Historic Houses Castles & Gardens

IN GREAT BRITAIN & IRELAND

1984

Editor: Patricia M. Wickens

This Guide to Historic Houses and Castles includes most of the habitable properties open to the public. Houses open by appointment only or very infrequently will be found on pages 185, 186, 187 and 188. Other Houses and Gardens in England, Wales and Scotland are listed in order of counties. An alphabetical index of Houses, Castles and Gardens throughout Great Britain and Ireland appears in the last pages.

Scale maps on pages 12, 14, 17, 18 and 20 indicate all properties shown in the classified section together with the nearest important towns, *map 1A* denotes map number and square reference.

The properties include privately owned and "lived-in" Mansions regularly opened to the public, together with the majority of Houses and Gardens under the control of *The National Trust* and *The National Trust for Scotland.* Castles and estates administered by the *Department of the Environment*, *Secretary of State for Scotland* and the *Welsh Office* are included where applicable as are the Houses under the care of local Civic Authorities.

Gardens open by courtesy of the owners in aid of the *National Gardens Scheme* and *Scotland's Garden Scheme* or the *Gardeners' Charities* are included where these Gardens are open on several occasions during the Summer months.

Some Houses are situated some distance from the towns, but many are regularly visited by coach companies in the summer months who are licensed to run straight to the House. Where these operate on regular days in the week details are shown. Other frequent coach services and local bus transport which serve roads adjacent or near to the properties are mentioned in detail.
Guided tours are organised at many Houses and these are indicated by a symbol. Connoisseur Days are generally not guided.

- △ Denotes guided tours of the House
- Denotes gardens open to the public
- Denotes properties recognised by the Countryside Commission
- ♿ Denotes the majority of the property is accessible by wheelchairs
- Denotes tea and light refreshments
- ✕ Denotes lunches or high teas
- Ⓔ Denotes educational services recognised by the Heritage Education Trust, see page 8

All admission charges quoted are subject to change without notice.

All dates are inclusive i.e. 'May to September—Weds' means first Wednesday in May to the last Wednesday in September.

Whilst every care has been taken in compiling this list no responsibility can be taken by the Publishers for any errors or omissions.

The front cover illustration is of Brympton d'Evercy, Somerset.

ABC HISTORIC PUBLICATIONS
WORLD TIMETABLE CENTRE, CHURCH STREET, DUNSTABLE, BEDFORDSHIRE.
Telephone: 0582 600111

ISSN 0073-2567 ISBN 0 900486 36 8

HISTORIC HOUSES TEN YEARS ON

by

MICHAEL SAUNDERS WATSON

President of the Historic Houses Association

1984 has long been immortalised in our minds with the dire prognostications of George Orwell's great classic. Now we have arrived and, as if to dispel any possibility of this gloomy view of our future, the British Tourist Authority has launched a major promotion "Heritage '84" to celebrate the great British heritage of which our historic houses form a major part.

Yet ten years ago George Orwell's picture could almost have been a possibility. Certainly the future of Britain's historic houses, if not our political system, lay in the balance. Those houses which remained in private hands had survived through a sort of Russian roulette whereby, provided the previous owner lived for seven years, he could pass the property on to his successor free of tax and, where he failed, the National Trusts could usually be relied upon to pick up the pieces. In 1974, however, a Labour Government came to power committed to a fundamental redistribution of wealth with a programme of swingeing taxation which, if carried through in its entirety, would have spelt the end of private ownership of historic houses in one generation. The number of properties which would then be abandoned by their owners as a result would be far more than the Government, National Trusts or any other body could possibly have maintained and the majority would have been lost for all time. Sir Roy Strong, newly arrived at the Victoria and Albert Museum, drew public attention to the issue in a major exhibition, "The Destruction of the Country House", listing more than 1,200 major houses which had disappeared in the previous 100 years.

In the event, of course, the worst did not occur. The Historic Houses Association now numbers well over 1,000 owner members, many whose properties are included in these pages as being regularly open to the public, with more open by appointment. What has happened in the intervening years and what does the future hold?

Any discussion of the survival of historic houses inevitably centres on two major issues: politics and economics. This is because in every sense of the word they are exceptional. Exceptional not only in their value but in their cost. The political issue is concerned with the importance of maintaining them as part of Britain's cultural heritage and as major tourist attractions, while the economic question is about who is to maintain them and how. Both issues have undergone major changes in the past ten years.

Probably the single most important political advance in this period, and possibly this century, has been the acceptance by politicians of all major political parties, reinforced by public opinion expressed in the largest petition ever presented to Parliament (1¼ million signatures), that Britain's historic houses are an important part of our cultural heritage which must be maintained and that the best way of doing this is, where possible, to leave them in private ownership.

As a result of this, various measures have been incorporated in the tax legislation to exempt outstanding houses, their amenity land and their contents from the effects of capital tax on death or gift. This was something which had never been done before and is a major achievement.

For their part, the owners had to undertake to maintain their property and secure reasonable public access to it. It was a fair deal for all parties but it left a number of questions unanswered. Was it sufficient, for instance, to protect only the heritage property from capital tax? Would there not be a need for some capital to support it? Reasonable access is fine in principle but what does it mean in practice and will the public avail themselves of it in a manner which does not leave the owner worse off than before? Most important of all, perhaps, is whether the next generation of owners will be prepared to commit themselves to maintaining their houses subject to the conditions on which the tax exemption depends.

The first question of the protection of capital required to support the property has been answered by provision for a maintenance fund which can be exempted from Capital Transfer Tax provided it is used exclusively for the maintenance of designated heritage property. Unfortunately, there is no similar exemption from Income Tax and herein lies a problem. The second and third questions remain unanswered and only time will tell. One thing is clear, however, and that is that the problems involved in maintaining and showing an historic house are constantly changing and if these measures are to work, successive owners must have adequate freedom of action within the law to conduct their difficult task. Subject to this, however, and where the will exists on the part of the owner, the spectre raised by capital taxes appears now to have been laid, at least temporarily, to rest. Income Tax and VAT still loom large, however, and make considerable inroads on the cash required to maintain these houses.

If the political position has improved, what has been happening on the economic front? In brief, we have all been confronted with the phenomenon known as inflation and this has borne particularly heavily on historic houses which, by their nature, are bound to be very expensive to run, but the problem has been confounded by the increasing scarcity, and thus cost, of the special materials and skills required for their maintenance.

The Great Hall

Michael Saunders Watson

For many of the larger, better-known houses, however, the increase in costs was to some extent off-set by the boom in tourism which occurred throughout the 1970s. Visitor numbers grew year by year, reaching a peak around 1978. They then levelled out for two years and since 1980 have declined by some 5% per year. Of course individual properties have been able to reverse the trend by additional promotion or special attractions but the trend is there nevertheless. There is no one obvious reason for this decline in visitor numbers but various factors have contributed to it. There are of course, many more properties open to the public. The number of houses advertised in this Journal as being regularly open to the public has increased by 35% in the past ten years but the circulation which peaked at 119,000 in 1978, fell to 88,000 in 1982. There is the effect of the recession on the home market and the strong pound affecting overseas visitors. One encouraging factor which is emerging is that, while attendances may be dropping at individual properties, the indications are that visitors are prepared to spend rather more where good value for money is offered.

The fact is, however, that more and more attractions are competing in a market which is not itself expanding, and those of us involved have to look to our operations to see whether we are providing what the public want in the manner best suited to the house and its economic requirements. For the smaller houses this poses special problems. They are first and foremost homes and are not able to attract or handle many visitors. For them, casual public access, far from being a commercial asset, can be a financial burden. Yet they have relatively the same expenses as their larger counterparts, often with less resources behind them.

So what of the future? The political problem of the '70s has been overtaken by the cash problem of the '80s. If the survival of the historic house is in question today, and there are a number of major properties whose future still lies in the balance, it will not be as a result of deliberate political action by the Government. It is more likely to be that the resources of the owner after tax are simply not adequate for the job. What, therefore, can be done?

Firstly, on the political front, we need to recognise the special problems of maintaining an historic house, indeed any listed building. France, Italy, Germany, Holland and, more recently, Denmark, all have arrangements by which the cost of maintaining historic houses can be offset against tax. In Britain there are none and the problem is further compounded by VAT which, with new construction work zero-rated and repairs standard-rated, positively discriminates against restoration in favour of demolition and new building. This anomaly must be removed and some incentive given through the income tax system to enable owners of all listed buildings to offset at least those additional costs which arise from the historic nature of the building against Income Tax. Such a move can only be to the National benefit in the long term.

Secondly, on the economic front, we, the owners and administrators, must look more closely at our opening arrangements. If we are to attract the casual visitor it may no longer be good enough to open only when it suits us. We may need to do more than simply offer the visitor a guided tour, followed by cream tea. We may have to review the method in which we show our houses and interpret them for the public. Interpretative technology is improving all the time and we must take advantage of it. Our unique selling point, to coin a phrase, is our quality and perhaps we should recognise this by going up-market, rather than by competing for visitors with the local amusement park. Education is a field where the historic house can play a meaningful role, recognised in the Journal by its sponsorship of the Sandford Award for houses offering proven educational facilities. Historic houses can provide good settings for business conferences, promotional activities and functions involving the Arts. These are all areas of benefit to the public interest which we the owners must explore. The criterion of success by which an historic house is measured should no longer be the number of visitors that have passed through its gates but the satisfaction of those members of the public who have used its facilities and enjoyed the special ambience that its offers.

In this context, the fact that the house is still a family home can give it a special quality of intimacy often appreciated by the visitor. On the other hand the more days the house is opened, the more difficult it is to maintain the homely atmosphere, or in fact to actually live in the place. I believe that one of the principal attractions of our smaller historic houses is that they are still homes, and as a result they will never be as efficient or as commercially viable as those which are run exclusively as leisure operations. They will, however, retain that human quality which breathes life into our architectural heritage.

In conclusion, therefore, ten years is a short time in the life of many of our historic houses but the past ten years have been significant ones. The political battle may have been won for the time being but the economic battle rages and here there is a need for Government assistance on Income Tax and VAT. Given this, for the historic house owner, the future offers an exciting challenge with the opportunity to own and manage a piece of Britain's heritage in the context of the 20th century.

To those of you readers who, in an idle moment, have lighted upon this page and actually read this article, you too can help by becoming Friends of the Historic Houses Association. Application forms for Membership are available at most members' houses or from the Historic Houses Association, 38 Ebury Street, London SW1W 0LU. By doing so, not only will you be purchasing a bargain in terms of free visits to 270 properties, but you will be encouraging us owners in our task and playing a part in the preservation of our National Heritage. What better year to take this step than 1984?

EDUCATIONAL SERVICES AT HISTORIC HOUSES AND CASTLES

In recent years there has been an increase in the number of school groups making educational visits to historic properties and also in the number of such properties which are providing some form of educational service. The Council for Environmental Education has welcomed these developments and in 1977 established a working party under the Chairmanship of Lord Sandford to co-ordinate activities and provide support and advice to owners, managers and teachers. This has led to the establishment of the Heritage Education Trust 1982 which now administers the Sandford Awards. The Sandford Group includes teachers, lecturers, members ot specialist teacher groups and representatives ot Local Educational Authorities, the Department of the Environment, the Historic Houses Association and both National Trusts.

One of the objectives of the Sandford Group is to encourage the attainment of high standards by education services based on historic properties. In furtherance of this aim the Group invited owners and managers of historic properties to submit details of their education services for consideration for entry in this separate section of Historic Houses, Castles and Gardens.

Detailed consideration of these submissions was made according to the following criteria

1. Evidence of good liaison between the historic property and Local Education Authorities and teachers.
2. The imaginative way in which the full educational potential of the property nad been or was being realised.
3. Design of educational materials and facilities.
4. Attention to adequate preparation, good management during the visit and effective follow-up.
5. The way in whicn a child's first visit is designed to kindle in him a lasting interest in a particular topic related to the property.

The Group considers that the houses in the list below are making determined efforts to meet the criteria outlined above and are therefore worthy of inclusion. It must be stressed however that these services vary greatly in their scope and degree of development. It is therefore essential that teachers contact the properties in advance of their visit to determine what services are available in the current year.

ABBOT HALL
Kendal, Cumbria

ASTON HALL
Birmingham, West Midlands

BEAULIEU ABBEY
nr. Lyndhurst, Hampshire

BELTON HOUSE
Grantham, Lincolnshire

BENINGBROUGH HALL
Shipton, North Yorkshire

BICKLEIGH CASTLE
nr. Tiverton, Devon

BLENHEIM PALACE
Woodstock, Oxfordshire

BOLLING HALL
Bradford, West Yorkshire

BREAMORE HOUSE
Fordingbridge, Hampshire

CASTLE WARD
Co. Down, N. Ireland

CHRISTCHURCH MANSION
Ipswich, Suffolk

CLAVERTON MANOR
nr. Bath, Avon

COVENTRY CATHEDRAL
Coventry, West Midlands

CROXTETH HALL & COUNTRY PARK
Liverpool, Merseyside

CULZEAN CASTLE
Maybole, Strathclyde Region

DODDINGTON HALL
Doddington, Lincolnshire

ERDDIG
nr. Wrexham, Clwyd

GEORGIAN HOUSE
Edinburgh, Lothian Region

GOODWOOD HOUSE
Chichester, West Sussex

HAGLEY HALL
nr. Stourbridge, West Midlands

HAREWOOD HOUSE
Leeds, West Yorkshire

HARRINGTON HALL
Spilsby, Lincolnshire

HOUSE OF THE BINNS
By Linlithgow, Lothian Region

KENTWELL HALL
Long Melford, Suffolk

LANGTON HALL
nr. Market Harborough, Leicestershire

LEIGHTON HALL
Carnforth, Lancashire

LITTLECOTE
nr. Hungerford, Wiltshire

LYME PARK
Disley, Cheshire

MOSELEY OLD HALL
Wolverhampton, West Midlands

NEWSTEAD ABBEY
Linby, Nottinghamshire

NORTON PRIORY MUSEUM
Runcorn, Cheshire

PENHOW CASTLE
nr. Newport, Gwent

RANGERS HOUSE
Blackheath, London

ROCKINGHAM CASTLE
nr. Corby, Northamptonshire

ST. FAGANS CASTLE
Cardiff, South Glamorgan

SUDBURY HALL
nr. Derby, Derbyshire

TATTON PARK
Knutsford, Cheshire

TOWER OF LONDON
Tower Bridge, London

TURTON TOWER
Blackburn, Lancashire

WESTON PARK
nr. Shifnal, Shropshire

WOLLATON HALL
Nottingham, Nottinghamshire

Awards are presented to Houses which are making an **outstanding contribution to Heritage Education.** Presentation of an Award is not based simply on material submitted for examination but also on independent assessment following visits by representatives of the Sandford Group. Recipients of the SANDFORD AWARD appear below:

BEAULIEU ABBEY
nr. Lyndhurst, Hampshire

BELTON HOUSE
Grantham, Lincolnshire

BICKLEIGH CASTLE
nr. Tiverton, Devon

BLENHEIM PALACE
Woodstock, Oxfordshire

BOLLING HALL
Bradford, West Yorkshire

CASTLE WARD
Co. Down, N. Ireland

CROXTETH HALL & COUNTRY PARK
Liverpool, Merseyside

DODDINGTON HALL
Doddington, Lincolnshire

GEORGIAN HOUSE
Edinburgh, Lothian Region

HAGLEY HALL
nr. Stourbridge, West Midlands

HAREWOOD HOUSE
Leeds, West Yorkshire

HOLKER HALL
Cark-in-Cartmel, Cumbria

HOPETOUN HOUSE
South Queensferry, Lothian Region

IXWORTH ABBEY
nr. Bury St. Edmunds, Suffolk

LEIGHTON HALL
Carnforth, Lancashire

MARGAM PARK
nr. Port Talbot, West Glamorgan

MOSELEY OLD HALL
Wolverhampton, West Midlands

PENHOW CASTLE
nr. Newport, Gwent

RANGER'S HOUSE
Blackheath, London

ROCKINGHAM CASTLE
nr. Corby, Northamptonshire

SUDBURY HALL
nr. Derby, Derbyshire

TATTON PARK
Knutsford, Cheshire

TOWER OF LONDON
Tower Bridge, London

The list of Houses providing educational services will continue to be published in the future. Owners or Managers wishing to submit their services for possible inclusion in this list should send samples of materials, together with the questionnaire, by March 22nd to **Martyn Dyer, Acting Director, Heritage Education Trust, St. Mary's College, Strawberry Hill, Twickenham TW1 4SX.** In addition any teacher who wishes to comment on the services provided at a particular house is invited to write with details to the same address.

THE MARQUESS AND MARCHIONESS
OF HERTFORD

invite you to

Ragley Hall

NOW RESTORED
TO ITS 18TH CENTURY PERFECTION

Ragley is one of the finest Palladian Houses in England. Designed in 1680, Rupert Hooke's magnificent architecture provides a superb setting for the famous Ragley art collection.

Paintings by Reynolds, Hoppner and Wooton. English and French 18th Century furniture and Sèvres and Meissen china decorate the newly restored rooms. "The Temptation", a new mural by Graham Rust, is the greatest addition to Ragley's beauty since the 18th century.

Whilst Ragley contains treasures collected over 3 centuries, it is not a museum, it is still the home of the Seymour family.

The Great Hall with the finest baroque plaster work in England is available for banquets, conferences and concerts throughout the year.

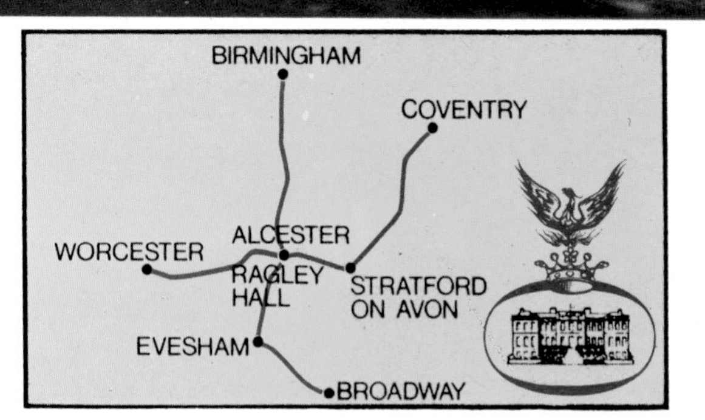

RAGLEY HALL, ALCESTER, NEAR STRATFORD-ON-AVON, WARWICKSHIRE.

The park contains the Adventure Wood, Country Trail and lakeside picnic places.

OPENING TIMES FOR 1984

House, Garden & Park open 1st April to 30th September, every day except Mondays and Fridays but open Bank Holiday Mondays. Park open 11.00 a.m. to 6.00 p.m. (*also* open Mondays and Fridays July and August). Licensed Coffee Shop open 12.30 p.m. House & Gardens open 1.30 to 5.30 p.m. Coach parties welcome at any time of the year by arrangement.

For further information: Lord Hertford, Ragley Hall, Alcester, Warwickshire.
Telephone: Alcester (STD 0789) 762090 or 762455.

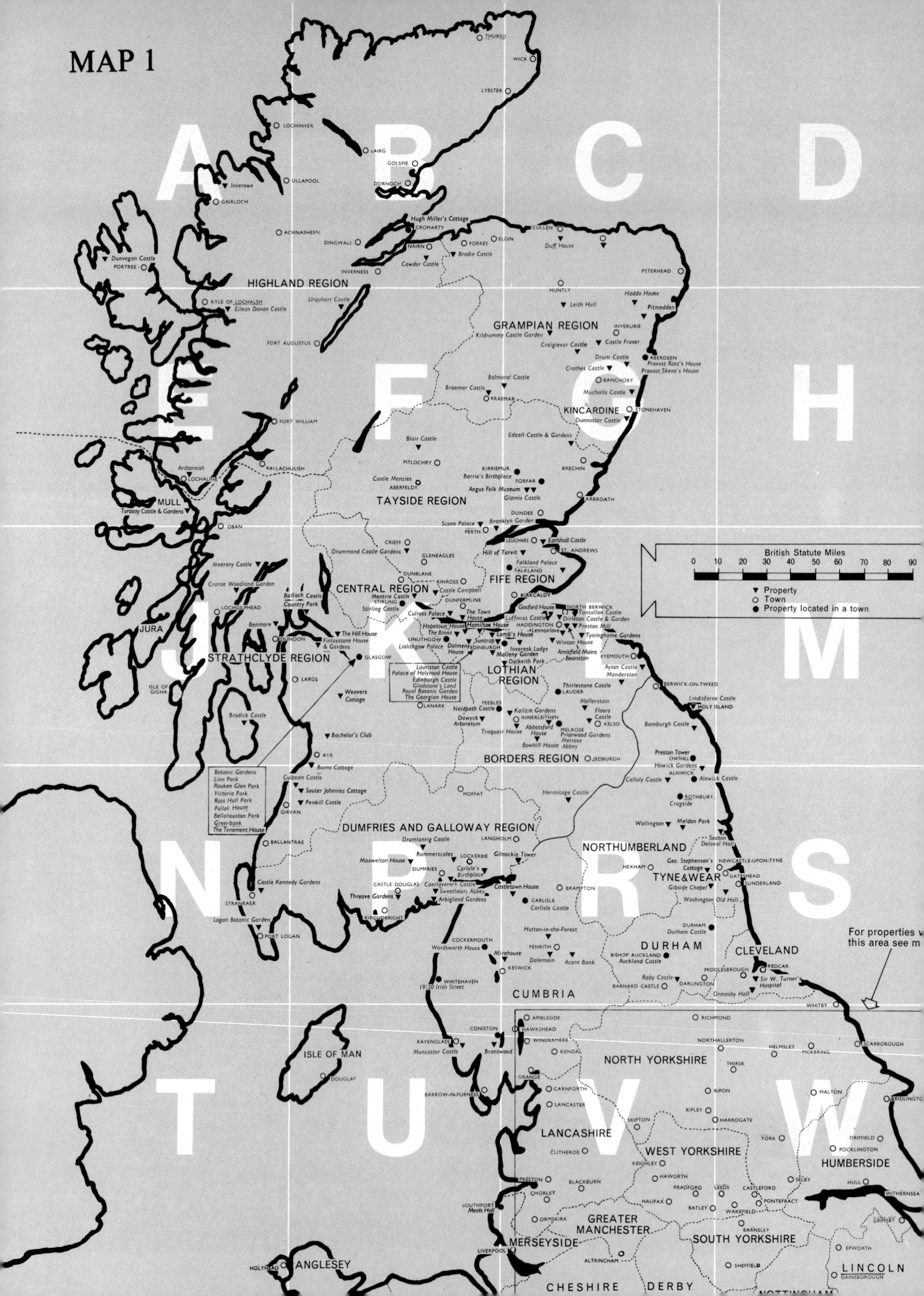
MAP 1
A
B
C
D
E
F
G
H
J
K
L
M
N
P
R
S
T
U
V
W
THURSO
WICK
LYBSTER
LOCHINVER
LAIRG
GOLSPIE
DORNOCH
ULLAPOOL
Inverewe
GAIRLOCH
Hugh Miller's Cottage
CROMARTY
ACHNASHEEN
DINGWALL
NAIRN
FORRES
ELGIN
CULLEN
Duff House
Brodie Castle
Cawdor Castle
INVERNESS
Dunvegan Castle
PORTREE
HIGHLAND REGION
PSTERHEAD
HUNTLY
Leith Hall
Hadda House
Pitmedden
KYLE OF LOCHALSH
Eilean Donan Castle
Urquhart Castle
GRAMPIAN REGION
INVERURIE
Kildrummy Castle Garden
Craigievar Castle
Castle Fraser
FORT AUGUSTUS
Drum Castle
ABERDEEN
Provost Ross's House
Provost Skene's House
Crathes Castle
BANCHORY
Balmoral Castle
Braemar Castle
BRAEMAR
Muchalls Castle
KINCARDINE
STONEHAVEN
Dunnottar Castle
FORT WILLIAM
Edzell Castle & Gardens
Blair Castle
PITLOCHRY
BRECHIN
KIRRIEMUIR
Barrie's Birthplace
FORFAR
Ardtornish
LOCHALINE
Castle Menzies
ABERFELDY
Angus Folk Museum
Glamis Castle
MULL
Torosay Castle & Gardens
TAYSIDE REGION
ARBROATH
DUNDEE
OBAN
Scone Palace
Branklyn Garden
PERTH
LEUCHARS
Earlshall Castle
CRIEFF
Drummond Castle Gardens
Hill of Tarvit
ST. ANDREWS
GLENEAGLES
Falkland Palace
FALKLAND
Inverary Castle
British Statute Miles
0
10
20
30
40
50
60
70
80
90
Property
Town
Property located in a town
DUNBLANE
KINROSS
FIFE REGION
Crarae Woodland Garden
CENTRAL REGION
Castle Campbell
Balloch Castle
Country Park
Mentrie Castle
STIRLING
Stirling Castle
DUNFERMLINE
KIRKCALDY
LOCHGILPHEAD
NORTH BERWICK
Tantallon Castle
Gosford House
Dirleton Castle & Garden
Luffness Castle
Culross Palace
The Town House
Hopetoun House
Hamilton House
HADDINGTON
Preston Mill
Lennoxlove
Tyninghame Gardens
JURA
Benmore
The Binns
Lamb's House
LINLITHGOW
Linlithgow Palace
Dalmeny House
Suntrap
EDINBURGH
Winton House
The Hill House
Finlaystone House & Gardens
DUNOON
Inveresk Lodge
Mallony Garden
Amisfield Mains
Beanston
EYEMOUTH
STRATHCLYDE REGION
GLASGOW
Dalkeith Park
Ayton Castle
Manderston
Lauriston Castle
Palace of Holyrood House
Edinburgh Castle
Gladstone's Land
Royal Botanic Garden
The Georgian House
LOTHIAN REGION
LARGS
ISLE OF GIGHA
Weavers Cottage
Thirlestane Castle
LAUDER
BERWICK-ON-TWEED
Lindisfarne Castle
HOLY ISLAND
LANARK
PEEBLES
Neidpath Castle
Mellerstain
Floors Castle
KELSO
Kailzie Gardens
INNERLEITHEN
Dawyck Arboretum
Abbotsford House
MELROSE
Priorwood Gardens
Melrose Abbey
Brodick Castle
Traquair House
Bowhill House
Bamburgh Castle
Bachelor's Club
BORDERS REGION
JEDBURGH
AYR
Burns Cottage
Preston Tower
CHATHILL
Howick Gardens
ALNWICK
Alnwick Castle
Botanic Gardens
Linn Park
Rouken Glen Park
Victoria Park
Ross Hall Park
Pollok House
Bellahouston Park
Greenbank
The Tenement House
Culzean Castle
Souter Johnnies Cottage
MOFFAT
Callaly Castle
Penkill Castle
Hermitage Castle
ROTHBURY
Cragside
GIRVAN
Wallington
Meldon Park
DUMFRIES AND GALLOWAY REGION
Seaton Delaval Hall
BALLANTRAE
Drumlanrig Castle
LANGHOLM
NORTHUMBERLAND
Rammerscales
LOCKERBIE
Gilnockie Tower
Maxwelton House
DUMFRIES
Carlyle's Birthplace
HEXHAM
Geo. Stephenson's Cottage
NEWCASTLE-UPON-TYNE
TYNE&WEAR
GATESHEAD
Castle Kennedy Gardens
CASTLE DOUGLAS
Caerlaverock Castle
Castletown House
BRAMPTON
Gibside Chapel
SUNDERLAND
Sweetheart Abbey
Threave Gardens
Arbigland Gardens
CARLISLE
Carlisle Castle
Washington Old Hall
STRANRAER
KIRCUDBRIGHT
Logan Botanic Garden
PORT LOGAN
DURHAM
Durham Castle
Hutton-in-the-Forest
COCKERMOUTH
Wordsworth House
Mirehouse
PENRITH
Dalemain
Acorn Bank
BISHOP AUCKLAND
Auckland Castle
CLEVELAND
For properties
this area see m
KESWICK
MIDDLESBROUGH
REDCAR
Raby Castle
DARLINGTON
Sir W. Turner's Hospital
WHITEHAVEN
19/20 Irish Street
BARNARD CASTLE
Ormesby Hall
CUMBRIA
WHITBY
AMBLESIDE
RICHMOND
HAWKSHEAD
CONISTON
RAVENGLASS
Muncaster Castle
WINDERMERE
Brantwood
NORTHALLERTON
HELMSLEY
PICKERING
SCARBOROUGH
KENDAL
NORTH YORKSHIRE
ISLE OF MAN
THIRSK
DOUGLAS
GRANGE
BARROW-IN-FURNESS
CARNFORTH
RIPON
MALTON
BRIDLINGTON
LANCASTER
RIPLEY
HARROGATE
SKIPTON
LANCASHIRE
YORK
DRIFFIELD
POCKLINGTON
CLITHEROE
WEST YORKSHIRE
HUMBERSIDE
KEIGHLEY
HAWORTH
PRESTON
BLACKBURN
BRADFORD
LEEDS
CASTLEFORD
SELBY
HULL
WITHERNSEA
CHORLEY
HALIFAX
BATLEY
WAKEFIELD
PONTEFRACT
SOUTHPORT
Meols Hall
ORMSKIRK
GREATER MANCHESTER
BARNSLEY
SOUTH YORKSHIRE
GRIMSBY
MERSEYSIDE
LIVERPOOL
EPWORTH
ALTRINCHAM
SHEFFIELD
HOLYHEAD
ANGLESEY
LINCOLN
GAINSBOROUGH
CHESHIRE
DERBY

Home of the Eleventh Duke of Marlborough

Birthplace of Sir Winston Churchill

OPEN DAILY 11 a.m. — 6 p.m. (last admission 5 p.m.)

12 MARCH — 31 OCTOBER 1984

For full details write or telephone: The Administrator,
Blenheim Palace, Woodstock, Oxford OX7 1PX
Telephone: Woodstock 811325

Lords Taveners Charity Cricket Match and Woodstock Horse Show
take place on Sunday 27 & Monday 28 May 1984.
On these days special times and rates apply.

THE RIGHT TO CLOSE THE PARK & PALACE WITHOUT NOTICE IS RESERVED.

MAP 2
MAP 5
This Map does not include Properties which are open by appointment only or very infrequently
British Statute Miles
0 5 10 15 20 25 30 35 40 45
Property
Town
Property located in a town
A
B
C
D
E
F
G
H
J
K
L
M
N
P
R
S
T
U
V
W
MERSEYSIDE
LIVERPOOL
Bluecoat Chambers
BIRKENHEAD
Ness Gardens
DIDSBURY
ALTRINCHAM
HOLYHEAD
ANGLESEY
Beaumaris Castle
BEAUMARIS
Aberconwy House
CONWY
Conwy Castle
Plas Mawr
Plas Newydd
BANGOR
Penrhyn Castle
Bryn Bras Castle
CAERNARVON
Caernarvon Castle
ABERGELE
RHYL
Gyrn Castle
HOLYWELL
Bodrhyddan Hall
Rhuddlan Castle
Bodnant Garden
Ewloe Castle
DENBIGH
Denbigh Castle
LLANRWST
Gwydir Castle
Ty Mawr
CLWYD
WREXHAM
Erddig
LLANGOLLEN
Chirk Castle
Tyn-y-Rhos Hall
GWYNEDD
Criccieth Castle
PORTHMADOG
PWLLHELI
BALA
Harlech Castle
DOLGELLAU
MACHYNLLETH
ABERYSTWYTH
CHESTER
CHESHIRE
TARPORLEY
Peover Hall
NORTHWICH
Nether Alderley Mill
Capesthorne
Vale Royal Abbey
Swythamley Park
CONGLETON
Rode Hall
Little Moreton Hall
NANTWICH
Churche's Mansion
Dorfold Hall
Woodhey Chapel
Cholmondeley Castle Gardens
Elds Wood
STAFFORD
MARKET DRAYTON
Hodnet Hall Gardens
STAFFORD
Pillaton
Adcote
SHREWSBURY
Attingham
OAKENGATES
Trelydan Hall
WELSHPOOL
Powis Castle
SHROPSHIRE
Weston Park
TONG
Boscobel House
Modeley Court
Benthall Hall
Broseley Hall
Condover Hall
MUCH WENLOCK
Wenlock Priory
Long Mynd & Carding Mill Valley
Acton Round Hall
BRIDGNORTH
Wilderhope Manor
Shipton Hall
NEWTOWN
BISHOP'S CASTLE
Dudmaston
Upton Cressett Hall
Hagley Hall
CRAVEN ARMS
Stokesay Castle
The White House
KIDDERMINSTER
LUDLOW
Mawley Hall
Stone House Cottage Gardens
STOURPORT
Hartlebury Castle
KNIGHTON
POWYS
TENBURY WELLS
DROITWICH
Croft Castle
Berrington Hall
Hergest Croft Garden & Park Wood
Burton Court
LEOMINSTER
KINGTON
LLANDRINDOD WELLS
BROMYARD
The Commandery
The Greyfriars
WORCESTER
Brilley, Cwmmau Farmhouse
Lower Brockhampton
BUILTH WELLS
HEREFORD & WORCESTER
Dinmore Manor
GREAT MALVERN
The Weir
LEDBURY
Little Malvern Court
Moccas Court
HEREFORD
Eastnor Castle
Brobury Garden & Gallery
Abbey Dore Court Garden
Hellen's
TEWKESBURY
CARDIGAN
LAMPETER
Pentre Mansion
DYFED
BRECON
Tretower Court & Castle
Kentchurch Court
Ryelands House
CHELTENHAM
Trebinshwn House
ROSS-ON-WYE
CRICKHOWELL
Llanfihangel Court
Pembridge Castle
GLOUCESTER
Westbury Court Garden
LLANDILO
ABERGAVENNY
CARMARTHEN
Picton Castle
NARBERTH
HAVERFORDWEST
MONMOUTH
Dean Hall
STROUD
Clearwell Castle
Lydney Park
Berkeley Castle
GWENT
USK
Colby Lodge Garden
Kidwelly Castle
PEMBROKE
Chavenage
Chepstow Castle
CHEPSTOW
Westonbirt Arboretum
Manorbier Castle
TENBY
Tudor Merchant's House
WEST GLAMORGAN
SWANSEA
Margam Country Park
PORT TALBOT
MID GLAMORGAN
Penhow Castle
NEWPORT
Tredegar House
Caerphilly Castle
Horton Court
Badminton House
Little Sodbury Manor
BRIDGEND
Llanharan House
Castell Coch
CARDIFF
Cardiff Castle
St. Fagans Castle
SOUTH GLAMORGAN
The Manor House
Vine House
Blaise Castle House
CLEVEDON
Clevedon Court
Barstaple House
Georgian House
Red Lodge
St Vincents Priory
BRISTOL
Dyrham Park
St. Catherine's Court
Corsham Court
Wick Manor
Beckford's Tower
BATH
No. 1 Royal Crescent
Great Chalfield Manor
Herschel House
Claverton Manor
WESTON-SUPER-MARE
AVON
Orchard House
Lyncombe Court
King John's Hunting Lodge
RADSTOCK
BRADFORD-ON-AVON
CHEDDAR
Westwood
Oakhill Manor
WILTSHIRE
Chalcot House
WARMINSTER
Longleat House
ILFRACOMBE
MINEHEAD
WATCHET
Coleridge Cottage
Dunster Castle
CROWCOMBE
The Church House
WELLS
The Bishop's Palace
GLASTONBURY
Arlington Court
Barford Park
BRIDGWATER
Marwood Hill
Woodside
BARNSTAPLE
Combe Sydenham Hall
SOMERSET
Stourhead
Lytes Cary
Stowell Hill
Hadspen House
Pythouse
Castle Hill
Tapeley Park Gardens
Gaulden Manor
Priest's House
Midelney Manor
Tintinhull House
ILCHESTER
SHAFTESBURY
TAUNTON
MARTOCK
Rosemoor
WELLINGTON
Poundisford Park
Hatch Court
East Lambrook Manor
Montacute House
Stoke-sub-Hamdon Priory
YEOVIL
Sandford Orcas Manor House
Purse Caundle Manor House
SHERBORNE
Sherborne Castle
Compton House
Brympton d'Evercy
Tiverton Castle
TIVERTON
Knightshayes Court
Barrington Court
ILMINSTER
Bickleigh Castle
CULLOMPTON
CREWKERNE
Melbury House
Minterne
CHARD
DORSET
Clapton Court
Forde Abbey
Milton Abbey
BUDE
Ebbingford Manor
HOLSWORTHY
Fursdon House
Killerton Gardens
Dewlish House
Parnham House
Mapperton
Athelhampton
DEVON
Cadhay
OTTERY ST. MARY
Wolfeton House
Hardy's Cottage
Fernwood
LYME REGIS
BRIDPORT
DORCHESTER
OKEHAMPTON
Sand
EXETER
A La Ronde
SIDMOUTH
Abbotsbury
TINTAGEL
Tintagel, Old Post Office
Castle Drogo
Powderham Castle
EXMOUTH
BUDLEIGH SALTERTON
Clouds Hill
WEYMOUTH
LAUNCESTON
STARCROSS
Long Cross Victorian Gardens
DAWLISH
NEWTON ABBOT
TEIGNMOUTH
TAVISTOCK
Bradley Manor
CORNWALL
The Garden House
Buckland Abbey
Pencarrow House & Gardens
Compton Castle
Torre Abbey
TORQUAY
BODMIN
Cotehele House
Bickham House
PAIGNTON
TOTNES
Kirkham House
Bowden House
Lanhydrock
NEWQUAY
Hemerdon House
Trerice
Antony House
PLYMOUTH
DARTMOUTH
Coleton Fishacre Garden
Dartmouth Castle
FOWEY
LOOE
Saltram House
PROBUS
Trewithen
Mount Edgcumbe
Flete
TRURO
KINGSBRIDGE
Trelissick Gardens
Sharpitor
Trengwainton Gardens
Godolphin House
FALMOUTH
Pendennis Castle
PENZANCE
St. Michael's Mount
Glendurgan Garden
HELSTON
Trelowarren House & Chapel

LONGLEAT
LONGLEAT
WARMINSTER
WILTSHIRE
ENGLAND
Telephone:
Maiden Bradley
(09853) 551.
Look in
and lord it
for a day

Medieval Jousting Tournaments on:
Sunday, May 27th &
Monday, May 28th
(Spring Bank Holiday)

Sunday, June 24th
Sunday, July 29th

Sunday, August 26th &
Monday, August 27th
(Summer Bank Holiday)
Sunday, September 16th

Performed by Professionals with no punches pulled
No extra charges
As seen on television worldwide

Belvoir Castle

(Home of the Duke & Duchess of Rutland)

Open from March 27th — September 30th, 1984

A Stately Home occupying a commanding position overlooking the beautiful Vale of Belvoir. Once inside Belvoir Castle you are free to enjoy the magnificent State Rooms, beautiful works of art, a historic Armoury of Weapons and a permanent Military Museum of 17/21st Lancers. The attractive Statue Garden also open to the Public. Refreshments available inside Castle — Self Service Tea Rooms. Waitress Service for Lunches and Teas for Pre-booked Parties only on Tues., Weds., Thurs., Sat. Over 90,000 visitors in 1983. Schools Educational facilities available.

Easter Bank Holiday
Sunday, April 22nd &
Monday, April 23rd
The Robin Hood Society
'Hunt the Outlaws'
Great Family Entertainment

Sunday, June 3rd
Archery Display

Sunday, July 1st
Miniature Steam Fair
Working Models

Sunday, August 12th
Stars & Bars Society
Mock Battle & Display

Sunday, July 22nd
Teddy Bears' Picnic

LITTLE LORD FAUNTLEROY FILMED HERE IN 1980
Special events most Sundays, no extra charge. Details on request

Opening Hours: Tuesdays, Wednesdays, Thursdays, Saturdays: 12 noon-6 p.m. Sundays: 12 noon-7 p.m. (Oct. 2 p.m.-6 p.m.) Bank Holiday Mondays only: 11 a.m.-7 p.m. Good Friday only: 12 noon-6 p.m.

Admission Charges: Adults £1.80. Children £1. Party Bookings: Parties of 30 or more O.A.Ps. £1. Parties of 30 or more Adults £1.30. Parties of 30 or more Schoolchildren £1. (Accompanying Teachers Free). All Coach Excursion Passengers £1.30. Free car and coach park.

Castle sometimes available to hire for Large Banquets, Dances, Conferences, Filming & T.V. Commercials, etc.

Futher information from: J. W. Durrands, Estate Office, R2, Belvoir Castle, Grantham, Lincs.
Telephone: Grantham (0476) 870262.

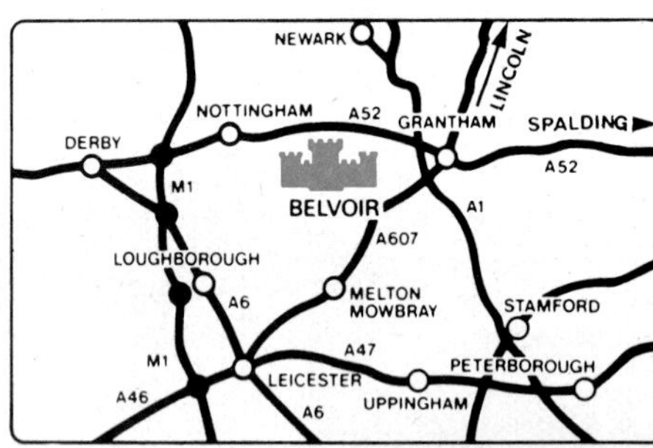

MAP 3
MAP 5
This Map does not include Properties which are open by appointment only or very infrequently
For properties within this area see map 6
British Statute Miles
0 5 10 15 20 25 30 35 40 45
Property
Town
Property located in a town
A B C D E F G H J K L M N P R S T U V W
DONCASTER
EPWORTH
SOUTH YORKSHIRE
BAWTRY
SHEFFIELD
GAINSBOROUGH
ALFORD
CHESTERFIELD
LINCOLN
BAKEWELL
The Old House Museum
Chatsworth
Haddon Hall
Winster Market House
Hardwick Hall
OLLERTON
Carlton Hall
Doddington Hall
HORNCASTLE
Harrington Hall
SPILSBY
Gunby Hall
Aubourn Hall
SKEGNESS
MANSFIELD
WOODHALL SPA
Thorpe Tilney Hall
Tattershall Castle
Newstead Abbey
Newark Town Hall
NEWARK
Lea Rhododendron Gardens
Fulbeck Hall
NOTTINGHAM
LINCOLN
DERBY
Marston Hall
BOSTON
Fydell House
ASHBOURNE
Clifton Hall
NOTTINGHAM
Kedleston Hall
DERBY
Sudbury Hall
Holme Pierrepont Hall
Belton House
GRANTHAM
Grantham House
HUNSTANTON
WELLS
SHERINGHAM
CROMER
Holkham Hall
Walsingham Abbey
Felbrigg Hall
Melbourne Hall
Belvoir Castle
Mannington Hall Gardens
Hoar Cross Hall
Thrumpton Hall
Woolsthorpe Manor
Sandringham Grounds
Trinity Hospital
FAKENHAM
Blickling Hall
AYLSHAM
Prestwold Hall
RUGELEY
MELTON MOWBRAY
SPALDING
Springfields Gardens
Houghton Hall
STAFFORD
LOUGHBOROUGH
KING'S LYNN
Medieval Merchants House
Beeston Hall
Hanch Hall
Manor House
LICHFIELD
OAKHAM
Oakham Castle
NORFOLK
LEICESTER
WISBECH
Peckover House
TAMWORTH
Tamworth Castle
STAMFORD
Burghley House
Priest's House
SWAFFHAM
Oakleigh House
NORWICH
GREAT YARMOUTH
Battlefield of Bosworth
LEICESTER
Belgrave Hall
Guildhall
Wygston's House
PETERBOROUGH
Asbury Cottage
Kirby Hall
Deene Park
Elton Hall
Oxburgh Hall
Rainthorpe Hall & Gardens
Hales Hall
Fritton Lake & Gardens
NUNEATON
Southwick Hall
Somerleyton Hall
LOWESTOFT
BIRMINGHAM
Aston Hall
Blakesley Hall
Arbury Hall
Langton Hall
Rockingham Castle
OUNDLE
CORBY
Lyveden New Bield
Lilford Park
CAMBRIDGE
Packwood House
Stanford Hall
Rushton Hall
Boughton House
ELY
THETFORD
Kenilworth Castle
KENILWORTH
Stoneleigh Abbey
RUGBY
Baddersley Clinton
KETTERING
Hinchingbrooke House
HUNTINGDON
DISS
HALESWORTH
Euston Hall
Wingfield College
Wingfield Castle
SOUTHWOLD
WARWICK
WARWICK
Warwick Castle
Lord Leycester Hospital
Coton Manor Wildlife Garden
Guilsborough Grange
Lamport Hall
KIMBOLTON
Kimbolton Castle
Island Hall
Anglesey Abbey
Ixworth Abbey
YOXFORD
Badingham
Coughton Court
Holdenby House Gardens
WELLINGBOROUGH
NORTHAMPTON
Althorp
Charlecote Park
ALCESTER
STRATFORD-ON-AVON
NORTHAMPTON
Hinwick House
CAMBRIDGE
University Botanic Garden
BURY ST. EDMUNDS
Haughley Park
STOWMARKET
SAXMUNDHAM
Ragley Hall
The Grammar School
Shakespeare's Birthplace Trust Properties
Harvard House
Delapre Abbey
Castle Ashby
Wimpole Home Farm
Wimpole Hall
Ickworth
Helmingham Hall
Glemham Hall
Farnborough Hall
Stoke Park Pavilions
SUFFOLK
Upton House
Honington Hall
OLNEY
Canon's Ashby House
TOWCESTER
Cowper & Newton Museum
Stagsden Bird Gardens
Docwra's Manor
The Priory
LAVENHAM
Otley Hall
Manor Gardens
Brook Cottage
Sulgrave Manor
Chicheley Hall
BEDFORD
Kentwell Hall
Little Hall
WOODBRIDGE
Wroxton Abbey
BANBURY
The Swiss Garden
BIGGLESWADE
Nether Hall
Melford Hall
IPSWICH
CHIPPING CAMPDEN
BRACKLEY
Stowe
BEDFORD
SUDBURY
The Guildhall
HADLEIGH
Christchurch Mansion
Ipswich Museum
Pykenham Gatehouse
Batsford Arboretum
Broughton Castle
Aynhoe Park
BUCKS
Wrest Park
SAFFRON WALDEN
Hedingham Castle
Belchamp Hall
Gainsborough's House
MORETON-IN-MARSH
WOBURN
Woburn Abbey & Wild Animal Kingdom
Audley End House
FINCHINGFIELD
Sezincote Garden
Chastleton House
BUCKINGHAM
HITCHIN
THAXTED
Spains Hall
HALSTEAD
DEDHAM
Castle House
Winslow Hall
WINSLOW
DUNSTABLE
Rousham House
Claydon House
St. Paul's Walden Bury
Benington Lordship
Saling Hall
Gosfield Hall
Ditchley Park
Waddesdon Manor
Ascott
LUTON
Knebworth House
COLCHESTER
Luton Hoo
BISHOP'S STORTFORD
COGGESHALL
Paycocke's
Beth Chatto Gardens
Waddon House
Mentmore Towers
HERTFORD
BRAINTREE
WOODSTOCK
Blenheim Palace
Hartwell House
AYLESBURY
Shalom Hall
Arlington Mill
BURFORD
OXFORD
Stanton Harcourt Manor
University Botanic Garden
Colleges
OXFORD
Dorton House
Nether Winchendon House
Ashridge
Shaw's Corner
WELWYN
HEMEL HEMPSTEAD
HERTFORD
ESSEX
Yew Tree Cottage
Kelmscott Manor
LECHLADE
FARINGDON
Kingston House
Waterperry Horticultural Centre
PRINCES RISBOROUGH
Princes Risborough Manor House
ST. ALBANS
ST. OSYTH
CLACTON
CHELMSFORD
MALDON
Buscot Old Parsonage
Buscot Park
ABINGDON
Nuneham
AMERSHAM
RICKMANSWORTH
The Great Barn
Pusey House Gardens
Milton Manor House
West Wycombe Park
HIGH WYCOMBE
ENFIELD
Lydiard Mansion
WANTAGE
Ardington House
Stonor Park
Divine Mercy College & Museum
SWINDON
Kingstone Lisle Park
Greys Court
HENLEY-ON-THAMES
HAMPSTEAD
Ashdown House
UXBRIDGE
MAIDENHEAD
SLOUGH
GREATER LONDON
SOUTHEND-ON-SEA
Basildon Park
Mapledurham House
WINDSOR
Littlecote
BERKSHIRE
READING
RICHMOND
Avebury Manor
HUNGERFORD
The Old Rectory
GREENWICH
DARTFORD
KINGSTON
MARLBOROUGH
NEWBURY
Swallowfield Park
CARSHALTON
BROMLEY
FARNINGHAM
MARGATE
BROADSTAIRS
Sandham Memorial Chapel
The Vyne
West Green House
CROYDON
Quex Park
FAVERSHAM
WOKING
Stratfield Saye House
CANTERBURY
WILTSHIRE
BASINGSTOKE
SEVENOAKS
AYLESFORD
SURREY
LEATHERHEAD
MAIDSTONE
Goodnestone Park
ANDOVER
HAMPSHIRE
GUILDFORD
FARNHAM
DORKING
KENT
Jenkyn Place
DEAL
Deal Castle
Avington Park
Jane Austen's Home
ALTON
TONBRIDGE
Walmer Castle
Heale House
TUNBRIDGE WELLS
LINGFIELD
HASLEMERE
EAST GRINSTEAD
ASHFORD
Sandling Park
DOVER
Dover Castle
FOLKESTONE
Mompesson House
SALISBURY
King's House
STOCKBRIDGE
Houghton Lodge
WINCHESTER
The Pilgrim's Hall
Oates Memorial Museum & Gilbert White Museum
Alresford House
LAMBERHURST
TENTERDEN
Saltwood Castle
HYTHE
Mottisfont Abbey
ROMSEY
Broadlands
PETERSFIELD
Hurst Mill
Malt House
HORSHAM
CROWBOROUGH
Newhouse
Hole Park
PETWORTH
HAYWARDS HEATH
UCKFIELD
BURWASH
Breamore House
SOUTHAMPTON
Uppark
WEST SUSSEX
Beeches Farm
Horsted Place Gardens
Bodiam Castle
Great Dixter
Brickwall House
Cranborne Manor Gardens
Grove Place
West Dean Gardens
St. Roche's Arboretum
The Weald and Downland Open Air Museum
Heaselands
EAST SUSSEX
RYE
Lamb House
Haremere Hall
Furzey Gardens
LYNDHURST
Coates Manor
Coke's Cottage
PULBOROUGH
Parham
Danny
Bentley Wildfowl
BATTLE
Goodwood House
STEYNING
Newtimber Place
RINGWOOD
Exbury Gardens
Beaulieu Abbey and Palace House
National Motor Museum
Chidmere
Denmans
BRAMBER
St. Mary's
LEWES
Glynde Place
Michelham Priory
Highbury
CHICHESTER
Arundel Castle
Monk's House
Firle Place
HAILSHAM
HASTINGS
Macpenny's
Spinners
BRIGHTON
Royal Pavilion
Preston Manor
Alfriston Clergy House
The Old Minthouse
Russell-Cotes Art Gallery and Museum
CHRISTCHURCH
COWES
Osborne House
GORING-BY-SEA
SEAFORD
EASTBOURNE
BOURNEMOUTH
NEWPORT
BRADING
YARMOUTH
Newtown Old Town Hall
Carisbrooke Castle
Nunwell House
ISLE OF WIGHT
SWANAGE

MAP 4
This Map does not include Properties which are open by appointment only or very infrequently
A
B
C
D
E
F
G
H
J
K
L
M
N
P
R
S
T
U
V
W
DONEGAL
LONDONDERRY
ANTRIM
TYRONE
NORTHERN IRELAND
FERMANAGH
ARMAGH
DOWN
MONAGHAN
SLIGO
LEITRIM
MAYO
CAVAN
LOUTH
ROSCOMMON
LONGFORD
MEATH
WEST MEATH
GALWAY
REPUBLIC OF IRELAND
OFFALY
KILDARE
DUBLIN
LEIX
WICKLOW
CLARE
CARLOW
TIPPERARARY
LIMERICK
KILKENNY
WEXFORD
WATERFORD
KERRY
CORK
COLERAINE
Mussenden Temple, Bishops Gate & Black Glen
LONDONDERRY
Printing Press STRABANE
Arthur House
LARNE
AHOGHILL
MONEYMORE
ANTRIM
Templetown Mausoleum
Springhill
Ulster American Folk Park
DONEGAL
OMAGH
BELFAST
NEWTOWNARDS
Mount Stewart Garden Temple of the Winds
Wellbrook Beetling Mill
MOY
The Argory
Ardress House
Rowallane Garden
PORTADOWN
Lissadell
ENNISKILLEN
Castle Coole
Florence Court
ARMAGH
DOWNPATRICK
Castle Ward
Derrymore House
MONAGHAN
NEWCASTLE
NEWRY
DUNDALK
LEITRIM
CAVAN
CASTLEBAR
WESTPORT
LONGFORD
CLAREMORRIS
Clonalis House
ROSCOMMON
DROGHEDA
KELLS
DUBLIN AIRPORT
National Botanic Gardens
LUCAN
DUBLIN
ATHLONE
Castletown House
Fernhill
GALWAY
TULLAMORE
BRAY
KILDARE
Russborough
PORT LAOIS
Mount Usher Garden
WICKLOW
CARLOW
ENNIS
SHANNON AIRPORT
KILKENNY
TIPPERARY
CASHEL
WEXFORD
Johnstown Castle
TRALEE
WATERFORD
TRAMORE
KILLARNEY
LISMORE
Lismore Castle
Riverstown House
Fota
CORK
COBH
KINSALE
GLENGARIFF
BANTRY
Bantry House
British Statute Miles
0 5 10 15 20 25 30 35 40 45 50 55 60 65
Property
Town
Property located in a town

You don't have to come to London to come to Christie's

Northumbria
Aidan Cuthbert
Eastfield House
Main Street
Corbridge
Northumberland
(043471) 3181

North-West
Victor Gubbins
St. Andrew's Place
Penrith
Cumbria
(0768) 66766

Yorkshire
Sir Nicholas Brooksbank, Bt.
46 Bootham
York
(0904) 30911

West Midlands
Michael Thompson
Stanley Hall
Bridgnorth
Shropshire
(07462) 61891

Mid-Wales
Sir Andrew Duff Gordon, Bt.
Downton House
New Radnor
Presteigne
Powys
(0242) 518999

East Anglia
Veronica Bowring
Davey House
Castle Meadow
Norwich NR1 3DE
(0603) 614546

Cotswolds
Rupert de Zoete
(Consultant)
111 The Promenade
Cheltenham
Gloucester
(0242) 518999

West Country
Richard de Pelet
Monmouth Lodge
Yenston
Templecombe
Somerset
(0963) 70518
and
Nigel Thimbleby
Wolfeton House
Dorchester
Dorset
(0305) 68748
and
39 Poole Hill
Bournemouth
Dorset
(0202) 292740

Cornwall
Christopher Petherick
Tredeague
Porthpean
St. Austell
Cornwall
(0726) 64672

South-East
Kim North
Cotlands
Cowfold
West Sussex
(040386) 850

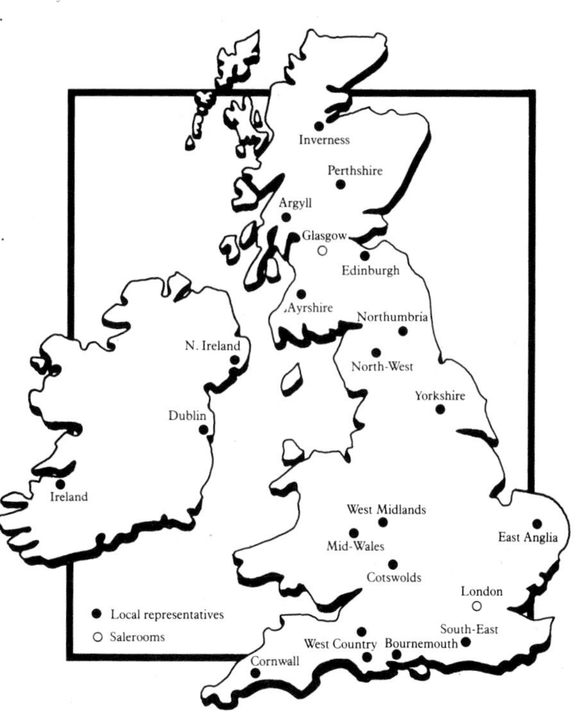

Our representatives throughout the British Isles offer convenient local access to the full range of services centred on Christie's salerooms in London.

Wherever you live, whether you are contemplating sale by auction or you would like advice on the valuation of works of art for insurance or other purposes, please consult your nearest Christie's representative.

He will be pleased to see you by appointment and, if you decide to sell, will arrange for property to be transported to one of our London salerooms.

Christie's. International Fine Art Auctioneers

CHRISTIE'S

Inverness
Jack Buchanan
111 Church Street
Inverness
(0463) 234603

Perthshire
Sebastian Thewes
Strathgarry House
Killiecrankie by Pitlochry
Perthshire
(079681) 216

Argyll
Sir Ilay Campbell, Bt.
Cumlodden Estate Office
Crarae, Inveraray
Argyll PA32 8YA
(05466) 633

Edinburgh
Michael Clayton
5 Wemyss Place
Edinburgh
(031) 225 4756/7

Ayrshire
James Hunter Blair
Blairquhan
Maybole
Ayrshire
(06557) 239

Ireland
Desmond Fitz-Gerald
Knight of Glin
Glin Castle, Glin
Co. Limerick

Dublin Office
(0001) 680585

N. Ireland
John Lewis-Crosby
Marybrook House
Raleagh Road
Crossgar
Downpatrick
Co. Down
(0396) 830574

Channel Islands
Richard de la Hey
8 David Place
St. Helier, Jersey
(0534) 77582

City of London
Simon Birch
10/12 Copthall Avenue
(Second Floor)
London EC2R 7DJ
(01) 588 4424

Salerooms

Christie, Manson & Woods Ltd
8 King Street
St. James's
London SW1Y 6QT
(01) 839 9060

Christie's
South Kensington
85 Old Brompton Road
London SW7 3JS
(01) 581 2231

Glasgow
Christie's & Edmiston's Ltd
164-166 Bath Street
Glasgow
(041) 332 8134

MAPS 5 & 6

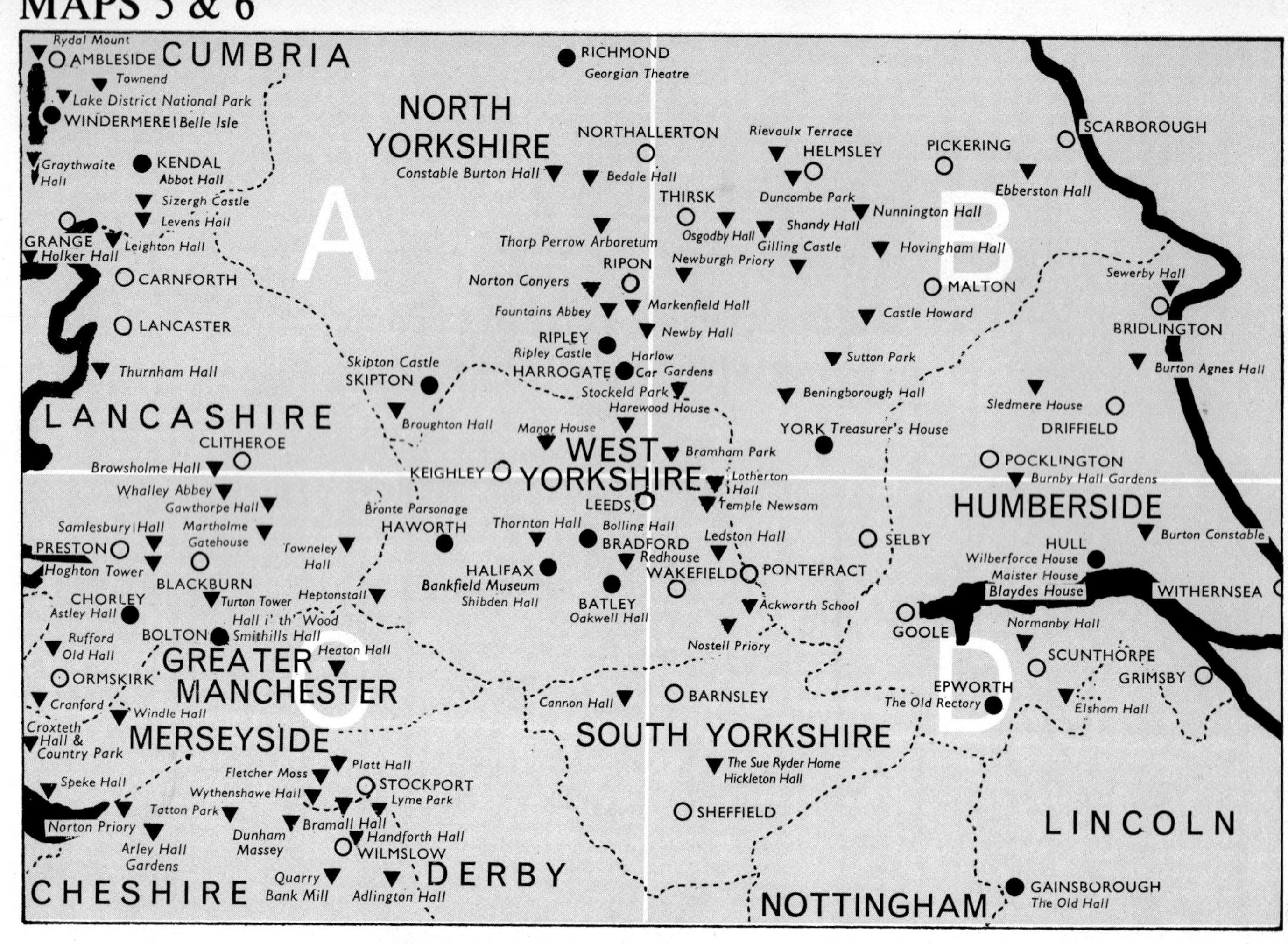

Rydal Mount
AMBLESIDE
CUMBRIA
Townend
Lake District National Park
WINDERMERE
Belle Isle
Graythwaite Hall
KENDAL
Abbot Hall
Sizergh Castle
Levens Hall
GRANGE
Holker Hall
Leighton Hall
CARNFORTH
LANCASTER
Thurnham Hall
LANCASHIRE
CLITHEROE
Browsholme Hall
Whalley Abbey
Gawthorpe Hall
Samlesbury Hall
Martholme Gatehouse
PRESTON
Hoghton Tower
BLACKBURN
Towneley Hall
CHORLEY
Astley Hall
Turton Tower
Rufford Old Hall
BOLTON
Smithills Hall
Hall i' th' Wood
ORMSKIRK
GREATER MANCHESTER
Heaton Hall
Cranford
Windle Hall
Croxteth Hall & Country Park
MERSEYSIDE
Speke Hall
Norton Priory
Fletcher Moss
Platt Hall
Wythenshawe Hall
STOCKPORT
Lyme Park
Tatton Park
Bramall Hall
Arley Hall Gardens
Dunham Massey
Handforth Hall
WILMSLOW
Quarry Bank Mill
Adlington Hall
CHESHIRE
DERBY
RICHMOND
Georgian Theatre
NORTH YORKSHIRE
NORTHALLERTON
Constable Burton Hall
Bedale Hall
Rievaulx Terrace
HELMSLEY
PICKERING
SCARBOROUGH
Ebberston Hall
THIRSK
Duncombe Park
Nunnington Hall
Osgodby Hall
Shandy Hall
Gilling Castle
Hovingham Hall
Thorp Perrow Arboretum
Newburgh Priory
RIPON
Norton Conyers
MALTON
Sewerby Hall
Markenfield Hall
Fountains Abbey
Castle Howard
BRIDLINGTON
Newby Hall
RIPLEY
Ripley Castle
Harlow Car Gardens
HARROGATE
Sutton Park
Burton Agnes Hall
Skipton Castle
SKIPTON
Stockeld Park
Beningborough Hall
Harewood House
Sledmere House
Broughton Hall
DRIFFIELD
Manor House
WEST YORKSHIRE
YORK
Treasurer's House
Bramham Park
POCKLINGTON
KEIGHLEY
Lotherton Hall
Burnby Hall Gardens
LEEDS
Temple Newsam
Bronte Parsonage
HUMBERSIDE
HAWORTH
Thornton Hall
Bolling Hall
BRADFORD
Ledston Hall
SELBY
Burton Constable
HULL
Wilberforce House
Maister House
Blaydes House
WITHERNSEA
Redhouse
HALIFAX
Bankfield Museum
Shibden Hall
Heptonstall
WAKEFIELD
PONTEFRACT
BATLEY
Oakwell Hall
Ackworth School
GOOLE
Normanby Hall
Nostell Priory
SCUNTHORPE
GRIMSBY
EPWORTH
The Old Rectory
Elsham Hall
Cannon Hall
BARNSLEY
SOUTH YORKSHIRE
The Sue Ryder Home
Hickleton Hall
SHEFFIELD
LINCOLN
GAINSBOROUGH
The Old Hall
NOTTINGHAM
A
B
C
D

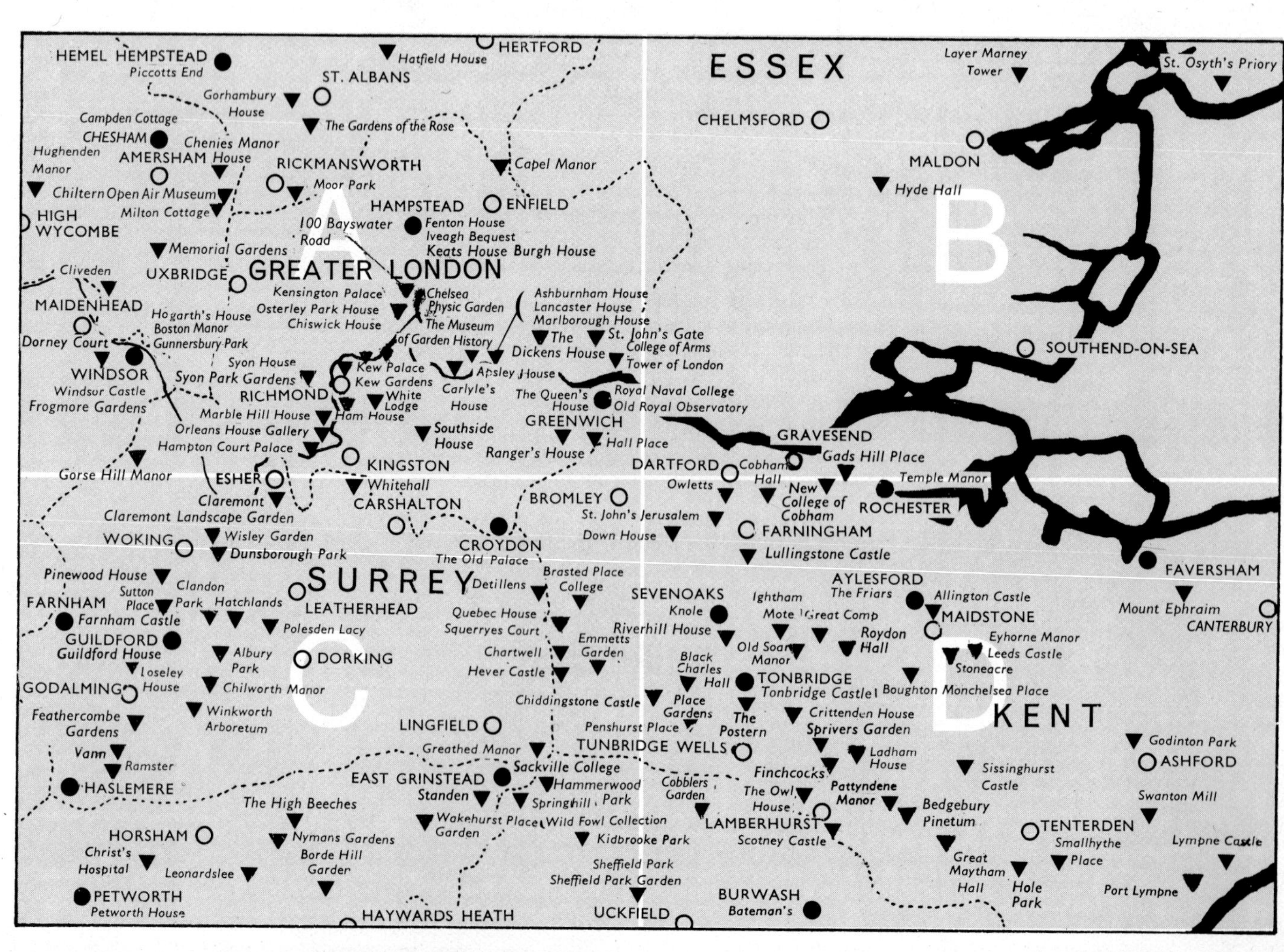

HEMEL HEMPSTEAD
Piccotts End
Hatfield House
HERTFORD
ESSEX
Layer Marney Tower
St. Osyth's Priory
ST. ALBANS
Gorhambury House
The Gardens of the Rose
Campden Cottage
CHESHAM
Chenies Manor House
CHELMSFORD
Hughenden Manor
AMERSHAM
RICKMANSWORTH
Capel Manor
MALDON
Chiltern Open Air Museum
Moor Park
Hyde Hall
HIGH WYCOMBE
Milton Cottage
HAMPSTEAD
ENFIELD
100 Bayswater Road
Fenton House
Iveagh Bequest
Keats House
Burgh House
Memorial Gardens
Cliveden
UXBRIDGE
GREATER LONDON
Kensington Palace
Chelsea Physic Garden
MAIDENHEAD
Hogarth's House
Osterley Park House
Boston Manor
Chiswick House
Gunnersbury Park
The Museum of Garden History
Ashburnham House
Lancaster House
Marlborough House
The Dickens House
St. John's Gate
College of Arms
Tower of London
Dorney Court
Syon House
Kew Palace
Kew Gardens
Carlyle's House
Apsley House
SOUTHEND-ON-SEA
WINDSOR
Windsor Castle
Frogmore Gardens
Syon Park Gardens
RICHMOND
White Lodge
The Queen's House
Royal Naval College
Old Royal Observatory
Marble Hill House
Ham House
Orleans House Gallery
Southside House
GREENWICH
Hampton Court Palace
Ranger's House
Hall Place
GRAVESEND
Gads Hill Place
Gorse Hill Manor
ESHER
KINGSTON
Whitehall
DARTFORD
Cobham Hall
Owletts
Temple Manor
Claremont
CARSHALTON
BROMLEY
New College of Cobham
ROCHESTER
Claremont Landscape Garden
St. John's Jerusalem
FARNINGHAM
WOKING
Wisley Garden
Dunsborough Park
CROYDON
The Old Palace
Down House
Lullingstone Castle
AYLESFORD
The Friars
FAVERSHAM
Pinewood House
Clandon Park
Sutton Place
SURREY
Detillens
Brasted Place College
SEVENOAKS
Ightham Mote
Allington Castle
MAIDSTONE
Mount Ephraim
CANTERBURY
FARNHAM
Farnham Castle
Hatchlands
LEATHERHEAD
Quebec House
Knole
Great Comp
Polesden Lacy
Squerryes Court
Riverhill House
Roydon Hall
Eyhorne Manor
GUILDFORD
Guildford House
Albury Park
DORKING
Chartwell
Emmetts Garden
Old Soar Manor
Black Charles Hall
Leeds Castle
Stoneacre
Loseley House
Hever Castle
TONBRIDGE
Tonbridge Castle
GODALMING
Chilworth Manor
Chiddingstone Castle
Place Gardens
Boughton Monchelsea Place
Feathercombe Gardens
Winkworth Arboretum
LINGFIELD
Penshurst Place
The Postern
Crittenden House
Sprivers Garden
KENT
Godinton Park
Vann
Ramster
Greathed Manor
TUNBRIDGE WELLS
Ladham House
ASHFORD
Sissinghurst Castle
HASLEMERE
EAST GRINSTEAD
Sackville College
Standen
Hammerwood Park
Cobblers Garden
Finchcocks
The Owl House
Pattyndene Manor
Bedgebury Pinetum
Swanton Mill
The High Beeches
Springhill
Wakehurst Place Garden
Wild Fowl Collection
LAMBERHURST
Scotney Castle
TENTERDEN
Smallhythe Place
Lympne Castle
HORSHAM
Nymans Gardens
Kidbrooke Park
Christ's Hospital
Borde Hill Garden
Leonardslee
Sheffield Park
Sheffield Park Garden
Great Maytham Hall
Hole Park
Port Lympne
PETWORTH
Petworth House
HAYWARDS HEATH
UCKFIELD
BURWASH
Bateman's
A
B
C
D

FOUR HISTORIC FAMILY HOMES

within easy reach of London

STRATFIELD SAYE HOUSE

Family home of the Dukes of Wellington.
See Page 70

HATFIELD HOUSE

Family home of the Marquess of Salisbury.
See Page 76

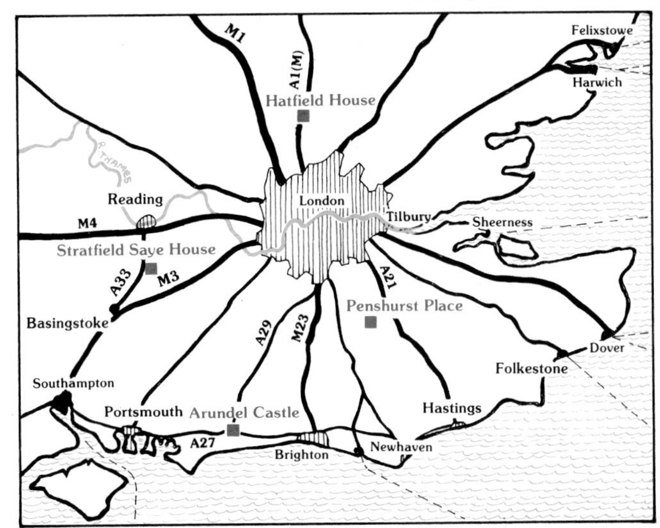

ARUNDEL CASTLE

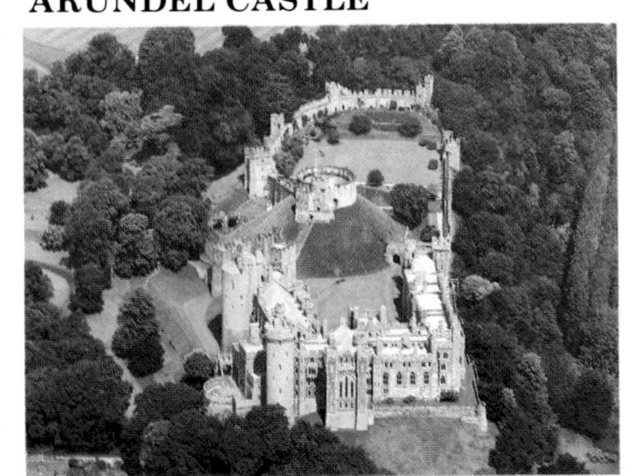

Family home of the Dukes of Norfolk.
See Page 145

PENSHURST PLACE

Family home of William Sidney, Viscount De L'Isle, VC, KG. See Page 86

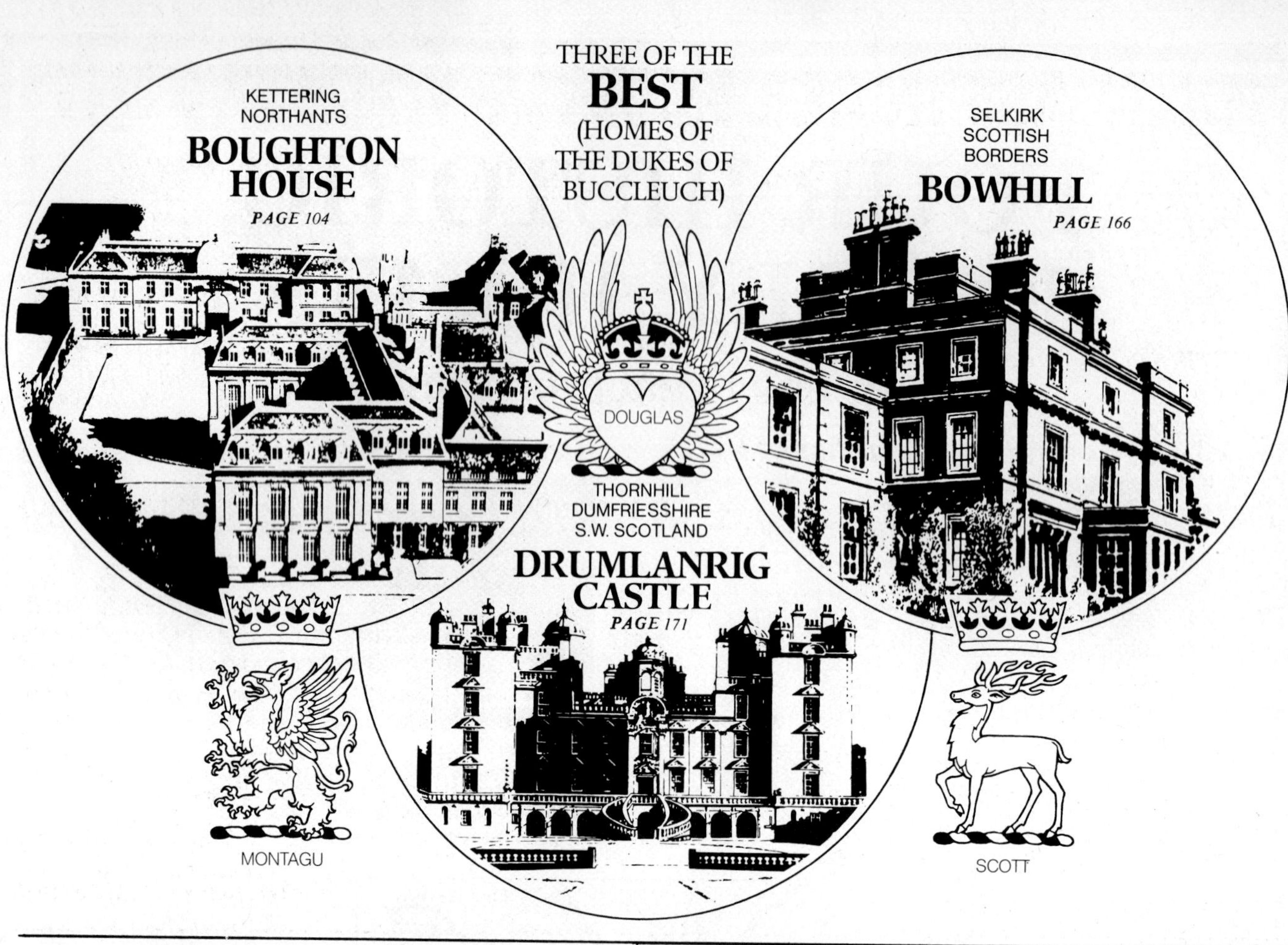
THREE OF THE
BEST
(HOMES OF
THE DUKES OF
BUCCLEUCH)
KETTERING
NORTHANTS
BOUGHTON
HOUSE
PAGE 104
SELKIRK
SCOTTISH
BORDERS
BOWHILL
PAGE 166
DOUGLAS
THORNHILL
DUMFRIESSHIRE
S.W. SCOTLAND
DRUMLANRIG
CASTLE
PAGE 171
MONTAGU
SCOTT

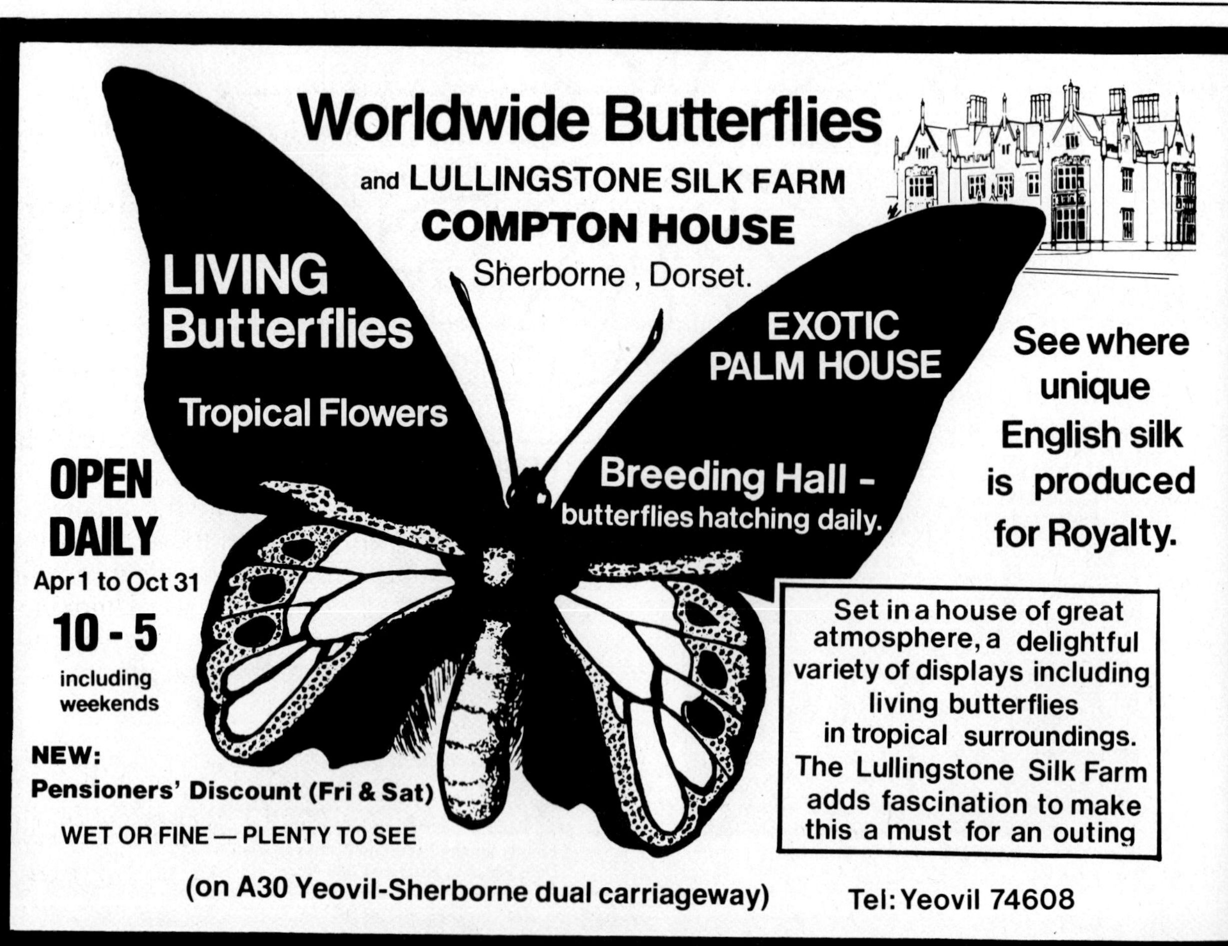
Worldwide Butterflies
and LULLINGSTONE SILK FARM
COMPTON HOUSE
Sherborne, Dorset.
LIVING
Butterflies
Tropical Flowers
EXOTIC
PALM HOUSE
Breeding Hall -
butterflies hatching daily.
See where
unique
English silk
is produced
for Royalty.
OPEN
DAILY
Apr 1 to Oct 31
10 - 5
including
weekends
NEW:
Pensioners' Discount (Fri & Sat)
WET OR FINE — PLENTY TO SEE
Set in a house of great
atmosphere, a delightful
variety of displays including
living butterflies
in tropical surroundings.
The Lullingstone Silk Farm
adds fascination to make
this a must for an outing
(on A30 Yeovil-Sherborne dual carriageway)
Tel: Yeovil 74608

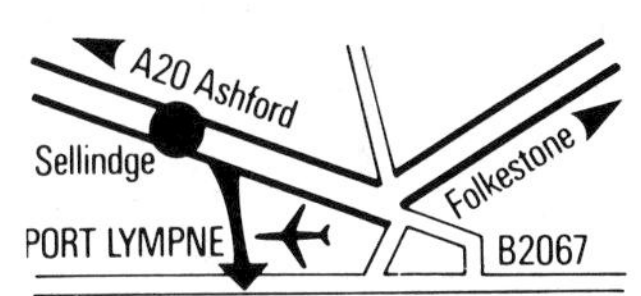

A20 Ashford
Sellindge
Folkestone
PORT LYMPNE
B2067

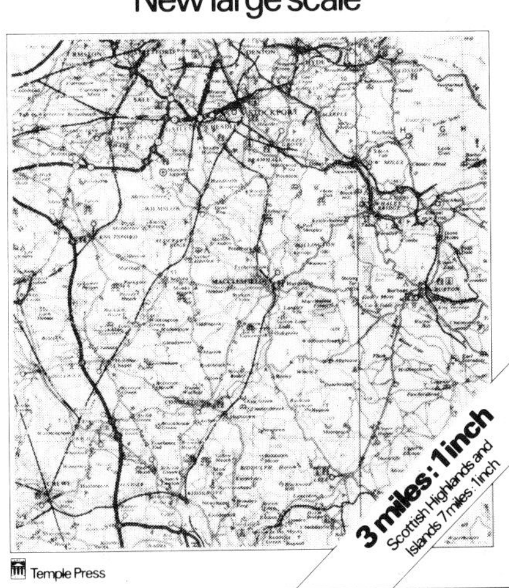

OS
Ordnance Survey
Motoring Atlas
New large scale
3 miles: 1 inch
Scottish Highlands and Islands 7 miles: 1 inch
Temple Press

CLAVERTON MANOR

BATH

THE AMERICAN MUSEUM

The American Museum stands high above the Avon Valley. Eighteen furnished period rooms combine with galleries of textiles, pewter, glass and silver to illustrate the background of American domestic life between the 17th and 19th centuries. Special sections are devoted to the American Indians, Pennsylvania Germans and the Shakers. American gardens and teas with American cookies.

OAKHILL MANOR

Near BATH

MUSEUM OF MODELS RELATING TO TRANSPORT

High in the Mendip Hills this is a fine example of one of England's smaller country estates of 45 acres and features:

* One of the world's finest private collections of models covering air, sea and land transport.
* Furnished Mansion House set in 8 acres of delightful gardens.
* One of Europe's finest and most spectacular miniature railways transports visitors from the car park to the museum.

Refreshment buffet, picnic area, gift shop. Free car park.

Open Easter to November 4th; daily (including weekends) 12 noon to 6 p.m.

Entrance: off A37 4 miles north of Shepton Mallet, turn at side of Mendip Inn. Telephone: Oakhill 840210
High in the Mendip Hills

CLOSE TO WELLS, GLASTONBURY, CHEDDAR GORGE & CRANMORE

No. 1 ROYAL CRESCENT

BATH

The Royal Crescent has been described as "the summit of the Palladian achievement in Bath", a city of unique period character, famous for its splendid Georgian architecture. This magnificent semi-elliptical terrace of thirty houses overlooking the Victoria Park was built between 1767 and 1774 by John Wood, the Younger—the climax of his father's grand design for a new city on the classical ideal. In 1970 No. 1 Royal Crescent was completely restored and the main rooms have been decorated and furnished as they might have been in the eighteenth century when the fashionable world flocked to Bath for the season and to take the waters.

DYRHAM PARK

AVON

12 miles east of Bristol; 8 miles north of Bath

THE NATIONAL TRUST

A fine William and Mary house built for William Blathwayt, Secretary at War and Secretary of State to William III. Blathwayt married Mary Wynter in 1686 and five years later began to rebuild Dyrham, her family home. The entrance or east front was designed by Talman, who also worked at Chatsworth and Hampton Court, in 1698 whereas the garden front, which overlooks the tranquil aspect of medieval church, small lake with waterfowl and old Ilex and lime trees, was completed six years earlier by a Dutchman, Hauduroy.

Within the house there has been little change in the rooms since they were furnished by Blathwayt, according to the inventory drawn up by his housekeeper. Some are panelled in cedar or Virginian walnut and one still has its original leather wall hangings. The furniture, pictures and tapestries have associations with Pepys, Evelyn and other men of letters, friends of Thomas Povey, Blathwayt's uncle.

Picnics and controlled dogs welcome in the historic deer park.

Historic Houses Castles & Gardens

in Great Britain and Ireland

- △ Denotes guided tours of the House
- ✿ Denotes gardens open to the public
- ♈ Denotes properties recognised by the Countryside Commission
- ☕ Denotes tea and light refreshments
- ✕ Denotes lunches or high tea
- ♿ Denotes the major part of the property is suitable for wheelchairs
- Ⓔ Denotes educational services recognised by the Heritage Education Trust, see page 8

PROPERTY (*showing map reference*)	LOCATION (*with nearest Rly. Stn.*)	OPENING TIMES AND ADMISSION CHARGES CATERING FACILITIES	COACH AND RAIL TOURS BUS SERVICES (*showing alighting points*)
AVON			
BADMINTON HOUSE, Badminton *map 2 M* *His Grace the Duke of Beaufort, K.G., G.C.V.O.* Built for the first Duke of Beaufort in Charles II's reign. Altered by Kent c. 1740	In the village of Badminton, 5 m E of Chipping Sodbury *Stn: Chippenham (10m)*	Wednesdays only: June 6, July 11, Aug. 8 & Sept. 5: 2.30–5. Adm. £1, O.A.Ps. 50p, Chd. 10p. ☕ Buffet teas available in the Orangery	Tours from West Country & South Wales National tours from Cheltenham
BARSTAPLE HOUSE (TRINITY ALMS-HOUSES), Bristol *map 2 M* *Bristol Municipal Charities* ✿ Victorian almshouse with garden courtyard	Old Market St., Bristol; ½ m from City centre on A42 *Stn: Bristol*	GARDEN & EXTERIOR OF BUILDINGS ONLY: All the year—Weekdays 10–4. Adm. free. *The Almshouse is occupied mainly by elderly residents & their rights for privacy should be respected* ☎ *Bristol* (0272) 25777 (Warden)	Local City bus service
BECKFORD'S TOWER, Bath *map 2 M* *The Beckford Tower Trust* Built 1827 by William Beckford of Fonthill. A Beckford Museum (first floor); fine views from Belvedere (156 steps)	2 m from Bath Spa Stn. via Lansdown Rd. *Stn: Bath Spa (2 m)*	April 1 to Oct. 28—Sats., Suns. & Bank Hol. Mons. 2–5. Adm. 30p, Chd. & O.A.Ps. 20p. *Parties other days by arrangement.* ☎ *Bath* (0225) 336228	Bristol Omnibus 2 from Bath (*alight Lansdown Cemetery*) (*not Suns. or B. Hols.*)
BLAISE CASTLE HOUSE, Henbury *City of Bristol* *map 2 M* 18th century house set in landscaped park; containing collections illustrating everyday life of the last 300 years	4 m NW of central Bristol *Stns: Bristol Temple Meads (5 m); Sea Mills (2 m)*	All the year—Sats. to Weds. 10–1, 2–5, *Closed Thurs. & Fris.; Christmas Day, Boxing Day, New Year's Day & Good Friday*. Adm. free ☎ *Bristol* 506789 ☕ tea bar (in park)	Bristol City services 1, 2, 26, 47, 49
CLAVERTON MANOR, nr Bath *map 2 M* △ *The American Museum in Britain* ✿ A Greek Revival house high above the valley of the Avon. Completely furnished rooms, 17th, Ⓔ 18th and 19th century brought from the U.S.A.	2½ m from Bath Stn. via Bathwick Hill; 3½ m SE of Bath via Warminster rd (A36) & Claverton village *Stn: Bath Spa (2½ m)*	March 24 to Oct. 28—Daily (except Mons.) 2–5; Bank Hols. and preceeding Sun. 11–5. ***Mornings and winter months on application only.*** School parties by previous arrangement except Jan. Educational Tel. 63538. ***Pre-arranged parties over 30 at reduced rate.*** Adm. (1983 rates) House & Grounds £1.60, Chd. & O.A.Ps. £1.40, Grounds only 50p. Parties of children not admitted during normal opening hours. ☎ *Bath* (0225) 60503 ☕ with American cookies (*Gingerbead cooked in 18th century oven*)	National tours from Cheltenham & Gloucester London Transport tour *Bus:* 18 from Bath (*alight The Avenue, 10 minutes walk*) (*only 18/264 Suns.*)
CLEVEDON COURT, nr Clevedon *The National Trust* *map 2 M* ✿ A 14th cent. manor house incorporating a 12th cent. tower and a 13th cent. hall with terraced 18th cent. garden; rare shrubs and plants	1½ m E of Clevedon off the Bristol rd B3130 *Stn: Yatton (3 m)*	April to end of September—Weds., Thurs. & Suns., also Bank Hol. Mons. 2.30–5.30 (last adm. 5). Adm. £1.30. Chd. 65p (children under 17 must be accompanied by an adult). No dogs. Unsuitable for wheelchairs & coaches. ☕ **at the House**	Bristol 350, 357, 362, X5 (*not Suns.*), Bristol—Clevedon (*alight gates*)
DYRHAM PARK, nr Bristol and Bath *The National Trust* *map 2 M* ✿ Late 17th century house in a remarkable setting. The Blathwayt furniture and Dutch paintings in a fine series of panelled rooms. ♿ Deer Park	12 m E of Bristol, approach from Bath–Stroud rd (A46), 2 m S of Tormarton interchange with M4 8 m N of Bath *Stn: Bath Spa (8 m)*	Park—Daily 12–6 (or dusk if earlier). House & Garden: April, May & Oct.—Daily (except Thurs. & Fris.) 2–6. June, July, Aug. & Sept.—Daily (except Fris.) 2–6. Last admission 5.30. Adm. House, Gardens & Park £2, Chd. £1. *Prebooked parties of 15 or more* £1.50. Park only 50p, Chd. 25p. Dogs in park on leads, please. Wheelchairs provided. ☕ **in the Orangery**	Bristol 236 Yate–Bath (*Weds. & Sats. only*) 334, Bristol—Doynton (*not Suns.*) (1½ *m*) 388 Bristol—Dyram (*Tues./Thurs. only*)
GEORGIAN HOUSE (1790) *map 2 M* *City of Bristol* Completely equipped in the style of the period	7 Great George St., Bristol 1 *Stn: Bristol Temple Meads (¾ m)*	All the year—Mon. to Sat. 10–1, 2–5. *Closed Christmas Day, Boxing Day, New Year's Day, Good Friday, May 7 & Spring B.H. Mon. & Tues.* Adm. free ☎ *Bristol* 299771	City buses (*frequent*)
HERSCHEL HOUSE, Bath *map 2 M* *William Herschel Society* Small Georgian house of Sir William Herschel from which he discovered the planet Uranus in 1781. Furnished museum of his music and astronomy	19 New King St. 3 mins. walk from Queen Sq. *Stn: Bath Spa*	March 3 to Oct. 27—Weds. & Sats. 2–5. Adm. 50p. Parties other days by arrangement. ☎ *Bath* (0225) 336228	Local bus services
HORTON COURT, Horton *map 2 M* *The National Trust* ♿ A Cotswold manor house restored and altered in the 19th century. 12th century hall and late Perpendicular ambulatory in garden only shown.	3 m NE of Chipping Sodbury, ¾ m N of Horton, 1 m W of Bath-Stroud rd (A46)	Hall & Ambulatory only: April to October—Weds. & Sats. 2–6 (or sunset if earlier) ***Other times by written appointment with the tenant*** Adm. 50p *No reduction for parties or children.* No dogs. Unsuitable for coaches. Wheelchairs—ambulatory only.	
LITTLE SODBURY MANOR, Chipping Sodbury *map 2 M* *Gerald Harford, Esq.* Medieval House with fine Great Hall. There are Tudor, Jacobean and Queen Anne additions	2½ m from Chipping Sodbury off A46 *Stn: Bristol Parkway (10 m)*	April to Sept.—By appointment only. Adm. £1. ☎ *Chipping Sodbury* 312232	Bristol 323 to Little Sodbury (*except Weds., Sats. & Suns.*)
LYNCOMBE COURT, Bath *map 2 M* *Captain Francis Burne* ✿ Victorian garden of 1½ acres; winter garden, water garden; herbaceous plants and shrubs; wood walks. Magnificent views.	In Lyncombe Vale Rd.: from Claverton St. turn l. up Lyncombe Hill on to Lyncombe Vale Rd. *Stn: Bath*	GARDEN ONLY: Suns. May 20 & 27; June 3 & 10: 2–6. Adm. 50p, Chd. 20p. *In aid of National Gardens' Scheme. No dogs.* ☕ tea & biscuits	Local bus services

PROPERTY (*showing map reference*)	LOCATION (*with nearest Rly. Stn.*)	OPENING TIMES AND ADMISSION CHARGES CATERING FACILITIES	COACH AND RAIL TOURS BUS SERVICES (*showing alighting points*)
AVON—*continued*			
THE MANOR HOUSE, Walton-in-Gordano *Mr. & Mrs. Simon Wills* *map 2 M* 4 acres—mainly shrubs and fine trees. Much new planting including bulbs, alpines, ground cover and silver plants	W of Bristol; via B3124 from Clevedon to Portishead; driveway on left before 1st houses in Walton-in-Gordano *Stn: Yatton (6 m)*	GARDEN ONLY: April 2 to Sept. 27—Mons., Weds. & Thurs. 10–4. Also Bank Hol. Sun. & Mon., Aug. 26/27: 2–6. Open by appointment all year. Adm. 50p, Chd. 25p. *In aid of National Gardens' Scheme, Gardeners' Sunday & St. Peter's Hospice.* Plants for sale. No dogs. Coaches by appointment only. teas—Bank Hols. only *Clevedon* (0272) 872067	Bristol X5 (*not Suns.*), 360 (*not Suns.*), 124 (*peak Suns. only*)
OAKHILL MANOR, Oakhill, nr Bath *map 2 S* *W. W. Harper, Esq.* Attractive small country estate of 45 acres, Mansion House set in 8 acres of gardens in the Mendip Hills. Collection of models relating to transport; miniature railway	Entrance to car pk on A37, 4 m N of Shepton Mallet at side of Mendip Inn	Good Friday to Nov. 4—Daily 12–6. Adm. (1983 rates, all inclusive including 2 rides on the railway) £2.25, O.A.Ps. & Chd. 6-15 yrs. £1.50, Chd. 2-5 yrs. 95p. Suitable in part to disabled. Miniature railway transports visitors from car park to house. Picnic area. Gilft shop. light lunches; refreshments *Oakhill* 840210	Bristol 176 (*not Suns.*), Bath–Oakhill 175 (*not Suns.*), Bath–Gurney Slade
ORCHARD HOUSE, Claverton *map 2 M* *Rear Adm. & Mrs. Hugh Tracy* Plantsman's garden of 2½ acres in which owners have tried to combine botanical interest with attractive and informal layout. Collections of herbs, alpines, ground-cover and silver plants; rock gardens, herbaceous borders, lawns, shrubs, views.	3½ m from centre of Bath; turn off at signpost for Claverton Village or ½ m down hill from American Museum, Claverton. *Stn: Bath Spa (2½ m)*	GARDEN ONLY: Wednesdays April 25; May 2, 9 & 16; June 6 & 13 and Sunday July 15: 2–6. Adm. 50p, Chd. 20p. *In aid of National Gardens' Scheme & Bath Skyline Appeal (N.T.).* No dogs. Plants for sale. Small (wholesale) nursery. teas, July 15	Local buses from Bath (*alight Claverton village*)
RED LODGE, Bristol *map 2 M* *City of Bristol* Late 16th cent. house with period panelling and plasterwork together with furniture	Park Row, Bristol, 1 *Stn: Bristol Temple Meads (¾ m)*	All the year—Mon. to Sat. 10–1, 2–5. *Closed Christmas Day, Boxing Day, New Year's Day, Good Friday, May 7 & Spring B.H. Mon. & Tues.* Adm. free *Bristol* 299771	Bristol City services (*near city centre*)
No. 1 ROYAL CRESCENT, Bath *map 2 M* *Bath Preservation Trust* A Georgian House as it was when built by John Wood the Younger 1767	Close to city centre. *Stn: Bath Spa (¾ m)*	March to Oct.–Tues. to Sats. 11–5; Suns. & Bank Hol. Mons. 2–5. Last adm. 4.40. *Closed Mons. (except B. Hols.) & Good Friday.* Adm. 75p; Chd., Students& O.A.Ps. (U.K.) 45p. Parties by arrangement with the House Manager. *No dogs.* *Bath* (0225) 28126	From Bus Station (¾ m)—51 (open top) (*alight at door*); 20 (3 *mins, walk*); 2, 7, 8, 9 (6 *mins. walk*)
ST. VINCENT'S PRIORY, Clifton *map 2 M* *G. Melhuish, Esq.* A small Gothic revival house, built over caves which were traditionally once a Christian sanctuary	Overlooking Clifton Suspension Bridge *Stn: Bristol Temple Meads (2½ m)*	July & Aug.—Sats. & Suns. 2.15–6. *Other times by appointment only.* Adm. 25p. Avon Gorge Hotel *Bristol* 739621	Bus service X62 (*not Suns.*) 8 & 83 from City centre
VINE HOUSE, Henbury, Bristol *map 2 M* *Professor & Mrs. T. F. Hewer* Two acres. Trees shrubs, small water garden; bulbs; naturalised garden landscape.	4 m NW of Bristol *Stns: Bristol Parkway (5 m); Bristol Temple Meads (5 m)*	GARDENS ONLY: Suns. & Mons. April 22/23 & May 27/28; 2–7. Also open by appointment throughout the year. Adm. 40p. Chd. & O.A.Ps. 20p. *In aid of National Gardens' Scheme & 'Friends of Blaise'.* *Bristol* 503573	Bristol City Services 1, 2, 26 (daily); 47, 49 (*not Suns.*) (*alight Henbury 'The Salutation'*)
BEDFORDSHIRE			
LUTON HOO, Luton *map 3 K* *The Wernher Family* Exterior commenced by Robert Adam, 1767. Interior remodelled in the French style early in this century. Magnificent art collection includes Fabergé jewels and unique Russian collection. Park landscaped by 'Capability' Brown.	Ent. at Park St. Gates Luton 30 m N of London via M1 (exit 10, jct. A1081 — formerly A6). Rail & Bus stns. 3 m *Stn: Luton (3 m)*	HOUSE & GARDENS—March 31 to Oct. 14—Mons., Weds., Thurs., Sats. & Good Friday 11–5.45 (Gardens 6); Suns. 2–5.45 (Gardens 6). Last adm. 5. Adm. £1.60, Chd. 80p. Gardens only: Adm. 80p, Chd 50p. Reduced rates for parties prepaid 14 days prior to visit (minimum 30 adults). No dogs admitted to House or Gardens. refreshments *Luton* (0582) 22955	British Rail, London (*St. Pancras*) to Luton (*fast trains in 30 mins.*) Green Line 707, 717, 727, 757 (London–Luton express via M1) to Luton Bus Station London Country 321, Uxbridge–Watford–St. Albans–Luton National Coaches from London, Northampton & Milton Keynes via Luton Premier/Percivals 39, Cambridge–Luton–Oxford
STAGSDEN BIRD GARDENS, Stagsden *Mr. & Mrs. R. E. Rayment* *map 3 F* A large Bird Zoo and breeding establishment for birds with over 1,300 specimens in approximately 150 species and varieties, with collection of shrub roses	5 m W of Bedford, 7 m E of Newport Pagnell, N of A422; turn N at Stagsden Church *Stn: Bedford Midland (5 m)*	Open every day of the year 11–6 (or dusk if earlier). Adm £1, Chd. (3–15 inc.) 50p, O.A.Ps. 80p. *Oakley* 2745 *Picnics welcomed in the gardens*	United Counties 132, Bedford–Newport Pagnell–Stony Stratford (*alight Stagsden village*)
THE SWISS GARDEN, Old Warden, nr Biggleswade *map 3 F* *Bedfordshire County Council* An unusual Romantic garden dating from the early 19th century, containing original buildings, ironwork and other features together with many interesting plants and trees, some of great rarity. Attractive lakeside picnic area in adjoining woodlands.	2½ m W of Biggleswade, adjoining Biggleswade – Old Warden rd; approx. 2m W of A1. *Stn: Biggleswade (3 m)*	March 24 to Oct. 28—Weds., Thurs., Sats., Suns., Good Friday, Spring & Summer (Aug.) Bank Hol. Mons. 2–6 (last adm. 5.15). N.B. *The Garden will be closed on April 29, May 27, June 24, July 29, Aug. 26, Sept. 30 & Oct. 28.* Adm. (1983 rates) 30p, Chd. (5–14) 15p. Special rates for School parties & group visits by prior arrangement. Wheelchair access—by special arrangement. Lakeside picnic area open at all times. Public lavatory (facilities for disabled). Cafeteria at adjoining Shuttleworth Aeroplane Collection *Bedford* (0234) 63222, *Ext.* 30	United Counties 179, Bedford, Biggleswade (*not Suns.*)
WOBURN ABBEY *map 3 K* *Home of the Marquess of Tavistock and his Family (Trustees of the Bedford Estates).* Home of the Dukes of Bedford for over 300 years. Rebuilt by Henry Flitcroft & Inigo Jones in mid 18c. and added to by Henry Holland in early 1800's. Situated in a beautiful 3000 acre deer park with many different species, including the famed Père David Herd. Contains one of the world's most important private art collections, including paintings by Canaletto, Van Dyck, Cuyp, Teniers, Rembrandt, Gainsborough, Reynolds, Velazquez and many other famous artists. Important collections of French and English 18 cent. furniture, silver and the fabulous Sèvres dinner service, presented to 4th Duke, by Louis XV of France. Unique forty-shop Antiques Centre, Pottery; catering, banqueting and conference facilities. (SEE PAGE 5)	In Woburn 8½ m NW of Dunstable on A50 42 m from London off M1 at junction with A5120, exit 12 (3 m from Woburn) *Stns: Woburn Sands (4 m); Ridgmont (3½ m); Flitwick (5 m)*	Jan. 1 to March 25 & Oct. 27 to Dec. 30—Sats. & Suns. only. House 11–4.45; Park 10.30–3.45. March 26 to Oct. 26—Daily. House: Weekdays 11–5.45; Suns. 11–6.15. Park: Weekdays 10–4.45; Suns. 10–5.45. *Last adm: to House 45 mins. before closing time every day.* Adm. charges not available at time of going to press. *Party rates are available* THE THORNERY. This single room thatched summer house was designed by Humphry Repton in the early 19th century and has recently been restored. Frequently used by Mary the 'Flying Duchess' as a retreat, the building may now be visited by special appointment. Free Car Park. Licensed restaurants. Enquiries 052 525 666, Catering 052 525 662. Antiques Centre 052 525 350	Trains from Euston to Bletchley Frames tours from London East Kent Tours National tours from London, Northampton, Birmingham & the Midlands Grey-Green Tours from London United Counties 141, Bedford–Woburn–Aylesbury, 67 Luton–Woburn–Bletchley National Coach 556, London–Woburn–Northampton
WREST PARK, Silsoe *map 3 K* *Dept. of the Environment* Fine example of a formal canal garden	10 m N of Luton on Bedford rd (A6) *Stn: Flitwick (4½m)*	Gardens & part of House: April to Sept.—Sats., Suns. & Bank Hol. Mons. 9.30–6.30. Adm. 50p, Chd. (under 16) & O.A.Ps. 25p. in the Orangery.	United Counties 142, 143, Luton–Bedford (*alight Silsoe Church*)

LUTON HOO

WERNHER COLLECTION

LUTON, BEDFORDSHIRE

Famous pictures (Rembrandt, Titian etc.), magnificent tapestries and furniture, English china, mediaeval ivories, silver gilt, 16th and 17th century jewels. Russian Fabergé jewels and unique collection of portraits and mementoes of the Russian Imperial Family.

Times of Opening:
HOUSE AND GARDENS:
March 31st to October 14th:
Mons., Weds., Thurs., Sats. and Good Friday: 11a.m.—5.45 p.m. (Gardens 6 p.m.); Sun. 2—5.45 p.m. (Gardens 6 p.m.).

Last admissions 5 p.m.

Admission £1.60; Children 80p.

Gardens only: 80p; Children 50p.

Reduced rates for parties prepaid 14 days prior to visit (minimum 30 adults). Dogs not admitted to House or Gardens.

Refreshments.

Facilities available for filming, still photography, conferences, banquets and similar functions.

Flowers from Luton Hoo Garden arranged in the House.

Illustrated Guide Book, price £1 (£1.25 inc. post).

Telephone: Luton (0582) 22955

A Treasure House in a perfect setting

Aerial view of House commenced by Robert Adam

ST. VINCENT'S PRIORY

SION HILL, CLIFTON
BRISTOL

A small Gothic revival house, built over caves, which were traditionally once a Christian sanctuary. It has unusual caryatid figures adorning the facade. The hall-conservatory is illuminated by coloured glass, portraying Christian symbols. The ground floor reception room has a chimney piece depicting David and Goliath; the first floor music room is outstanding for a frieze modelled in relief from Pompeian murals.

OPEN July and August on Saturdays and Sundays from 2.15 p.m. to 6.00 p.m. At other times by appointment. Admission 25p.

STAGSDEN
BIRD GARDENS
STAGSDEN BEDFORD

An extensive bird breeding and conservation centre specialising in pheasants, waterfowl, and old breeds of poultry, together with a wide variety of other birds in all numbering over 150 species and varieties. Surplus stock available at certain times during the year. There is also a large collection of shrub roses, and extensive free parking facilities. Reduced rates are charged for parties which book in advance, and school parties are particularly welcome. The Zoo is open every day of the year from 11 a.m., and is situated 200 yards north of the A422 Bedford to Newport Pagnell road. Visitors should take the Turvey Road at Stagsden Church.

Tel. Oakley 2745.

BASILDON PARK

Near PANGBOURNE, BERKSHIRE

THE NATIONAL TRUST

Classical late-Georgian house of Bath stone, built by John Carr of York for Sir Francis Sykes, in a beautiful setting overlooking the Thames Valley and surrounded by parkland. The focal point is a spacious Octagon room, and there is much fine plasterwork. Given to the National Trust by Lord Iliffe in 1978, with its notable collection of pictures and furniture. Interesting Anglo-Indian room, connected with the East India Company. Unusual decorated Shell room.

OPENING TIMES PAGE 27

"Country Life" photograph

BERKSHIRE

PROPERTY (*showing map reference*)	LOCATION (*with nearest Rly. Stn.*)	OPENING TIMES AND ADMISSION CHARGES CATERING FACILITIES	COACH AND RAIL TOURS BUS SERVICES (*showing alighting points*)
BASILDON PARK, nr Pangbourne *map 3 J* *The National Trust* Classical house, built 1776. Unusual Octagon room; fine plasterwork; important paintings and furniture. Garden	7 m NW of Reading between Pangbourne & Streatley on A329 *Stns: Pangbourne (2 m); Goring & Streatley (3 m)*	April to Oct.—Weds. to Sats. 2–6; Suns. & Bank Hol. Mons. 12–6. *Last adm. to house half-hour before closing.* Adm. House & Grounds £1.50, Chd. 75p, O.A.Ps. £1 (except Suns.). Grounds only 50p, Chd. 25p, O.A.Ps. 30p (except Suns.). Reduction (except Suns.) to House & Grounds for parties of 20 or more £1, Chd. 50p. *Closed Mons. (except Bank Hols.), Tues. & Good Friday.* Shop. Dogs in grounds only, on leads. Unsuitable for wheelchairs. ☕ Tea room in house ☎ *Pangbourne* (073 57) 3040	Alder Valley/Oxford 5, Reading–Wallingford–Oxford
FROGMORE GARDENS, Windsor *map 6 A* *Her Majesty the Queen* Beautifully landscaped gardens with trees, shrubs and lake.	Entrance to garden-thro' Long Walk Gate. (*Visitors are requested kindly to refrain from entering grounds of the Home Park*). *Stns: Windsor & Eton Central; Windsor & Eton Riverside (both 20 mins: walk)*	GARDEN open *only* on Wed. May 2 & Thurs. May 3: 11–7 (last admission 6.30). Adm. 60p. Chd. (under 14) 15p. No dogs. COACHES BY APPT. ONLY (apply to Nat Gardens' Scheme, 57 Lower Belgrave St., London SW1W 0LR. Tel. 01-730 0359). The Royal Mausoleum also open on above 2 days, adm. free. (In addition, Mausoleum open Wed. May 23: 11–4, but *not* the gardens). ☕ refreshment tent at car park—May 2 & 3.	
MAPLEDURHAM HOUSE—SEE UNDER OXFORDSHIRE			
THE OLD RECTORY, Burghfield *map 3 J* *Mr. & Mrs. R. R. Merton* Garden of horticultural interest; roses, hellebores, lilies, many rare and unusual plants from China and Japan; old-fashioned cottage plants; autumn colour.	5½ m SW of Reading, between M4 junctions 11 & 12 *Stns: Mortimer (3½ m); Theale (2½ m)*	GARDEN ONLY: Weds.—Feb. 29; March 28; Apr. 25; May 30; June 27; July 25; Sept. 26; Oct. 31; 11–4. Also by appointment. Adm. 40p. Chd. 10p. *In aid of National Gardens' Scheme* Plants & produce for sale.	*Bus:* Alder Valley 9, 9B, from Reading Bus Station (*half-hourly*)
SAVILL GARDEN, Windsor Great Park *Crown Property* *map 6 A* Mainly a woodland garden of 35 acres together with a formal area of roses and herbaceous plants, all of which offer great interest and beauty at every season of the year.	To be approached from A30 via Wick Rd. & Wick Lane, Englefield Green *Stn: Egham (3 m)*	Open daily 10–6. *Closed for a short period at Christmas.* Adm. £1.30, O.A.Ps. £1.10, Parties of 20 & over £1.10; accompanied Chd. (under 16) free	Green Line 718 London–Windsor; 724 Harlow–Watford–Windsor London Country 441, 442, 443 Staines–Windsor–High Wycombe/Uxbridge Alder Valley X20 London–Farnham; 200, 201 Heathrow–Camberley–Basingstoke
SWALLOWFIELD PARK, Swallowfield *Mutual Households Association* *map 3 J* Built by the Second Earl of Clarendon in 1678	In the village of Swallowfield 6m SE of Reading *Stn: Mortimer (4 m)*	May to September—Weds. & Thurs. 2–5. Adm. 50p, Chd. 25p. Free car park. No dogs admitted.	Alder Valley 6, 6A Reading–Basingstoke, 12 Reading–Aldershot
VALLEY GARDENS, Windsor Great Park *Crown Property* *map 6 A* Extensive woodland gardens of 400 acres which include a large heather garden offering beauty and charm at all seasons of the year.	To be approached from Wick Rd., off A30 (1 *m walk*) *Stn: Egham (3 m)*	Open daily from sunrise to sunset. Adm. free to pedestrians. Car park adjoining gardens 80p per car.	See Savill Garden transport facilities
WINDSOR CASTLE, Windsor *map 6 A* *Royal Residence* Largest inhabited castle in the world, stands besides the Thames, 21 m from London. None of the original fortress of William I remains, the Castle is now largely mediaeval, Stuart and Regency. *The State Apartments* are full of historical treasures, including valuable collection of pictures, rich in examples of the work of Van Dyck; furniture, porcelain and armour		CASTLE PRECINCTS: open daily from 10. Closes 4.15 (Jan. 1 to March 24 & Oct. 21 to Dec. 31); 5.15 (March 25 to April 30 & Sept. 1 to Oct. 27); 7.15 (May 1 to Aug. 31). *Closed Mon: June 18.* HOURS OF OPENING (except as stated below): Jan. to late March—Weekdays 10.30–3.15. *Closed Suns:* Late March to late Oct.—Weekdays 10.30–4.45; Suns. (May 1 to Oct. 16) 1.30–4.45. Late Oct. to Dec. 31—Weekdays 10.30–3.15. *Closed Suns.* The State Apartments etc. will be CLOSED as follows: STATE APARTMENTS: Jan. 1–2, March 12 to May 4, June 4 to 29, Dec. 3–26. Adm. £1.20, Chd. (5–15) & Retirement Pensioners 60p. QUEEN MARY'S DOLLS' HOUSE — EXHIBITION OF DRAWINGS — ROYAL MEWS EXHIBITION: Jan. 1–3, April 1, June 13 (except Royal Mews Exhibition), Dec. 23–26. Adm. 50p, Chd. (5–15) & Retirement Pensioners 20p. *Whilst there is every intention to adhere to the above schedule this cannot be guaranteed as Windsor Castle is always subject to closure, sometimes at short notice* ☎ *Windsor* (075 35) 68286 ST. GEORGE'S CHAPEL: All enquiries to the Chapter Clerk, Windsor Castle, tel: *Windsor* 65538 ✕☕ Castle Hotel (*opposite*)	National tours from London, Essex, Bournemouth and the Midlands Rail tour from London (Waterloo)—Daily (*summer*) (*Stns: Windsor & Eton Central or Windsor & Eton Riverside–few mins: walk*) Barton tours from Nottingham & Leicester London Trans. conducted tour—(*summer*) Rickards tour from London—Daily Green Line 700, 701, 704, 718, 724, 726 London Country 335, 353, 441, 442, 443 Alder Valley (also 62 to Windsor Bridge)

BUCKINGHAMSHIRE

PROPERTY (*showing map reference*)	LOCATION (*with nearest Rly. Stn.*)	OPENING TIMES AND ADMISSION CHARGES CATERING FACILITIES	COACH AND RAIL TOURS BUS SERVICES (*showing alighting points*)
ASCOTT, Wing *map 3 K* Δ *The National Trust* Anthony de Rothschild collection of fine pictures. French and Chippendale furniture, exceptional Oriental porcelain containing examples of the Ming, K'ang Hsi and Chun ware of the Sung dynasty. 12 acres of grounds. Gardens contain unusual trees, flower borders, topiary sundial, naturalised bulbs and water lilies	½ m E of Wing; 2 m SW of Leighton Buzzard, on the S side of Aylesbury–Leighton Buzzard rd (A418) *Stn: Leighton Buzzard (2 m)*	April to end of Sept.—Weds. & Thurs.; also Sats. in Aug. & Sept. and Mon. Aug. 27 (Bank Hol.): 2–6. Gardens also open last Sun. each month April to Sept.; 2–6. Last adm. to House & Gardens half-hour before closing. Adm. House & Gardens £1.80, Chd. £1.30; Gardens only £1, Chd. 50p. *No reduction for parties.* Dogs on leads, in car park only. Wheelchair access to part of garden only. Enquiries: Estate Manager ☎ *Wing* 242 N.B. Owing to large number of visitors, entry is by timed ticket. Occasionally there will be considerable delays in gaining admission to the House.	United Counties 141, Bedford–Leighton Buzzard Aylesbury (*alight gates*)
CAMPDEN COTTAGE, Chesham Bois, Amersham *map 6 A* *Mrs. P. A. Liechti* ½ acre plantsman's garden of year round interest created and maintained by present owner. Featured on B.B.C. Tv's "Gardeners' World," September 1983.	51 Clifton Rd., midway between Amersham-on-the-Hill & Chesham (A416); behind Catholic Church. *Stn: Amersham (1½m)*	GARDEN ONLY: Suns. April 22; May 27; June 24; July 15; Sept. 16; Oct. 7: 2–6. Adm. 50p, Chd. 20p. *In aid of National Garden's Scheme.* Also open Feb. to Oct. by appointment. Parties by written arrangement. *No dogs.* Unsuitable for wheelchairs. Parking on open Suns. in school grounds opposite church. Plants for sale.	No reasonable public transport
CHENIES MANOR HOUSE, Chenies *map 6 A* *Lt. Col. & Mrs. MacLeod Matthews* Charming 15th/16th century Manor House and garden in picturesque village	Off A404 between Amersham & Rickmansworth *Stn: Chorley Wood Rickmansworth*	First week in April to end of Oct. Weds. & Thurs. 2–5. Also open Bank Hol. Mons. May 28 & Aug. 27 2–6. Adm. £1.30, Chd. (under 14) half-price. Gardens only 65p. Parties throughout the year by prior arrangement—min. charge £25. Free parking. No dogs. ☕ home-made teas ☎ *Little Chalfont* 2888	London Country 336, Watford–Chenies–Chesham (*not Suns.*); 309 (*passes Chorley Wood Stn.*)
CHICHELEY HALL, Newport Pagnell *map 3 F* *Trustees of the Hon. Nicholas Beatty* Beautiful Baroque house and gardens built 1719–1723. Fine panelling, Naval pictures and mementos of Admiral Lord Beatty. Sir John Chester's unique Hidden Library.	2 m E of Newport Pagnell: 11 m W of Bedford on A422. M13 m (junction 14) *Stn: Wolverton (6½ m)*	April 20 to Sept. 30—Every Sunday, also Good Friday & Bank Hol. Mons. plus Weds. in August 2.30–6. DAY OR EVENING PARTIES—WITH MEALS —AT AMY TIME. Adm. £1.50, Chd. 90p. Parties £1.30. ☎ *North Crawley* (023 065) 252	United Counties 132 (*alight at entrance*)
CHILTERN OPEN AIR MUSEUM, *map 6 A* **Newland Park, nr Chalfont St. Peter** *Chiltern Open Air Museum Ltd.* Set in beautiful wooded ground the buildings reflecting 500 years of life in the Chiltern Hills; plus an Iron Age House and Nature Trails	Between Cht. St. Peter & Cht. St. Giles; 4½ m Amersham, 8 m Watford, 6 m Beaconsfield; 2 m A413 at Cht. St. Peter, 2 m A412 at Maple Cross, Rickmansworth *Stn: Chorleywood (2 m via footpath)*	Easter Sun. to Sept. 30—Weds., Suns. & Bank Hols. 2–6. Parties & School parties by arrangement. Adm. £1, Chd. & O.A.Ps. 50p. ☕ home-made teas ☎ *Chalfont St Giles* 71117	

THE HOME OF GOOD PLANTS AND TRULY A GARDEN FOR ALL SEASONS.

IN WINDSOR GREAT PARK

Clearly signposted from Ascot, Egham and Windsor.

Ample Free Car/Coach parking adjoining the garden in Wick Lane, Englefield Green.

The Garden is open daily throughout the year from 10 a.m. to 6 p.m. or sunset if earlier. (Closed December 25-28, 1984.)

Admission: Adults £1.30. Senior Citizens £1.10. Parties of 20 or more £1.10. Half price Nov./Feb. Accompanied children under the age of 16 free. (Large groups of children by arrangement)

A Licensed Self Service Restaurant is open from March 1st to October 31st. Also our well stocked Plant-Gift-Shop is open throughout the season.

CLAYDON HOUSE

BUCKINGHAMSHIRE

THE NATIONAL TRUST

A fine 18th century house. The staterooms contain unique and exotic wood carvings these reach their height in the extraordinary Chinese Room, the only one of its kind in the country. Magnificent wrought ironwork staircase, inlaid with holly, ebony and ivory. Florence Nightingale frequently stayed at Claydon and her bedroom and a museum containing mementoes of her life and the Crimean War are on display.

OPENING TIMES OPPOSITE

CHENIES MANOR

CHENIES BUCKINGHAMSHIRE

15th/16th century Manor House with fortified tower. Original home of the Earls of Bedford, visited by Henry VIII and Elizabeth I. Home of the MacLeod Matthews family. Contains contemporary tapestries and furniture. Early examples of English brickwork, hiding places, "secret passages". Surrounded by beautiful gardens — sunken garden, "white" garden, physic garden, penitential maze, 12th century undercroft, 14th century well and collection of recovered items.

Fine collection of antique dolls.

OPEN: First week in April to end of October, 2.00 p.m. to 5.00 p.m. Wednesdays and Thursdays, also Bank Holiday Mondays 28th May and 27th August.

Open, by prior arrangement, for parties throughout the year.

No dogs, no indoor photography. Wheelchair access to garden only.

Free parking.

Gift shop in old forge.

Teas with home-made cakes.

Chiltern Open Air Museum

NEWLAND PARK, nr CHALFONT ST. PETER, BUCKINGHAMSHIRE

A Museum, set in beautiful wooded grounds of buildings reflecting 500 years of life in the Chiltern Hills—plus an Iron Age House and Nature Trails through ancient Chalk Pits.

Free Car Park | Teas | Picnic Areas

Chicheley Hall

near Newport Pagnell — Buckinghamshire

Home of the Hon. Nicholas Beatty

Chicheley Hall, still a lived-in family home, is an exceptionally fine early Georgian House built 1719-1723 by Francis Smith of Warwick. Here is some of the most notable brickwork to be found in any house of the period, with the four sides of the house displaying a carefully graduated crescendo of architectural effect.

The interior has a striking Palladian Hall designed by Flitcroft and beautiful panelled rooms including Sir John Chester's ingenious hidden library. The rooms are furnished with fine period furniture and pictures.

The BEATTY NAVAL MUSEUM at Chicheley contains many fascinating momentoes of Admiral Earl Beatty and World War I at sea. The gardens contain a formal three-sided canal designed in 1700 by George London who also worked at Hampton Court. Tea room and Gift Shop.

OPEN: April 20th–Sept. 30th—EVERY SUNDAY, plus Good Friday and Bank Hol. Mons. plus Weds. in August 2.30–6.00. DAY OR EVENING PARTIES—WITH MEALS—AT ANY TIME. Tel. North Crawley (023065) 252.

PROPERTY (*showing map reference*)	LOCATION (*with nearest Rly. Stn.*)	OPENING TIMES AND ADMISSION CHARGES CATERING FACILITIES	COACH AND RAIL TOURS BUS SERVICES (*showing alighting points*)

BUCKINGHAMSHIRE—*continued*

CLAYDON HOUSE, Middle Claydon, nr. Winslow *map 3 J* *The National Trust* Built mid 18th cent., as an addition to an earlier house. The stone-faced West front contains a series of magnificent and unique rococo state-rooms including Florence Nightingale Museum, her bedroom and sitting room	Nr. the village of Middle Claydon, W of E Claydon, 3½ m SW of Winslow	April to end of Oct.—Sats. & Mons. to Weds. 2–6; Suns. & Bank Hol. Mons. 12–6. Last adm. 5.30. *Closed Thurs. & Fris. (inc. Good Friday).* Adm. £1.50, Chd. 75p. O.A.Ps. £1 (except Suns.). Parties of 20 or more £1 (except Suns.). Parties write to Custodian. Dogs in car park only. Wheelchairs provided. available at house *Steeple Claydon* 349	Red Rover 15 Aylesbury–Steeple Claydon (*not Suns.*) 22 Aylesbury–Claydon House (*Suns. only*) Entrance by North drive only
CLIVEDEN, Maidenhead (1851) *map 6 A* *The National Trust* Gardens contain temples by Giacomo Leoni. Box parterre, fountain, formal walks; historic open-air theatre, water garden, rose garden, herbaceous borders. View of Thames	3 m upstream from Maidenhead; 2 m N of Taplow on Hedsor rd (B476) Main Entrance opp Feathers Inn *Stns: Bourne End (1½ m) (not Suns.); Taplow (3 m) (not Suns.); Maidenhead (4½ m)*	GARDENS: March to Dec. Daily 11–6. *Closed January & February.* HOUSE (2 rooms only shown): April to end of Oct.—Sats. & Suns. 2–6 (last adm. half-hour before closing). *Closed Bank Hols. & Good Friday.* Adm. House & Grounds £2, Chd. £1, O.A.Ps. £1.40 (except Suns.); Parties of 20 or more £1.40 (except Suns.). Grounds only £1.50, Chd. 75p, O.A.Ps. £1 (except Suns.); Parties of 20 or more £1 (except Suns.). *Parties must give advance notice. No dogs in House or formal gardens but allowed in woods only.* Wheelchairs (available) in parts of garden & house. Shop (April to Oct., Weds. to Suns. & B.H. Mons. 2–5.30. Nov. to end of Dec., Sats. & Suns. 11–4). Estate Office *Burnham* 5069 Light lunches, coffee, teas in Cliveden Restaurant (Weds. to Suns.) *Burnham* 61406	Alder Valley (Thamesline) 68 Slough–Maidenhead (*not Suns.*) (*alight Feathers Inn*)
COWPER & NEWTON MUSEUM, Olney *map 3 F* Personal belongings of William Cowper and Rev. John Newton. Bobbin lace and items of local interest	Market Place, Olney; N of Newport Pagnell via A509	All the year—Tues. to Sats. 10–12, 2–5. *Closed Good Friday, Christmas & New Year's Day.* Adm. 40p *Bedford* (0234) 711516	
DORNEY COURT, nr Windsor *Mr. & Mrs. Peregrine Palmer* *map 6 A* Beautiful Tudor pink brick and timber Manor House which has been in the family for over 350 years. Superb collection of furniture and paintings.	2 m W of Eton & Windsor in village of Dorney on B3026 *Stns: Taplow (1½ m) (not Suns.); Burnham (2 m); Windsor & Eton Riverside (3 m)*	Easter weekend Friday to Monday then Suns. & Bank Hol. Mons. to second Sun. in Oct.; also Mons. & Tues. in June, July, Aug. & Sept.: 2–5.30. Adm. £1.80, Chd. £1. Parties at other times by arrangement. home-made cream teas *Burnham* (062 86) 4638	No reasonable public transport
DORTON HOUSE, Aylesbury *map 3 J* *Ashfold School Trust Ltd.* Jacobean mansion built by Sir John Dormer in 1626. Fine Jacobean ceilings.	6 m N of Thame, 11 m W of A'bury, 15 m E of Oxford; off A418	May to July & Sept.—Sats & Suns. 2–5. *Closed June 4 & 5.* At other times by arrangement. Adm. 25p, Chd. free *Brill* (0844) 238 237 at House (during school terms only)	No reasonable public transport
HUGHENDEN MANOR, High Wycombe *The National Trust* *map 6 A* Home of Benjamin Disraeli, Earl of Beaconsfield (1847–1881). Small formal garden.	1½ m N of High Wycombe on W side Gt. Missenden rd (A4128) *Stn: High Wycombe (2 m)*	House & Garden: March—Sats. & Suns. only 2–6 (or sunset if earlier), April to end of Oct.—Weds. to Sats. 2–6; Suns. & Bank Hol. Mons. 12–6. *Closed Good Friday.* Adm. £1.50. Chd. 75p, O.A.Ps. £1 (except Suns.). Parties of 20 or more £1 (except Suns.). Shop: open mid-March to Dec. *Parties must book in advance.* Dogs in Park & car park only. Wheelchairs provided. tea & biscuits available Sats., Suns. & Bank Hols. (*Mar. to Oct.* 3–5). Parties Weds. to Fris. only if booked in advance.	**Barton tours from Nottingham** **Green Line 790/Oxford 290 to High Wycombe, then** Alder Valley (Chilternlink) 323, 324, 333, 334 from High Wycombe (*alight gates*)
MEMORIAL GARDENS, Stoke Poges *South Bucks. District Council* *map 6 A* Gardens of Remembrance. Of outstanding beauty and unique design, adjoining the historic churchyard famous for Gray's "Elegy"	Off Church Lane, approx. 2 m N of Slough; adjacent to St. Giles' Church *Stn: Slough (2 m)*	All the year—Daily (except Sats.) 9–dusk. *Closed Sats.*	London Country 353, Windsor–Slough–Berkhamsted (*approx. hourly*)
MENTMORE, Mentmore *map 3 K* *The World Government of the Age of Enlightenment—Great Britain* Magnificent Victorian mansion designed by Sir Joseph Paxton. Last surviving example of his architecture in England. Outstanding interiors. Former home of Mayer Amschel de Rothschild and the Earls of Rosebery. Now the administrative headquarters of Maharishi University of Natural Law which was founded by His Holiness Maharishi Mahesh Yogi to bring the life of Great Britain and the whole world in alliance with natural law and create a problem-free society through the application of Vedic Science, Modern Science and the Transcendental Meditation and T.M. Sidhi Programme. Exhibitions, scientific laboratories for research on higher states of consciousness. 83 acres of grounds. Beautiful views. Peaceful atmosphere	12 m NE of Aylesbury; 5 m SE of Leighton Buzzard. 53 m from London (M1 exit 11 via Dunstable) *Stns: Cheddington (1 m), Leighton Buzzard (5 m)*	April 4 to Oct. 17—Suns. & Bank Hols. 1–5 (last adm. 4.30). Remainder of year—Suns. & Bank Hols. 1–4. Parties other days by arrangement. Adm. House & Grounds £1.50. Chd. 75p. Reduced rates for parties by prior arrangement. Free car park. Gift Shop. Picnic facilities. home-made cream teas available at the house. SEASONAL FESTIVALS: Spring, Summer, Autumn, Winter. Banquets, presentation of Maharishi Awards, Entertainment. For further information please contact the Secretary. *Cheddington* (0296) 661881	British Rail from London (Euston) to Cheddington & Leighton Buzzard
MILTON COTTAGE, Chalfont St. Giles *Milton's Cottage Trust* *map 6 A* The Cottage where John Milton completed 'Paradise Lost' and began 'Paradise Regained', contains many Milton relics and a library including first and early editions. Preserved as it was in 1665. Charming Cottage Garden	½ m W of A413; on B4442 to Beaconsfield *Stn: Sear Green 2½ m)*	Feb. to Oct.—Tues. to Sats. 10–1, 2–6; Suns. 2–6. Spring & Summer Bank Hol. Mons. 10–1, 2–6. *Closed Mons. (except Bank Hols.) & Jan., Nov. & Dec.* Adm. 60p, Chd. (under 15) 20p. Parties of 20 or more 40p. *Chalfont St. Giles* 2313	London Country 305, High Wycombe—Uxbridge, (*passes door*), 353 Berkhamsted—Windsor (*alight Pheasant, ¼ m*)
NETHER WINCHENDON HOUSE, Aylesbury *map 3 J* *Mrs. John Spencer Bernard* Tudor manor house with 18th cent. additions. Home of Sir Francis Bernard, Governor of New Jersey and Massachusetts, 1760	1 m N of A418 Aylesbury-Thame rd nr village of Lower Winchendon, 6 m SW Aylesbury *Stn: Aylesbury (7½ m)*	May to Aug.—Thurs. 2.30–5.30. Also Bank Hol. Sats. Suns. & Mons. in May & Aug. and Sats. & Suns., June 9/10 & July 7/8. Parties at any time of year by written appointment. Adm. £1.20, Chd. (under 12) 60p; O.A.Ps. 60p (Thurs. only). *Haddenham* 290101	Oxford 260, 261, Aylesbury–Thame
PRINCES RISBOROUGH MANOR HOUSE Princes Risborough *The National Trust* *map 3 K* 17th century red-brick house with Jacobean oak staircase	Opp. church off market sq. in town centre. *Stn: Princes Risborough (1 m)*	Open by written appointment only—Weds. 2.30–4.30. Last admission 4 p.m. Two rooms only shown. Adm. 50p, Chd. 25p. No reductions for parties. No dogs. Wheelchair access.	
STOWE (STOWE SCHOOL), **Buckingham** *Governors of Stowe School* *map 3 J* Famous 18th cent. house formerly the home of the Duke of Buckingham. Garden and garden buildings by Bridgeman, Kent, Gibbs, Vanburgh and 'Capability' Brown	3 m N Buckingham town	GROUNDS & GARDEN BUILDING ONLY: April 20-23 inc. and July 14 to Sept. 9—Fris., Sats. & Suns. only plus Aug. Bank Hol. Mon. 1–6. Adm. 60p, Chd. & O.A.Ps. 40p. light refreshments	Midland Red 500 Banbury–Brackley–Stowe–Buckingham (*Tues. & Sats. only*)

CLIVEDEN

BUCKINGHAMSHIRE

THE NATIONAL TRUST

Extensive and historic gardens with hanging woods, overlooking the Cliveden Reach of the Thames; the present house, third to be constructed on the site, was built in 1851. The gardens are remarkable for their colourful flower borders, box parterre, fountain, water garden, rose garden and rustic theatre. Once the home of Nancy, Lady Astor.

HUGHENDEN MANOR

HIGH WYCOMBE, Buckinghamshire

THE NATIONAL TRUST

A. F. Kersting photograph

Hughenden Manor was bought by Benjamin Disraeli, Earl of Beaconsfield, in 1847. He rebuilt it and lived there until his death in 1881. The house, with its contemporary decoration, is a typical example of a Victorian gentleman's country seat, and contains many relics of the statesman. There are portraits of his friends, letters from Queen Victoria and some of the manuscripts of his novels. His study is arranged exactly as he left it at the time of his death.

OPENING TIMES OPPOSITE

 **MENTMORE** 

BUCKINGHAMSHIRE

ADMINISTRATIVE HEADQUARTERS OF MAHARISHI UNIVERSITY OF NATURAL LAW

COME TO MENTMORE AND ENJOY THE PEACEFUL ATMOSPHERE OF THIS GREAT HISTORIC HOUSE

Magnificent Victorian mansion, best surviving example of the work of Sir Joseph Paxton, architect of the Crystal Palace. Former home of Baron Mayer Amschel de Rothschild and the Earls of Rosebery. Beautiful banqueting hall, well-preserved gilt interiors, Rubens fireplace, fine grounds with panoramic views of the Chilterns. Now the administrative headquarters of Maharishi University of Natural Law which was founded by His Holiness Maharishi Mahesh Yogi to bring the life of Great Britain and the whole world in alliance with natural law and create a problem-free society through the application of Vedic Science, Modern Science and the Transcendental Meditation and T.M. Sidhi Programme.

For details of facilities available see alphabetical listing. Tel: Cheddington (0296) 661881

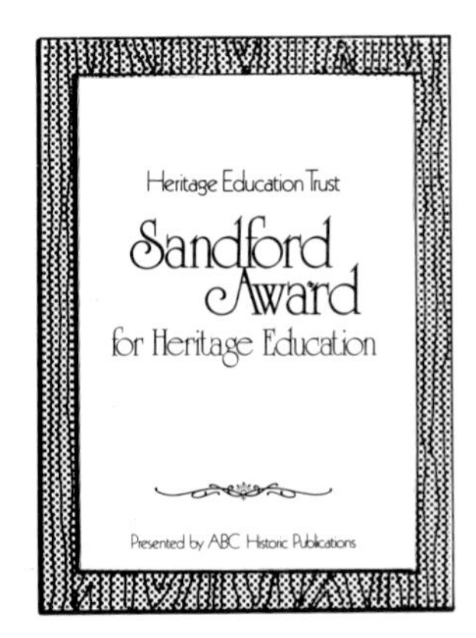

For information on

EDUCATIONAL SERVICES

SEE PAGE 8

DORNEY COURT

Nr. Windsor

"One of the finest Tudor Manor Houses in England". *Country Life.*

A visit to Dorney is a most welcome, refreshing and fascinating experience. Built about 1500 and lived in by the present family for nearly 400 years this enchanting, many gabled, pink brick and timbered manor house is a joy to behold. The rooms are full of the atmosphere of history: early fifteenth and sixteenth century oak, beautiful seventeenth century lacquer furniture, eighteenth and nineteenth century tables, 400 years of family portraits, stained glass and needle-work. Here once Charles II came to seek the charms of Barbara Palmer, Countess of Castlemaine, the most intelligent, beautiful and influential of ladies. St. James' Church, next door, is a lovely cool, cheerful and very English village Church.

Our coffee and shortbread or home-made cream teas will refresh you as surely will a stroll around the gardens, noted for the yew hedges, tall trees and happy, bright flowers. We have a small shop specialising in home grown vegetables, plants and honey. Home-made cream teas.

PROPERTY (*showing map reference*)	LOCATION (*with nearest Rly. Stn.*)	OPENING TIMES AND ADMISSION CHARGES CATERING FACILITIES	COACH AND RAIL TOURS BUS SERVICES (*showing alighting points*)
BUCKINGHAMSHIRE—*continued*			
WADDESDON MANOR, nr Aylesbury △ *The National Trust* *map* 3 *K* French decorative art and drawings of 17th and 18th centuries and other works of earlier centuries. Important English, Dutch, Flemish and Italian paintings. Textiles, buttons, lace etc.; mementoes and pastimes of the family. Exhibition of dresses of the 1860s. Extensive grounds with 18th century style aviary and small herd of Sika deer. Fine trees and views. Play area for young children.	At W end of Waddesdon Village: 6 m NW Aylesbury on Bicester rd (A41) *Stn: Aylesbury* (6 *m*)	March 28 to Oct. 28. House: Weds. to Suns. 2–6. Grounds: Weds. to Sats. from 1; Suns. from 11.30. Good Friday & Bank Hol. Mons. House & Grounds 11–6. *Completely closed Weds. following Bank Hol. Mons.* Adm. House, Grounds & Aviary £1.80. Fris. (except Good Friday) Bachelors' Wing, 60p extra. Grounds & Aviary only 80p, Chd. 25p. Parties by arrangement (no reduction except pre-booked parties of O.A.Ps. Weds., Thurs. & Sats.). Special morning guided tours £3.50. *Children under* 12 *not admitted to House. No indoor photography.* Free car park. Home grown produce stall. Dogs in grounds only. Wheelchairs provided. ☕ Tea room ☎ (0296) 651211 *or* 651282 ✕ **Five Arrows Hotel in village**	Tours: Alex Smith, Nottingham. Birds, Blackheath. Conway Hunt, Chertsey. Epsom Coaches. Grey-Green, London. Keiths, Aylesbury. National, London, Oxford & Cheltenham. Safeguard, West Surrey. Sampsons, Enfield. Smiths, Reading. Supreme, Hadleigh (Essex). Venture Transport, Harrow. Weyfarer, Alder Valley, Haslemere, Guildford, Woking. *Buses:* Red Rover from Aylesbury to Waddesdon (*alight village*); service into Manor grounds on Sun. & B.H. afternoons, April to Sept.
WEST WYCOMBE PARK (1750) *map* 3 *K* △ *The National Trust* Palladian house with frescoes and painted ceilings. 18th century landscape garden with lake and various classical temples, including the newly reconstructed Temple of Venus	At W end of West Wycombe S of Oxford rd (A40), 3 m W High Wycombe *Stn: High Wycombe* (2½ *m*)	House & Grounds: June—Mons. to Fris.; July to end Aug.—Daily (except Sats.) & inc. Summer Bank Hol. Mon. 2–6 (last adm. half-hour before closing). Grounds only: Easter Sun. & Mon.; Spring Bank Hol. Sun. & Mon., 2–6. Adm. House & Grounds £1.80; Grounds only £1; Chd. half-price. *No reduction for parties.* Dogs in car park only. Unsuitable for wheelchairs. ☎ *High Wycome* 24411	**National tour from London** **Oxford 290, Oxford–High Wycombe–London** **Green Line 790 to High Wycombe, then** Alder Valley (Chilternlink) 321, 332, 339, 341 Oxford 232 from High Wycombe (*alight village*).
WINSLOW HALL, Winslow *map* 3 *K* △ *Sir Edward & Lady Tomkins* Built 1698-1702, almost certainly by Sir Christopher Wren. One of the few country houses designed by him which has survived without major structural alteration, retaining most of its original features. 18th cent. furniture; Chinese art; objets d'art. Garden	At ent. to town on A413 between Aylesbury & Buckingham. *Stn: Aylesbury* (10 *m*) *or Bletchley* (10 *m*)	July 1 to Sept. 15—Daily (except Mons. but open Bank Hol. Mons.) 2.30–5.30, Sept. 15 to 30—Weekends only. Gardens only open Suns. in May & June 2–5. Other times by appointment. Adm. £1. Parties 75p per person. ☕ Teas & refreshments available; other catering by arrangement. ☎ *Winslow* 2323 *or* 3433 (*Administrator*)	Red Rover, Aylesbury–Buckingham United Counties 336, 337, Aylesbury–Northampton 377, 381, Bletchley–Steeple Claydon (***alight town centre***) (***no Sun. buses***)
WOTTON HOUSE nr Aylesbury *map* 3 *J* ***Administrator Mrs Patrick Brunner.*** **Built 1704, on the same plan as Buckingham House, which later became Buckingham Palace Interior remodelled by Soane 1820. Wrought iron by Tijou and Thomas Robinson. 'Capability' Brown landscape 1757-1760**	**In Wotton Underwood; 2 m S of A41, midway between Aylesbury and Bicester**	August to end of September—Weds. Tours 2, 3 & 4 (last tour). Parties by arrangement.	Red Rover 3, Aylesbury–Brill (***Weds. & Sats. only***)
CAMBRIDGESHIRE			
ANGLESEY ABBEY, nr Cambridge *The National Trust* *map* 3 *G* Founded in the reign of Henry I. An Elizabethan manor was created from the remains by the Fokes family. Contains Fairhaven collection of art treasures. About 100 acres of grounds, including flower borders, trees, avenues and many garden ornaments	**In village of Lode 6 m NE of Cambridge on B1102** *Stn: Cambridge* (6 *m*)	House & Gardens: March 31 to April 15—Weekends only. April 21 to Oct. 14—Daily (except Mons. & Tues. but open Bank Hol. Mons.) 2–6. *Closed Good Friday.* Adm. £1.80. Pre-booked parties of 15 or more £1.40 (Weds., Thurs. & Fris. only). Garden only: April 21 to Oct. 12—Mons. & Tues. 2–6. Adm. £1, Chd. (with adult) half-price. *Closed Good Friday.* No dogs. Indoor photography by permission only. Wheelchair access (house difficult); chairs provided. Free car park & picnic area. Shop (*closed Mons. & Tues.*). Lode Mill: March 31 to Oct. 14—Sat., Suns. & Bank Hol. Mons. ☕ **Tea room** ☎ ***Cambridge* (0223) 811200**	Eastern Counties 111, 122 from Cambridge (*alight Lode*) (*not Suns.*)
DOCWRA'S MANOR, Shepreth *map* 3 *F* *Mrs. John Raven* 2 acres of choice plants in a series of enclosed gardens	In Shepreth; 8 m SW of Cambridge *Stn: Shepreth* (*not Suns.*)	GARDEN ONLY: Suns., April 1, May 6, June 3, July 1, Aug. 5, Sept. 2 & Oct. 7; 2–6. Also April 4 to Oct. 3—Weds. 10–5. Adm. 50p, Chd. free. Proceeds for garden upkeep. Also Sun. July 8, 2–7 *in aid of National Gardens' Scheme and Cambs. & Isle of Ely Naturalists Trust.* Also open by appointment. Plants for sale. No dogs. ☕ teas Sun. July 8 only. ☎ *Royston* 60235 *or* 61008	
ELTON HALL, nr Peterborough *map* 3 *F* *Mr. & Mrs. William Proby* The home of the Proby family for over 300 years. A mixture of styles dating from the 15th century Gatehouse Tower and Chapel with numerous 18th and 19th century additions. A very fine library and collection of pictures and furniture	8 m W of Peterborough on A605. *Stn: Peterborough* (10 *m*)	Bank Hols. May 6/7 & 27/28; Aug. 23, 24, 26, 27 & 28 (*closed Aug.* 25). May to July—Weds. August—Weds. & Suns. Parties other days by appointment. Open 2–5. Adm. House & Garden £1.50, Chd. 75p. ☕ home-made teas available ☎ *Elton* (083 24) 468	*Bus:* Peterborough–Oundle
HINCHINGBROOKE HOUSE, Huntingdon ***Hinchingbrooke School*** *map* 3 *F* **Early 13th cent. Nunnery converted mid 16th cent. into Tudor house with additions, late 17th cent. and 19th cent. Former home of Cromwells and of Montagus, Earls of Sandwich**	**½ m W of Huntingdon on A604, 2 m E of A1, 16 m NW of Cambridge** ***Stn: Huntingdon* (½*m*)**	April, May, June, July & Aug.—Suns. & Bank Hol. Mons. only 2–5. Adm. 60p, Chd. 40p. *Parties other days by arrangement. Special rate of* 40p *per person for parties of* 30 *or more.* ☕ at the House. ☎ *Huntingdon* 51121	United Counties 211-212, St. Ives–Huntingdon–Bedford; 227, Thrapston–Huntingdon (***not Suns***).
ISLAND HALL, Godmanchester *map* 3 *F* *Mr. Christopher & The Hon. Mrs. Vane Percy* A mid 18th century Mansion, of architectural importance and fine panelled rooms, in a tranquil riverside setting.	In centre of Godmanchester; 1 m S of Huntingdon (A1); 15 m NW of Cambridge (A604) *Stn: Huntingdon* (1*m*)	June 3 to Sept. 16—Suns., Tues. & Thurs.; also Bank Hols. May 6/7, 27/28 & Aug. 27: 2.30–5.30. Parties at any time by arrangement. Adm. £1, Chd. 50p (with adult 70p). ☕ teas	*B.R.* King's Cross to Huntingdon United Counties 151, Cambridge–Godmanchester; 221, Huntingdon–Godmanchester
KIMBOLTON CASTLE, Kimbolton *map* 3 *F* ***Governors of Kimbolton School*** **Tudor manor house, associated with Katherine of Aragon, completely remodelled by Vanbrugh (1708–20); courtyard c. 1694 Fine murals by Pellegrini in chapel, boudoir and on staircase. Gatehouse by Robert Adam**	**8 m NW of St. Neots on A45 ; 14 m N of Bedford** *Stn: St. Neots* (9 *m*)	**Easter Sun. & Mon.; Spring Bank Hol. Sun. & Mon.; Summer Bank Hol. Mon.;** **also July 22 to September 2—Suns. only: 2–6.** **Adm. 40p, Chd. & O.A.Ps. 15p.**	**No reasonable public transport**
PECKOVER HOUSE, Wisbech (1722) △ *The National Trust* *map* 3 *F* **Important example of early 18th cent. domestic architecture. Fine rococo decoration. Interesting Victorian garden contains rare trees, flower borders, roses. Under glass are orange trees Stables**	**Centre of Wisbech town on N bank of River Nene (B1441)** *Stn: March* (9½ *m*)	Principal Rooms & Gardens: March 31 to April 15—Sats. & Suns. only. April 21 to Oct. 14—Daily (except Thurs. & Fris.) 2–5.30. Adm. £1.10. Chd. (*with adult*) 55p. No dogs. Wheelchairs—garden only. ☕ in the Old Kitchen ☎ *Wisbech* 583463	E. Counties 336 Peterborough–Wisbech–Kings Lynn 354 March–Wisbech (*not Suns.*) Embling's, March–Wisbech

WADDESDON MANOR

near AYLESBURY, Buckinghamshire

THE NATIONAL TRUST

"Aerofilms Ltd." photograph

Built 1874-89 for Baron Ferdinand de Rothschild in the style of a French Renaissance château and bequeathed to the National Trust by Mr. James A. de Rothschild in 1957. Rooms with 18th century panelling furnished with French royal furniture, porcelain and Savonnerie carpets. Dutch, Flemish and Italian paintings and portraits by Gainsborough, Reynolds and Romney.
Other rooms contain French 17th and 18th century drawings, textiles, lace and buttons and an **exhibition of dresses of the 1860s**, also personal mementoes and pastimes of the family. In the Bachelors' Wing, open on Fridays only, are 15th, 16th and 17th century works of art and European small arms.

OPENING TIMES OPPOSITE

WEST WYCOMBE PARK

BUCKINGHAMSHIRE

THE NATIONAL TRUST

Early Georgian house, rebuilt 1745–71 by Sir Francis Dashwood, Lord le Despencer, with additions derived from buildings at Vicenza by Palladio and from early Greek temples. The interior is richly decorated and has ceilings and frescoes copied from famous palaces in Rome and from the temples at Palmyra near Damascus. The fine collection of pictures, mirrors and furniture, much of which was made for the house, belongs to Sir Francis Dashwood who lives here with his family. The landscape garden is in a beautiful setting of rolling hills and beechwoods. The main features are the famous church with the golden ball and the splendid mausoleum perched on the nearby hilltop, the lake with Revett's Temple of Music and Cascade and various Roman and Greek temples, including the newly reconstructed Temple of Venus.

OPENING TIMES OPPOSITE

WINSLOW HALL

BUCKINGHAMSHIRE

Winslow Hall built for Sir William Lowndes between 1698 and 1702. It is almost certainly by Sir Christopher Wren and is one of the very few country houses designed by him which has survived without major structural alteration. It still retains most of its original features but has been modernised and redecorated by the present owners, Sir Edward and Lady Tomkins. The house is furnished for the most part with early 18th century English furniture. There are also several good examples of Chinese art, particularly of the Tang period, and a collection of objets d'art, bibelots and jade as well as some fine pictures and clocks. Extensive and beautiful gardens.

ANGLESEY ABBEY

near CAMBRIDGE

THE NATIONAL TRUST

"Aerofilms Ltd." photograph

The Abbey was founded in 1135 for Canons of the Augustinian order and converted after 1591 into a private house. Thomas Hobson, a carrier of the phrase "Hobson's choice" was one of several secular owners before it was bought and altered by the first Lord Fairhaven in 1926 to house his great collection of European paintings, porcelain, clocks, tapestries, silver and furniture.
The gardens (100 acres) were created between 1926 and 1966. Avenues of beautiful trees; hedges enclosing small intimate gardens; groups of statuary. Working water mill.

OPENING TIMES OPPOSITE

ELTON HALL NR. PETERBOROUGH

Elton Hall, which dates from 1475, has been the home of the Proby Family (later created the Earls of Carysfort) since 1660. The house is remarkable in that it represents a procession of periods as it was gradually enlarged and altered from the 15th century onwards. The interior reflects this progression as a notable collection of paintings, books and furniture was acquired by each generation.

OPENING TIMES OPPOSITE

ISLAND HALL

GODMANCHESTER, CAMBRIDGESHIRE

On the banks of the River Great Ouse; this beautiful house contains lovely rooms with fine period detail and interesting possessions relating to the owners' family since their first occupation of the house in 1800.

OPENING TIMES OPPOSITE

PROPERTY (*showing map reference*)	LOCATION (*with nearest Rly. Stn.*)	OPENING TIMES AND ADMISSION CHARGES CATERING FACILITIES	COACH AND RAIL TOURS BUS SERVICES (*showing alighting points*)

CAMBRIDGESHIRE—*continued*

PROPERTY	LOCATION	OPENING TIMES AND ADMISSION CHARGES CATERING FACILITIES	COACH AND RAIL TOURS BUS SERVICES
UNIVERSITY BOTANIC GARDEN, Cambridge *map 3 F* *Cambridge University* Fine specimen trees and shrubs. Founded 1761	In Cambridge, 1 m S of City Centre *Stn: Cambridge* (¼ *m*)	All the year—Daily [illegible]-7.30 (*dusk in winter*). Adm. free, weekdays (Suns., May to Sept. only, 2.30–6.30). *Open to keyholders only on Suns. at other times throughout year*. Picnic area.	All buses going down Trumpington Road or Hills Road (*entrance to garden in Trumpington Rd., Hills Rd, or Bateman St.*)
UNIVERSITY OF CAMBRIDGE—SEE PAGE 184			
WIMPOLE HALL, nr Cambridge *map 3 F* *The National Trust* An architecturally refined house of aristocratic proportions, sumptuous 18th and 19th century staterooms, set in a beautifully undulating park devised by the best of the Landscapists.	8 m SW of Cambridge; signposted off A603 at New Wimpole *Stns: Shepreth (5 m) (not Suns.), Royston (7 m)*	House, Garden & Park: March 31 to Nov. 4—Daily (except Fris.) & Bank Hol. Mons. 2–6. *Closed Fris. (inc. Good Friday)*. Adm. £1.80, Chd. (with adult) 90p, O.A.Ps. £1.40 (weekdays only). Pre-booked parties of 15 or more £1.10 (Mons. to Thurs. only). Park 50p, refundable on entering House or Farm (see entry below). Picnic area. Shop. Dogs allowed in park only, on leads. Wheelchair access—3 chairs provided. ✕ ☕ lunches & teas in the Dining Room ☎ *Cambridge* (0223) 207257 208987 (*Farm*)	United Counties 175, Cambridge–Biggleswade (*alight New Wimpole, 1½ m*) (*not Suns.*)
WIMPOLE HOME FARM, nr Cambridge *The National Trust* *map 3 F* An historic farm, faithfully restored by the National Trust, set in 350 acres of beautiful parkland. Approved Rare Breeds Centre. Children's corner, Agricultural museum	8 m S of Cambridge; signposted off A603 at New Wimpole *Stns: Shepreth (5 m)*; Royston (*7 m*)	April 1–20 & Oct.—Sats. & Suns. only 11–5.30. April 21 to end of September—Daily (except Fris.) 11–5.30. Adm. £1.20, Chd. 60p ✕☕ Lunches & teas at Wimpole Hall	United Counties 175 Cambridge–Biggleswade (*alight New Wimpole, 1½ m*) (*not Suns.*)

CHESHIRE

PROPERTY	LOCATION	OPENING TIMES AND ADMISSION CHARGES CATERING FACILITIES	COACH AND RAIL TOURS BUS SERVICES
ADLINGTON HALL, Macclesfield *map 5 C* *Charles Legh, Esq.* Great Hall dates from about 1450. Elizabethan half-timbered "black and white" portion 1581	5 m N of Macclesfield on the Stockport–Macclesfield rd (A523) *Stn: Adlington (¼ m)*	Good Friday to Oct. 7—Suns. & Bank Hols.; also Aug.—Weds. & Sats. 2.30–6. Adm. £1.20, Chd. 60p. *Special parties by arrangement other days (over 25 people, 80p).* ☕ at the Hall ☎ *Prestbury* 829206	National tours from Lancashire towns Yelloway tours from Oldham & Rochdale districts National coach 451, Manchester–Derby (*alight Adlington P.O., ¼ m*)
ARLEY HALL AND GARDENS, Northwich *map 5 C* *The Hon. M. L. W. Flower* Victorian country house and private Chapel (c. 1840). Gardens of great variety and charm—topiary, rhododendrons, azaleas, herbaceous border, shrub roses, walled gardens, herb garden, woodland garden, woodland walk and farm animals.	5 m N of Northwich 6 m W of Knutsford 7 m S of Warrington 5 m off M6 at junc. 19 & 20; 5 m off M56 at junc. 9 & 10 *Stn.: Lostock Gralam (7½ m) (not Suns.)*	April 8 to Oct. 7—Tues. to Suns. & Bank Hol. Mons. 2–6 (June, July & Aug. 12–6). Last adm. Hall 5 Gardens 5.30. Adm. Gardens, Chapel & Grounds £1.20, Hall 75p extra. Chd. half-price. Special rates, opening hours and catering for organised parties by appointment. ☕ in converted Tudor Barn ☎ *Arley* (056 585) 353, 284 *or* 203 *after office hours* 203 *only*	No reasonable public transport
BRAMALL HALL, Bramhall, Stockport *Metro. Borough of Stockport* *map 5 C* Important large timber-framed hall dating from the 14th century.	4 m S of town centre; off A5102 *Stn: Stockport* (4 *m*)	Jan. to Nov.—Daily (except Mons. but open Bank Hol. Mons.). April to Sept. 12–5; Oct. & Nov. and Jan. to March 12–4. Open Bank Hols. Schools & other organised parties by appointment Tues. to Fris. 10–12. Adm. (subject to alteration) 80p, Chd. 40p. ☎ 061-485 3708	Local bus service to and from Stockport passes gates
CAPESTHORNE, Macclesfield *map 2 D* *Lt. Col. Sir Walter Bromley-Davenport* Recent research has revealed that Francis and William Smith of Warwick were almost certainly the original architects of this Jacobean style house built in 1722. Later alterations were made by Blore and Salvin. Pictures, furniture, family muniments and Americana	7 m S of Wilmslow, on Manchester–London rd (A34), 6½ m N of Congleton *Stns: Chelford (3½ m); Macclesfield (6m)*	April to Sept.—Suns.; also Weds. & Sats. May to Sept. and Tues. & Thurs. July to Sept.; open Good Friday & Bank Hol. Mons. Hall 2–5; Garden 12–6. Organised parties by appointment (except Mons. & Fris.) Adm. Hall, Park & Gardens £1.50, Chd. 70p; Gardens only 75p, Chd. 35p. Car park free ✕☕ ☎ *Chelford* 861221 *or* 861439	National tours from Lancashire, Dewsbury & Halifax and the Potteries Crosville E26, E27, Northwich–Knutsford–Macclesfield. E29, E30, Manchester–Macclesfield (*alight Monks Heath 1½ m*)

ARLEY HALL AND GARDENS near NORTHWICH, CHESHIRE

close to M6 (Junctions 19 & 20) and M56 (Junctions 9 & 10)

the home of the Hon. Michael and Mrs. Flower

Arley Hall lies at the centre of an estate owned by one family for over 500 years. Built about 1840 in the 'Victorian Jacobean' style, it contains fine plaster work, oak panelling and carving, furniture and interesting pictures, including a unique collection of late 19th century watercolours of houses in the area. Adjacent to the House is a private Chapel built by Anthony Salvin. The Gardens, which have been open for many years, won a premier award in the British Tourist Authority's Landscape Heritage Competition in 1975. Overlooking beautiful parkland, and providing great variety of style and design, the Gardens rank among the finest in the country. The twin herbaceous borders are among the first to have been established in England and the avenue of 14 large Ilex trees clipped to the shape of cylinders is most unusual. Other features include

Lime Avenue *"Smith Collection" photograph*

an avenue of pleached lime trees, yew hedges and lawns, walled gardens, small formal gardens, shrub roses, herb garden, azaleas and rhododendrons and a newly developing woodland garden.

New attractions in 1984 are a short woodland walk beyond the woodland garden and a display of farm animals in the Home Farm.

Teas are served in a fine 16th century converted barn adjoining an earlier "Cruck" barn—Gift Shop—Plants for Sale.

For opening times and admission charges see entry in alphabetical listing.

Enquiries: The Administrator, Arley Hall & Gardens, Northwich, Cheshire, CW9 6NB. Telephone: Arley (056 585) 353, 284 or 203 (after office hours 203 only).

ADLINGTON HALL

near MACCLESFIELD, Cheshire
(off A523)

"Country Life" photograph

Adlington Hall is a Cheshire Manor and has been the home of the Leghs since 1315. The Great Hall was built between 1450 and 1505, the Elizabethan "Black & White" in 1581 and the Georgian South Front in 1757. The Bernard Smith Organ was installed c. 1670.

A " Shell Cottage," Yew Walk and Lime Avenue are features of the gardens.

Open Good Friday to October 7th—Sundays and Bank Holidays (also Wednesdays and Saturdays during August) from 2.30 p.m. to 6 p.m.

Admission £1.20, Children 60p. Car Park free. Home-made teas, refreshments and Sunday lunches.

Organised Parties on other days by arrangement (over 25 people, 80p). Gift shop.

Enquiries to The Guide. ☎ Prestbury 829206.

" Photo Precision " photograph

PECKOVER HOUSE

CAMBRIDGESHIRE

THE NATIONAL TRUST

Peckover House, Wisbech, one of a series of Georgian Houses on the North Brink facing the river Nene. Built in 1722, the house was bought by Jonathan Peckover in the late 18th century and remained the home of that family until given to the National Trust in 1948. The interior has rococo decoration, in plaster and wood, of a very refined order. There is a fascinating Victorian garden and in the glasshouse are orange trees which bear good fruit. The Georgian stables are also of interest.

OPENING TIMES OPPOSITE

BRAMALL HALL

STOCKPORT, CHESHIRE

One of the finest Black and White houses in England, Bramall Hall was largely built between the 14th and 16th centuries. For 500 years the Hall was the home of the Davenport family. Inside are important early wall paintings, a family chapel and elaborate plasterwork.

The house is set in a large landscaped park.

Bramall Hall is owned and administered by Stockport Metropolitan Borough Council.

OPENING TIMES OPPOSITE

CAPESTHORNE near MACCLESFIELD, CHESHIRE

(close to Radio Telescope, Jodrell Bank)

Capesthorne is the home of the Bromley Davenport family where they and their ancestors have lived since Domesday times. Adjoining the house is a beautiful little Georgian chapel. The gardens and tea room overlook a chain of pools.

Open Sundays, April to September and Wednesdays & Saturdays from May to September and Tuesdays & Thursdays from July to September; also Good Friday & Bank Holiday Mondays. Hall 2–5 p.m. Gardens 12–6 p.m. Admission Hall, Park & Gardens £1.50p, Children 70p, Gardens only 75p, Children 35p. Car park free. Organised parties by appointment.

Enquiries to Hall Manager, Capesthorne, Macclesfield, Cheshire.
☎ Chelford 861221 or 861439.

PROPERTY (*showing map reference*)	LOCATION (*with nearest Rly. Stn.*)	OPENING TIMES AND ADMISSION CHARGES CATERING FACILITIES	COACH AND RAIL TOURS BUS SERVICES (*showing alighting points*)
CHESHIRE—*continued*			
CHOLMONDELEY CASTLE GARDENS, Malpas *map 2 D* *The Marquess of Cholmondeley* Gardens, lake-side picnic area. Farm with collection of rare breeds of farm animals. Ancient private Chapel in Park. Evening service 6.30 every third Sunday in month.	Off A41 Chester/ Whitchurch rd. & A49 Whitchurch/ Tarporley rd. *Stn: Whitchurch* (*7½ m*)	HOUSE NOT OPEN TO PUBLIC GARDENS & FARM ONLY: Easter Sun. to Sept. 30—Suns. & Bank Hols. only 12–6. Adm. £1, Chd. 25p. Enquiries to: The Estate Office, Cholmondeley, Malpas, Cheshire. Gift shop. Plants for sale. ☕ Tea room ☎ *Cholmondeley* (082 922) 383 *or* 203	No reasonable public transport
CHURCHE'S MANSION, Nantwich *map 2 D* Δ *Mr. & Mrs. R. V. Myott* A half-timbered H-plan mansion built 1577. Being restored to its original state. Fine oak panelling. Furnished. Walled garden	In Nantwich at junc. of A534 & A51. *Stns: Nantwich* (*1½ m*) (*not Suns*); *Crewe* (*6 m*)	April to October—Daily 10–5. Adm. 50p. ✕ Licensed restaurant in the Mansion (open all year) Lunch 12–2; Dinner 7–8.30. ☎ 0270 625933	Crosville C84, Chester–Crewe–Newcastle K43, Crewe–Nantwich (*alight Mansion*)
DORFOLD HALL, Nantwich *map 2 D* Δ *R. C. Roundell, Esq.* Jacobean country house built 1616. Beautiful plaster ceilings and panelling	1 m W of Nantwich on A534 Nantwich–Wrexham Rd. *Stn: Nantwich* (*1¼m*)	April to October—Tues. & Bank Hol. Mons. 2–5. Adm. £1, Chd. 50p. *At other times by appointment only.* ☎ *Nantwich* (0270) 625245	Crosville C84, Chester–Newcastle–under Lyme (*alight gates*)
DUNHAM MASSEY, Altrincham *map 5 C* *The National Trust* Fine 18th century park and house. Portraits of Lady Jane Grey and later Greys, Earls of Stamford, Huguenot silver	3 m SW of Altrincham off A56; junc. 19 off M6 *Stns: Altrincham* (*3 m*); *Hale* (*3 m*)	April to Oct.—Daily (except Fris.). Open Bank Hol. Mons. *Closed Good Friday*. Garden, restaurant & shop 12–5.30 (Sats., Suns. & Bank Hol. Mons. 11–5.30). House 1–5 (Sats., Suns. & Bank Hol. Mons. 12–5). *Timed tickets to avoid delay. Parties should book timed entry to House.* Adm. House & Garden £1.80; booked adult parties of 15 or more Mons. to Thurs. only £1.40. Garden only 70p. Car park 50p. Coaches free. Dogs in park only on leads. Wheelchairs provided—access to shop, garden, park, kitchen & outbuildings only. Information from the Administrator, Dunham Massey Hall, Altrincham, Cheshire. ✕☕ lunches & teas available ☎ 061-941 1025	Crosville/Warrington 38, Warrington—Altrincham (*alight Dunham Town ½m*); also 37 & H50 on A56 (*¼ m*).
GAWSWORTH HALL, Macclesfield *Mr. & Mrs. Timothy Richards* *map 2 D* Tudor half-timbered manor house with tilting ground. Former home of Mary Fitton, Maid of Honour at the Court of Queen Elizabeth I, and the supposed "dark lady" of Shakespeare's sonnets. Pictures, sculpture and furniture.	3 m S of Macclesfield on the Congleton–Macclesfield rd (A536) *Stn: Macclesfield* (4 m)	March 24 to October 28—Daily 2–6 Adm. £1.30, Chd. 65p. *Evening parties by arrangement.* Free car park. ✕☕ in the Pavilion ☎ *North Rode* (026 03) 456	Crosville K38, Macclesfield–Congleton–Crewe National tours from the Potteries, Lancashire, the Midlands, Chester, Wirral & Liverpool
HANDFORTH HALL, Handforth, nr. Wilmslow *map 5 C* *Dr. J. C. Douglas* Small 16th century half-timbered manor house. Fine Elizabethan staircase. Collection of oak furniture.	½ m E of Handforth on B5358 *Stn: Handforth* (*few mins. walk*)	June to September by written appointment only.	Frequent train & bus services.
HARE HILL GARDEN, Over Alderley nr. Macclesfield *map 2 D* *The National Trust* Walled garden with pergola, rhododendrons and azaleas; parkland.	Between Alderley Edge & Prestbury off B5087 at Greyhound Rd. *Stns: Alderley Edge* (*2½ m*); *Prestbury* (*2½ m*)	GARDEN ONLY: April to end of Oct.—Weds., Thurs. & Suns., 2–5.30. Adm. 70p. Parties by appointment in writing to the Head Gardener. Unsuitable for school parties. Dogs admitted on leads. Wheelchair access—some assistance needed.	Crosville E59 passes nearby—limited service only (*not Suns.*)

CHOLMONDELEY CASTLE GARDENS

MALPAS, CHESHIRE

Home of The Marquess and Marchioness of Cholmondeley

Gardens, lakeside picnic area, farm, including a collection of rare breeds of farm animals.

Ancient Private Chapel in the Park.
Evening Services 6.30 p.m. every third Sunday in month.

Open SUNDAYS and BANK HOLIDAYS ONLY from EASTER SUNDAY to end of SEPTEMBER: 12 noon to 6 p.m.
Weekday visits accepted by prior arrangement.

Admission £1 Adults
25p Children

Tea Room and Gift Shop
Plants for Sale

Situated off Whitchurch/Tarporley Road and Chester/Whitchurch Road.

All enquiries to The Estate Office, Cholmondeley, Malpas, Cheshire.
Telephone Cholmondeley 383 or 203.

THE HOUSE IS NOT OPEN TO THE PUBLIC

CHURCHE'S MANSION

NANTWICH, CHESHIRE

This half-timbered mansion was completed on Saturday, 4th May, 1577 for Rychard and Margerye Churche. Restoration and repairs commenced in 1930 continue to reveal the splendours of this fine H-plan mansion.
April to October—Daily 10.00 a.m.–5.00 p.m.
Closed November to March.
Admission 50p. Car Park Free.
Licensed Restaurant in the Mansion (open throughout the year).

GAWSWORTH HALL

near MACCLESFIELD, CHESHIRE

This beautiful 16th century half timbered Manor House is situated half-way between Macclesfield and Congleton in an idyllic setting close to the lovely medieval Church. The mile long park wall encloses the famous tilting ground formed by the Fitton family, who were seated at Gawsworth from 1306 until the late 17th century. Pictures, Sculpture and Furniture.

Open daily from 24th March to 28th October: 2–6 p.m.
Evening parties by arrangement.
Admission: Adults £1.30, Children 65p.
Teas and refreshments available in the Pavilion.
FREE CAR PARK
OPEN AIR SHAKESPEARE and OPERA June/July.
Tel. North Rode (026 03) 456

LYME PARK

DISLEY

Lyme Park and Hall were given by Lord Newton in 1947 to the National Trust who lease it to Stockport and Greater Manchester Councils. The present appearance of the Hall is mainly due to the work of the Italian architect, Giacomo Leoni, who was commissioned in 1720 to alter the existing structure built by Sir Piers Legh VII in 1541 on the site of a still older building which is mentioned in a manuscript dated 1465. The State Rooms in the Hall are furnished with period furniture and tapestries. Exhibitions about the Hall and Park are open at the same time as the Hall.

PROPERTY (*showing map reference*)	LOCATION (*with nearest Rly. Stn.*)	OPENING TIMES AND ADMISSION CHARGES CATERING FACILITIES	COACH AND RAIL TOURS BUS SERVICES (*showing alighting points*)
CHESHIRE—*continued*			
LITTLE MORETON HALL, Congleton *The National Trust* *map 2 D* A moated building of 15th and 16th century half-timbered work. Remarkable carved gables. The recently discovered and restored 16th century wall paintings are on view	4 m SW of Congleton off Newcastle-under-Lyme – Congleton rd (A34) *Stns: Kidsgrove (3m); Congleton (4½ m)*	March & Oct.—Sats. & Suns. 2–6 (or sunset if earlier). *School parties March to end Oct. mornings only, except Tues.* April to Sept.—Daily (except Tues.) 2–6 (or sunset if earlier). *Closed Good Friday. Parties by prior arrangement. Guided tours* 2.15, 3.15 & 4.30. Adm. £1.40, Chd. 70p. No dogs. Wheelchairs provided. Shop. at the Hall (*parties to pre-book*) *Congleton* (02602) 2018	National tours from Buxton & Lancashire towns P.M.T. 18, 18a Hanley–Congleton (*alight Scholar Green, 1 m*)
LYME PARK, Disley *map 5 C* *The National Trust (who lease it to Stockport & Greater Manchester Councils)* House dating from Elizabethan times. Impressive Palladian exterior (1720) by Giacomo Leoni. Home of Leghs for 600 years. Grinling Gibbons carvings. Extensive garden, formal bedding, herbaceous borders, stream. Park of 1,320 acres. Herds of red and fallow deer. Nature trail. Pitch and putt course. Cycle hire.	¼ m W of Disley on the Stockport-Buxton rd (A6). 6½ m SE of Stockport *Stn: Disley (¼ m)*	HOUSE: March 31 to end of Oct.—Tues. to Sats. 2–5; last adm. 4.30 (Oct. 4 p.m.). Suns., Good Friday & Bank Hol. Mons. 1–6; last adm. 5.30 (Oct. 4.30). *Closed Mons. except Bank Hols.* PARK & GARDENS open all year 8 to sunset. Adm. House 70p; Park & Gardens free. Special bookings for large parties (no reductions) on application to the Administrator. Car park 60p, motor cycles 40p (inc. N.T. members); half price after 4 p.m. (except Suns. & Bank Hols.). Coaches free. *All charges subject to review.* April to end Oct.—Daily; remainder of year weekends & Bank Hols. only *Disley* (066 32) 2023	National tours from Lancashire towns Trent 199 Stockport–Buxton; 200 Manchester–Nottingham National 952, Manchester–Nottingham (*alight Disley, Ram's Head*) Gt. Manchester 361, 362 Stockport-Hayfield (*half hourly*) (*alight gates*) 360 direct Stockport to Lyme Hall (*Suns. only*).
NESS GARDENS, Wirral *map 2 D* *Liverpool University Botanic Gardens* Finest collection of rhododendrons and azaleas in the N.W. Superb specimen trees and shrubs. Large rock, water, heather and terrace gardens. Visitor centre with slide shows and indoor exhibitions.	Between Neston & Burton ; NW of Chester off A540 *Stn: Neston (1½ m)*	All the year—Daily 9 to sunset. *Closed Christmas Day*. Adm. £1, Chd. & O.A.Ps. 50p. Picnic area. Tea room (Party catering by prior arrangement) 051-336 2135	Crosville C22 Chester–Meols; 72C Birkenhead–Ness
NETHER ALDERLEY MILL, Nether Alderley *map 2 D* *The National Trust* 15th century corn-mill in use until 1929 and now restored	1½m S of Alderley Edge on E side of A34. *Stn : Alderley Edge (2 m)*	April, May, June & Oct.—Weds., Suns. & Bank Hol. Mons. 2–5.30. July, Aug. & Sept.—Daily (except Mons. but open Bank Hol. Mon.) 2–5.30. *Closed Good Friday*. Adm. 80p, Chd. 40p. Dogs on leads only, at owners' risk. Unsuitable for disabled or visually handicapped. Parties by prior arrangement with Mr. R. Allen, 7 Oak Cottage, Styal, Wilmslow. *Wilmslow* (0625) 523012	Crosville-E29 Manchester-Macclesfield.
NORTON PRIORY MUSEUM, Runcorn *Norton Priory Museum Trust* *map 5 C* Excavated remains of medieval priory, including 12th century undercroft, set in beautiful woodland gardens. New museum building with displays of excavated floor tiles, carved stonework, ceramics etc.; auditorium, museum shop etc.	From M56 (jct. 12) follow Norton Priory road signs *Stn: Runcorn (3 m)*	March to Oct.—Sats., Suns. & Bank Hols. 12–6; Mons. to Fris. 12–5. Nov. to Feb.—Daily 12–4. *Closed Dec.* 24 & 25. Special arrangements for groups. Adm. 70p; Chd., Students & O.A.Ps. 30p. *Runcorn* (092 85) 69895	Crosville T3, T4 Busway from rail & bus stations (*alight Haddocks Wood—10 min. walk*)
PEOVER HALL, Over Peover, Knutsford *Randle Brooks* *map 2 D* Dates from 1585. Caroline stables. Mainwaring Chapel. Landscaped park. Extensive gardens.	4 m S of Knutsford off A50 at Whipping Stocks Inn *Stn: Knutsford (3½m)*	May to September (except Bank Holidays). HALL, STABLES & GARDENS: Mons. 2–5. Adm. £1.20, Chd. 60p. STABLES & GARDENS ONLY: Thurs. 2–4.30. Adm. 75p. Enquiries: N. Brooks, Peover Hall Farm. teas *Lower Peover* 2135	Crosville E26, Macclesfield–Knutsford–Northwich (*alight Over Peover*)

The National Trust in CHESHIRE

LITTLE MORETON HALL near CONGLETON

Friars Gate Studio photograph

Considered the most perfect example of a moated, half-timbered manor house in Britain. Dating from the 15th Century, the house was finally completed by the Moreton family in the 16th Century and illustrates the merging of the mediaeval Gothic with the exuberances of the English Renaissance. Restored 16th Century wall paintings are on view.

Great Hall, Long Gallery and Chapel, where a short service is held at 4.30 p.m. every Sunday. Knot and Herb Garden. Shop. Tea Room.

DUNHAM MASSEY near ALTRINCHAM

Molyneux Photography photograph

Dunham Massey is one of the most notable Cheshire estates, until 1976 the home of the Earl of Stamford who left it to the National Trust. The house contains much outstanding 18th century furniture and Huguenot silver and a series of portraits of the Grey family, Earls of Stamford. Large gardens, grounds and a magnificent formal deer park and Elizabethan mill in working order.

NETHER ALDERLEY MILL NETHER ALDERLEY

A fascinating overshot water mill, originally fifteenth century, with a stone-tiled low pitched roof. Now restored to full working order and is grinding flour again.

HARE HILL GARDEN

OVER ALDERLEY near MACCLESFIELD

Camera 7 Ltd. photograph

Walled garden with pergola, rhododendrons and azaleas; parkland.

PROPERTY (*showing map reference*)	LOCATION (*with nearest Rly. Stn.*)	OPENING TIMES AND ADMISSION CHARGES CATERING FACILITIES	COACH AND RAIL TOURS BUS SERVICES (*showing alighting points*)
CHESHIRE—*continued*			
QUARRY BANK MILL, Styal *map 5 C* *The National Trust* *(Quarry Bank Mill Trust Ltd.)* Styal is the most complete and least altered factory colony of the Industrial Revolution. The model village, chapels, school, shop and Apprentice House were built for the work force of Samuel Greg in the decades following the establishment of cotton spinning at Quarry Bank Mill in 1784. The Mill is being developed as a working museum, with working weaving shed and spinning demonstrations. The Apprentice House contains an exhibition and A.V. on the social history of the village.	1½ m N of Wilmslow off B5166 *Stns: Styal (½ m not Suns.); Wilmslow (1½ m)*	April, May & Sept.—Tues. to Suns. & Bank Hol. Mons. 11–5. June, July & Aug.—Daily 11–5. Oct. to March—Tues. to Suns. 11–4. *Closed Christmas Day.* Country Park open all year during daylight hours. Adm. to end of May £1.50, Chd. £1; from June 1 £1.80, Chd. £1.20. Parties should apply to the Quarry Bank Mill Trust (send s.a.e. or tel. Wilmslow 527468) for details of special rates & a booking form at least 3 weeks before visit. Disabled visitors please tel. before visit. No coach parties Suns. or Bank Hols. Shop sells cloth woven in Mill. ☎ *Wilmslow* 527468	*Trains:* Regular service from Manchester & Wilmslow *(Mons. to Sats.)*
RODE HALL, Scholar Green, Stoke-on-Trent *Sir Richard Baker Wilbraham Bt.* *map 2 D* 18th century country house with Georgian stable block. Later alterations by S. Wyatt and Darcy Braddell.	5 m SW of Congleton between A34 & A50 *Stn: Alsager (2½ m)*	April to Sept.—Tues. & Bank Hol. Mons. 2–5. Adm. £1. ☎ *Alsager* 3237 ✕ ☕ Bleeding Wolf Restaurant, Scholar Green	PMT 318, 319 Hanley-Sandbach *(alight Odd Rode Church)*
TATTON PARK, Knutsford *map 5 C* *The National Trust (financed, maintained & administered by Cheshire County Council)* Seat of the late Lord Egerton of Tatton. Fine Georgian house by Samuel and Lewis Wyatt, beautifully furnished and decorated. Family museum. Restored 15th century Old Hall. 1930s working Farm. Magnificently varied 50 acre garden, showhouse, fernery, waterfowl, 1,000 acre deer park, two large meres, swimming, sailing, fishing, riding. Medieval village trail. Historical nature trail.	2 m N of Knutsford, 3½ m off M6 (exit 19) 4 m S of M56 (exit 7) fully signposted *Stn: Knutsford (2 m)*	PARK & GARDENS open all year. HOUSE open daily April to October. Hours (Suns. & Public Hols. in brackets): April to mid-May & Sept./Oct.: Park 11–6 (10–6); Garden 12–4.30 (11–5); House 1–4 (1–5); Old Hall 12–4 (12–5); Farm 12–4 (12–4). Mid-May to Aug.: Park 10.30–7 (10–7); Garden 11–5.30 (11–6); House 1–5 (12–5); Old Hall (July/Aug.) 12–5 (12–5); Farm 11–4 (11–4). Nov. to April 1: Park 11–dusk (11–dusk); Garden 1–4 (12–4); *House, Old Hall & Farm closed but open Suns. in Nov. & March* 1–4. Exits remain open for 1 hr. after adm times. Adm. House £1; Old Hall 80p; Garden 70p; Farm 70p. Reduction for parties of 12 or more weekdays on application only. Park: cars 95p (inc. N.T. members); coaches free. Knitsford Gate car park: cars 45p (inc. N.T. members). Information from the Information Officer, Tatton Park, Knutsford. ✕ ☕ Restaurant ☎ *Knutsford* (0565) 3155	National tours from the Potteries, Lancashire Chester, Liverpool & Birkenhead Buses to Knutsford from Wilmslow, Northwich, Macclesfield etc
VALE ROYAL ABBEY, Whitegate *map 2 D* *Barry Hertzog, Esq.* Abbey built 1540, with additions, on site of original Abbey founded in 1281. Grounds, gardens with new plantings; the Nun's Grave, an historic monument.	3½ m NW of Winsford off A54 to Chester *Stn: Winsford (4½ m)*	All the year—Sats., Suns. & Bank Hols. 11–5. *Closed Christmas weekend.* Adm. Abbey & Grounds £1, Chd. 50p. Shop. Educational tours. Wheelchair access to ground floor & Grounds only. ✕ ☕ Snack lunches, teas (usually available) ☎ *Sandiway* (0606) 888684 *or* 882164	Buses via A556 Northwich By-pass *(alight near end of North Drive of Abbey)*. Bus from Winsford B.R. Stn. to Whitegate–Helipad area (Pooley's Guide).
WOODHEY CHAPEL, Faddiley, nr. Nantwich *The Trustees of Woodhey Chapel* *map 2 D* "The Chapel in the Fields." A small private chapel, recently restored, dating from 1699.	1 m SW of Faddiley off A534 Nantwich—Wrexham rd. *Stn: Nantwich (4 m)*	April to Oct.—Sats. & Bank Hol. Mons. 2–5. Adm. 50p, Chd. 25p. At other times by appointment. ☎ *Faddiley* (027 074) 215	No reasonable public transport
CLEVELAND			
ORMESBY HALL, nr Middlesbrough *The National Trust* *map 1 S* Mid-18th century house. Contemporary plasterwork. Small garden	3 m SE of Middlesbrough, *Stns: Marton (1½ m) (not Suns. April, Sept., Oct.); Middlesbrough (3 m)*	April to October—Weds., Sats., Suns. & Bank Hol. Mons. 2–6. Educational & party visits at other times by appointment. **Adm. 90p, Chd. (accompanied) 40p.** ***Pre-booked parties of 15 or over 60p each adult, 30p chd.*** **No dogs. Wheelchairs ground floor only.**	United 254, 255, 256 Middlesbrough–Whitby; 266, 267 Middlesbrough *(Swan's Corner Circular) (alight Ormesby crossroads, ¼ m)*

Thundering looms

... intricate spinning ... a mill apprentice's day (and his master's) 150 years ago ... two centuries of British textiles ... Experience all this and more at **Quarry Bank Mill, Styal,** best-preserved cotton mill and factory colony of the Industrial Revolution, in its unspoilt woodland setting. Tea Room, Pie Shop, Gift Shop; facilities for special functions.

For information, phone or send s.a.e. Parties are welcome (at reduced rates) all year, advance booking is essential. Quarry Bank Mill, Styal, Cheshire SK9 4LA tel Wilmslow (0625) 527468.

Styal is a National Trust property.

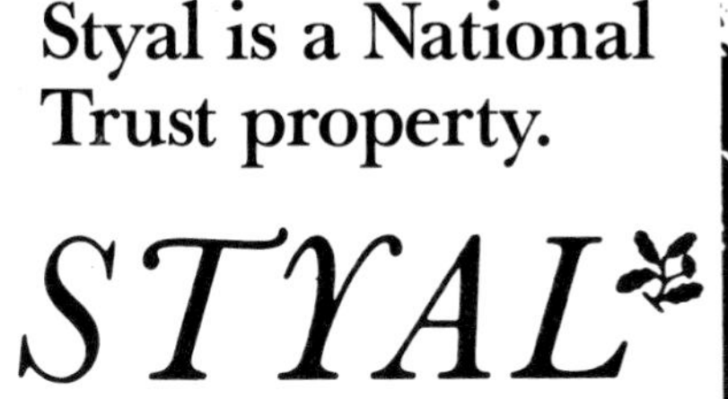

STYAL

VALE ROYAL ABBEY

WHITEGATE, CHESHIRE

The present Abbey was built in 1540, with additions, on the site of the original Abbey founded in 1281. The Great Hall, Library, Armoury, Dining Hall and Delamere lobby are undergoing extensive restoration. The Nun's Grave, in the grounds, is an historic monument. The Gardens have new planting with rhododendrons, azaleas, camellias etc. and the Abbey shop sells antiques, souvenirs, solid oak furniture and some plants.

Some luxury flats available on new 99 year leases in Blore wing (shown above).

OPENING TIMES OPPOSITE

ORMESBY HALL

Near Middlesbrough

THE NATIONAL TRUST

The main house was built in about 1750, and though not very grand by 18th century standards, both the design and decoration of the house reflect taste and craftsmanship of a high order.

The decoration inside is opulent and varied and includes fine plaster-work by contemporary craftsmen.

The stable block, attributed to Carr of York, is a particularly fine mid-eighteenth century building with an attractive courtyard.

CORNWALL

PROPERTY (*showing map reference*)	LOCATION (*with nearest Rly. Stn.*)	OPENING TIMES AND ADMISSION CHARGES AND CATERING FACILITIES	COACH AND RAIL TOURS BUS SERVICES (*showing alighting points*)
ANTONY HOUSE, Torpoint *map 2 U* Δ *The National Trust* The home of Sir John Carew Pole, Bt. Built for Sir William Carew 1711–1721. Unaltered Queen Anne house, panelled rooms. Fine furniture	5 m W of Plymouth via Torpoint car ferry. 2 m NW of Torpoint, N of A374 *Stn: Plymouth (6 m) (via Ferry)*	April to end of October—Tues., Weds. & Thurs.; also Bank Hol. Mons.: 2–6 (last adm. 5.30). Adm. £1.80, Chd. 90p. *No reduction for parties but organisers should please notify the Secretary.* No dogs. Unsuitable for wheelchairs. Shop. *Plymouth* (0752) 812191	National tours from Truro and Plymouth Western National 79 from Plymouth to Great Parks Estate (¼ *m*)
COTEHELE HOUSE, Calstock *map 2 U* *The National Trust* Fine medieval house, former home of Earls of Mount Edgcumbe. Armour, furniture, tapestries. Terrace garden falling to the sheltered valley, ponds, stream, unusual shrubs	On W bank of the Tamar, 2 m W of Calstock (*by footpath, 6 m by road*). 8 m SW of Tavistock; 14 m from Plymouth via Tamar Bridge *Stn: Calstock (1¼ m) (not Suns.)*	April to end of Oct.—Daily 11–6 (last adm. 5.30). Closes sunset if earlier. Nov. to March—Garden open daily during daylight. Adm. House, Gardens & Cotehele Mill £2.30, Chd. £1.15; Gardens & Cotehele Mill £1, Chd. 50p. *Reduced fee of £1.80 for pre-booked coach parties. Organisers should book visits & arrange for meals beforehand with the Administrator:* No dogs. Wheelchairs provided; house only accessible. Shop. in the barn & on Cotehele Quay *St. Dominick* 50434	No reasonable public road transport Can be reached by water from Devonport (contact Millbrook Steamship Co.)
GLENDURGAN GARDEN, Helford River *map 2 T* *The National Trust* A valley garden with fine trees and shrubs, overlooking estuary. Giant's Stride and maze	4 m SW of Falmouth ½ m SW of Mawnan Smith on road to Helford Passage *Stn: Penmere (4 m)*	March to end of October—Mons., Weds. & Fris. (except Good Friday) 10.30–4.30. Adm. £1, Chd. 50p. *No reduction for parties* No dogs. Unsuitable for wheelchairs.	Cornwall Busways 62, 64 from Falmouth (*alight Trebath Cross*)
GODOLPHIN HOUSE, Helston *map 2 T* *S. E. Schofield, Esq.* Tudor house. Colonnaded front added 1635. A former house of the Earls of Godolphin.	5 m NW of Helston; between villages of Townshend & Godolphin Cross.	May & June—Thurs. 2–5. July, Aug. & Sept.—Tues. & Thurs. 2–5. Adm. £1, Chd. 50p. Open at other times times for pre-booked parties & all year round for arranged parties.	
LANHYDROCK, nr Bodmin *map 2 U* *The National Trust* 17th cent. long gallery. Fine plaster ceilings. Family portraits 17th to 20th centuries. The extensive kitchen quarters (1883) are also shown. Formal garden with clipped yews, and parterre, laid out in 1857. Rhododendrons, magnolias, rare trees and shrubs.	2½ m SE of Bodmin on Bodmin–Lostwithiel rd (B3268) *Stn: Bodmin Road (1½ m by signposted carriage - drive to house; 3 m by road)*	November to end of March—Garden open daily during daylight hours. April to end of Oct.—Daily 11–6 (last adm. 5.30). Adm. £2.30, Chd. £1.15; Garden only £1, Chd. 50p. Pre-booked parties £1.80. *Organisers should book visits & arrange for meals beforehand with The Administrator, Lanhydrock House, Bodmin.* Dogs in park only on leads. Wheelchairs provided. Shop (also open Nov. & Dec.). teas in restaurant at House; snacks in stable block (*last adm.* 5.30) *Bodmin* 3320	
LONG CROSS VICTORIAN GARDENS, nr. Wadebridge *map 2 U* *Mr. & Mrs. R. Y. Warrillow* Late Victorian gardens set amidst majestic pines with panoramic sea views	7 m N E of Wadebridge, Trelights, St. Endellion; just off B3314 between Port Isaac & Portquin	Easter to Oct.—Daily 11–2, 5.30 to dusk. Children's playground; family room. Adm. free. *Collection box in aid of National Gardens' Scheme.* Beer Garden, coffee & refreshments *Port Isaac* (020888) 243	
MOUNT EDGCUMBE HOUSE & COUNTRY PARK, nr Plymouth *map 2 U* Δ *City of Plymouth & County of Cornwall* The Edgcumbe Family Seat. Varied contrasts in outstanding scenery, formal gardens, mature woodland, open parkland and unique coastline.	Just across the Tamar from Plymouth by Cremyll Ferry or B3247 to Cremyll *Stn: Plymouth (2 m) (viafoot ferry)*	House and Higher Gardens: For details of opening times & adm. charges telephone Plymouth (0752) 822236. Country Park & Formal Gardens open all year free of charge. Information office. available in the Orangery	*Bus:* 28, 29 from Royal Parade, Plymouth to Durnford Street then Cremyll Pedestrian Ferry to Park entrance
THE OLD POST OFFICE, Tintagel *map 2 P* *The National Trust* A miniature 14th century manor house with large hall	Nos. 3 & 4 in the centre of Tintagel	April to end of October—Daily 11–6 (or sunset if earlier). Adm. 80p, Chd. 40p. *No reduction for parties.* No dogs. Wheelchair access. Shop.	National tours from Devon & Cornwall **Fry's from Launceston** Wadebridge–Tintagel (*not Suns*)

GODOLPHIN HOUSE

near HELSTON, CORNWALL

A former home of the Earls of Godolphin and the birthplace of Queen Anne's famous Lord High Treasurer—Sidney, first Earl of Godolphin. Parts of the house are of early Tudor date and additions were made in Elizabethan and Carolean times. The unique front was completed shortly before the Civil War and rests on massive columns of local granite. The fine "Kings Room" is traditionally said to have been occupied by Charles II (then Prince of Wales) at the time of his escape from Pendennis Castle to the Scilly Islands. Pictures include "The Godolphin Arabian" by John Wootton.

May & June—Thursdays. July, August & September—Tuesdays & Thursdays. 2–5 p.m. Admission £1, Children 50.

Parties by arrangement all year round.

MOUNT EDGCUMBE HOUSE AND COUNTRY PARK

Nr. PLYMOUTH

Across the Sound from Plymouth stands this Tudor style mansion, restored following its destruction in the 1941 Plymouth Blitz. Visitors to the House and Country Park will enjoy its relaxed atmosphere, occupying a unique site overlooking Plymouth Sound, comprising 800 acres of quiet countryside with scenic walks along 10 miles of coastline.

OPENING TIMES ABOVE

PROPERTY (*showing map reference*)	LOCATION (*with nearest Rly. Stn.*)	OPENING TIMES AND ADMISSION CHARGES CATERING FACILITIES	COACH AND RAIL TOURS BUS SERVICES (*showing alighting points*)
CORNWALL—*continued*			
PENCARROW HOUSE & GARDENS, Bodmin *map 2 U* *The Molesworth—St. Aubyn family* Georgian mansion, fine collection of 18th century paintings. English, French and Oriental furniture and china. Large formal garden and woodlands, with granite rockery, ancient encampment and lake. Noted specimen conifer collection.	4 m NW of Bodmin off A389 & B3266 at Washaway. *Stn: Bodmin Road (7 m)*	House: Easter Sat. to September 30—Tues., Weds., Thurs., Fris. & Suns. 1.30–5.30 (June 1 to Sept. 10: 11–5.30); Bank Hol. Mons. 11–5.30. Last tour at 5. Grounds: Daily during season. Adm. (1983 rates): House & Gardens £1.50, Chd. 75p; Garden only 75p, Chd. 35p. No reduction for O.A.P. Guided tours. *Special arrangements for pre-booked parties.* Free car & coach park. Car park & toilet facilities for disabled. Plant shop. Picnic area. Children's play area & pets corner. Craft Centre. Self-pick strawberries & raspberries in season. available at the House *St. Mabyn* 369	Cornwall Busways 55 Bodmin Road–Padstow (*not Suns.*) (*alight Washaway*)
PENDENNIS CASTLE, Falmouth *map 2 T* *Dept. of the Environment* Castle fort built by Henry VIII, c. 1540	On Pendennis point (headland) *Stn: Falmouth (¾ m) (Suns. May–Sept. only)*	All the year: March 15 to Oct. 15—Weekdays 9.30–6.30; Suns. 2–6.30. Oct. 16 to March 14—Weekdays 9.30–4; Suns. 2–4. *Closed Dec. 24, 25, 26 & Jan. 1.* Adm. 50p, Chd. (under 16) & O.A.Ps. 25p.	All Cornwall Busways routes serving Falmouth (65 passes Castle). *No buses Suns. except in peak*
ST. MICHAEL'S MOUNT, Penzance *The National Trust* *map 2 T* Home of Lord St. Levan. Mediaeval and early 17th century with considerable alterations and additions in 18th and 19th century	½ m from the shore at Marazion (A394), connected by causeway, 3 m E Penzance *Stn: Penance (3 m)*	All the year: April 1 to end of May—Mons., Weds. & Fris.; June to end of Oct.—Mons. to Fris.: 10.30–4.45 (last adm.). Nov. 1 to March 31—Mons., Weds. & Fris. by conducted tours only, leaving at 11.0, 12.0, 2.0, 4.0 (*weather & tide permitting— N.B.: ferry boats do not operate a regular service during this period*). Adm. £2, Chd. £1. Shop—April to end of Oct., daily. No dogs. Unsuitable for wheelchairs. at the Island Café & Tea Gardens (*summer only*) *Marazion* 710507	National tours from Truro and Perranporth. Ferry boat from Marazion 40p. No ferry boats during winter months. Cornwall Busways 2, 3 Penzance–Marazion–Helston–Falmouth (*alight Marazion Sq*)
TRELISSICK GARDEN, nr Truro *map 2 T* *The National Trust* Beautiful wooded park at head of Falmouth harbour. Large shrub garden. Woodland walks. Particularly rich in rhododendrons and hydrangeas	4 m S of Truro on both sides of B3289 overlooking King Harry Passage *Stns: Perranwell (4m) (not Suns. April & Oct); Truro (5m)*	Gardens only; March to end of Oct.—Mons. to Sats. 11–6 (or sunset if earlier), Suns 1–6 (or sunset if earlier). Entrance on road to King Harry Passage. Adm. £1.40, Chd. 70. *No reduction for parties.* Shop, with special plants section. Dogs in woodland walk & park only, on leads. Wheelchairs provided. in the barn *Devoran* 862090	Cornwall Busways 88 Truro–Feock (*not Suns.*) (*alight Feock Downs crossroads* 1¼ m)
TRENGWAINTON GARDEN, Penzance *The National Trust* *map 2 T* Large shrub and woodland garden. Fine views. A series of walled gardens contain rare sub-tropical plants	2 m NW of Penzance ½ m W of Heamoor on Morvah rd (B3312) *Stn: Penzance (2 m)*	March to October—Weds., Thurs., Fris., Sats. & Bank Hol. Mons. 11–6. Adm. £1, Chd. 50p. *No reduction for parties.* No dogs. Wheelchair access.	Cornwall Busways 10, 12 Penzance–St. Just (*alight Boswedman Turn or Madron, ¾ m.*)
TRERICE, St. Newlyn East (1571) *map 2 T* *The National Trust* A small Elizabethan house, plaster ceilings and fireplaces, in a recently planted garden. A small museum in the Barn traces the development of the lawn mower.	3 m SE of Newquay A392 & A3058 (*turn right at Kestle Mill*) *Stns: Quintrel Downs (1½ m); Newquay 3½ m) (not Suns. April, Sept. & Oct.)*	April to end of October—Daily 11–6 (last adm. 5.30). Adm. £1.80, Chd. 90p. *Reduced rate of £1.50 for prebooked parties.* No dogs. Wheelchairs provided; access to house only. Shop. in the barn 11–6 (last adm. 5.30). *Parties must book.* *Newquay* 5404	Cornwall Busways 90 Newquay–Truro–Falmouth (*not Suns: April, May, Sept. & Oct.*) (*alight Kestle Mill, 1 m*)
TREWITHEN, Probus, nr Truro *map 2 U* *Mr. & Mrs. A. M. J. Galsworthy* Guided tours around this charming and intimate privately owned Country House. Occupied by the same family since built in 1720. The gardens covering some 20 acres are outstanding and internationally famous. Renowned for their magnificent collection of camellias, rhododendrons, magnolias and many rare trees and shrubs seldom found elsewhere. The woodland gardens are surrounded by peaceful parkland landscaped and planted in the 18th century. The gardens, which include a natural water garden, have been considerably extended with the introduction of many new plants and rare species. Magnolias and early rhododendrons March to May, camellias and later flowering rhododendrons May to end of June.	1½ m E of Probus. Just S of A390 St. Austell–Truro *Stns: St: Austell (7 m); Truro (7 m)*	GARDEN: March to September—Weekdays (inc. Bank Hols.). 2–4.30. *Closed Suns.* Adm. March to June 90p. Chd & O.A.Ps. 80p; July to Sept. 80p. Chd. & O.A.Ps. 60p. Chd. under 10 years free. Season ticket £5. HOUSE: April to July only—Mons. & Tues. (inc.. Bank Hols.) 2–4.30. Adm. £1.70. NURSERY: March to Nov.—retail & wholesale. *Enquiries* *St. Austell* (0726) 882418 *or* 882764	Cornwall Busways 32 St. Austell–Truro (connections from Penzance) (*alight gate,* ½ m.)
TRELOWARREN HOUSE & CHAPEL, Mawgan-in-Meneage, Helston *map 2 I* *Sir John Vyvyan, Bt.* *Leased to the Trelowarren Fellowship* Home of the Vyvyan family since 1427 the main part of the house dates from early Tudor times. The Chapel, part of which is pre-Reformation, and the 17th century part of the house are leased to the Trelowarren Fellowship, an Ecumenical Charity.	3 m S of Helston off B3293 to St. Keverne	HOUSE: Easter Monday (April 23) to Oct. 31—Weds. & Bank Hols.; also open Suns. from mid June to Sept. 30: 2.30–5. Conducted tours 80p, Chd. 40p. (under 12 yrs. free). CHAPEL: Easter to Sept. 30—Daily 11–5. Organised tours by arrangement. Weekly concerts throughout the year & Sunday services during the holiday season. Ground floor only suitable for disabled. tea & light refreshments *Mawgan* (032 622) 366	
CUMBRIA			
ABBOT HALL ART GALLERY & MUSEUM OF LAKELAND LIFE & INDUSTRY, Kendal *map 5 A* *Lake District Art Gallery & Museum Trust* 18th cent. house reputably built by Carr of York. Collections of fine pictures, water-colours, glass, furniture and china of the period. Modern galleries for frequent changing exhibitions. Garden landscaped in 1759	In Kendal next to Parish Church *Stn: Kendal*	All the year—Daily. Art Gallery—Mons. to Fris. 10.30–5.30; Sats. & Suns. 2–5. Museum—Mons. to Fris. 10.30–5; Sats & Suns. 2–5. *Both closed two weeks Christmas to New Year, also Good Friday.* Adm. charge; special rates for O.A.Ps., Chd. & Students. *Lift for disabled* Mons. to Fris. only. Mons. to Fris. 11–4 *Kendal* 22464	Ribble services from Lancaster, Ulverston, Keswick Ambleside, Windermere
ACORN BANK, Temple Sowerby *map 1 R* *The National Trust* Spring bulbs, walled garden with herbaceous plants, outstanding herb garden. Red sandstone house, part 16th century (not open)	Just N of Temple Sowerby, 6 m E of Penrith on A66. *Stn: Penrith (6 m)*	GARDEN ONLY: April to end October—Daily 10–5.30. Adm. 50p, Chd. 25p. No reduction for parties. No dogs. Wheelchair access to parts of garden only.	Ribble 620, 621, 623, 624, 625 Penrith–Appleby–Kirkby Stephen (*not Suns.*) (½ *m*)
BELLE ISLE, Bowness-on-Windermere *Mr. & Mrs. E. S. C. Curwen* *map 5 A* Built in 1778 on a 38 acre island in the middle of Lake Windermere. Interior by the Adams brother. Portraits by Romney and furniture by Gillow. Nature walk.	On Lake Windermere *Stn: Windermere (1½m)*	May 21 to Sept. 13—Mons., Tues., Weds. & Thurs. 10.30–5. Adm. to island £1, Chd. 60p. Guided tour of house 50p. Café adjacent to the house	*Bus:* Ribble 519, Ambleside–Windermere–Bowness Pier; 517, Ambleside–Bowness Pier–Ulverston (*with connections from Barrow*) *Ferry:* British Rail, Ambleside–Bowness Pier–Lake side

TREWITHEN

TRURO, CORNWALL

"Country Life" photograph

"ONE OF THE OUTSTANDING CORNISH COUNTRY HOUSES OF THE 18th CENTURY" according to Christopher Hussey in "Country Life." A blend of landscape and woodland gardening at its finest.

PENCARROW HOUSE & GARDENS

near BODMIN, CORNWALL

A Georgian country mansion built c. 1750 by Sir John Molesworth, Bt., containing a fine collection of 18th century paintings, including works by Reynolds, Devis Scott, Wilson, Neefs, Raeburn and Northcote, set amongst typical English, French and Oriental furniture and china. The mile-long entrance drive and American Gardens, laid out in the 1840s by the Victorian statesman, Sir William Molesworth, Bt., contain a noted collection of specimen conifers and specialise in rhododendrons, camellias and azaleas.

TRELOWARREN

MAWGAN-IN-MENEAGE, HELSTON, CORNWALL

Home of the Vyvyan family since 1427 the main part of the house dates from early Tudor times. The Chapel, parts of which are pre-Reformation, and the 17th century part of the house are leased to the Trelowarren Fellowship, an Ecumenical Charity. The Chapel and main rooms, containing family portraits and various Exhibitions, are open to the Public with guided tours. Weekly Concerts take place throughout the year and Sunday Services during the holiday season.

ABBOT HALL ART GALLERY

KENDAL CUMBRIA

The old front of Abbot Hall facing the river Kent

The house, built in 1759 by Carr of York, contains 18th century furnished rooms; upstairs—modern galleries with pictures, prints, sculpture and pottery. Changing exhibitions.

Open Weekdays 10.30 to 5.30; Saturdays and Sundays 2.0 to 5.0.

Closed for two weeks from Christmas to New Year and Good Friday.

Car Park

BRANTWOOD

CONISTON, CUMBRIA

Home of John Ruskin 1872-1900. Brantwood is one of the most beautifully situated houses in the Lake District. The views of the mountains across Coniston Water are amongst the finest in England. House contains a large collection of Ruskin's exquisite paintings and drawings, his furniture, coach and boat 'Jumping Jenny'. Delightful nature trail around the Brantwood Estate. Tea room, quality book shop, Gift shop.

OPENING TIMES PAGE 46

BELLE ISLE

WINDERMERE, CUMBRIA

Built in 1778 on a 38 acre island in the middle of Lake Windermere. Interior by the Adams brothers. Portraits by Romney and furniture by Gillow. Nature walk.

Open May 21st to September 13th on Mondays, Tuesdays, Wednesdays and Thursdays, 10.30 a.m. to 5 p.m. Admission to Island £1, Chd. 60p. Guided tour of house 50p. Cafeteria.

CUMBRIA—*continued*

PROPERTY (*showing map reference*)	LOCATION (*with nearest Rly. Stn.*)	OPENING TIMES AND ADMISSION CHARGES CATERING FACILITIES	COACH AND RAIL TOURS BUS SERVICES (*showing alighting points*)
BRANTWOOD, Coniston *map 1 U* *Brantwood Educational Trust* The home of John Ruskin from 1872–1900. Large collection of pictures by Ruskin and his associates, Ruskin's coach, boat, furniture and other associated items. Ruskin's woodland gardens and part of the 250 acre estate now form a Nature Trial in three consecutive sections—total length approximately 3 miles.	2½ m from Coniston. Historic House signs at Coniston, Head of Coniston Water & Hawkshead	Open all year. Mid-March to mid-Nov.—Daily 11–5.30. Winter season—Weds. to Suns. 11–4. Adm. House & Nature Trails £1. Chd. 50p; Special Family Day Ticket £2.50 (father, mother & their children up to 16 yrs.); Nature Trails only 35p, Chd. 25p. Free car park. Parking for disabled near house. Toilets (inc. for disabled). Gift & Book shop. Tea room/coffee; light meals available	Ribble Bus service Coniston—Hawkshead (*at Head of Coniston Water, 1½ m*)
CARLISLE CASTLE, Carlisle *map 1 R* *Dept. of the Environment* Earliest remains keep c. 1170. Outer gatehouse construction 13th cent. **Regimental Museum**	In Carlisle N end of town *Stn: Carlisle (1 m)*	All the year: March 15 to Oct. 15—Weekdays 9.30–6.30; Suns. 2–6.30. Oct. 16 to March 14—Weekdays 9.30–4; Suns. 2–4. *Closed Dec. 24, 25, 26 & Jan. 1.* Adm.: summer—90p, Chd. (under 16) & O.A.Ps. 50p; winter—50p, Chd. (under 16) & O.A.Ps. 25p.	All bus services serving Town Hall
CASTLETOWN HOUSE, Rockcliffe, Carlisle *map 1 R* *Giles Mounsey-Heysham, Esq.* Georgian Country House set in attractive gardens and grounds. Fine ceilings. Naval pictures and furnishings.	5 m NW of Carlisle on W side of A74. *Stn: Carlisle (5 m)*	HOUSE ONLY: April to Sept.—Weds. & Bank Hol. Mons. 2–5. Other times & parties by prior arrangement. Adm. £1, Chd. (accompanied) & O.A.Ps. 50p. ☎ *Rockcliffe* (0228 74) 205 Hotels & refreshments in Carlisle	Western SMT from Carlisle to Lodge Gates
DALEMAIN, nr Penrith *map 1 R* *Mr. & Mrs. Bryce McCosh* Medieval, Tudor and early Georgian house and gardens lived in by the same family for over 300 years. Fine furniture and portraits. Countryside park and picnic areas. **Agricultural Museum, Westmorland and Cumberland Yeomanry Museum and Adventure Playground.**	**3 m from Penrith on A592. Turn off M6 exit 40 onto A66 (A592) to Ullswater** *Stn: Penrith (3½ m)*	Easter Sat. to Oct. 14—Daily (except Fris. & Sats. but open Sats. of Bank Hol. weekends) 12–6. Last adm. 5.15. Adm. £1.50, Chd. (under 16) 60p, (under 5 free). Gardens & Museums only 60p, Chd. free. Parties of 10 or more £1.20, Chd. 50p (*out of opening hours parties will pay full normal rate*). Car park, picnic area free. Shop. ☎ *Pooley Bridge* (085 36) 450 Bar Lunches (wine bar) 12–2.30; home-made teas 2.30–5.15. Hotels at Pooley Bridge & along lakeside	No reasonable public transport
GRAYTHWAITE HALL, Ulverston *M. C. R. Sandys, Esq.* *map 5 A* Seven acres of landscaped gardens. Rhododendrons, azaleas and other shrubs	**4 m N of Newby Bridge on W side of Lake Windermere** *Stn: Windermere (6½ m) (via vehicle ferry)*	GARDENS ONLY: April to June—Daily 10–6. Adm. 50p; Children under 14 free.	No reasonable public transport
HOLKER HALL, Cark-in-Cartmel *map 5 A* *Hugh Cavendish, Esq.* Dates from 16th century with 19th century additions. Exhibitions. Gardens and deer park. Lakeland Motor Museum. Regular special park events during season. Hot air ballooning activities many Sundays, weather permitting.	**½ m N of Cark, off the Haverthwaite rd 4 m SW of Grange-over-Sands** *Stn: Cark-in-Cartmel (½ m)*	Easter Sun. to Oct. 28—Daily (except Sats.) 10.30. Last visitors hall 4.30. Adm. from £1.50, Chd. 75p, O.A.Ps. £1.30 & upwards. Group rates to parties of 20 or more. *Discounts offered to booked parties in early & late months.* Gift shop. Free Car & Coach Parks. Cafeteria ☎ *Flookburgh* (044-853) 328	National tours from Lancashire and the North-East. **Ribble 530 531, 532, 535 Kendal Grange-Cark-Ulverston.** *Daily departures from Grange every other hour from* 11. Connecting services from Ambleside, Windermere, Lancaster & Barrow
HUTTON-IN-THE-FOREST, Penrith *Lord Inglewood* *map 1 R* 14th cent. Pele Tower with later additions of great architectural interest. Pictures, tapestry and furniture over 4½ centuries. Gardens and terraces dating from 17th cent. Picnic Area and Woodland Walk through outstanding specimen trees.	**6 m NW of Penrith on B5305 Wigton Rd (from M6 exit 41)** *Stn: Penrith (6¾ m)*	Bank Hol. Suns. & Mons. also Thurs., May 24 to Oct 25 & Fris., July & Aug. House open other days by prior arrangement. Grounds open anytime—honesty box for donations. Private parties by arrangement any day. Adm. £1.50, Chd. 60p, O.A.Ps. £1. Parties at special rates. Free parking. Woodland Walk. Shop. fresh home-made teas available. ☎ *Skelton* (085-34) 500	No reasonable public transport
19/20 IRISH STREET, Whitehaven *map 1 P* *Copeland Borough Council* 1840–50 Italianate design, possibly by S. Smirke. Stuccoed 3-storey building now occupied by the Council Offices	In town centre *Stn: Whitehaven*	Open all the year during office hours. For details & appointments telephone Mr. J. A. Pomfret. Ground floor only suitable for disabled. Hotels & restaurants in town centre ☎ *Whitehaven* (0946) 3111, *Ext.* 287	
LAKE DISTRICT NATIONAL PARK VISITOR CENTRE, Brockhole, nr Windermere *map 5 A* Set in 32 acres of gardens overlooking Lake Windermere and enjoying magnificent views. Audio-visual exhibitions on the Lake District; film shows, lake-shore walks, summer boat trips.	Between Windermere & Ambleside on A591 *Stn: Windermere (2¾ m)*	Late March to early Nov.—Daily. Adm. £1 (under 18 years 50p). Parties by arrangement. Special events. New "LIVING LAKELAND" Exhibition. Terrace cafeteria specialises in Lakeland teas & Cumbrian pastries & salad lunches ☎ *Windermere* (096 62) 2231	Ribble 555/556, Keswick–Ambleside–Windermere Kendal–Lancaster 517, Ulverston–Windermere–Ambleside Lake launch service in summer
LEVENS HALL, Kendal *map 5 A* *O. R. Bagot, Esq.* Elizabethan house with fine plaster-work, panelling, and notable furniture. Famous topiary garden laid out in 1692.	5 m S of Kendal on the Milnthorpe rd (A6); Exit 36 from M6. *Stn: Kendal (6 m)*	Easter Sun. to September 30. HOUSE (& Gift Shop): Tues., Weds., Thurs., Suns. & Bank Hol. Mons. 11–5. STEAM COLLECTION: 2–5. TOPIARY GARDEN: Daily 10–5. Adm. House & Garden £1.90; Garden only £1. Reductions for Children & Groups. *House not suitable for wheelchairs.* light lunches & home-made teas at House (open days only) ☎ *Sedgwick* 60321	National-Ribble express services from London **Liverpool, Manchester, Bolton & Preston** **National tours from Lancashire, Dewsbury, Halifax & Wakefield** **Ribble 553, 554, Kendal–Arnside; 555, Keswick–Lancaster; 533, Kendal–Ulverston** (*alight Levens Bridge*)
LINGHOLM, Keswick *map 1 P* *The Viscount Rochdale* Formal and extensive woodland gardens; rhododendrons, azaleas etc. Exceptional views of Borrowdale.	Turn off A66 at Portinscale 1 m along Grange Rd (C511)	GARDEN ONLY: April to October—Weekdays 10–5. Adm. £1, Chd. (accompanied) free. *No dogs.* Free car park ***Proportion of proceeds to National Gardens' Scheme & Gardeners' Charities.***	**Cumberland 34, Whitehaven–Workington–Keswick** (*alight Braithwaite, 1 m*); **certain journeys from Keswick to Braithwaite operate via Portinscale**
MIREHOUSE, Keswick *map 1 P* *Mr. & Mrs. Spedding* Seventeenth century Manor House with 19th century additions. Portraits and manuscripts of Francis Bacon and many literary friends of the Spedding family including Tennyson, Wordsworth, Southey. Walk through grounds to Bassenthwaite Lake. Adventure Playgrounds.	4½ m N of Keswick on A591 (Keswick to Carlisle rd). *Stn: Penrith (15m; connecting bus to Keswick)*	Lakeside Walk, Adventure Playgrounds—Daily 10.30–5.30. House—Suns., Weds. & Bank Hol. Mons. 2–5. Parties welcome by appointment. ☎ *Keswick* (0596) 72287 Adm. Grounds only 40p, Chd. & Students 25p. House & Grounds £1.20, Chd. & Students 50p. Old Sawmill Tearoom open daily 10.30–5.30; Specialises in salad & sandwiches made to order, home baking. Parties please book. ☎ *Keswick* (0596) 74317	**Cumberland 35, Whitehaven–Castle Inn–Keswick** **71, Carlisle–Wigton–Keswick** (*alight at Dodd Wood*)

HOLKER HALL
Cark-in-Cartmel Cumbria

"Aerofilms" photograph

Standing on the threshold of Lakeland, 20 minutes from Windermere, this former home of the Dukes of Devonshire is now owned and lived in by a relative, Mr. Hugh Cavendish. Dating from the 16th century, with extensive rebuilding in 1873, the Hall is renowned for its furniture, paintings and exquisite woodcarvings. 120 acres of park including 22 acres formal and woodland gardens, particularly beautiful in early spring and summer. Red and Fallow deer in the park.
Housed in the old yard buildings is the superb Lakeland Motor Museum. Over 100 exhibits of rare and antique cars, cycles and automobilia. 1920s petrol station re-creation, B.B.C.-T.V. replica of Campbell's 'Bluebird'. Other exhibits in the grounds include a Craft Countryside Museum, Marklin Model Railway, Baby Animal Farm and Children's Playground. Café, Shop, Picnic facilities. Coach parties particularly welcome. Ballooning some weekends. Regular schedule of special events. For further information: The Manager, Holker Hall and Park, Cark-in-Cartmel, Grange-over-Sands, Cumbria. Tel. Flookburgh (044-853) 328.

DALEMAIN
PENRITH, CUMBRIA

Home of Mr. & Mrs. Bryce McCosh

Medieval, Tudor and early Georgian House and Gardens, Countryside Museum, Great Barn housing Agricultural bygones. Westmorland and Cumberland Yeomanry Museum. Adventure Playground. Gift shop; Home-made teas.

LEVENS HALL
near KENDAL CUMBRIA

This beautiful house shows the evolution of the North Country Pele Tower and Hall into a magnificent mansion of 1580. The panelled interior, plasterwork and contents are exceptional. The Topiary Garden, planted to the original plan of 1692, forms a splendid complement to the house. There is also a collection of steam engines illustrating the progress of steam from 1820 to 1930, which is under steam on House Open Days from 2.00 p.m. to 5.00 p.m. On Sundays and Bank Holiday Mondays traction engines are in steam, including a Fowler Showman's Engine 'Bertha', a Foden Steam Wagon, a 1901 Steam Car and a half-size traction engine giving children rides, weather and availability permitting.

B.T.A. photograph

For opening times see Page 44.

On House Open days only light lunches, snacks, ices and teas are available.

Gift Shop in Undercroft of original Pele Tower.

Plants for sale.

Children's play area.

NO DOGS admitted beyond Car Park.

Further information:
Mrs. Hal Bagot,
Levens Hall, Kendal,
Cumbria LA8 0PB
Telephone:
Sedgwick (0448) 60321

HUTTON IN-THE-FOREST
PENRITH, CUMBRIA

14th cent. Pele Tower with later additions of great architectural interest. Pictures, tapestry and furniture over 4½ centuries. Gardens and terraces dating from from 17th cent. Picnic Area and Woodland Walk through outstanding specimen trees

OPENING TIMES OPPOSITE

LAKE DISTRICT NATIONAL PARK VISITOR CENTRE
Brockhole, near Windermere

Mid way between Ambleside and Windermere on A591

Brockhole is set in 32 acres of beautiful terraced gardens overlooking Lake Windermere and enjoying magnificent views. Exciting audio-visual exhibitions on the Lake District. Hourly film shows on topics ranging from Geology and Natural History to Wordsworth. Lake shore walks. Terrace cafeteria specialises in Lakeland Teas and Cumbrian pastries. Films, by arrangement, in French, German, Dutch etc. for parties. Special 1984 Exhibition: "World of Beatrix Potter". Motor launch trips on the lake in summer and conducted tours of the gardens. Children's playground. Special holiday events for families. Admission £1 (under 18 years, 50p).

Open daily, late-March to early-November. Parties by arrangement.
Telephone: Windermere (096 62) 2231.

PROPERTY (*showing map reference*)	LOCATION (*with nearest Rly. Stn.*)	OPENING TIMES AND ADMISSION CHARGES CATERING FACILITIES	COACH AND RAIL TOURS BUS SERVICES (*showing alighting points*)
CUMBRIA—*continued*			
MUNCASTER CASTLE, Ravenglass *map 1 U* Δ *Sir William Pennington-Ramsden, Bt.* ✿ Seat of the Penningtons family since 13th cent. Famed rhododendron and azalea gardens. Superb views over Esk Valley (Ruskin's Gateway to Paradise)	1 m SE of Ravenglass village on A595 (entrance ½ m W of Church) *Stn: Ravenglass (¼ m) (no B.R. service Suns.)*	GROUNDS & BIRD GARDEN: April 20 to Sept. 30—Daily (except Mons. but open Bank Hols.) 12–5. CASTLE: April 20 to Sept. 30—Daily (except Mons. but open Bank Hols.) 1.30–4.30 (last adm.). Adm. Grounds only £1, Chd. 60p; Inclusive Ticket £2, Chd. £1. Special party rates	National tours from Lancashire towns, Furness & Keswick Cumberland 12, Whitehaven–Ravenglass–Millom (*not Suns.*) (*alight Castle gates*)
RYDAL MOUNT, Ambleside *map 5 A* *Mrs. Mary Henderson—nee Wordsworth* ✿ Wordsworth's home from 1813–1850. Family portraits, furniture, many of the poet's personal possessions, and first editions of his works. The garden has been described as one of the most interesting small gardens to be found anywhere in England and was designed by Wordsworth. Two long terraces, many rare trees and shrubs. Extends to 4½ acres.	Off A591, 1½ m from Ambleside, 2½ m from Grasmere *Stn: Windermere (6½ m)*	March 1 to October 31—Daily 10–5.30. November 1 to mid-January—Daily 10–12.30, 2–4. Adm. House & Gardens £1, Chd. 50p. ☎ *Ambleside* (096 63) 3002	Ribble buses run regularly between Lancaster, Kendal Ambleside and Grasmere (*alight at Rydal*).
SIZERGH CASTLE, Kendal *map 5 A* *The National Trust* ✿ Home of Stricklands for 700 years. 14th century pele tower. Additions 15th, 16th and 18th century.	3½ m S of Kendal nr NW of A6/A591 interchange; 2 m from Levens Hall *Stns : Oxenholme (3 m); Kendal (3½ m)*	Castle & Garden: April to end of Sept.—Weds., Thurs., Suns. & Bank Hol. Mons., also all Mons. in Aug.; 2–5.45. Adm. £1.30, Chd. half-price. Garden only: Oct.—Weds. & Thurs. 2–5.45. Adm. 50p, Chd. half price. *N.B. Special reduction for pre-booked, conducted parties.* Parties by arrangement with The Administrator, Sizergh Castle. Please send s.a.e. Shop. No dogs. Wheelchairs (one provided) in garden only.	National tours from Blackpool Ribble 555, 556, Keswick–Kendal–Lancaster 500, 533, Kendal–Grange–Barrow 554, Kendal–Arnside (*alight North Lodge entrance, via old North drive*)
STAGSHAW, Ambleside *map 5 A* *The National Trust* ✿ Woodland garden on steep slope with rhododendrons, azaleas, camellias and spring bulbs. Views over Windermere	½ m S of Ambleside from A591 turn off East *Stn : Windermere (5 m)*	GARDEN ONLY: April to end of June—Daily 10–6.30 (or sunset if earlier); thereafter by appointment with the Warden; please send s.a.e. Adm. 50p, Chd 25p. No reduction for parties. *N.B. Parking limited; please park at Waterhead car park & walk to Stagshaw (½ m).* No dogs or guide dogs. Unsuitable for disabled. ☎ *Ambleside* 3265	Ribble 517, 518, 519, 20, 555, 556, Keswick–Kendal–Lancaster (*hourly*) 517, Ulverston–Ambleside (*alight Waterhead, ½ m*)
TOWNEND, Troutbeck *map 5 A* *The National Trust* 17th c. Lakeland farmhouse with original furnishings including much woodcarving in traditional style. Home of the Brownes for 300 years.	At S end of Troutbeck village, 3 m SE of Ambleside *Stn : Windermere (3 m)*	April to end of October—Daily (except Mons. & Sats. but open Bank Hol. Mons.) 2–6 (or sunset if earlier). *Closed Good Friday & November to March:* Adm. 90p, Chd. 45p. *No reductions for parties. No dogs.* Unsuitable for wheelchairs. ☎ *Ambleside* (0966) 32628	Access by motor coach by prior arrangement only with Highway & Transportation Dept. The Courts, Carlisle. Ribble/Cumberland 559 from Ambleside (*Tues & Thurs in July & Aug*); from Keswick (*Thurs. in July & Aug*). Ribble 517, 555, 556 & Troutbeck Bridge (*2 m*). *Bus:* (Mountain Goat) Ambleside–Windermere–Glenridding (*April to Sept.*)
WORDSWORTH HOUSE, Cockermouth Δ *The National Trust* *map 1 P* Built 1745, birthplace of the poet Wordsworth. The pleasant garden is referred to in his 'Prelude'. Static and audio-visual display	In Main Street *Stn: Maryport (6½ m)*	April to end of October—Mons. to Sats. (except Thurs.) 11–5; Suns. 2–5. *Closed Good Friday.* Adm. £1.20, Chd. 60p. Reductions for pre-booked parties except on Suns. No dogs. Shop open daily in summer & Nov. to Dec. 24 (except Thurs. & Suns.) 10–5. Unsuitable for wheelchairs. ☕ light refreshments & lunches in the old kitchen. ☎ *Cockermouth* (0900) 824805	National Coach, 903, 908, 913, London–Whitehaven Cumberland 34, 35, Whitehaven–Workington–Keswick; 58, Maryport–Cockermouth; 60, Wigton–Cockermouth 65, Cockermouth–Buttermere (*alight main street*)
DERBYSHIRE			
CHATSWORTH, Bakewell *map 3 A* *Chatsworth House Trust* ✿ Built by Talman for 1st Duke of Devonshire between 1687 and 1707. Splendid collection of pictures, drawings, books and furniture. Gardens with elaborate waterworks surrounded by a great park	½ m E of village of Edensor on A623, 4 m E of Bakewell, 10 m W of Chesterfield *Stns: Matlock (7½ m) Grindleford (7½ m)*	HOUSE & GARDEN: March 25 to Oct. 28—Daily 11.30–4.30. FARMYARD & ADVENTURE PLAYGROUND: March 25 to Sept. 30—Daily 10.30–4.30. Adm. charges not available at time of going to press. Gift shops. Baby Room. All details subject to confirmation. ☕ home-made refreshments. ☎ *Baslow* (024 688) 2204	Keith Tours from Aylesbury National tours from the Potteries and Midlands, Stockport, Bradford, Harrogate, Halifax, Dewsbury, Wakefield, Blackpool, etc. E. Mid. 58, Chesterfield–Buxton (*Sats. only*); Hulleys 1, Chesterfield–Bakewell; Trent 111, Matlock–Baslow; South Yorkshire 237, 240, Sheffield–Bakewell; E. Mid/Ribble 67, Manchester–Mansfield (*alight Cuttings from Bakewell (¾ m); Edensor village from Matlock (½ m); Devonshire Arms Baslow from Sheffield, Manchester, Mansfield & Chesterfield, 1 m*)
ELVASTON CASTLE COUNTRY PARK, nr Derby *map 3 A* *Derbyshire County Council* Country estate with formal gardens and landscaped parkland. Walled Old English Garden; extensive topiary gardens. Unique Working Estate Museum.	4 m SE of Derby on B5010 (Borrowash–Thulston rd.) app. from A6 Derby–Loughborough or A6005 Derby–Long Eaton rds. (signposted)	PARK open all year. Adm. free. ESTATE MUSEUM: Easter to Oct.—Weds. to Sats. 1–5; Suns. & Bank Hol. Mons. 10–6. Adm. charge. Car park, free midweek. ☕ light refreshments daily Easter to Oct. 31; remainder of year weekends only ☎ *Derby* (0332) 71342	Trent & Barton bus services from Nottingham & Derby (*alight Elvaston*)
HADDON HALL, Bakewell *map 3 A* *His Grace the Duke of Rutland* ✿ Fine example of medieval and manorial home. Delightful terraced garden noted for wall and bed roses	2 m SE Bakewell & 6½ m N of Matlock on Buxton–Matlock rd (A6) *Stn: Matlock (6½ m)*	April 3 to September 29—Daily (except Suns. & Mons.) 11–6; also Easter, early May, Spring & Summer Bank Hol. Suns. & Mons. (Suns. 2–6, Mons. 11–6). Adm. £1.70, Chd. £1. Party rate £1.30. ✕☕ at the Hall ☎ *Bakewell* 2855 ✕ Peacock Hotel, Rowsley; Rutland Arms, Bakewell	National tours from Stockport & the Potteries Trent 4 & 4A, Buxton–Derby (*alight gates*); Hulley's Bakewell–Youlgreave (connections from Chesterfield (*alight gates*) South Yorkshire 237, 240, Sheffield–Bakewell (thence by Trent or Hulley's buses)
HARDWICK HALL, nr Chesterfield *The National Trust* *map 3 A* ✿ Built 1591–1597 by "Bess of Hardwick". Notable furniture, needlework, tapestries. Gardens with yew hedges and borders of shrubs and flowers. Extensive collection of herbs	2 m S of Chesterfield–Mansfield rd (A617) 6½ m NW of Mansfield and 9½ m SE of Chesterfield *Stns: Alfreton & Mansfield Parkway (8 m); Chesterfield (9½ m)*	HOUSE & GARDEN open April to October 31. House—Weds., Thurs., Sats., Suns. & Bank Hol. Mons. 1–5.30 (or sunset if earlier). Last adm. to Hall 5 p.m. Garden open daily during the season, 12–5.30. *Closed Good Friday.* Adm.: House & Garden £2, Chd. £1; Garden only £1, Chd. 50p. *No reduction for parties (including schools). School parties must book.* Car park (gates close 6.30). Dogs in park only, on leads. Wheelchairs in garden only. ***Enquiries to The National Trust, Hardwick Hall, Doe Lea, nr Chesterfield, Derbys. Liable to serious overcrowding on Suns. & Bank Hols.*** ☕ in the Great Kitchen of Hall 2.15–4.45 (on days Hall open). ✕ lunches 12–2, April to Oct. 31, on days when Hall is open. ☎ *Chesterfield* 850430	National tours from Stockport, Blackpool, etc. East Midland/Trent 63, Nottingham–Mansfield–Chesterfield East Midland/Mansfield District/Lincolnshire X67, X68, Manchester–Chesterfield–Mansfield–Newark–Lincoln/Chesterfield Trent 331, Nottingham–Alfreton–Chesterfield East Midland/Trent X53, Nottingham–Glapwell–Sheffield (*alight Glapwell for E. Midland & Trent, 2 m Hardstoft for Trent 1½ m*)
KEDLESTON HALL, Derby *map 3 A* *The Viscount Scarsdale,* ✿ Probably the finest Robert Adam house in England, with unique Marble Hall, contemporary furniture and fine pictures	4½ m NW of Derby on Derby – Hulland rd via the Derby Ring rd Queensway *Stns: Duffield (4 m); Derby (6 m)*	Easter Sun., Mon. & Tues., then Suns. from last Sun. in April to last Sun. in September, also Bank Hol. Mons. & Tues. Hall & Museum 1–5.30; Park, Gardens & Church 12–5.30. Adm. House, Museum, Park, Gardens & Church £1.80, Cnd. 90p; Park, Gardens & Church—all persons 90p. Private parties (min. charge £35) can be arranged Mons. to Thurs. by writing to the Curator. ☕ in the Great Kitchen of Hall ☎ *Derby* (033 2) 842191	Barton tours from Nottingham, etc National tours from Chesterfield, Stockport, Birmingham & the Potteries

HADDON HALL

Bakewell, Derbyshire

The Best Loved of Derbyshire's Great Houses

"English Life" photograph

Probably the most complete and authentic example of a medieval and manorial home to be seen in England.
The Hall and terraced rose gardens are open to the public from Tuesday to Saturday (not Sundays and Mondays) from April 3rd to September 29th. 11 a.m.–6 p.m. Open Sundays and Mondays at Easter, May 6th & 7th, Spring and Summer Bank Holidays (Sundays 2–6 p.m., Mondays 11 a.m.–6 p.m.).

No dogs allowed. Admission £1.70. Children £1.
Car Park 20p. Coaches free.
Party rate £1.30 per person.

Morning refreshments, luncheons, and afternoon teas available.
Haddon Estate Office, Haddon Hall, Bakewell, Derbys. ☎ Bakewell 2855.

HARDWICK HALL Derbyshire

THE NATIONAL TRUST

"A. F. Kersting" photograph

Built 1591–1597 by Elizabeth, Countess of Shrewsbury ("Bess of Hardwick"), mother of the 1st Earl of Devonshire. An example of Elizabethan domestic architecture almost without a rival. Both in its structure and in its contents—furniture, needlework, tapestries and portraits—Hardwick is a faithful picture of an earlier epoch.

OPENING TIMES OPPOSITE

MUNCASTER CASTLE RAVENGLASS, CUMBRIA

This magnificent Castle with its famous Rhododendron gardens and superb views of the Esk Valley dates back to the 13th cent., although the Pele Tower is actually built on Roman Foundations. There is a superb collection of Tapestries, China and Pictures which include examples by Van Dyck, Velasquez, Reynolds, Gainsborough, Hoppner and Lely. Also a magnificent collection of 16th and 17th century furniture in outstanding condition. The library contains over 6,000 books and there are many other objets de vertu in this superb collection.

The gardens offer a variety of walks which can all offer some of the finest views in England.

Open daily except Mondays but open all Bank Holidays: GOOD FRIDAY to SEPTEMBER 30th.

CASTLE: 1.30–4.30 (last admission).

GROUNDS: 12.00–5.00 (last admission).

TEENAGERS COMMANDO COURSE; BIRD GARDENS; GIFT SHOP; LUNCHES; TEAS; LIGHT REFRESHMENTS; TABLE LICENCE.

Write or phone for Party Bookings and details of events during the season to:
CURATOR: MUNCASTER CASTLE, RAVENGLASS, CUMBRIA.
Tel: RAVENGLASS 614 or 203.

Access is from A595, 1½ miles east of Ravenglass.
Free Car Park opposite Main Gates.

KEDLESTON HALL (Derby, 4 m.)

For over 800 years the home of the Curzon family

The Residence of Viscount and Viscountess Scarsdale

Built in 1759–65 on the site of the original XIIth century manor house, Kedleston is the finest untouched example of the work of Robert Adam in the country, with its world-famous Marble Hall and magnificent Staterooms, containing an important collection of Old Masters and contemporary furniture. Visitors can also see the XIIth century Church including the Marquis Curzon of Kedleston Memorial Chapel, the spacious gardens and also the Museum containing the magnificent collection of Silver, Ivories and works of art made by the Marquis when Viceroy of India 1898–1905. For further information—write The Curator, Estate Office, Kedleston Hall, Derby. Telephone Derby 842191.

(For days open to General Public see opposite)

MELBOURNE HALL near Derby

Home of the Marquis of Lothian

A House of history—a world famous garden. Open throughout the year by previous appointment for prebooked parties over twenty persons.

Public opening: Sundays June 1st to October 1st. 2 p.m.–6 p.m. Admission £2.00; Children £1.00.

State Rooms available Day Conferences. Apply Miss Dorehill, Melbourne Hall. Tel. (03316) 2502.

Tearoom, Craft Sales Centre, Gift Shop.

MELBOURNE HALL GARDENS

Open daily. Admission £1.00. Wardens Cottage, Melbourne Hall Courtyard. Tel. (03316) 3347.

DERBYSHIRE—*continued*

PROPERTY (*showing map reference*)	LOCATION (*with nearest Rly. Stn.*)	OPENING TIMES AND ADMISSION CHARGES CATERING FACILITIES	COACH AND RAIL TOURS BUS SERVICES (*showing alighting points*)
LEA RHODODENDRON GARDENS, Lea *Mr. & Mrs. Tye* *map 3 A* Large garden of hybrid and species rhododendrons and azaleas in woodland setting. Rock garden	**5 m SE of Matlock, off A6** *Stn: Whatstandwell (2¼ m)*	GARDEN ONLY. March 19 to July 31—Daily 10–7. Adm. 50p (May 5 to June 17. 70p), Chd. 10p. Wheelchairs free. Coaches by appointment only. Plants for sale. tea & homemade cakes	No reasonable public transport
MELBOURNE HALL, Melbourne *map 3 A* *The Marquess of Lothian* Lord Melbourne, the great Prime Minister, lived here. Lady Palmerston inherited it. One of the most famous formal gardens in Britain. Contains an important collection of pictures and antique furniture	**8 m S of Derby on Derby–Ashby-de-la-Zouch rd (A514)** *Stn: Derby (7½ m)*	June 1 to Oct. 1—Suns. 2–6. Adm.: House & Gardens £2, Gardens only £1; Chd. (under 16 years) half-price. Pre-booked parties (over 20 persons) by previous appointment throughout the year. Gardens open daily. Adm. £1, Chd. half-price. Gift Shop. Craft Sales Centre. For all information apply: Miss Dorehill, Melbourne Hall, Melbourne, Derby. Tearoom *Melbourne* (03316) 2502 *Melbourne* (03316) 2460	National tours from Birmingham, the Potteries & other Midland towns Trent 19, 19A, Derby–Melbourne; 21, 21A, Derby–Ashby; 22 & 23, Derby–Swadlincote (*hourly*) Barton 3c, Nottingham–Melbourne.
THE OLD HOUSE MUSEUM, Bakewell *Bakewell Historical Society* *map 3 A* An early Tudor house with original wattle & daub screen and open chamber. Costumes and Victorian kitchen, craftsmen's tools and toys.	**In Bakewell above the Church** *Stns: Grindleford (7½ m); Matlock (8 m)*	Easter to end of October—Daily 2.30–5. Adm. 50p, Chd. 25p. *Parties by appointment* *Bakewell* 3647	Trent, Derby–Matlock–Bakewell–Buxton Hulley's Chesterfield–Bakewell South Yorkshire P.T.E. Sheffield–Bakewell National Coach, Nottingham—Manchester
SUDBURY HALL, nr Derby *map 3 A* *The National Trust* A 17th century brick built house. Contains plasterwork ceilings, Laguerre murals staircase carved by Pierce and overmantel by Grinling Gibbons	**At Sudbury, 6 m E of Uttoxeter off A50 road** *Stn: Uttoxeter (6 m)*	April 1 to end of Oct.—Weds. to Suns. & Bank Hol. Mons. 1–5.30 (or sunset if earlier). *Closed Mons. (except Bank Hols.), Tues. & Good Friday.* Adm. £1·80, Chd. 90p. Pre-booked parties (Thurs. & Fris. 1–5) special rates. Museum small adm. charge. Shop. Dogs in grounds only. Wheelchairs in garden only. light lunches & teas in Coach House, same open days as property, 12.30–5.30. *Sudbury* 028 378) 305	Potteries, 23 Hanley–Uttoxeter–Derby (*Sats. only*) Stevenson's Uttoxeter–Burton (*alight Sudbury, Vernon Arms*)
WINSTER MARKET HOUSE, nr Matlock *The National Trust* *map 3 A* A stone market house of the late 17th or early 18th century in main street of Winster	**4 m W of Matlock on S side of B5057** *Stn: Matlock (4 m)*	April to end of Sept.—Weds., Sats., Suns. & Bank Hol. Mons. 2–6 (or sunset if earlier). Adm. free. Shop. No dogs. Unsuitable for wheelchairs. *Thorpe Cloud* (033 529) 245	Silver Service 170 Matlock–Winster–Bakewell–Chesterfield (*alight in village*)

DEVON

PROPERTY (*showing map reference*)	LOCATION (*with nearest Rly. Stn.*)	OPENING TIMES AND ADMISSION CHARGES CATERING FACILITIES	COACH AND RAIL TOURS BUS SERVICES (*showing alighting points*)
A LA RONDE, Exmouth *map 2 R* *Mrs. Ursula Tudor Perkins* A unique sixteen sided house designed in 1795 by the Misses Jane and Mary Parminter. Almost unchanged and still owned by the same family, it combines contrived 18th century fashions with total practicability. Parkland. Panoramic views of sea and estuary; Shell Gallery, Gothic grottos.	**2 m N of Exmouth on A376** *Stn: Lympstone (1¼ m)*	April to Oct.—Mons. to Sats. 10–6; Suns. 2–7. Adm. House & Grounds £1.20, Chd. (under 14) 50p. Coaches—day & evening visits by appointment. Devon cream teas (in old kitchen). *Exmouth* (0395) 265514	Devon General 356, 357 Exeter–Exmouth (*alight Courtlands*)
ARLINGTON COURT, Barnstaple *map 2 R* *The National Trust* Regency house furnished with the collections of the late Miss Rosalie Chichester; including shells, pewter and model ships. Display of horse-drawn vehicles in the stables. Good trees, Victorian formal garden	**8 m NE of Barnstaple on E side of A39** *Stn: Barnstaple (8 m)*	Nov. to end of March: Garden & park open daily during daylight hours. House, Carriage Collection, Stables, Shop: April to end of Oct.— Daily (except Sats. but open Sats. of Bank Hol. Weekends) 11–6. Garden & Park: April to Oct.—Daily 11–6. Open Good Friday. Adm.: House & Carriage Collection £2.30, Chd. £1.15. Gardens, Ground & Stables £1.30. Chd half-price. *Reduced fee of £1.70 for parties of 25 or more at certain times on application to the Administrator. Parties who do not pre-book will be charged full rate.* Shop. Dogs in grounds only, on leads. Wheelchairs provided. Carriage rides. Licensed restaurant at the House: April to end of Oct.—days as for House, 11–5.30. *Shirwell* (027 182) 296	North Devon Red Bus 309 Ilfracombe–Barnstaple (*one a day Tues. & Fris. only*) (*alight Arlington Turn ½ m.*) 310 Barnstaple–Lynton (*not Suns.*) (*alight Blackwater Gate 3 m*) National tours from Ilfracombe
BICKHAM HOUSE, Roborough *map 2 U* *The Lord Roborough* Shrub garden; camellias, rhododendrons, azaleas, cherries, bulbs, trees. Lovely views	**8 m N of Plymouth on Roborough Down turn for Maristow** *Stn: Plymouth (8¼ m)*	GARDEN ONLY: April & May—Suns.; also Suns. June 10 & 24 and Bank Hol. Mons. April 23 (Easter), May 7 & 28: 2–6. Adm. 50p. *In aid of National Gardens Scheme. No dogs.* home-made teas.	Western National 83, 84, Plymouth–Tavistock, half-hourly, (*alight Clearbrook Road, Roborough Down, ¾ m*)

PROPERTY (*showing map reference*)	LOCATION (*with nearest Rly. Stn.*)	OPENING TIMES AND ADMISSION CHARGES CATERING FACILITIES	COACH AND RAIL TOURS BUS SERVICES (*showing alighting points*)
DEVON—*continued*			
BICKLEIGH CASTLE, nr Tiverton *map* 2 *R* *Mr. & Mrs. O. N. Boxall* Medieval romantic home of the heirs of the Earls of Devon. Great Hall. Armoury. Guard Room, Stuart farmhouse, Elizabethan bedroom. 11th century Chapel. Tower. Museum and spy & escape gadgets, Exhibition of treasures recovered from the "Mary Rose". Moated Gardens.	4 m S of Tiverton A396. At Bickleigh Bridge take A3072 and follow signs	Easter Week then Weds., Suns. & Bank Hol. Mons. to end of May. June to mid Oct.—Daily (except Sats.): 2–5. *Parties of 20 or more by prior appoint. only (preferably at times other than above) at reduced rates.* Adm. £1.50, Chd. half-price. Free coach & car park. Souvenir shop. tea in the thatched Barn. *Bickleigh* (088 45) 363	Devon General 354 or 355 Exeter–Tiverton (*alight Trout Inn, Bickleigh, 10 mins. walk*)
BOWDEN HOUSE, Totnes *map* 2 *V* *Mr. & Mrs. C. V. Petersen* Dating back to the 9th century Bowden became the residence of the De Broase family, builders of 13th century Totnes Castle. Parts of the house date from this period. An Elizabethan mansion was created in 1510 with a Queen Anne facade added in 1704. The Grand Hall is decorated in Neo-classical Baroque style	1 m from centre of Totnes. *Stn: Totnes*	April to Oct.—Tuesdays. Grounds open from 1.30. House tours 2–5. Adm. £1.25, Chd. half-price (under 10 yrs. free). Coach parties by appointment. (0803) 863664	Local bus services
BRADLEY MANOR, Newton Abbot *map* 2 *V* *The National Trust* Small, roughcast 15th cent. manor house with great hall, screens passage, buttery and Perpendicular chapel	W end of town, 7½m NW of Torquay opp. Old Totnes Rd. jct. on W side of A381 *Stn: Newton Abbot,* (1½ *m*)	April 4 to end of Sept.—Weds. 2–5; also Thurs., April 5 & 12, Sept. 20 & 27. Adm. £1, Chd. half-price. *No reduction for parties.* Parties of 15 or more must book in writing. No indoor photography. No access for coaches—Lodge gates too narrow. No dogs. Unsuitable for disabled or visually handicapped.	Devon General 175, 176, 183 from Newton Abbot (*alight Bradley rd*); other buses from all parts at bus station. (1 *m*)
BUCKLAND ABBEY *map* 2 *U* *The National Trust* *(administered by Plymouth Corporation)* 13th cent. Cistercian monastery bought by Sir Richard Grenville in 1541, altered by his grandson Sir Richard Grenville, of the 'Revenge', in 1576. Home of Drake from 1581 and now a naval and Devon Folk Museum. Drake's drum may be seen. Garden and large medieval tithe barn.	11 m N of Plymouth 6 m S of Tavistock between the Tavistock – Plymouth rd (A386) & River Tavy *Stn: Bere Alston* (4½ *m*) (*not Suns.*)	Good Friday to end of Sept.—Mons. to Sats. (inc. Banks Hols.) 11–6; Suns. 2–6 (last adm. 5.30). Oct. to April 6—Weds., Sats. & Suns. 2–5 (last adm. 4.30). Adm. £1.20 (1983 rates). Chd. half-price. 20% *reduction for pre-arranged parties (booked at least one week in advance) by tel. or writing to: City Museum & Art Gallery, Drake Circus, Plymouth* (0752) 668000 Dogs in grounds only. Shop. Unsuitable for disabled or visually handicapped. *Yelverton* (082 285) 3607	Tours from all parts of the West Country Plymouth Jt. 55, 55A, 63, Plymouth–Milton Combe (*alight Abbey entrance*)
CADHAY, Ottery St. Mary *map* 2 *R* *Lady William-Powlett* An Elizabethan manor house built 1550. A charming "lived in" home	½ m from Fairmile on Honiton – Exeter rd (A30) *Stns: Feniton (2½ m) (not Suns.); Honiton (6 m)*	Spring (May 27/28) & Summer (Aug. 26/27) Bank Hol. Suns. & Mons.; also Tues., Weds. & Thurs. in July & Aug.: 2–6 (last adm. 5.30). Adm. £1, Chd. 50p. *Parties by arrangement* *Ottery St. Mary* 2432	National Coach 705, 706, 726 (*alight Fairmile Inn*) Devon General 381, 382, Sidmouth-Ottery St. Mary; 380, 381, 382, Exeter—Ottery St. Mary (*alight Ottery St. Mary 1 m*)
CASTLE DROGO, nr Chagford *map* 2 *R* *The National Trust* Granite castle designed by Sir Edwin Lutyens, standing at over 900ft. overlooking the wooded gorge of the River Teign. Terraced garden and miles of splendid walks	4 m NE of Chagford; 6 m S of A30 *Stn: Yeoford (8m) (not Suns.)*	April to end of October—Daily 11–6 (last adm. 5.30). Adm. £2; Grounds only £1. Chd. half-price. *Reduced rates for parties* (£1.40) *at certain times of day on application to the Administrator. Parties who do not pre-book will be charged at full rate.* No dogs. Wheelchairs provided. Shop. coffee, light lunches (licensed) & teas at the castle 11–5.30 *Chagford* (064 73) 3306	Devon General 362 Exeter–Okehampton (*not Suns.*) (*alight gates*) 173 Newton Abbot–Chagford (*not Suns.*) (*alight Sandypark or Easton Cross 2 m*) 359 Exeter–Chagford (*not Suns.*) (*alight Easton Cross, 2 m*)
CASTLE HILL, Filleigh, Barnstaple *map* 2 *R* *Lady Margaret Fortescue* A seat of the Fortescue family. Palladian mansion built c. 1730–1740. Fine 18th cent. furniture, tapestries, porcelain and pictures. Ornamental garden and large shrub and woodland garden and arboretum	3½ m W of South Molton on A361 *Stn: Umberleigh (5m)*	April to October. Telephone or write to owner for appointment for a conducted tour. Parties (20 to 50) £1.50 per person. *Filleigh* (059-86) 227 Gardens only (30p per person) can be seen by tel. Estate Office. *Filleigh* (059-86) 336	North Devon Red Bus 307 Barnstaple–South Molton (*alight Stagshead*)
COLETON FISHACRE GARDEN, Coleton *The National Trust* *map* 2 *V* 18 acre garden in a stream-fed valley. Garden created by Lady Dorothy D'Oyley Carte between 1925 and 1940; planted with wide variety of uncommon trees and exotic shrubs.	2 m from Kingswear; take Lower Ferry Rd., turn off at tollhouse & follow 'Garden Open' signs.	All the year—Weds., Fris. & Suns. 11–6. Adm. £1, Chd. 50p. Parties please book with Mr. or Mrs. Taylor. Limited wheelchair access.	Devon General/Barton Coaches 118 from Brixham Bus Stn. (*not Suns.*) (*alight Hillhead, Lower Ferry Rd., ¼ m*)
COMPTON CASTLE, nr Paignton *map* 2 *V* *The National Trust* Fortified manor house. Great Hall (restored), Solar and Kitchen	1 m N of Marldon off A381 *Stns: Paignton (3 m); Torre (3 m)*	April to end of October—Mons., Weds. & Thurs. 10–12.15, 2–5 (last adm. 30 mins. before closing). Other times by appointment. Adm. £1.10, Chd. half-price. Parties £1—*organisers should please notify the Secretary*. No dogs. *Kingkerswell* (080 47) 2112	Devon General 107 Paignton–Marldon (1½ *m*) Please check local timetables

PROPERTY (*showing map reference*)	LOCATION (*with nearest Rly. Stn.*)	OPENING TIMES AND ADMISSION CHARGES CATERING FACILITIES	COACH AND RAIL TOURS BUS SERVICES (*showing alighting points*)

DEVON—*continued*

PROPERTY	LOCATION	OPENING TIMES	BUS SERVICES
DARTMOUTH CASTLE, Dartmouth *Dept. of the Environment* *map 2 V* 15th century castle designed for coastal defence	**1 m SE of Dartmouth on W side of estuary** *Stn: Kingswear (Torbay Steam Rly)*	All the year: March 15 to Oct. 15—Weekdays 9.30–6.30; Suns. 2–6.30. Oct. 16 to March 14—Weekdays 9.30–4; Suns. 2–4. *Closed Dec. 24, 25, 26 & Jan. 1.* Adm. 60p, Chd. (under 16) & O.A.Ps. 30p.	Western National 93 from Plymouth (*peak Suns only*) Devon General/Burton coaches 118 from Brixham (*peak Suns. only*) via lower ferry to Dartmouth, & Devon General (*peak Suns. only*)
FERNWOOD, Ottery St. Mary *map 2 R* *Mr. & Mrs. H. Hollinrake* 2 acre woodland garden; wide selection of flowering shrubs, conifers and bulbs giving colour over a long period; species and hybrid rhododendrons and azaleas	1½ m W of Ottery St. Mary; ¼ m down Toadpit lane (off B3174) *Stn: Whimple (3 m) (not Suns.)*	GARDEN ONLY: April 1 to September 30—Daily, all day. Adm. 25p. *In aid of National Gardens' Scheme.* No dogs.	Western National 380, 381, 382 from Exeter, Sidmouth & Axminster to Ottery St. Mary (1½ *m*) (*not Suns.) for all services*)
FLETE, Ermington, Ivybridge *map 2 V* *Mutual Households Association* Built around an Elizabethan manor	11 m E of Plymouth	May to September—Weds. & Thurs., 2–5. Adm. 50p. Chd. 25p. Free car park. No dogs admitted.	Western National 91/93, Plymouth–Dartmouth
FURSDON HOUSE, Cadbury, Thorverton *E. D. Fursdon, Esq.* *map 2 R* Georgian fronted manor house, home of the Fursdon family who have lived here for over 700 years in unbroken male succession. Regency Library, family portraits, costumes and mementoes. Park and grounds, superb views, woodland walks	9 m N of Exeter, 6 m SW of Tiverton; ¾ m off A3072 Tiverton—Crediton rd. *Stns: Crediton (7 m); Exeter St. Davids (9½ m)*	Easter Sun. (April 22) to Sept. 30—Suns., Thurs. & Bank Hol. Mons. Tours only at 2 p.m., 3 p.m. & 4 p.m. (last adm.). Parties at other times by arrangement (reduced price). Adm. House & Grounds £1.60, Chd. under 16, 75p; under 10, free. Grounds only reduced. *No dogs.* Shop. Free car park. Tea room (open days) ☎ *Exeter* (0392) 860860 Inns at Bickleigh (2 *m*) & Thorverton (2 *m*)	
THE GARDEN HOUSE, *map 2 U* **Buckland Monachorum, Yelverton** *The Fortescue Charitable Trust* 8-acre garden of interest throughout the year and including a 2-acre walled garden that is one of the finest in the country. Fine collections of herbaceous and woody plants.	5 m S of Tavistock; from Yelverton on A386 turn W; 10 m N Plymouth *Stn : Bere Alston (4½ m) (not Suns.)*	GARDENS ONLY: April 1 to Sept. 30—Mons. to Fris. 2–6. Adm. £1, Chd. 25p. *Closed Bank Hol. Mons. & Good Friday. In aid of National Gardens' Scheme.* No dogs. Coaches & parties by appointment. Car park. Unusual plants for sale. ☎ *Yelverton* 854769	Plymouth Jt. 55, Plymouth–Milton Combe (*alight Knighton Cnr., Crapstone 200 yds*)
HEMERDON HOUSE, Plympton, Plymouth *J. H. G. Woollcombe, Esq.* *map 2 U* Small early 19th century house containing West country paintings and prints, also furniture and a Library.	2 m from Plympton *Stn: Plymouth (7 m)*	May 7-28 inclusive then Aug. 20-27 inclusive: 2–5.30. For further information please contact the Administrator. Adm. £1. ☎ *Plymouth* (0752) 23816 (Office hours)337350 (weekend & evenings	Local bus service
KILLERTON, nr Exeter *map 2 R* *The National Trust* Late 18th cent. house in a beautiful setting containing the Paulise de Bush Collection of Costume. Lovely throughout the year, with flowers from early spring, and splendid late autumn colours. 19th century Chapel and Ice House. Paths lead up the hill to the Dolbury, an isolated hill with an Iron Age hill fort site.	**7 m NE of Exeter on W side of Exeter Cullompton (B3181—formerly A38); from M5 s'bound exit 28/B3181; from M5 n'bound exit 29 via Broadclyst & B3181** *Stns: Exeter Central & Exeter St. Davids (7½m); Whimple (6m) (not Suns.)*	HOUSE: April to end of October—Daily 11–6 (last adm. 5.30). Garden: all the year during daylight hours. Adm. House & Garden £2 (tickets available at Stable Block), Chd. half-price; Garden only £1.30. *Reduced rates for parties (£1.50) on application to the Administrator. Parties who do not pre-book will be charged at full rate.* The Conference Room may be booked for meetings etc. Applications (in writing) to: The Administrator, Killerton House, Broadclyst, Exeter, Devon. Shop in Stables. Dogs in Park only. Wheelchairs provided. ☎ *Exeter* (0392) 881345 Licensed restaurant at House, 11–6 (last adm. 5.30); entrance from garden—tickets necessary, available at shop. Light refreshments in Stables.	Devon General 373, 374, 375, Exeter–Cullompton (*alight Killerton turning, ¾ m*)
KIRKHAM HOUSE, Paignton *map 2 V* *Dept. of the Environment* Interesting example of 15th cent. architecture	In Kirkham Street, nr. Parish Church. *Stn: Paignton (¼ m)*	April to September—Weekdays 9.30–6.30; Suns. 2–6.30. Adm. 30p, Chd (under 16) & O.A.Ps. 15p.	Devon General services from Newton Abbot, Brixham, Torquay & Plymouth Western Nat. services from Totnes & Plymouth
KNIGHTSHAYES COURT, nr Tiverton *The National Trust* *map 2 R* Large garden of interest at all seasons. House by William Burges, begun in 1869, decorated by J D. Crace.	2 m N of Tiverton; turn off A396 (Bampton - Tiverton rd) at Bolham *Stn: Tiverton Jct. (8 m) (not Suns.)*	April to end of Oct.—Daily: Garden 11–6, House 1.30–6 (last adm. 5.30). Adm. £2, Chd. £1. Garden & Grounds only £1.30. *Reduced rates for parties (£1.50) on application to the Administrator. Parties who do not pre-book will be charged at full rate.* Shop. Plants available at garden shop. No dogs. Wheelchairs provided. coffee, lunches (licensed) & teas 11–5.30 ☎ *Tiverton* (0884) 254665	Kingdom tours, Tiverton–Dulverton (*alight Bolham 1 m*) (*no Sunday buses*)
MARWOOD HILL, nr Barnstaple *map 2 P* *Dr. J. A. Smart* Extensive collection of camellias under glass and in the open, daffodils, rhododendrons, rare flowering shrubs: rock and alpine garden, rose garden, waterside planting. Bog garden. Large greenhouse of Australian native plants.	4 m N of Barnstaple; opp. church in Marwood *Stn: Barnstaple (4 m) (not Suns.)*	GARDENS ONLY. All the year—Daily (except Christmas Day) dawn to dusk. Adm. 50p, Chd. 10p. *In aid of National Gardens' Scheme* Plants for sale. Dogs allowed, on leads only.	
OVERBECKS MUSEUM & GARDEN, Sharpitor, Salcombe *map 2 V* *The National Trust* 6 acres of garden with rare and tender plants and beautiful views eastwards over Salcombe Bay. Part of house forms museum of local interest and of particular interest to children	1½ m SW of Salcombe signposted from Malborough & Salcombe	Gardens: All the year—Daily. Museum: April 1 to Oct. 31—Daily 11–1, 2–6. Last adm. 12.45 & 5.30. Adm. Museum & Garden £1.10, Chd. half-price. Garden only 80p. *No reduction for parties.* Dogs allowed in gardens & conservatory only, not in Museum. Shop. Picnicking allowed in gardens. Not suitable for coaches. ☎ *Salcombe* (054 884) 2893	Western National 92 Kingsbridge–Salcombe (*peak Suns. only*); 93 Dartmouth–Kingsbridge–Plymouth connecting at Kingsbridge with buses from Totnes (*peak Suns. only*) (*alight top of Salcombe, 1½ m*) Frequent ferries from Salcombe to South Sands (¾ *m*) May to Oct. at ½ hr. intervals weather permitting

PROPERTY (*showing map reference*)	LOCATION (*with nearest Rly. Stn.*)	OPENING TIMES AND ADMISSION CHARGES CATERING FACILITIES	COACH AND RAIL TOURS BUS SERVICES (*showing alighting points*)
DEVON—*continued*			
POWDERHAM CASTLE, nr Exeter *The Earl & Countess of Devon* *map 2 R* Medieval castle built c. 1390 by Sir Philip Courtenay, ancester of the present Earl of Devon. Damaged in the Civil War and restored and altered in 18th and 19th centuries. Music Room by Wyatt. Park stocked with deer.	8 m SW of Exeter off A379 to Dawlish *Stn: Starcross* (1½ *m*)	For opening arrangements please contact: The ADMINISTRATOR ☎ *Starcross* (0626) 890 243 Dogs admitted to shaded car park only	Devon General 186, 187 Exeter–Teignmouth–Newton Abbot, half-hourly (*alight Castle Gates*) B.R.(W) to Starcross (1 *m*) Ferry service from Exmouth to Starcross (1 *m*)
ROSEMOOR GARDEN CHARITABLE TRUST, Great Torrington *map 2 P* *Lady Anne Palmer* Garden started in 1959; rhododendrons (species and hybrid), ornamental trees and shrubs; primulas; species roses. Scree and alpine beds. Young arboretum.	1 m SE of Torrington on B3220 to Exeter	GARDENS ONLY: April 1 to October 31—Daily, dawn–dusk. Adm. 70p, Chd. 30p, O.A.Ps. 50p. Parties 50p per person. Unusual plants for sale. teas Suns., Weds. & Bank Hols. (any day for pre-booked parties)	North Devon Red Bus 315, 317 from Bideford to Torrington 315 (*not Suns.*) (*passes gates*)
SALTRAM HOUSE, Plymouth *map 2 U* *The National Trust* A George II house, built around and incorporating remnants of a late Tudor mansion, in a landscaped park. Two exceptional rooms by Robert Adam. Furniture, pictures, fine plasterwork and woodwork. Great Kitchen. Beautiful garden with Orangery. Octagonal summerhouse, rare shrubs and trees. Shop in stables.	2 m W of Plympton 3½ m E of Plymouth city centre, between A38 & A379 main rds *Stn: Plymouth* (3½ *m*)	Nov. to end of March: Garden open daily during daylight hours. April to end Oct.: Daily (except Mons. but open Bank Hol. Mons.): House 12.30–6; Kitchen, Shop & Art Gallery 11–6; Garden 11–6 (open daily inc. Mons.). Last adm. 5.30. Adm. £2.30. Chd. half-price; Garden only 80p. *Reductions for parties* (£1.70) *at certain times of day by prior arrangement for visits/meals with the Administrator*. The Chapel may be booked for meetings, etc. Applications (in writing) to: The Administrator, Saltram House, Plympton, Plymouth. No dogs. Wheelchairs admitted. Licensed restaurant in House (entrance from Garden); Tues. to Suns. & Bank Hols. 11–6 (last adm. 5.30). ☎ *Plymouth* (0752) 336546	National tours from Truro, Exeter, **Exmouth** & Birmingham Plymouth Joint 22 (*alight top of Cot Hill* ½ *m*); other buses to Marsh Mills Lodge (½ *m*) Glenton Tours from London.
SAND, Sidbury, nr. Sidmouth *map 2 R* *Lt. Col. P. V. Huyshe* Lived in Manor house in unspoilt valley owned by Huyshe family since 1560, rebuilt 1592-4. Screens passage, panelling, family documents, heraldry.	¾ m NE of Sidbury; 400 yds. from A375 Grid ref. 146925 *Stn: Honiton* (6½ *m*)	Bank Hol. Suns. & Mons.—Easter (April 22/23), Spring (May 27/28) & Summer (Aug. 26/27): 2–6. Last tour 5.15. Adm. 80p, Chd. & Students 20p. light teas in house cream teas in Sidbury (free car parking)	Local bus service to Sidbury (¾ *m*)
TAPELEY PARK, Instow *map 2 P* *Miss Rosamond Christie* Italian style garden of great beauty. Magnificent view of Taw and Torridge estuary. House contains fine plasterwork ceilings, furniture, porcelain and objets d'art.	Between Barnstaple & Bideford on A39; 1 m S of Instow *Stn: Barnstaple* (7 *m*)	April to Oct.—Bank Hols. & daily (except Mons. but open Bank Hol. Mons.) 10–6, Nov. to April—Gardens only during daylight hours. N.B.—*Tours of HOUSE only when numbers permit*. Adm. charges not available at time of going to press. *Coach parties welcome by appointment*. Dogs must be on leads. Pets, Putting, Play areas & Picnic places. Craft shop. Plants & produce for sale. The Queen Anne Dairy is open all day for light lunch, cream tea & other refreshments. ☎ *Instow* (0271) 860528	North Devon Red Bus 301, Westward Ho!–Bideford–Barnstaple–Ilfracombe 302 Appledore–Barnstaple
TIVERTON CASTLE, nr Tiverton *map 2 R* *Mr. & Mrs. Ivar Campbell* Historic fortress of Henry I. Joan of Arc gallery. Clock collection. Chapel of St. Francis	Outskirts of Tiverton by St. Peter's Church (entrance through main gate) *Stn: Tiverton Junct.* (6 *m*)	Easter, April 21–26 inc. then May 20 to Sept. 22—Suns. to Thurs. 2.30–5.30. Adm. (1983 rates, subject to amendment) £1.20. Chd. & O.A.Ps. 90p. Party bookings at special rates. ☎ *Tiverton* (0884) 253200	Devon General 373, 354, 355 Exeter–Tiverton
TORRE ABBEY, Torquay *map 2 V* *Torbay Borough Council* 12th century monastery converted into a private residence after the Dissolution in 1539. Extensively remodelled during the early 18th century. Contains furnished period rooms, family chapel and extensive collection of paintings and other works of art. Ruins of medieval Abbey also on show. Formal gardens containing tropical palm house, rose garden, rockeries and spring bulbs	On Torquay Sea front. *Stn: Torquay* (¼ *m*)	HOUSE: April to Oct.—Daily 10–5. Nov. to March—Mons. to Fris. only by appointment. Adm. (1983 rates) 30p, Chd. & O.A.Ps free. GARDENS: All the year—Daily. Palm House open weekdays 10–3.30; restricted hours weekends & Bank Hols. Adm. free. Tea rooms in grounds (June to Mid-Sept.) ☎ *Torquay* (0803) 23593	Local bus services 132, 133, 136 pass Abbey Gates; 120, 121 to Sea Front (¼ *m*)
WOODSIDE, Barnstaple *map 2 P* *Mr. & Mrs. Mervyn Feesey* 2 acre plantsman's garden, south sloping, many raised beds. Collection of ornamental grasses, bamboos, sedges and other monocots; unusual and rare dwarf shrubs and rock plants; troughs; variegated and peat-loving shrubs and conifers; New Zealand collection.	N outskirts of Barnstaple; off A39 to Lynton (400 yds. beyond Fire Stn.). *Stn: Barnstaple Jct.* (1 *m*)	GARDEN ONLY: Sundays May 6, June 3, July 1 & August 5: 2–6. Adm. 50p, Chd. 25p. *In aid of National Gardens' Scheme*. Other days by appointment. ☎ *Barnstaple* (0271) 43095	

PROPERTY (*showing map reference*)	LOCATION (*with nearest Rly. Stn.*)	OPENING TIMES AND ADMISSION CHARGES CATERING FACILITIES	COACH AND RAIL TOURS BUS SERVICES (*showing alighting points*)
DORSET			
ABBOTSBURY—SWANNERY & SUB-TROPICAL GARDENS *map 2 S* *Strangways Estates* Owned by the Strangways family since 1541 it received a Conservation award in 1975. The Swannery—unique colony of mute swans; 17th century duck decoy; reed bed walk. Sub-Tropical Gardens—17 acres of woodland and formal gardens containing tender and exotic plants growing outdoors. Peacocks. Aviary.	On B3157 Weymouth–Bridport rd; may be apprch'd from A35 at Winterbourne Abbas	The Swannery: Opening times not available at time of going to press. Sub-Tropical Gardens: Opening times not available at time of going to press. Tea kiosk (in Gardens). *Abbotsbury* (030587) 387	Southern National 412 Weymouth–Abbotsbury (*infrequent*) (*not Suns.*)
ATHELHAMPTON, Athelhampton *map 2 S* *Sir Robert Cooke* One of the finest medieval houses in England. 10 acres of formal and landscape gardens	½ m E of Puddletown on Dorchester–Bournemouth rd (A35), 5 m NE of Dorchester *Stns: Dorchester South & West (6m); Moreton (4 m)*	April 18 to Oct. 14—Weds., Thurs. & Suns.; Good Friday & Bank Hols; also Tues. & Fris. in Aug.: 2–6. Adm. charge (children free of charge in gardens). Party rates by arrangement. Dogs admitted only to shaded car park. at the House *Puddletown* 363	National tour from Bournemouth Wilts & Dorset 184, Salisbury–Weymouth (*alight Puddletown, 1 m*) 186/187 Bournemouth–Weymouth *not Suns: (alight Hall gates)* X20 Swanage–Weymouth (*summer only*)
CLOUDS HILL, nr Wool *map 2 S* *The National Trust* The home of T. E. Lawrence (Lawrence of Arabia) after the first World War; contains his furniture and other relics	1 m N of Bovington Camp, 1½ m E of Waddock crossroads (B3390), 9 m E of Dorchester *Stns: Wool (3½ m); Moreton (3½ m)*	April to end Sept.—Weds., Thurs., Fris. (inc. Good Friday) Suns. & Bank Hol. Mons. 2–5. October to March—Suns. only 1–4. Adm. £1. *No reduction for children or parties.* No photography. Dogs in grounds only. Unsuitable for wheelchairs & coaches.	National tours from Bournemouth Barry's Coaches, Dorchester–Wool–Bovington (*alight at Camp, 1½ m*) Wilts & Dorset X20 Swanage–Weymouth (*summer only*)
COMPTON ACRES GARDENS *map 2 S* *J. R. Brady, Esq.* **Famous gardens in the south of England. Valuable bronze and marble statuary and ornaments. Seven separate secluded gardens**	Canford Cliffs rd midway between Bournemouth and *Stn: Poole or Bournemouth* (3 *m*)	April 1 to October 31—Daily 10.30–6.30 (*closes at dusk on Thurs., June to August*). No dogs. Adm. £1.20. Chd. 60p. *Reduced rates for parties of 35 or over.* in the grounds	National tours from Kent and Dorset Surrey Motors tours from Sutton Wilts & Dorset 150, 151 from Bournemouth 151 from Poole (*alight gates*)
COMPTON HOUSE, nr Sherborne *map 2 S* *Worldwide Butterflies Ltd.* 16th cent. Manor House with 19th cent. Tudor style front. Set in tranquil surroundings with lawns and 13th cent. church, an historic building with a difference: here butterflies are bred and visitors see all stages of their development. Tropical Jungle, Breeding Hall, Palmhouse and other display areas. House still lived in. Visitors also see the Lullingstone Silk farm which produced the silk for two coronations and other Royal occasions	On A30 dual carriageway, midway between Sherborne & Yeovil *Stns: Yeovil Pen Mill (2 m); Sherborne (3 m)*	April 1 to Oct. 31—Daily 10–5. Adm. charges not available at time of going to press. *The gardens of the house are now open to visitors and it is possible to see some of the fine outbuildings which are gradually to be restored.* light refreshments *Yeovil* (0935) 74608 Compton Manor Farm Restaurant *Yeovil* (0935) 23795 Little Chef Restaurant at entrance gates *Yeovil* (0935) 23980	Local buses from Sherborne & Yeovil will usually stop at entrance gates (10-15 *mins. walk*)
CRANBORNE MANOR GARDENS *The Marquess of Salisbury* *map 3 N* **Walled gardens, yew hedges and lawns; wild garden with spring bulbs, herb garden, Jacobean mount garden, flowering cherries and collection of old-fashioned and specie roses. Gardens originally laid out by John Tradescant**	**18 m N of Bournemouth, B3078; 16 m S of Salisbury, A354, B3081**	GARDENS ONLY. April to October—first Sat. & Sun. in month & Bank Hols. also other days as advertised locally (not Sun. morns.) Free car park. Garden centre open daily Mons.–Sats. 9–5, Suns. 2–5. Something for every gardener, but specialising in old-fashioned and specie roses, herbs, ornamental pots and Italian statuary and garden furniture. *Cranborne* 248	Stanbridge Motor Services from Wimborne (*Sats. only*) (*alight Square*)
DEANS COURT, Wimborne *map 2S* *Sir Michael & Lady Hanham* Partly wild garden, specimen trees, interesting birds, organic kitchen garden. House, formerly the Deanery, enlarged 1725, some rebuilding 1868.	2 m walk from Wimborne Minster & Square; nr free car parks in town.	GARDEN: Easter Sun. 2–6, Easter Mon. 10–6. Spring & Summer Bank Hol. Mons. (May 28 & Aug. 27) 10–6. May 31 to Sept. 30—Thurs. & Suns. 2–6. Adm. 60p, Chd. 30p. No dogs or unaccompanied children. *Special arrangements for disabled on application at gate.* Organically-grown produce for sale. Vegetable sanctuary. HOUSE: By written appointment. Wholefood teas.	Wilts & Dorset services to Poole, Bournemouth Blandford, Shaftesbury to the Square. *Trains:* from Poole & Bournemouth
DEWLISH HOUSE, Dewlish *map 2 S* *J. Anthony Boyden, Esq.* **Queen Anne house built 1700**	**8 m NE of Dorchester**	May to September—Thurs (except Bank Holidays) 2–5. Adm. £1.20, Chd. 60p. *Milborne St. Andrew* 224	Wilts & Dorset 184, Weymouth–Salisbury (*alight Dewlish Turn, 1 m*)
FORDE ABBEY, nr Chard *map 2 S* *Trustees of G. D. Roper, Esq.* 12th century Cistercian Monastery. Famous Mortlake tapestries. 25 acres of beautiful gardens.	1 m E of Chard Jnc. 4 m SE of Chard. 7 m W of Crewkerne *Stns: Crewkerne (8m); Axminster (8 m)*	House & Gardens: Easter Sun. & Mon. then May to Sept.—Suns., Weds. & B. H. Mons., 2–6. Gardens only: March, April & October—Suns., 2–4.30. Adm. £1.75, Chd. 75p, Parties £1.	National tours from Bournemouth, Torquay, Paignton, Seaton & main towns in Dorset and Somerset
HARDY'S COTTAGE, Higher Bockhampton *The National Trust* *map 2 S* Birthplace of Thomas Hardy 1840–1928. A thatched cottage, built by his grandfather; little altered	3 m E of Dorchester; ½ m S of Blandford Rd (A35) *Stn: Dorchester South & West (4 m)*	Interior by prior appointment with the tenant between April & end of Oct. (except Tues. a.m.) from 11–6 or sunset if earlier. Adm. £1. Exterior from end of garden. Approached by 10 mins. walk from car park via woods. *Dorchester* 62366	Wilts & Dorset, 184, Weymouth–Salisbury 186/187 Bournemouth–Weymouth (*not Suns.*) (*alight Higher Bockhampton turn, Cuckoo Lane ½ m*)
HIGHBURY, West Moors *map 3 N* *Mr. & Mrs. Stanley Cherry* Half acre garden in mature setting; many rare and unusual plants and shrubs. Specialist collections. Botanical and horticultural interest with everything labelled	8 m N of Bournemouth. In Woodside Rd off B3072 B'mouth – Verwood (last rd N end of village) *Stn: Bournemouth (8½ m)*	GARDEN ONLY: April 1 to Sept. 2—Suns. & Bank Hol. Mons. 2–6. Parties other days by appointment. Adm. 25p. Chd 5p. *In aid of National Gardens' Scheme & Gardeners' Sunday.* No dogs. *Ferndown* 874372	No reasonable public transport

ATHELHAMPTON

DORSET

Surrounded by one of the Great Gardens of England

Legendary site of Athelstan's palace. Thomas Hardy's Athel Hall. A family home for more than five hundred years. Great Hall with unique roof, oriel window, heraldic glass and linenfold panelling. Tudor Great Chamber. Wine Cellar. State Bedroom. Twelve architectural and water gardens. Rare plants and trees. Thatched stable. 15th century Dovecote. Tour the House at leisure. Guides for consultation.

OPENING TIMES
April 18th to October 14th.

Wednesdays, Thursdays and Sundays, Good Friday and Bank Holidays; also Tuesdays and Fridays during August: 2–6. Children free of charge in gardens. Party rates by arrangement. Dogs admitted only to shaded car park.

Antiques and craft shop. Plants for sale.

Cream Teas at the House.

Telephone: Puddletown 363.

COMPTON ACRES GARDENS

Canford Cliffs, Poole, Dorset (Bournemouth 3 miles)

John T. Etches photograph

REPUTED TO BE THE FINEST IN EUROPE

These famous private gardens overlook Poole Harbour and Brownsea Island and the Purbeck Hills beyond. There are seven separate and distinct gardens, including Rock and Water Gardens, Semi-Tropical Glen, Heather Dell, Japanese Garden, Roman and English Gardens, Italian Garden and Palm Court.

The public are admitted from April 1 to October 31, every day including Sundays from 10.30 a.m. to 6.30 p.m. During June, July and August open Thursdays until dusk.

Admission £1.20. Children 60p. Reduction for parties of 35 and over
Teas and refreshments available. Free car and coach park. Sorry no dogs.

CRANBORNE MANOR GARDENS

CRANBORNE, WIMBORNE, DORSET

One of the "Great Gardens of Great Britain"

Cecil Beaton photograph

These beautiful and historic gardens, laid out in the 17th century by John Tradescant, and much embellished and enlarged in the 20th century, feature several gardens surrounded by walls and yew hedges—enclosing a White garden, Herb, Mount and Knot garden planted with Elizabethan flowers. There are also Water and Wild gardens. Visitors will find many interesting plants, fine trees and avenues.

GARDEN CENTRE

Specialising in rare and uncommon plants, Italian pots and statuary, old fashioned and specie roses, herbs, etc. Large Gift Shop. Open daily Monday to Saturday 9–5; Sunday 2–5.

FORDE ABBEY

CHARD
SOMERSET

Forde Abbey was founded in 1138 as a Cistercian Monastery and was "modernised" in 1500 by Abbot Chard whose Great Hall and Tower remain. In 1640 the Abbey was converted into a Country House, whose magnificent interior is untouched, and includes a series of unique plaster ceilings and an outstanding set of Raphael Tapestries.

Today the Abbey, surrounded by 25 acres of Gardens and Lakes, on the bank of the River Axe is the home of the Roper family.

THE GARDEN CENTRE

Trees, shrubs and plants are available on weekdays throughout the year.

THE FRUIT GARDENS

From mid June to mid August Forde Abbey Fruit Gardens are open daily 9 a.m.–7 p.m.

Visitors are able to pick strawberries, raspberries, currants, loganberries and vegetables according to the season.

There are extensive car parks and the whole is set in delightful countryside.

PROPERTY (showing map reference)	LOCATION (with nearest Rly. Stn.)	OPENING TIMES AND ADMISSION CHARGES CATERING FACILITIES	COACH AND RAIL TOURS BUS SERVICES (showing alighting points)
DORSET—*continued*			
MELBURY HOUSE, nr Yeovil *map 2 S* *The Lady Teresa Agnew* Large garden; very fine arboretum; shrubs and lakeside walk; beautiful deer park	13 m. N of Dorchester *Stn: Chetnole (2 m)*	GARDEN ONLY: Thurs. June 28; July 12, 19; Aug. 2: 2–6. Adm. 50p, Chd. 20p. ***In aid of the National Gardens' Scheme***	Local rail services
MILTON ABBEY, nr Blandford *map 2 S* Fine Abbey Church completed 15th century on site of 10th century Abbey. Georgian gothic house built 1771, with ceilings designed by James Wyatt. Abbot's hall completed in 1498 with carved screen and hammerbeam roof.	**9 m SW of Blandford just N of A354 at Winterborne Whitchurch**	April 14 to 23 & July 22 to Sept. 2—Daily 10–7.30 Adm. to Grounds & House 50p, Chd. free	National tours from Bournemouth. Wilts & Dorset tours from Bournemouth Wilts & Dorset 184, Salisbury–Weymouth ***(alight Winterborne Whitchurch or Milborne St. Andrew, 3 m)***
MINTERNE, Dorchester *map 2 S* *The Lord Digby* Important Rhododendron Garden set in a beautiful valley, landscaped in the 18th cent. with streams, small lakes and rare trees.	On A352 2 m N of Cerne Abbas; 10 m N of Dorchester, 9 m S of Sherborne	April to June—Suns. & Bank Holidays, 2–7. Adm. £1, Chd. free. Free car park. Parties by appointment. ☎ *Cerne Abbas* 370	No reasonable public transport
PARNHAM HOUSE, Beaminster *map 2 S* *John Makepeace, Esq.* Tudor Manor House with additions by John Nash. Home of The John Makepeace Furniture Workshops and The School for Craftsmen in Wood. The house stands in fourteen acres of varied gardens, with formal terraces bisected by water courses and cascades leading down towards the river.	**1 m S of Beaminster 6 m S of Crewkerne** *Stn: Crewkerne (6 m)*	April 1 to Oct. 31—Weds., Suns. & Bank Hols. 10–5 Adm. Principal rooms, gardens, workshops, car parks, picnic areas: £1.75, Chd. (10–15) 75p; under 10, free. *Parties & functions by arrangement.* **teas, light lunches etc. in 17th cent. Oak Room.** ☎ ***Beaminster* (0308) 862204**	Western National 400, Bridport-Beaminster *(not Suns). (alight opposite entrance)*
PURSE CAUNDLE MANOR, Purse Caundle *R. E. Winckelmann, Esq.* *map 2 S* 15th/16th century manor (great hall and chamber and gardens)	**4 m E of Sherborne; ½ m S of A30** *Stn : Sherborne (4½ m)*	April 22 to October—Thurs., Suns. & Bank Hols. 2–5. Also by appointment. Adm. £1, Chd. 30p. Free car park. ☎ *Milborne Park* 250 400	Western National 468, 469 ***to 1 mile east of Milbourne Port***
RUSSELL-COTES ART GALLERY & MUSEUM *map 3 N* *Bournemouth Corporation* Victorian House designed by Fogerty in 1894 as the East Cliff Hall	**Russell-Cotes Road, East Cliff, Bournemouth** *Stn : Bournemouth (¾ m)*	**All the year—Weekdays 10.30–5.30. Gardens open June 1 to September 30** Adm. 50p, Chd. 10p (under 5 yrs. free). Consideration is being given to re-opening on Sunday afternoon 3–5.30.	**Local corporation services with a red indicator** Wilts & Dorset via Lansdowne from Salisbury & Lymington
△ **SANDFORD ORCAS MANOR HOUSE, Sandford Orcas, Sherborne** *map 2 S* *M. T. Medlycott, Esq.* Tudor house; fine panelling, furniture, pictures and stained glass	4 m N of Sherborne; ent. next to church *Stn: Sherborne (4 m)*	Easter Monday 10–6 then May to Sept.—Suns. 2–6 & Mons. 10–6. Adm. £1. Chd. 50p. Parties by appointment. ☎ *Corton Denham* (096 322) 206	No reasonable public transport
SHERBORNE CASTLE, Sherborne *map 2 S* *Simon Wingfield Digby, Esq.* 16th-cent. mansion in continuous occupation of the Digby family since 1617	**5 m E of Yeovil off A30 to S** *Stn: Sherborne (few mins. walk)*	Easter Sat. to end of Sept.—Thurs., Sats., Suns. & Bank Hol. Mons. 2–6. Adm. charges available on request by telephone. *Special terms & days for parties by arrangement.* Gift shop. at the house ☎ *Sherborne* (093581) 3182	**National Coach 705, 706, from London and West Country** **Western National 470, Yeovil–Corton Denham** *(Thurs. only)*; 468 Yeovil–Sherborne/Wincanton; **469 Yeovil–Sherborne–Stalbridge**
SMEDMORE, Kimmeridge *map 2 W* *Major & Mrs. John Mansel* 17th/18th cent. manor house, still lived in by the family who built it. Dutch marquetry furniture, antique dolls. Walled gardens, interesting shrubs, fuchsias and hydrangeas.	**7 m S of Wareham** *Stn: Wareham (8 m)*	June 6 to September 12—Weds. 2.15–5.30 (last adm. 5). Also Sun., Aug. 26, 2.15–5.30. Adm. House & Gardens £1.10, Chd. 55p. Gardens only 55p, Chd. free. *Organised parties Thurs. afternoons during same period by arrangement only.* Written guides in French, German & Dutch. **at Kimmeridge (1 m)** ☎ ***Corfe Castle* 480717**	**No public transport facilities**
WOLFETON HOUSE, Dorchester *map 2 S* *Capt. N. T. L. Thimbleby* Outstanding medieval and Elizabethan manor house with magnificent wood and stone work, fireplaces and ceilings; Great Hall and stairs; parlour, dining room, Chapel and Cider House. Furniture and pictures.	1¼ m from Dorchester on Yeovil rd (A37); indicated by Historic House signs *Stns: Dorchester South & West (1¼ m)*	May to Sept. — Tues., Thurs., Suns. & Bank Hol. Mons. also daily (except Sats.) in Aug.; 2–6. *At other times throughout the year by appointment.* Adm. charges not available at time of going to press. Cider for sale. Ploughman's lunches, teas & evening meals for parties by prior arrangement. ☎ *Dorchester* (0305) 63500	Bere Regis & District from Dorchester *(alight Charminster)*
DURHAM			
AUCKLAND CASTLE, Bishop Auckland *The Bishop of Durham* *map 1 R* Historic home of the Bishops of Durham with parts dating from 12th century. Very fine private Chapel remodelled by Bishop Cosin from 1660. 14th century Hall, gothicised by James Wyatt in 1795. Also large public park and unusual 18th century deerhouse.	In Bishop Auckland, at the end of Market Place. *Stn: Bishop A'land*	May 6 to Sept. 26—Suns., Mons. & Weds. 2–5. Adm. 75p, Chd. 30p, O.A.Ps. 50p. Parties by appointment. ☎ *Bishop Auckland* (0388) 663063	United 1 from Darlington Northern General X3 from Durham; X20 from Newcastle & Durham
DURHAM CASTLE, Durham *map 1 R* *The University of Durham* △ The Norman castle of the prince bishops has been used by Durham University since 1832	**In the centre of the city (adjoining Cathedral)** *Stn: Durham (¼ m)*	All the year; first three weeks in April then July, August & September—Weekdays 10–12, 2–4.30. Other months—Mons., Weds. & Sats. 2–4. Adm. (1983 rates) 75p, Chd. 35p.	National tours from Lancashire **Northern General & United Services. Frequent from all parts to Centre of City** ***(alight Market Place, ¼ m)***
RABY CASTLE, Staindrop, Darlington *The Lord Barnard, T.D.* *map 1 R* Principally 14th cent., alterations made 1765 and mid 19th century. Fine pictures and furniture. Collection of horse-drawn carriages and fire engines. Large walled Gardens.	**1 m N of Staindrop village, on the Barnard Castle–Bishop Auckland rd (A688)** *Stn: Bishop Auckland (7½ m) (not Suns.)*	Easter weekend (Sat.–Tues.) then April 25 to June 27 —Weds. & Suns.; July 1 to Aug. 31—Daily (except Sats.); Sept. 2 to 30—Weds. & Suns.; May, Spring & August Bank Hol. weekends (Sat.–Tues.). Hours: Castle 2–5, Park & Gardens 1–5.30. Adm. (1983 rates) Castle, Gardens & Carriage Collection £1.20, Chd. & O.A.Ps. 70p; Gardens & Carriages only 60p, Chd. & O.A.Ps. 40p. *Special terms for parties over 25 on above & other days by arrangement with Curator: Car park open from 12.30 on Bank Hols. Picnic area* tea at the Stables ☎ *Staindrop* (0833) 60202	**United 75 & 77, Darlington–Barnard Castle; United 8, Bishop Auckland–Barnard Castle** ***(alight Staindrop, North Lodge, ½ m)***

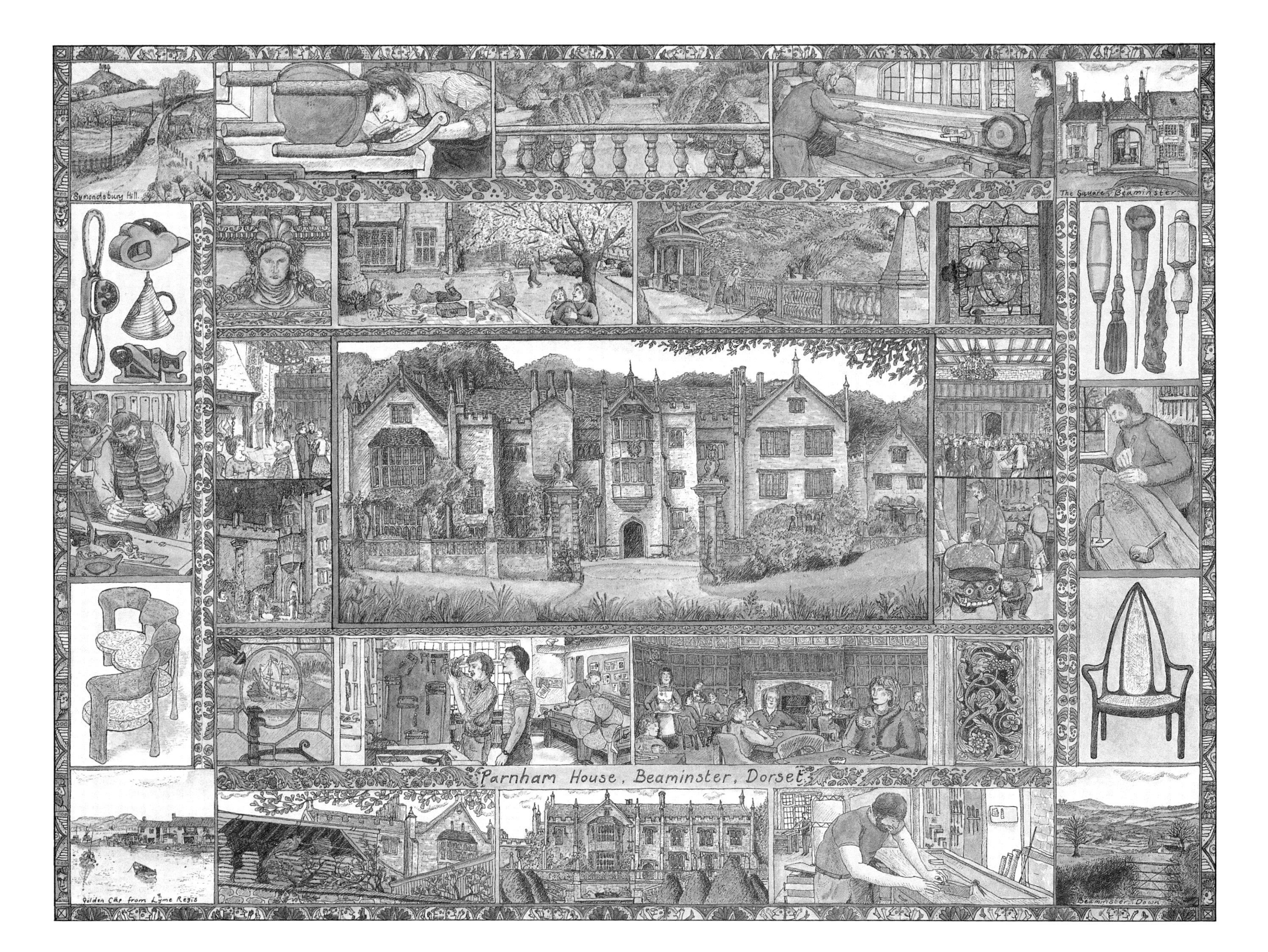
Symondsbury Hill.
The Square, Beaminster
Parnham House, Beaminster, Dorset.
Golden Cap from Lyme Regis
Beaminster Down

PARNHAM HOUSE

BEAMINSTER, DORSET.

Parnham House is a 16th-Century manor enlarged by John Nash in 1810; enchantingly set in idyllic gardens with terraces, topiary, cascading water and great trees, Parnham lies hidden in a valley amidst the hills of West Dorset.

Each month, the work of an eminent artist, designer or craftsman is featured in the Drawing Room. An international collection of wooden artefacts and antique wood-working tools is shown in the Library.

Individually-commissioned furniture is designed by John Makepeace and made by eight skilled craftsmen for private, business and public use. Recently-completed work is shown in the Great Hall.

The house and gardens and The John Makepeace Furniture Workshop are open to visitors on Wednesdays, Sundays and Bank Holidays from April to October.

The independent School for Craftsmen in Wood was founded by The Parnham Trust in 1977 to train young people in fine craftsmanship, design, marketing and business management, in preparation for setting up their own businesses. The School is not open to the general public.

Britain's woodlands, such an important part of our heritage, are suffering from neglect. Their future conservation depends upon our using them more intelligently. The Parnham Trust intends to respond to this national need by establishing a British School for Woodland Industries.

Having purchased a woodland three miles from Parnham with £250,000 most generously subscribed for the purpose, the Trustees are now seeking contributions towards the £700,000 urgently needed to build and equip the new School.

If you care about our native woodlands, not only as a valuable habitat for wild-life and as an amenity but also as a potential source of suitable industry and employment in the countryside, please do consider how you can help. I shall be pleased to send you details. 1984

John Makepeace
Director of The Parnham Trust

Parnham House, Beaminster, Dorset, DT8 3NA
Telephone: Beaminster (0308) 862204

RUSSELL-COTES ART GALLERY & MUSEUM

BOURNEMOUTH, DORSET

The Russell-Cotes Museum, designed in 1894 by Fogerty as a villa for Sir Merton Russell-Cotes, is a remarkable example of a late Victorian Residence. The interior is decorated in the Italian manner and there is a fine collection of paintings and other works of art. The nearby Rothesay Museum includes the important Lucas Collection of early Italian paintings and pottery, an Armoury and Britain's largest typewriter collection.

WOLFETON

DORSET

The home of Captain & Mrs. Thimbleby

A beautiful and romantic Tudor house with Elizabethan additions, fine stonework, interior woodcarvings and plaster ceilings; the mediaeval gatehouse, French in appearance, has two unmatched and far older towers.

PARNHAM HOUSE

BEAMINSTER DORSET

An idyllic Tudor house of honey-coloured stone, mullioned windows, pinnacles and battlements, columns and balustrades, among terraced gardens, topiary, rotundas and spring water cascading to the River Brit.

Home of John Makepeace, the designer and furniture-maker, whose workshops are open to visitors. Recent commissions are shown in the Great Hall.

Each month, an exhibition by a major artist or craftsman in the Drawing Room. In the Library—a fine collection of antique tools and wooden artefacts. The Painted Staircase, with *trompe l'oeil* murals of the gardens, leads to the Strode Bedroom, dominated by the great four-poster of yew-wood.

Parnham—where individual craftsmanship flourishes today.

Please see the separate colour insert

The School for Craftsmen in Wood at Parnham is not open to visitors.

SHERBORNE CASTLE

SHERBORNE, DORSET

Family home of Mr. Simon Wingfield Digby

John Mennell photograph

Built by Sir Walter Raleigh in 1594 and enlarged in 1625 by Sir John Digby, 1st Earl of Bristol. Home of the Digby family since 1617, the house contains fine furniture, porcelain and pictures by Vandyck, Gainsborough, Reynolds, Lely, Kneller and other famous artists. Twenty acres of lawns and pleasure grounds planned by 'Capability Brown' around the newly restored 50 acre lake are open to the public.

One of the two castles in the ancient and attractive town of Sherborne

OPENING TIMES OPPOSITE

RABY CASTLE

STAINDROP, CO. DURHAM

The Castle is one of the largest 14th century Castles in Britain and was built by the Nevills although one of the towers probably dates back to the 11th century. Interior mainly 18th and 19th century; medieval Kitchen and Servants' Hall.

There are some fine pictures of the English, Dutch and Flemish Schools and good period furniture. Collection of horse drawn carriages.

The large walled Gardens are also open to the public.

OPENING TIMES OPPOSITE

PROPERTY (*showing map reference*)	LOCATION (*with nearest Rly. Stn.*)	OPENING TIMES AND ADMISSION CHARGES CATERING FACILITIES	COACH AND RAIL TOURS BUS SERVICES (*showing alighting points*)
EAST SUSSEX (*see also West Sussex*)			
BATEMAN'S, Burwash *map 6 D* Δ *The National Trust* Built 1634. Rudyard Kipling lived here. Water-mill restored by the National Trust. Attractive garden, yew hedges, lawns, daffodils	**½ m S of Burwash on the Lewes–Etchingham rd (A265)** ***Stn:* Etchingham (3 m)**	April to end of Oct.—Daily except Thurs. & Fris. but open Good Friday) 11–6. Last adm. 5.30. Adm. House, Mill & Garden £1.70, Chd. 80p. Pre-booked parties by special arrangement £1.30—*apply to the Administrator*. No dogs. Tea room ☎ *Burwash* 882302	Southdown/East Kent 718, Brighton–Heathfield–Ashford–Canterbury (*Weds. & Sats. only, alight Burwash 'Bear Inn' P.H., ¾ m*)
BEECHES FARM, nr Uckfield *map 3 P* Δ *Mrs. Vera Thomas* 16th century tile hung farm house. Lawns, yew trees, borders, sunken garden, roses, fine views	Off A2102, 1½ m W Uckfield (on Isfield rd) *Stn: Uckfield (1½ m)*	All the year—Daily 10–5. Adm. Gardens 20p, House (by appointment) 75p. *Special quotations (inc. tea) for parties.* Suns., April 15 & June 17 *in aid of National Gardens' Scheme.*	Buses to Uckfield (1½ *m*) from Lewes, Eastbourne Tunbridge Wells, Haywards Heath, etc.
BENTLEY, Halland, nr Lewes *map 3 R* *East Sussex County Council* Wildfowl collection of over 1,000 birds. Motor Museum with veteran and vintage vehicles, Palladian style conversion of Tudor farmhouse by Raymond Erith R.A.	7½ m NE of Lewes; 1½ m off B2192; 1½ m off A22; 1½ m off A26 (well signposted) *Stn: Uckfield (3 m) (not Suns.)*	March 26 to Sept. 30 — Mons. to Sats. 11–6; Suns. & Bank Hols. 11–6.30. House open 1–5. Winter—Weekends only 11–5.30. Last adm. 1½ hrs. before closing. Adm. £1.80, Chd. 90p, O.A.Ps. £1.30. Parties 10% discount.	Southdown 180 Uckfield—Hailsham (*alight Iron Peartree Corner*) 118 Lewes–Heathfield (*alight Shortgate*) 119 Lewes–Crowborough (*alight Isfield Almshouses*); well signposted National tours from parts of Sussex & London area
BODIAM CASTLE, nr. Robertsbridge *map 3 R* *The National Trust* Built 1386–9, one of the best preserved examples of medieval moated military architecture	3 m S of Hawkhurst; 1 m E of A229 *Stn: Robertsbridge (5 m)*	April to Oct. 31—Daily 10–6 (or sunset if earlier). Nov. to March—Mons. to Sats. only, 10–sunset. Last adm. half-hour before closing. *Closed Dec. 25, 26 & 27.* Adm. 90p, Chd. 45p. *Parties of 15 or more by prior arrangement* 70p. Car park free to members. Museum. Audio visual. Shop. Dogs admitted except in shop & museum. Wheelchair access. ☎ *Staplecross* (058 083) 436 Tea room: ☎ *Staplecross* 212	National tours from London & Kent Maidstone 254, Tunbridge Wells–Hawkhurst–Hastings (*alight Bodiam*)
BRICKWALL HOUSE, Northiam, Rye *Frewen Educational Trust* *map 3 R* Home of the Frewen family since 1666. 17th cent. drawing room with richly decorated plaster ceiling. Garden now being restored.	7 m NW of Rye on B2088 *Stns: Rye (7 m); Doleham (6 m)*	April 28 to May 23 & June 2 to July 11—Weds. & Sats. 2–4. Adm. 50p. ☎ *Northiam* (07974) 2494	Maidstone 12 Hastings–Tenterden–Maidstone 411 Hastings–Northiam–Rye National Coach 034 London–Tunbridge Wells–Rye
CHARLESTON MANOR, West Dean, Seaford *map 3 R* Δ *Mr. & Mrs. Robert Headlam* Fine example of Norman, Tudor and Georgian architecture in a romantic setting. Famous Romanesque window and exquisite rose gardens. Norman dovecote and Tudor tithe barn.	½ m S of Litlington. Off B2108 3 m from Seaford, 7 m from Eastbourne *Stn: Seaford (3 m)*	GARDENS ONLY: April to Oct.—Daily. Adm. 75p. *Regret House not open.* Sorry, no dogs. Near Downs (good walking).	Southdown 712 Eastbourne–Seaford–Brighton–(*alight Exceat Corner* 1 *m*)
COBBLERS GARDEN, Crowborough *map 6 D* *Mr. & Mrs. Martin Furniss* **2 acre garden on sloping site designed and planted by owners since 1968 in informal manner for all-season colour; large range of herbaceous and shrub species: water garden. Featured in R.H.S. Journal, March 1978 and two B.B.C. television programmes Aug. 1978, 'Country Life' and 'Homes & Gardens' 1981**	**At Crowborough Cross (A26) turn on to B2100 (signposted C'borough stn & Rotherfield); at 2nd crossroads turn r. into Tollwood Rd.** *Stn: Crowborough*	GARDEN ONLY—Suns., May 20, 27; June 10, 24; July 8, 22; August 5, 12; 2.30–6. Adm. £1, Chd. 50p. *In aid of National Gardens' Scheme.* No dogs please. Ample free parking. **teas at the garden**	No reasonable public transport Trains from Charing Cross to Tonbridge, connections for Crowborough
FIRLE PLACE, nr Lewes *map 3 P* Δ *Viscount Gage* Important collection of Italian, Dutch and English pictures. Sèvres porcelain, French and English furniture and objects of American interest	5 m SE of Lewes on the Lewes–Eastb'rne rd (A27) *Stn: Glynde (3 m) Lewes (5 m)*	June, July, Aug. & Sept.—Mons., Weds. & Suns. (and Thurs. during August only); also Easter, May, Spring & Summer Bank Hol. Suns. & Mons.: 2.15–5. Adm. charges not available at time of going to press. First Wed. in month longer, unguided Connoisseurs' tour of House & Garden. Group parties of 25 on Open Days (except first Wed. in month) at reduced rate. Special exclusive viewings at other times of year for parties over 20 by arrangement. *Party bookings in writing to Showing Secretary, Firle Place, Nr. Lewes, East Sussex BN8 6LP.* at the House & Shop ☎ *Glynde* (079159) 335	National Express 064 from London, Brighton, Eastbourne Southdown 728 Eastbourne–Lewes–Brighton (*2 hourly*) (*not Suns.*), 825 Lewes–Glynde–Firle (*Mons. to Fris., 2 hourly*) (*alight Firle Gates*)
GLYNDE PLACE, nr Lewes *map 3 P* *Viscount Hampden* Δ Beautiful example of 16th cent. architecture. Pictures, bronzes, historical documents.	4 m SE of Lewes on Eastbourne – Lewes rd (A27) or A265 *Stn: Glynde (½ m)*	June 6 to Sept. 27—Weds. & Thurs. 2.15–5.30 (last adm. 5). Last Wed. each month—Connoisseurs' Day. Open Easter Sun. & Mon. and Bank Hols. House open for parties by prior arrangement (20 or more £1.10 per person). Adm. £1.50, Chd. 75p. Connoisseurs' Day: Adm. £1.75. Garden only 50p (rebate on entry into house). Free parking. home-baked teas in Coach House (parties to book in advance). ☎ *Glynde* (079 159) 248	British Rail. Brighton to Eastbourne line, stopping every hour at Glynde Stn.

BENTLEY

Halland, nr. Lewes, East Sussex

The famous Wildfowl collection contains over a thousand birds of 110 different species of waterfowl as well as cranes, peacocks, flamingoes and ornamental pheasants. The motor museum has a fascinating variety of veteran and vintage vehicles. Bentley House, also open to the public, is a Tudor farmhouse dating from 1558 and converted into a Palladian Style country house for Mr. and Mrs. Gerald Askew by Raymond Erith, R.A., who restored 10 and 11 Downing Street. It contains antique furniture and a unique collection of wildfowl paintings by Philip Rickman. Its walled gardens, the parkland and woodland walk can all be explored and the picnic area, the well appointed tea room, gift shop, children's play area and exhibition room all add to the attractions.

OPENING TIMES OPPOSITE

BODIAM CASTLE

near ROBERTSBRIDGE

THE NATIONAL TRUST

The romantic ruin—among the most beautiful in England—of a moated 14th century castle, built as a protection against French raids

OPENING TIMES OPPOSITE

FIRLE PLACE

near Lewes, East Sussex

Home of the Gage family since the 15th century. The original Tudor house was largely altered about 1730.

The House contains an important collection of European and English Old Masters. The pictures are further enhanced with a collection of French and English furniture by famous craftsmen. Also a quanity of Sèvres china of the finest quality. All these are largely derived from the Cowper collection and can be seen in a lovely spacious family setting.

"Country Life" photograph

Through General Gage, Commander-in-Chief of the British forces at the beginning of the War of Independence, and his wife Margaret Kemble of New Jersey, there are items of particular interest to visitors from the U.S.A.

OPENING TIMES

June to September: Mondays, Wednesdays and Sundays; also Thursdays during August only and Easter, May, Spring and Summer Bank Holiday Sundays and Mondays. Open 2.15 to 5.00 (last admission).

House is set in parkland under the South Downs. 55 miles from London by road. Hourly rail service Victoria to Lewes takes 64 minutes, thence by taxi (5 miles).

GLYNDE PLACE

near Lewes, East Sussex

A very beautiful example of 16th century architecture. The house, which is built round a Courtyard, is of flint and brick and stands in the picturesque village of Glynde. Interesting collection of pictures by Kneller, Lely, Snyders, Weenix and Zoffany. Bronzes by Francesco Bertos.

OPENING TIMES OPPOSITE

GREAT DIXTER

NORTHIAM, EAST SUSSEX

A half-timbered Hall House, A.D 1450

A beautiful example of a 15th century half-timbered manor house with a Great Hall of unique construction. Restorations and the addition of a smaller 16th century hall house were carried out by Sir Edwin Lutyens who also designed the gardens. Yew hedges, topiary and garden buildings create a delightful setting for flower borders. These contain a rich diversity of plants of horticultural interest. Naturalised daffodils and fritillaries; paeonies, primulas, fuchsias, rose garden, clematis, herbaceous and bedding plants informally arranged.

OPENING TIMES PAGE 60

PROPERTY (*showing map reference*)	LOCATION (*with nearest Rly. Stn.*)	OPENING TIMES AND ADMISSION CHARGES CATERING FACILITIES	COACH AND RAIL TOURS BUS SERVICES (*showing alighting points*)
EAST SUSSEX—*continued*			
GREAT DIXTER, Northiam *map 3 R* Δ *Quentin Lloyd, Esq.* 15th century half-timbered manor house in a Lutyens designed garden	½ m N of Northiam, 8 m NW of Rye, 12 m N of Hastings. Just off A28 *Stns: Doleham (7 m); Rye (8 m), Hastings (12 m)*	April 1 to Oct. 14—Daily (except Mons. but open all Bank Hol. Mons.) also weekends Oct. 20/21 & 27/28: 2–5.30 (last adm. 5). Gardens open at 11 on May 27/28, Suns. in July & Aug., also Aug. 27. Adm. House & Gardens £1.40, Chd. 40p; Gardens only 90p, Chd. 25p. *Special rates for parties by arrangement.* No dogs. locally, ask for list ☎ 07974 3160	National Coach 034 London–Rye 400 Ashford–Northiam–Hastings; 408 Rye–Northiam–Hastings (500 *yds from bus stop*)
HAMMERWOOD PARK, nr East Grinstead Δ *David Pinnegar, Esq.* *map 6 C* Built in 1792 by Latrobe, the architect of The White House and The Capitol, Washington D.C., U.S.A. This was his first main work. A fine house, in course of restoration, housing various displays of costume, kitchen items etc., with guided tours. Educational facilities.	3½ m E of East Grinstead on A264 to Tunbridge Wells; 1 m W of Holtye *Stn: East Grinstead (4 m)*	Easter Sat. to end of Sept.—Weds., Sats., Suns & Bank Hol. Mons. 11.30–5.30. Also Thurs. in August. Pre-booked parties of 15 or more any day by arrangement. Adm. House & Grounds £1, Chd. 75p. Evening events & concerts throughout the summer—write or telephone for details. ☎ *Cowden* (034286) 594 teas *or Woldingham* (088 385) 2366	British Rail, London Bridge to East Grinstead (*hourly*); Maidstone & District 900, Medway Towns–Maidstone–Tunbridge Wells–East Grinstead–Gatwick Airport (*alight entrance lane to W. of Hammerwood Church*)
HAREMERE HALL, Etchingham *map 3 R* *Jacqueline, Lady Killearn* Early 17th cent. Manor House with Minstrel staircase, panelled Great Hall, carved doors and Flemish fireplace. Period furniture. Collections of rugs, ornaments, pottery, plate from Middle and Far East. Terraced gardens	On A265 between Etchingham & Hurst Green, N of Battle *Stn: Etchingham (5 mins. walk)*	GARDENS—Daily from Easter to Sept. 30. SHIRE HORSE FARM—Daily from Easter to Sept. 30 (demonstrations at 11 a.m. & 3 p.m.). HOUSE open to public Bank Hol. Weekends only 2.30–5.30—otherwise to parties of 20 or more by appointment. Adm. Shire Horse Farm £1.60; Hall, Grounds & Gardens £1.50; Gardens only 60p. Registered with English Tourist Board. 5 star accomm., 4-poster beds etc., by arrangement with House Manager. luncheon & tea for parties by appointment Guests for Glyndebourne Opera Festival catered for ☎ *Etchingham* 245	Trains from Charing Cross to Etchingham
HORSTED PLACE GARDENS, nr Uckfield *Lady Rupert Nevill* *map 3 P* Charming Victorian garden, rose borders, rhododendrons, shaded walks. Picnic area	On A26 1 m S of Uckfield *Stn: Uckfield (1½ m) (not Suns.)*	Easter to end of September—Weds., Thurs., & Suns. & Bank Hol. Mons.2–6. Adm. (1983 rates) 70p. Chd. 35p. House open to parties by appointment.	Maidstone/Southdown, Brighton–Uckfield–Tunbridge Wells (*alight Little Horsted Church*)
KIDBROOKE PARK, Forest Row *map 6 C* *The Council of Michael Hall School* Sandstone house and stables built in 1730s with later alterations	1 m SW of Forest Row, off A22, 4 m S of E. Grinstead *Stn: E. Grinstead (4m)*	Spring Bank Hol. Mon. (May 25) then Aug.—Daily (inc. Bank Hol. Mon.). Application for admission to the Bursar. REPTON GROUNDS also open at all above weekends.	Maidstone 291, Tunbridge Wells–East Grinstead: Southdown 170, Haywards Heath–East Grinstead (*not Suns.*)
LAMB HOUSE, Rye *map 3 R* *The National Trust* Georgian house with garden. Home of Henry James from 1898 to 1916	In West Street facing W end of church *Stn: Rye (¼ m)*	House (hall & 3 rooms only) & garden; April to end of Oct.—Weds. & Sats. 2–6 (last admission 5.30) Adm. 80p. No reduction for children or parties. No dogs. Unsuitable for wheelchairs.	Maidstone 408, 409, 410, 414, 415 Hastings–Rye; 12, Maidstone–Tenterden–Rye; 401, 403 Tenterden–Rye; 416 Camber–Rye; 762 Folkestone–Lydd–Rye (*summer only*)
MICHELHAM PRIORY, nr Hailsham Δ *Sussex Archaeological Society* *map 3 R* Founded in 1229 this Augustinian Priory is surrounded by one of the largest moats in England. Elizabethan wing and 14th cent. gatehouse. Special exhibitions and events. Tudor barn. Working Watermill recently restored, grinding wholemeal flour.	½ m E of Upper Dicker just off London–Eastbourne rd (A22 & A27) 7 m N of Eastbourne *Stn: Berwick (3 m.)*	Good Friday April 20 to Oct. 21—Daily 11–5.30. (*House closed* 1–2). Adm. (inc. Watermill) £1.30, Chd 50p. Reduction for parties booked in advance. *No dogs.* at licensed restaurants in Grounds. *Special Events* 1984: Sussex Crafts & Small Industries Aug. 1–5. Festival of Music & Art Aug. 12–19 & many other events.	Coaches from Bexhill, Brighton, Hastings, Worthing Epsom, Gravesend, Folkestone National coaches from London Southdown services to Hailsham & Lower Dicker (2½ *m. walk*) to Upper Dicker, (½ *m. walk*) Weds. & Sats. only.
MONK'S HOUSE, Rodmell *map 3 P* *The National Trust* A small village house and garden. The home of Virginia and Leonard Woolf from 1919 until his death in 1969	2½ m SE of Lewes, off C7 in Rodmell village. *Stn: Southease (1 m)*	April to end of Oct.—Weds. & Sats. 2–6 (last admission 5.30). Adm. £1. No reductions for children or parties. No dogs. Unsuitable for wheelchairs. Maximum of 15 people in house at any one time	
THE OLD CLERGY HOUSE, Alfriston, nr Seaford *map 3 R* *The National Trust* A pre-Reformation parish priests' house, c. 1350. Bought in 1896, the first building acquired by the Trust	4 m NE of Seaford just E of B2108; adjoining The Tye & St. Andrew's Church *Stns: Berwick (2½m); Seaford (4 m)*	Exhibition Room, Hall & Garden. April to October—Daily 11–6 (or sunset if earlier). Last adm. half-hour before closing. Adm. 70p. Shop (open until Christmas). No dogs. Unsuitable for wheelchairs. ☎ *Alfriston* (0323) 870001	Southdown 126, Seaford–Alfriston–Eastbourne
PRESTON MANOR, Brighton *map 3 P* *Borough of Brighton* Georgian house with Thomas-Stanford/Macquoid bequests of fine furniture, pictures etc.	On main Brighton to London rd at Preston Park *Stn: Preston Park*	All the year—Weds. to Sats. 10–5; Suns. 2–5. *Closed Good Friday, Christmas & Boxing Day.* Adm. 75p, Chd. 45 (to end Mar. 1984 then 80p, Chd. 45p). Gardens free. *Parties by arrangement.* ☎ (0273) 603005	*Buses* 5, 5A, 5B pass the entrance (*South Rd. stop*)
ROYAL PAVILION, Brighton *map 3 P* *Borough of Brighton* Unique building by Henry Holland and John Nash, built for the Prince Regent	In centre of Brighton (Old Steine) *Stn: Brighton (½ m.)*	All the year—Daily 10–5 (June to Sept. 10–6.30; last adm. 6). *Closed Christmas Day & Boxing Day.* Adm. £1.45 to end Mar. 1984; from April £1.50 to £1.85 according to season. *Reduced rate for parties & children.* Ground floor accessible for the disabled. most days. ☎ (0273) 603005	Most bus services pass the main entrance

MICHELHAM PRIORY

Upper Dicker, near HAILSHAM, Sussex

(Sussex Archaeological Society)

Augustinian Priory founded 1229 on an earlier island site, became a Tudor farmhouse in the 16th century. Owned by the Sackville family 1603–1897. Beautiful grounds enclosed by a mediaeval moat. Imposing 14th century Gate House. Period Furniture, Tapestries, Sussex Ironwork, Ancient Stained Glass, Musical Instruments Collection, Doll's House, Forge and Wheelwrights' Shop, Wagons, Art Exhibitions in Great Barn. Sussex Crafts Shop.

Working Watermill grinding wholemeal flour "Physic" Garden.

Judges Ltd. of Hastings photograph

Open April 20th to October 21st

DAILY 11–5.30
(House closed 1–2)
Tel. Hailsham (0323) 844224.

MORNING COFFEES, FARMHOUSE LUNCHEONS and SUSSEX TEAS served daily.

Also buffet service available during peak periods.

Special Events 1984:

SUSSEX CRAFTS AND SMALL INDUSTRIES EXHIBITION
August 1st to 5th.

FESTIVAL OF MUSIC AND ART
August 12th to 19th

Many other events

HAREMERE HALL

ETCHINGHAM, EAST SUSSEX

As early as the end of the 12th century there was a Lord of the Manor, Miles de Haremere. Several members of the family are named as having witnessed Charters, among them Simon who is mentioned in the Battle Abbey register.

In 1612 the Manor became the property of John Busbridge whose son John inherited it. There is a story that this John, while sleeping, was awakened by the sound of horses. On looking from his bedroom window he saw Cromwell's soldiers advancing. They took the house and shot and killed John.

HORSTED PLACE GARDENS

UCKFIELD, EAST SUSSEX

The gardens of Horsted Place were re-designed and landscaped around the Victorian Gothic mansion, standing in a commanding position with a wide and agreeable prospect over the Sussex Downland.

Geoffrey Jellicoe, the designer, writes: 'Three influences were: first, the stately character of the Mid-Victorian house; second, the combined forces of Humphrey Repton and Lady Rupert Nevill which created the glades and rose baskets that are reminiscent of Brighton Pavilion; and third, the modern Brazilian landscape designer, Roberto Burle Marx, whose work inspired the sense of movement—the green rivers of grass on which the baskets appear to float.'

THE OLD CLERGY HOUSE

ALFRISTON, EAST SUSSEX

THE NATIONAL TRUST

Built for a group of priests about the time of the Black Death, the main hall has a crownpost roof, daub and wattle walls and a rammed chalk floor sealed with sour milk. The first building acquired by the National Trust in 1896.

OPENING TIMES OPPOSITE

THE ROYAL PAVILION **BRIGHTON**

The Royal Pavilion, which was the famous seaside Palace of King George IV, is one of the most dazzling and exotically beautiful buildings in the British Isles—"if not in the world." In it George, Prince of Wales, lived as Regent and as King, gathered about himself a brilliant and cultivated society.

First built by Henry Holland in 1787 as a simple classical villa, the Royal Pavilion was rebuilt by Nash from 1815–1820 in the "Indian" style. The interiors, on which George IV lavished enormous sums, were decorated in the "Chinese taste" which was here carried to unique heights of splendour and magnificence.

Throughout the year, the State and Private Apartments are open to the public. The furniture and works of art include superb original pieces lent by H.M. The Queen. Much has been done to restore the fantastic decorations to their original splendour. Current restoration work, fascinating in its own right, may entail the closure of certain rooms.

The general collections of Regency furniture in the Royal Pavilion, together with the original furniture of the building, supplemented by the important collections of furniture including Continental furniture of the Art Nouveau and Art Deco periods in the Art Gallery and Museum in Church Street form one of the most comprehensive and richest displays of furniture in Britain.

During the summer months the whole of the State and Private Apartments are open to the public fully furnished.

Open daily, including Sunday.

January to May—10 a.m. to 5 p.m. June to end of September—10 a.m. to 6.30 p.m. (last admission 6 p.m.). October to December—10 a.m. to 5 p.m.

Closed Christmas for either two or three days.

Admission £1.45 to end of March then £1.50 to £1.85 according to season. Reduced rates for children and O.A.Ps.

Tea room.

Further details and bookings for party visits, including services of a guide, from the Director, Royal Pavilion, Brighton, BN1 1UE.
Tel. (0273) 603005.

SHEFFIELD PARK GARDEN EAST SUSSEX

THE NATIONAL TRUST

"Photo Precision" photograph

Garden with five lakes laid out in the 18th century which assumed its present form in the 20th. Magnificent rhododendrons, maples, rare trees, shrubs and water-lilies give the garden interest all through the seasons. The house is not the property of the National Trust.

SPRING HILL WILDFOWL PARK

FOREST ROW, near EAST GRINSTEAD, EAST SUSSEX

Attractive new ponds and lay-out for one of the largest and finest collections in the country. It includes Hawaiian Ne-ne and Red-breasted geese bred at Spring Hill. Cranes, Rhea, Peacocks, Pheasants, Swans and Ducks, many rare. Most of them wander freely through the 14 acre grounds of a 15th century house in a beautiful Ashdown Forest setting.

Adults £1, Children 50p, O.A.Ps. 70p. Free car and coach park. Picnic area.

OPEN: Daily throughout the year, 10 a.m. to 6 p.m. or dusk if earlier. Cafeteria, light teas, wide selection of wild-life books, pictures and souvenirs from Aviary Gift shop. Tel. Forest Row (982) 2783.

SHEFFIELD PARK

Nr. UCKFIELD, EAST SUSSEX

First recorded owner of this ancient seat was Earl Godwin, King Harold's father. The present building is basically Tudor, but altered 1775–1778 by James Wyatt for John Baker Holroyd, later first Lord Sheffield. It is Wyatt's first Gothick country house. Guests have included Henry VIII. Edward Gibbon and Edward VII. The estate was acquired in 1972 by the present owners who have done much restoring and redecorating of the house. Much remains to be done. Beautiful staircase and fine rooms, most of which are those in which the owners actually live. Garden and grounds not open to the public. Open Easter Sunday and Monday then May and June. Closed July and August. Re-open September to October 31st–every Wednesday, Thursday, Sunday and Bank Holiday Monday from 2 p.m. to 5 p.m. Teas available for booked parties. All enquiries for this and such functions as lunches, wedding receptions, business lunches, dinners etc. or filming or similar use from: The Secretary, Sheffield Park, nr. Uckfield, Sussex. Telephone Dane Hill 790531.

HEDINGHAM CASTLE

ESSEX

The majestic Norman Keep was built in 1140 and is in an excellent state of preservation.

Situated in the lovely village of Castle Hedingham, Essex, near the Suffolk border, it is one of the finest examples of Norman architecture in Europe. Visitors may picnic in the peace and tranquillity of the Inner Bailey.

LAYER MARNEY TOWER

Nr. COLCHESTER, ESSEX

Lord Marney's Tudor masterpiece of 1520. The highest Tudor gatehouse in the country, flanked by 4 turrets each 8 stories. Terracotta windows and cresting to the turrets of Italian form. Excellent views of the Essex countryside and Blackwater Estuary from the tower. Teas provided for parties on application in writing.

"B.T.A." photograph

OPENING TIMES OPPOSITE

The tennis court and heated swimming pool may be used any day by organised parties for a fee by writing or telephoning COLCHESTER 330202.

SIR ALFRED MUNNINGS K.C.V.O.

(1878–1959)

HOME, PAINTINGS, STUDIOS & GARDENS

CASTLE HOUSE

DEDHAM, ESSEX

Exhibition of paintings, drawings, sketches and other works by this famous East Anglian artist (President of the Royal Academy 1944–1949) in the delightful setting of his home.

Open May 13th to October 14th Wednesdays, Sundays and Bank Holiday Mondays; also Thursdays and Saturdays in August: 2 p.m. to 5 p.m. Admission £1, Children 25p, O.A.Ps. 50p. Private parties by arrangement.

Free Car Park.

Tel. Colchester 322127.

PROPERTY (*showing map reference*)	LOCATION (*with nearest Rly. Stn.*)	OPENING TIMES AND ADMISSION CHARGES CATERING FACILITIES	COACH AND RAIL TOURS BUS SERVICES (*showing alighting points*)
EAST SUSSEX—*continued*			
SHEFFIELD PARK, nr Uckfield *map 6 C* *Mr. & Mrs. P. J. Radford* Tudor house remodelled by James Wyatt 1775–1778. First recorded owner, Earl Godwin King Harold's father. Dickens letters, rare books, weapons. Present owners are restoring the property—purchased 1972.	2 m N of Chailey cross roads (A275 & A272) *Stns : Haywards Heath (7 m); Uckfield (5 m)*	Easter Sun. & Mon. then May & June and Sept. & Oct.—Weds., Thurs., Suns. & Bank Hol. Mons. 2–5. *Closed July & Aug:* Adm. £1.25. teas available for booked parties *Dane Hill* 790531	Transport facilities as for Sheffield Park Garden (*see below*)
SHEFFIELD PARK GARDEN, nr Uckfield *The National Trust* *map 6 C* Large garden with series of lakes linked by cascades; great variety of unusual shrubs	Midway between East Grinstead & Lewes on E side of A275; 5 m NW of Uckfield *Stns : Haywards Heath (7 m); Buxted (7 m) ; Plumpton (6 m); Sheffield Pk (Bluebell Rly)*	April 1 to Nov. 18—Tues. to Sat. 11–6; Sun. 2–6 or sunset if earlier (open from 1 p.m.–sunset on Suns. in Oct. & Nov.). Bank Hol. Mons. 2–6. Last adm. one hour before closing. *Closed all other Mons. & Tues. following B.H. Mons. also Good Friday.* Liable to overcrowding Suns. & Bank Hols. Adm. May, Oct. & Nov. £2.20, Chd. £1.10; April & June to Sept. £1.70, Chd. 85p. Pre-booked parties £1.70 & £1.30 according to season. *No reduction for parties on Sats., Suns. & Bank Hols.* No dogs. Shop. Wheelchairs provided. *Dane Hill* 790655	National tours from London, Kent & South Coast Keith Tours from Aylesbury. Valliant Cronshaw tours from London Southdown 121, 122 Lewes—Chailey (*alight Chailey King's Head, 2½ m*) (also limited stop service from Brighton, summer only); 169 Horsham–Haywards Heath–Uckfield (*alight Chailey King's Head, 2½ m*); 769 Haywards Heath–Sheffield Park (*summer only*); 770 Brighton–Sheffield Park (*Suns. & B. Hols. only*) Bluebell Rly, Horsted Keynes–Sheffield Park *connecting buses from Brighton, Haywards Hth. and E. Grinstead to Horsted Keynes*
THE SPRING HILL WILDFOWL PARK, Forest Row *map 6 C* *R. A. Pendry, Esq.* 15th century farmhouse (not open). Beautiful Ashdown Forest setting, 14 acres, ponds, shrub and terraces. Rare Geese, Swans, Flamingos, Cranes, Rhea, Peacocks, Pheasants and Ducks.	1½m SW from Forest Row off A22. Turn between village church and Swan Hotel into Priory Road. Turn right opposite school. *Stn: East Grinstead (4 m)*	All the year—Daily 10–6 or dusk if earlier. Adm. £1, Chd. 50p, O.A.Ps. 70p. Free coach & car park. Picnic area. *Coach and other parties welcome at 10% reduction* light teas in Aviary gift shop *Forest Row* (034 282) 2783	Southdown 170, East Grinstead–Haywards Heath (*not Suns.*) 780 East Grinstead–Uckfield (*not Suns.*) (*1½ m from bus stop*)
ESSEX			
AUDLEY END HOUSE, Saffron Walden *Dept. of the Environment* *map 3 L* Palatial Jacobean mansion begun 1603 on site of Benedictine Abbey. State Rooms and Hall.	Just off old London—Cambridge Rd, 1m W of Saffron Walden, 15 m S of Cambridge. *Stn: Audley End (1 m)*	April to Sept.—Daily (except Mons.) 1–6.30. Grounds open 12 noon. Open Bank Hol. Mons. Adm. £1.80, Chd. (under 16) & O.A.Ps. 90p. at the House	National tours from Cambridge E. Counties 112, Cambridge–Saffron Walden E. Nat. 301, Bishop's Stortford–Saffron Walden Premier 38, London–S. Walden–Haverhill Premier 59, Haverhill–S. Walden–Audley End
BELCHAMP HALL, Belchamp Walter, Sudbury *M. M. J. Raymond, Esq.* *map 3 G* Queen Anne period house with period furniture and 17th and 18th cent. family portraits. Garden	5m SW of Sudbury *Stn: Sudbury (4 m)*	By appointment only. May to Sept.—Tues. & Thurs. and Easter, Spring & Summer Bank Hol. Mons.: 2.30–6. Adm. £1.10. Chd. 55p. Reduction for parties. *Sudbury* (0787) 72744	No reasonable public transport
BETH CHATTO GARDENS *map 3 L* **Elmstead Market** *Mrs. Beth Chatto* 5-acre garden, attractively landscaped with many unusual plants in wide range of conditions	4 m E of Colchester on A133 Colchester–Clacton *Stn: Alresford (2 m)*	GARDEN ONLY: all the year—Mons. to Sats. 9–1, 1.30–5 (closed at 4 in winter). *Closed Suns. & Bank Hols. also Sats. Nov. 19 to end of Jan.* Adm. 50p, Chd. free. Adjacent nursery also open. *Parties by arrangement.* No dogs please.	Eastern National 19 Clacton–Colchester–Maldon–Southend. 105, Colchester–Walton (*pass*); 80, 80A, Colchester–Harwich (*alight King's Arms, ¼ m*)
CASTLE HOUSE, Dedham *map 3 L* Home of the late Sir Alfred Munnings, K.C.V.O., President of the Royal Academy 1944–1949. The house and studios contain many paintings, drawings, sketches and other works	¾ m Dedham village, 7 m NE Colchester 2 m E of Ipswich rd (A12)	May 13 to October 14—Weds., Suns. & Bank Hol. Mons.; also Thurs. & Sats. in August; 2–5. Adm. £1, Chd. 25p, O.A.Ps. 50p. Le Talbooth, Gunhill (0206) 322127	E. Counties 207/208 (*not Suns.*), 208/209 (*Suns. only*) Colchester–Stratford St. Mary–Ipswich (*alight Stratford St. Mary, 1½ m*) E. National 87 (*Suns.—summer only*) & 87A (*not Suns.*) Colchester–Dedham
GOSFIELD HALL, Halstead *map 3 L* *Mutual Households Association* Very fine Tudor gallery	2½ m SW of Halstead on Braintree Haverhill rd (A131)	May to September—Weds. & Thurs. 2–5 Adm. 50p, Chd. 25p Free car park. No dogs admitted	National Coach 082, 095, London—Bury St. Edmunds. E. National 310, 311, Halstead—Braintree—Chelmsford (*alight Hall*)
HEDINGHAM CASTLE, Castle Hedingham *The Hon. Thomas & Mrs. Lindsay* *map 3 L* Home of the famous medieval family the de Veres, Earls of Oxford. Besieged by King John and visited by King Henry VII and Queen Elizabeth I. Visitors can see the Garrison Chamber, the Banqueting Hall with Minstrel's Gallery and the beautiful Tudor bridge built in 1496	On B1058 4 m N of Halstead, turn off A604; 9 m N of Braintree; 30 m SE of Cambridge *Stns: Sudbury (7m) Braintree (9m)*	Easter Weekend: Sat. & Sun. 1–5, Mon. 11–5. May to end of Oct.—Daily 10–5. Parties & schools welcome all year round by appointment with the Curator. Adm. £1, Chd. 50p. light refreshments *Hedingham* (0787) 60261 *or* 60804	
HYDE HALL, Rettendon *map 6 B* *Hyde Hall Garden Trust* Varied collection of trees and shrubs, spring bulbs, roses and ornamental greenhouse plants	7 m SE of Chelmsford (off A130)	GARDEN ONLY. Sundays April 15, May 27, June 24 & Aug. 19; 2–7. Other days by appointment. Adm. 75p, Chd. 25p. *In aid of National Gardens' Scheme & Gardeners' & other charities.* Plant stall. Dogs on leads allowed. teas	No reasonable public transport
LAYER MARNEY TOWER, nr Colchester *Major & Mrs. Gerald Charrington* *map 6 B* 1520. Tudor brick house with eight-storey gate tower. Terracotta dolphin cresting and windows. Formal yew hedges, rose bushes and lawns	3 m from Tiptree, 1 m S of B1022, Colchester–Maldon rd	April 1 to Sept. 30— Suns. & Thurs. 2–6; Bank Hols. 11–6; also Tues. 2–6 during July and August. Adm. 80p, Chd. 30p. *Parties other days by prior arrangement* *Colchester* 330202 at the House by arrangement	Eastern National 19 Clacton–Colchester–Maldon–Southend (*alight Roundbush Corner*)

PROPERTY (*showing map reference*)	LOCATION (*with nearest Rly. Stn.*)	OPENING TIMES AND ADMISSION CHARGES CATERING FACILITIES	COACH AND RAIL TOURS BUS SERVICES (*showing alighting points*)
ESSEX—*continued*			
PAYCOCKE'S, Coggeshall (1500) *map 3 L* *The National Trust* Richly ornamented merchant's house, dating from about 1500. Special display of local crafts.	On A120; S side of West St. Coggeshall next to Fleece Inn) 5½ m E of Braintree *Stn: Kelvedon (2½ m)*	April 1 to Oct. 14—Weds., Thurs., Suns. and Bank Hol. Mons.; also Fris. during July & Aug.: 2–5.30. Adm. £1, Chd. (accompanied) half-price. *Parties exceeding six should make prior arrangements with the tenant.* No reduction for parties. No dogs. Wheelchair access. ☕ in Coggeshall	Eastern National 70, Colchester–Braintree
ST. OSYTH'S PRIORY, St. Osyth *map 6 B* *Somerset & Lady Juliet de Chair* Described by "Country Life" as the finest monastic remains in Britain the Priory was an Augustinian Abbey for 400 years until the monasteries were dissolved by Henry VIII in 1537. It was then acquired by Lord D'Arcy, K.G., Controller to Edward VI, and since then has remained in private ownership.	4 m from Clacton, off B1027; 12 m from Colchester; 8 m from Frinton; 30 m from Southend *Stn: Gt. Bentley (4 m)*	Easter weekend then May 1 to Sept. 30. Gardens & Ancient Monuments—Daily 10–5. Whistlejacket Room & Vyntner Hall—Daily 10.30–12.30, 2.30–4.30. Inclusive Adm. £1, Chd. 50p. Car park free.	Buses from Clacton & Colchester
SALING HALL, Great Saling, nr Braintree *Mr. & Mrs. Hugh Johnson* *map 3 L* 12 acre garden: wall garden dated 1698; small park with fine trees, extensive new collection of unusual plants with emphasis on trees; water gardens.	6m NW of Braintree; mid-way between B'tree & Dunmow (A120); turn off N at Saling Oak Inn	GARDEN ONLY: May 16 to July 27 & Sept 5 to Oct. 19—Weds., Thurs. & Fris. 2–5. *Parties other days by arrangement.* Adm. 50p. No dogs please. *In aid of National Gardens' Scheme & Village Church Fund.*	No reasonable public transport
SHALOM HALL, Layer Breton, nr Colchester *Lady Phoebe Hillingdon* *map 6 B* 19th century house containing a collection of 17th and 18th century French furniture and porcelain and portraits by famous English artists including Thomas Gainsborough, Sir Joshua Reynolds etc.	7 m SW of Colchester; 2 m from A12 *Stn: Marks Tey (4½ m)*	August—Monday to Friday 10–1, 2.30–5.30. Adm. free	No reasonable public transport
GLOUCESTERSHIRE			
ARLINGTON MILL, Bibury *map 3 J* *D. C. W. Verey, Esq.* Large 17th-cent. Mill. Old Mill machinery. Country Museum. Staffordshire china. Furniture by Peter Waals. Trout pool. Victorian costumes and furniture. Very pretty village	7 m NE of Cirencester on the Cirencester to Burford rd (A433)	March to October—Daily 10.30–7 or dusk if earlier. Also open weekends in winter. Adm. 80p, Chd. 30p, O.A.Ps. 50p. Pottery and cards for sale ✕ Swan Hotel, Bibury ☎ *Bibury* 368	National excursions from Birmingham and the Midlands
BARNSLEY HOUSE GARDEN, Barnsley nr Cirencester *map 2 M* *Mr. & Mrs. D. C. W. Verey* Garden laid out 1770, trees planted 1840. Re-planned 1960. Many spring bulbs. Laburnum avenue (early June). Lime walk, herbaceous and shrub borders. Ground cover. Knotgarden. Autumn colour. Gothic summerhouse 1770. Classical temple 1780. House 1697 (NOT OPEN). Vegetable garden laid out as decorative potager.	4 m NE of Cirencester on Cirencester to Burford rd (A433) *Stn: Kemble (8 m)*	GARDEN ONLY: All the year—Weds. 10–6 (or dusk if earlier); also first Suns. in May, June & July. *Other days by appointment.* Adm. (March to Nov. inc.) Weds. 75p, O.A.Ps. 50p. Other days £1. Season ticket £2. Dec. to Jan. free. Plants for sale ☎ *Bibury* 281 ☕ The Greyhound Farm House, Barnsley ☎ *Bibury* 406	No reasonable public transport
BATSFORD PARK ARBORETUM, Moreton-in-Marsh *map 3 J* *The Batsford Foundation* Over 1,000 species of different trees in fifty acres of delightful Cotswold countryside overlooking the Vale of Evenlode.	1½ m NW of Moreton-in-Marsh A44 Evesham Rd, turn rt. into Park Drive just prior to Bourton on Hill *Stn: Moreton-in-Marsh (2 m)*	April to Oct.—Daily 10–5, including Bank Hols. Adm. £1, Chd. & O.A.Ps. 50p. *Coach parties by arrangement.* ☎ *Blockley* (0386) 700409 ☕ teas ✕ Hotels & restaurants in Moreton-in-Marsh	No reasonable public transport
BERKELEY CASTLE, nr Bristol *map 2 M* *Mr. & Mrs. R. J. Berkeley* One of the most historic castles, over 800 years old, and still lived in by the Berkeleys. Scene of the murder of Edward II (1327)	S of the town of Berkeley, midway between Bristol and Gloucester, just off A38	April—Daily (exc. Mons.) 2–5, May to August—Tues. to Sats. 11–5; Suns 2–5; *closed Mons.* September—Dail (exc. Mons.) 2–5, October—Suns only 2–4.30. Grounds open until 6 p.m. (5.30 in Oct.) also Bank Hol. Mons. 11–5. Adm. £1.70, Chd. 85p, O.A.Ps. £1.50. *Reduced terms for pre-arranged parties of 25 or over—apply Custodian* ☕ (✕ to order) at Castle ☎ *Berkeley* (0453) 810332	National tours from Bournemouth & Cheltenham Coliseum Coaches tours from Southampton Tours from W. Country, S. Wales and Midlands Venture Travel tours from London Bristol X20, Bristol–Berkeley–Gloucester (*every 2 hours*) (*not Suns.*)
CHAVENAGE, Tetbury *map 2 M* *David Lowsley-Williams, Esq.* Elizabethan Cotswold manor house with Cromwellian associations. Contents include 2 tapestried rooms. Also medieval Cotswold Barn	2 m N of Tetbury signposted off A46 B4014	Easter Bank Hol. then May to September—Thurs., Suns & Bank Hols. 2–5. Adm. £1, Chd. half price. *Previous notice of parties would be appreciated.* ☎ *Tetbury* 52329	Bristol 429 Malmesbury–Tetbury–Stroud (*not Suns*) (*alight Chavenage crossroads*, 1 *m*)
DEAN HALL, Littledean *map 2 M* *D. M. Macer-Wright, Esq.* Legend has it that a house has occupied the site since Roman times. Denes Hall was built for the Dene family, Lords of Dene from 1080 to 1327. Medieval core stands over remains of Saxon manorial church, the east wing added c. 1300. Gardens.	12 W of Gloucester; 2m E of Cinderford; 600 yds from A4151 on Littledean–Newnham-on-Severn rd., turn at King's Head	Gardens & House: April to Sept.—Daily 2–6. Coach parties by appointment. Adm. £1, Chd. 50p, O.A.Ps. 70p. No dogs. ✕☕ Littledean House Hotel.	National Welsh 31 Gloucester–Cinderford (*alight corner of Newham rd*)
HIDCOTE MANOR GARDEN, *map 3 F* **Hidcote Bartrim, nr Chipping Camden** *The National Trust* One of the most beautiful English gardens	4 m NE of Chipping Campden, 1 m E of A46 & B4081 *Stn: Honeybourne (4½ m)*	April to end of Oct.—Daily (except Tues. & Fris.) 11–8 (last adm. 7 or one hour before sunset). Adm. £1.90, Chd. 95p. *Parties by prior written arrangement only.* No dogs. Wheelchair access to part of garden only ✕☕ coffee, light lunches & cream teas 11–5 ☎ *Mickleton* 333	Midland Red 215, Stratford–Chipping Campden (*not Suns.*) (*alight Mickleton, Hidcote Turn, 1½ m*)
KELMSCOTT MANOR, nr Lechlade *Society of Antiquaries of London* *map 3 J* Cotswold-style manor of 16th and 17th cent. Summer home of William Morris from 1871 until his death in 1896. Original Morris possessions and examples of his designs. Small formal garden	1 m S of B4449, 2 m E of Lechlade, 3 m W of Faringdon	April to September—first Wed. only in each month, 11–1, 2–5. Adm. £2.	Baker's Coaches, Oxford–Lechlade (*alight Kelmscott Turn, ¾ m*)
KIFTSGATE COURT—SEE PAGE 66			
LYDNEY PARK, Lydney *map 2 M* *Viscount Bledisloe* Extensive woodland garden with lakes and a wide selection of fine shrubs and trees. Museums and Roman Temple site. Deer park (picnics)	½ m W of Lydney on A48 *Stn: Lydney (1½ m)*	Easter Sun. to Sun. June 10—all Suns., Weds. & Bank Hols. and daily May 27 to June 3: 11–6. Adm. £1, Chd. (under 15 yrs.) & parking free. Parties of 30 or more by appointment any day from Easter to June 10 (thereafter Roman site and Museum by appointment). Picnics. Fine shrubs for sale. ☕ at the house ☎ *Dean* 42844 (*Secretary*) ✕ in Lydney	National Welsh 731 Gloucester–Chepstow (*passes drive*)

BERKELEY  CASTLE GLOUCESTERSHIRE

Built in 1153, the castle stands in a state of perfect preservation. This, the oldest inhabited castle in England, has everything one expects to find in such an historic building.

Here is the massive Norman Keep, Dungeon, Great Hall and Kitchen, and the cell which was the SCENE OF THE MURDER OF KING EDWARD II.

The State Apartments contain a magnificent collection of furniture, rare paintings and tapestries. Part of the world-famous Berkeley silver is also on display. The lovely Elizabethan Terraced Gardens, with an ancient bowling alley, overlook the water-meadows, the Kennels of the Berkeley Hounds and, beyond, the Deer Park with its Red and Fallow Deer. Picnic area adjacent to coach and car parks.

The WILDFOWL TRUST is on the Estate 5 miles from the Castle.

John Bethell photograph

The Castle and Gardens are open to the public: April—Daily (except Mondays) 2—5. May to August—Weekdays (except Mondays) 11—5; Sundays 2—5. September—Daily (except Mondays) 2—5. October—Sundays only 2—4.30. Also Bank Holiday Mondays 11—5.

Refreshments and afternoon teas available.
Luncheons, to order only, for parties of 20 or more persons. Free Coach and Car Park. Dogs not allowed.

Charge for admission £1.70, *O.A.Ps.* £1.50. *Children* 85*p. Reductions for pre-arranged parties of* 25 *or over.* Special times arranged for organised parties.

For further information apply to the Custodian. Berkeley Castle, Glos. (stamped addressed envelope please). Telephone 0453 810332.

ENGLAND'S MOST HISTORIC HOME

BATSFORD PARK ARBORETUM

MORETON IN MARSH, GLOUCESTERSHIRE

Delightful scenic walks in fifty acres of glorious wooded countryside. Over a 1000 different species of trees, unique collection of bamboos, exotic shrubs and bronze statues from the Orient.

Picnic and play areas Toilets. Shop. Nursery. Teas & Garden Centre. Free parking.

Open daily April to October, 10 a.m.–5 p.m. (inc. Bank Hols).

Adults £1. Children & O.A.Ps 50p. (Coach parties by arrangement) Telephone: Blockley (0386) 700409.

LYDNEY PARK GARDENS

GLOUCESTERSHIRE

Extensive Rhododendron, Azalea and Flowering Shrub Gardens in Lakeland Valley. Garden around the House with Magnolias and Daffodils. Fine views across the Severn. Museums and Roman Temple Site.

OPENING TIMES OPPOSITE

DEAN HALL

LITTLE DEAN, GLOUCESTERSHIRE

Legend has it that a house has stood here since Roman times and recent research indicates that settlement continuity is likely, with the house standing over the remains of a substantial Roman building. Denes Hall was built for the Dene family, descendants of the Barons of Pontaudemer and Lords of Dene from at least 1080 until 1327. The house is particularly ancient, the North front encloses the remains of a 12th century hall which appears to be a conversion of a Saxon church constructed on top of the ruined Roman walls. The East wing, formerly an open hall, dates from the late 13th century. It is planned that from 1984 more of the early fabric of this remarkable house will be available for viewing. There are fine panelled rooms in the Jacobean front. The cellars were opened in 1983 where remains of the Norman undercroft and Saxon and Roman walls can be seen. Grounds include terraced lawns, magnificent trees and water garden.

HIDCOTE MANOR GARDEN

GLOUCESTERSHIRE

3 miles from Chipping Campden

THE NATIONAL TRUST

A. H. Lealand photograph

The gardens, among the most beautiful in England, were laid out over a period of forty years by Major Lawrence Johnston and given by him to the Trust in 1948. Hidcote is formed of a series of small gardens, each devoted to some particular kind of flower and enclosed by hedges of many varieties. Visitors will find a number of rare plants collected from distant parts of the world, and from the gardens there are fine views over the Vale of Evesham.

PROPERTY (*showing map reference*)	LOCATION (*with nearest Rly. Stn.*)	OPENING TIMES AND ADMISSION CHARGES CATERING FACILITIES	COACH AND RAIL TOURS BUS SERVICES (*showing alighting points*)
GLOUCESTERSHIRE—*continued*			
KIFTSGATE COURT, nr Chipping Campden *Mrs. J. G. Chambers* *map 3 E* Garden with many unusual shrubs and plants including collection of specie and old fashioned roses	3 m NE of Chipping Campden 1 m E of A46 and B4081 *Stn: Honeybourne (4 m)*	GARDENS ONLY: April 1 to September 30—Weds., Thurs. & Suns. 2–6; also Bank Hols. 2–6. Adm. £1.20, Chd. 40p. *Unusual plants for sale on open days.* Whit. Sun. to Sept. 2	Midland Red 524 Evesham — Stratford-on-Avon (*alight crossroads just south of Mickleton*)
PAINSWICK HOUSE, Painswick *map 2 M* *Baroncino Nicholas de Piro* Formerly the Seat of the Hyetts of Painswick. Fine example of Palladian architecture with magnificent rooms, Chinese wallpaper.	Just outside Painswick village; Gloucester 6 m; Cheltenham 10 m; Bristol 35 m	August 1 to 31—Daily 2–6. Coach parties (by appointment—1 week's notice) throughout the year. Adm. £1.50, O.A.Ps. £1, Chd. (14 yrs. & under) free; Granny in a family free. For further information write or telephone. tea available *Painswick* (0452) 813646	Bristol 558, Gloucester–Painswick (*not Suns.*) 564, Cheltenham–Painswick
RYELANDS HOUSE, Taynton *map 2 M* *Captain & Mrs. Eldred Wilson* Garden of 1½ acres with great variety of plants, many rare and unusual; also wild garden and landscaped lake; country walk (Spring only) to see abundance of wild flowers and spectacular views	8 m NW of Gloucester; on B4216 halfway between Huntley (A40) & Newent (B4215)	GARDEN ONLY: Suns. April 1, 8, 15; Easter Sun. & Mon. April 22/23; Suns. April 29; June 10, 17, 24; July 1, 8, 15; Aug. 26; Summer Bank Hol. Mon. Aug. 27: 2–6. Other days for parties by appointment. Adm. 50p, Chd. 15p. Country walk (Spring only) 25p. extra, Chd. 10p. *In aid of National Gardens Scheme & Peoples' Dispensary for Sick Animals.* No dogs in the garden but allowed on leads on Country Walk. Plants for sale. teas	
SEZINCOTE GARDEN, Moreton-in-Marsh *Mr. & Mrs. D. Peake* *map 3 J* Oriental water garden by Repton and Daniell with trees of unusual size. House in "Indian" style inspiration of Royal Pavilion, Brighton.	1½ m W of Moreton-in-Marsh on A44 to Evesham; turn l. by lodge before Bourton-on-the-Hill. *Stn: Moreton-in-Marsh (3½ m)*	GARDEN: Thurs. Fris. & Bank Hol. Mons. 2–6 (or dusk if earlier) throughout year, except Dec. Adm. £1, hd. 20p. HOUSE: May, June, July & Sept.—Thurs. & Fris. 2.30–6. Parties by appointment. Adm. House & Garden £2. No children or dogs. Hotels & restaurants in Moreton-in-Marsh	Oxford–South Midland/Midland Red West 191, Oxford – Chipping Norton – Evesham – Worcester (*alight Bourton-on-the-Hill, 1 m*)
SNOWSHILL MANOR, Broadway *map 3 J* *The National Trust* A Tudor manor house with a later facade containing a unique collection of musical instruments, clocks, toys, etc. Terraced garden	3 m S of Broadway 4 m W of junct of A424 & A44; 6½ m W of Moreton-in-Marsh *Stn : Moreton-in-Marsh (7 m)*	April & Oct.—Sats., Suns. & Easter Mon. 11–1, 2–5. May to end Sept.—Weds. to Suns. & Bank Hol. Mons.: 11–1, 2–6 (or sunset if earlier). Adm. £1.90, Chd. half-price. *Parties of 15 or more by prior written arrangement only. No reductions.* No dogs. Shop. Limited access for wheelchairs. Photographs by permission. No picnics. *Broadway* 852410	Midland Red 259, Evesham–Broadway (3 *m*)
STANWAY HOUSE, nr Broadway *map 3 J* *Lord & Lady Neidpath* Golden-stoned Cotswold Jacobean Manor House in perfect village setting. Gatehouse, Tythe Barn, fine Great Hall and old furniture	1 m off A46 Cheltenham–Broadway rd; on B4077 Toddington – Stow - on - the - Wold rd. M5 jct. 9	June, July & August—Weds. & Suns. 2–6. Flower Show, Saturday, Aug. 18. Adm. £1.50, Chd. 75p. teas in Old Bakehouse on Weds. *Stanton* 469	No reasonable public transport
SUDELEY CASTLE, Winchcombe *map 2 M* *The Lady Ashcombe* Beautiful 12th cent. Cotswold home of Queen Katherine Parr, rich in Tudor history. Art treasures include Constable, Rubens and Van Dyck. Beautiful gardens with historic Elizabethan garden as main highlight. Unique Toy and Doll collection. Falconry exhibition with displays every Wednesday and Thursday from May to August	6 m NE of Cheltenham on A46. Access A40, A438, M5 (at Tewkesbury turn off)	April to October—Daily (inc. Bank Hols.) 12–5.30. Grounds open from 11. All inclusive adm. £2.80, Chd. £1.60. Special rates for O.A.Ps. and parties. Free car parking. Winter period—Weekdays by appointment for parties of 20 or more. *Winchcombe* (0242) 602308	National tours from the Midlands and Cheltenham Barton tours from Nottingham Keith Tours from Aylesbury Tours from London, South Wales, etc. Castleway's services from Cheltenham Midland X68 from Stratford-upon-Avon
UPPER SLAUGHTER MANOR HOUSE, Cheltenham *map 2 M* *Eric Turrell, Esq.* Elizabethan manor house part 15th cent. Extensive terraced gardens	2½ m W of Stow-on-the-Wold. *Stn: Kingham (7 m)*	May 4 to September 28—Fris. 2–5.30. Adm. 70p. *Stow-on-the-Wold* (0451) 20927	Pulham's Coaches, Moreton-in-Marsh–Bourton-on-the-Water–Cheltenham (*alight Lower Slaughter Turn, 1¼ m*)
WESTBURY COURT GARDEN *map 2 M* Westbury-on-Severn *The National Trust* A formal water-garden with canals and yew hedges, laid out between 1696 and 1705; the earliest of its kind remaining in England	9 m SW of Gloucester on A48 *Stn: Gloucester (9 m)*	April & October—Sats., Suns. & Easter Mon. 11–5; May to end of Sept.—Daily (except Mons. & Tues. *but open Bank Hol. Mons.*) 11–6. Adm. £1, Chd. 50p. Parties 70p by prior written arrangement only. Picnic area. No dogs. Wheelchairs provided. *Westbury-on-Severn* 461	Nat. Welsh 31, Gloucester–Coleford 73 Gloucester–Cardiff. (*alight gates*)
YEW TREE COTTAGE, Ampney St. Mary *Mrs. B. Shuker & Miss P. Strange* *map 3 J* Garden of one acre with variety of interesting plants throughout the year.	4 m E of Cirencester via A417 to Ampney St. M.; at Red Lion P.H. turn off N, then 1st l. Cottage 1st r. in village	GARDEN ONLY: Sun. April 1; Easter Sun & Mon. April 22/23; Suns. May 20, June 17, July 15 & Aug. 26: 2–6. Weds., throughout the year, 10–6. Open at other times by appointment. Adm. 30p, Chd. free. *In aid of National Gardens' Scheme & Sue Ryder Foundation, Leckhampton.* Plants for sale. teas—Suns. only *Poulton* (028 585) 333	
GREATER MANCHESTER			
DUNHAM MASSEY HALL—SEE UNDER CHESHIRE			
FLETCHER MOSS, Didsbury *Manchester City Art Galleries* *map 5 C* A late Georgian and early Victorian parsonage set in pleasant gardens. A local heritage centre displaying works by artists related to the North West.	5 m S of City centre on main Wilmslow Road *Stns: East Didsbury (not Suns.); Stockport (3 m)*	April & May—Weds. to Suns. 10–6. *Closed June to March.* Times subject to alteration, please telephone before visit. Adm. free 061-236 9422	Greater Manchester Transport 42, 45, 46, 306, 316
HALL I' TH' WOOD, Bolton *map 5 C* *Bolton Metropolitan Borough* Dating from latter half of the 15th century and furnished throughout in the appropriate period. The Hall, built in the post and plaster styles, dates from 1483, a further extension was added in 1591, the last addition being made in 1648. Home of Samuel Crompton in 1779 when he invented the Spinning Mule. House contains Crompton relics.	In Green Way, off Crompton Way; 2 m NE of town centre off A58 (Crompton Way); signposted *Stn: Bolton*	April to Sept.—Mons. to Sats. 10–6; Suns. 2–6. *Closed Thurs.* Oct. to March—Mons. to Sats. 10–5. *Closed Thurs. & Suns.* Adm. 30p, Chd. (over 8) & O.A.Ps. 20p; Parties of more than 25, 20p per head. School parties free *Bolton* (0204) 51159	*Bus:* 546 from town centre
HEATON HALL, Heaton Park, Prestwich *Manchester City Art Galleries* *map 5 C* Former home of the Earls of Wilton and designed by James Wyatt in 1772 the Hall has a unique decorated interior. Described by Pevsner as one of the finest country houses of its period in the country.	6 m N of City centre *Stns: Heaton Park (not Suns.); Moston (4 m)*	May & June—Weds. to Suns. 10–6. Also open Spring & Summer Bank Hols. *Closed July to April.* Times subject to alteration, please telephone before visit. Adm. free at the Hall 061 236 9422	Greater Manchester Transport 21, 27, 35, 36, 63, 93

KIFTSGATE COURT

MICKLETON, NR. CHIPPING CAMPDEN

Mark Ellidge photograph

A magnificently situated house with fine views and trees. The Garden (adjacent to Hidcote Manor National Trust Garden) was made by Mrs. J. B. Muir between 1920 and 1950 and is carried on by her daughter, Mrs. D. H. Binny and grand-daughter, Mrs. J. G. Chambers.
There are many unusual shrubs and plants and a collection of specie and old-fashioned roses including "Filipes Kiftsgate"—the largest rose in England. Plants from the garden for sale each open day.

PAINSWICK HOUSE

GLOUCESTERSHIRE

Formerly the Seat of the Hyetts of Painswick; now the home of the Baroncino and Baronessina de Piro. This Grade I house, a fine example of Palladian architecture, is worth seeing for its Chinese wallpaper, its magnificent rooms and its beautiful setting, only half a mile outside Painswick village.
Open EVERY DAY IN AUGUST 2.00 p.m. to 6.00 p.m. Admission £1.50, O.A.Ps. £1, Children (14 or under) free. Granny in a family free. Coach parties by appointment (1 week's notice) ALL YEAR ROUND.
For further information please write or telephone Painswick (0452) 813646.

CITY OF MANCHESTER

HEATON HALL

"The finest house of its period in Lancashire and one of the finest in the country" (Pevsner). Designed for the Earl of Wilton by James Wyatt in 1772, the house has sumptuous decorated interiors and commands panoramic views of Manchester. Heaton Hall was Wyatt's first country house commission and a principal example of his classical style. Contents include a range of magnificent state rooms with plasterwork by J. B. Maini, one of the few surviving Etruscan rooms with decorations by Biagio Rebecca, library with fittings by Gillows of Lancaster, an organ built by Samuel Green (1790), furniture, paintings and sculpture of the period.
May and June: Wednesday to Sunday 10–6. Also open Spring and Summer Bank Holidays. *Closed July to April.* Times subject to alteration, please telephone 061-236 9422 before visit.

STANWAY HOUSE

GLOUCESTERSHIRE

"Country Life" photograph

Built of golden Limestone and standing in one of the most perfect of Cotswold villages amid planted parkland, this Jacobean Manor with its exquisite Gatehouse and Tythe Barn has changed ownership only once in the last 1,260 years when it passed from the Abbey of Tewkesbury to the Tracys of Stanway, from whom its present owners, the Earls of Wemyss, descend. Fine furniture (including a Shuffleboard and Chinese Day Beds) contributes to the mellow charm of this typical squire's house.

HALL I' TH' WOOD MUSEUM

Greenway, off Crompton Way, Bolton

Dating from the latter half of the 15th century and furnished throughout in the appropriate period. The Hall itself, built in the post and plaster styles, dates from 1483, a further extension was added in 1591 in the form of a north west wing, the last addition being made in 1648 during the Civil War. Home of Samuel Crompton in 1779 when he invented the Spinning Mule. House contains Crompton relics.

PROPERTY *(showing map reference)*	LOCATION *(with nearest Rly. Stn.)*	OPENING TIMES AND ADMISSION CHARGES CATERING FACILITIES	COACH AND RAIL TOURS BUS SERVICES *(showing alighting points)*

GREATER MANCHESTER—*continued*

PLATT HALL, Platt Fields, Rusholme *map* 5 C *Manchester City Art Galleries* A Georgian country house of the 1760's, designed by John Carr of York and Timothy Lightoler for the Worsleys, it is now the internationally famous Gallery of English Costume, showing the changing styles in clothes and accessories from the 17th century to the present day	In Platt Fields, Rusholme, 2 m S of City on Wilmslow road *Stn: Levenshulme*	April to Sept.—Tues. to Fris. 10–6. *Closed Oct. to March.* Times subject to alteration, please telephone before visit. Adm. free. ☕ in the Park ☎ 061-224 5217	Greater Manchester Transport 3, 40, 41, 42, 43, 44 45, 46, 47, 48, 49, 53, 54, 141, 157, 158
SMITHILLS HALL, Bolton *map* 5 C *Bolton Metropolitan Borough* Dating from the 14th century with later additions. Great Hall with open roof. Fine linenfold panelling. 16th and 17th century furnishings. Grounds contain nature trail and trailside museum.	Off Smithills Dean Rd.; 1½ m NE of town centre off A58 (Moss Bank Way); signposted *Stn: Bolton*	April to Sept.—Mons. to Sats. 10–6; Suns. 2–6. *Closed Thurs.* Oct. to March—Mons. to Sats. 10–5. *Closed Thurs. & Suns.* Adm. 30p, Chd. (over 8) & O.A.Ps. 20p; Parties of more than 25, 20p per head. School parties free ☎ *Bolton* (0204) 41265	*Bus:* 526 from town centre
WYTHENSHAWE HALL, Northenden *Manchester City Art Galleries* *map* 5 C A timber framed and Georgian brick manor house which was the home of the Tatton family for over 500 years. 17th century furniture, oil paintings, arms and armour. Oriental ceramics, hard stone carvings, ivories and Japanese prints.	7 m S of City centre in Wythenshawe Park, on the Altrincham–Stockport rd *Stns: Sale (2¾ m); Gatley (3 m) (not Suns.)*	Aug. & Sept.—Weds. to Suns. 10–6. *Closed Oct. to July.* Times subject to alteration, please telephone before visit. Adm. free. ☕ at the Hall ☎ 061-236 9422	Greater Manchester Transport 101, 102, 114, 116, 294, 295

HAMPSHIRE

ALRESFORD HOUSE, Alresford *map* 3 N *Mr. & Mrs. P. Constable Maxwell* Georgian country house built by Admiral Lord Rodney 1750	8 m E of Winchester on A31 Winchester–Alton rd. *Stn: Winchester (8 m)*	May to Sept.—Weds. to Suns. 2.30–6. Adm. £1. Fruit & vegetables—'Pick Your Own'. Picknicking allowed. Catering facilities available for parties, receptions, etc. by arrangement. ☕ teas in walled garden	Local bus services
AVINGTON PARK, Winchester *map* 3 N Δ *J. B. Hickson, Esq.* Red brick house in the Wren tradition	4 m NE of Winchester, just S of B3047 in Itchen Abbas *Stn: Winchester (4 m)*	May to September—Sats., Suns, & Bank Hols. 2.30–5.30. *Occasionally closed Sats. for wedding receptions.* Adm. £1, Chd. (under 10) 50p. *Other times for large parties by prior arrangement.* ☕ at the House (*Suns. & Bank Hols. only*) ☎ 0962–78 202	Alder Valley 214 (*Mons. to Sats.*); 453 (*Suns. & Bk. Hols.*), Winchester–Itchen Abbas–Alresford–Alton–Guildford (*alight The Plough Inn, Itchen Abbas*) (*connections with other services in Winchester*)
BEAULIEU, Beaulieu *map* 3 N *The Lord Montagu of Beaulieu* Ⓔ Palace House and Gardens, Beaulieu Abbey and Exhibition of Monastic Life and the superb National Motor Museum with more than 200 historic exhibits. Monorail, Veteran Bus Ride, Veteran Car Ride, Transporama, Model Railway, Radio Controlled Veteran Cars. Daily cavalcades of historic vehicles during peak summer season and many other events throughout the year.	In Beaulieu 7 m SE of Lyndhurst, 14 m S of Southampton, 6 m NE of Lymington *Stns: Brockenhurst (6 m); Beaulieu Rd. (3 m) (Suns. May–Sept. only)*	All facilities open throughout the year. Easter to September—Daily 10–6; October to Easter—Daily 10–5. *Closed Christmas Day.* Inclusive admission charge. Reduced rates for Children & O.A.Ps. *Parties at special rates.* ✕☕ at licensed Brabazon Restaurant ☎ *Beaulieu* 612345	National tours from London, Essex, Bournemouth & the Midlands White Line Cruises—regular boat services from Ryde & Yarmouth (I.O.W.) via Buckler's Hard Wilts & Dorset 112, Lymington–Beaulieu–Hythe. Connections at Hythe with ferry & buses from Southampton, services 58 & 59 (Hampshire Bus) at Lymington with buses from Bournemouth 123 direct from Bournemouth (*summer Suns. only; no service winter Suns.*)
BREAMORE HOUSE, nr Fordingbridge Δ *Sir Westrow Hulse, Bt.* *map* 3 N Elizabethan Manor House (1583) with fine Ⓔ collection of paintings, tapestries, furniture. Countryside Museum. Carriage Museum	3 m N of Fordingbridge off the main B'nemouth rd (A338) 8 m S of Salisbury.	April 1 to Sept. 30—Daily (except Mons. & Fris. *but open Bank Hols.*) 2–5.30. Adm. House £1.50, Chd. 80p; Countryside Museum £1.20, Chd. 60p; Carriage Museum 80p, Chd. 40p; COMBINED TICKET £2. Chd. £1. Reduced rates for parties & O.A.Ps. April, May & Sept. *Other times by appointment.* ☕ home-made teas *Downton* (0725) 22270 ✕ Albany Hotel, Fordingbridge	National tours from Bournemouth, Portsmouth and the Midlands Wilts & Dorset X3, X4, 238 Salisbury–Bournemouth (*approx half-hourly*) (*alight Breamore P.O., ¾ m*)
BROADLANDS, Romsey *map* 3 N *The home of Lord Mountbatten* Formerly the home of Lord and Lady Mountbatten and the Victorian Prime Minister Lord Palmerston, it is now the home of Lord and Lady Romsey. Landscape and architecture by 'Capability' Brown. The Mountbatten Exhibition now provides all visitors with a fascinating glimpse of the eventful lives of Lord and Lady Mountbatten	8 m N of Southampton (A3057); entrance from By-pass immediately S of Romsey (A31) *Stn: Romsey (¼ m)*	April to Sept.—Daily 10–6 (last adm. 5 *Closed Mons. except in August, Sept. & Bank Hols.* Adm. (1983 rates) £2.25, Chd. £1, O.A.Ps. £1.70. Reduced rates for parties of 15 or more. Free coach & car park ☎ *Romsey* (0794) 516778 N.B. Special opening & admission arrangements for July 26, 27 & 28—C.L.A. GAME FAIR.	Wilts & Dorset and Hampshire Bus services from Andover, Eastleigh, Salisbury, Southampton & Winchester to Romsey
EXBURY GARDENS, nr Southampton *map* 3 N *E. L de Rothschild, Esq.* Large woodland garden of botanical interest; lovely trees; rhododendrons, azaleas, camellias and other flowering shrubs	Exbury village, 15 m SW of Southampton. Turn S off B3054 Between Beaulieu & Dibden Purlieu	GARDENS ONLY: March 10 to July 15—Weekdays 1–5.30 (last entry); Weekends & Bank Hols. (April to July) 10–5.30 (last entry). Adm. March & end of season 80p, Chd. & O.A.Ps. 40p. April to June £1.50, Chd. 80p, O.A.Ps. 80p (weekdays only), Party rate £1.20. Suns. & Bank Hols. during May £2, Chd. £1, O.A.Ps. £1.50. Dogs on leads allowed. ☕ teas available	Hampshire Bus 58, 59, X8, X9 from Southampton (*alight Blackfield crossroad, 2 m*)
FURZEY GARDENS, Minstead, nr Lyndhurst *map* 3 N Lovely gardens in nearly eight acres of peaceful glades. There are many main attractions including Heathers throughout the year and Azaleas, Rhododendrons, Bluebells, Peonies, Irises and Roses in season, plus many other attractive plants to extend the beauty.	Southampton 10 m, Ringwood 8 m, Lyndhurst 3½ m *Stn: Lyndhurst Rd (4½ m)*	All the year—Daily 10–5. *Closes at dusk in winter.* Adm. Mar.–Oct. £1, Chd. (5–14) years 50p; Nov–Feb. 60p, Chd. (5–14 years) 30p. ☎ *Southampton* (0703) 812464 ✕☕ Compton Arms; Honeysuckle Restaurant	Hampshire Bus 30, 31 from Southampton through villages (*not Suns.*) Wilts & Dorset X2 Southampton–Bournemouth (*alight Castle Malwood stop*)

AVINGTON PARK

WINCHESTER

OPENING TIMES ABOVE

William Cobbett wrote of Avington that it was "one of the prettiest places in the County" and indeed it is true today. Avington Park, where Charles II and George IV both stayed at various times, is an old house enlarged in 1670 by the addition of two wings and a classical Portico surmounted by three Statues. The State Rooms on view include the Ballroom with its magnificent ceiling, the Red Drawing Room, Library etc. Avington Church, one of the most perfect Georgian Churches in Hampshire, is in the grounds close by and may be visited.
The facilities are available for filming or still photography.
The Library is also available for Wedding Receptions, Conferences etc.
Enquiries to the Secretary, Avington Park, Winchester, Hants. Tel.: Itchen Abbas (0962 78) 202.

SMITHILLS HALL MUSEUM

off Smithills Dean Road, Bolton

One of the oldest manor houses in Lancashire, a house has stood on this site since the 14th century. The oldest part of Smithills, the Great Hall, has an open timber roof. Smithills has grown piece by piece over the centuries and such irregularly planned buildings, with the cluster of gables at the west end, gives the hall its present day picturesque effect. Furnished in the styles of the 16th and 17th centuries. Withdrawing room contains linenfold panelling. Grounds contain a nature trail and trailside museum which is open to the public between Easter and October.

BREAMORE HOUSE

Breamore, Hampshire

ELIZABETHAN MANOR HOUSE with fine collection of Works of Art.
COUNTRYSIDE MUSEUM. Exhibition of Rural Arts and Agricultural Machinery.
CARRIAGE MUSEUM. "The Red Rover" and other Coaches.

Combined ticket £2.00, Children £1.00.
Reduced rates for Parties and O.A.Ps. in April, May and September.

OPEN April 1 to September 30: Tuesdays, Wednesday, Thursdays, Saturdays, Sundays and all Holidays: 2.0–5.30 p.m.
Salisbury-Bournemouth road A338. Tea Bar. Free Car Park.

BEAULIEU

Palace House, home of Lord and Lady Montagu — once the Great Gatehouse of Beaulieu Abbey and converted to a residence in 1538. Beaulieu is famous for the National Motor Museum founded by Lord Montagu — one of the most comprehensive Museums of its kind in the world. Over 200 cars, commercial vehicles and motorcycles present the history of road transport from 1895 to the present day. There are also the lovely Ruins of 13th century Beaulieu Abbey and an Exhibition of Monastic Life.

IN THE HEART OF THE NEW FOREST

Special Features include a high-level Monorail, the Transporama sound and vision presentation, the replica 1912 open-topped London Bus, Radio Controlled Model Veteran Cars, the Miniature Veteran Car Ride and Railway World in Miniature. Daily cavalcades of historic vehicles during peak summer season and many other events throughout the year.

Open:
SUMMER: Easter — September 10 a.m. — 6 p.m.
WINTER: October — Easter 10 a.m. — 5 p.m. (Closed Christmas Day).

BROADLANDS ROMSEY

The Home of Lord Mountbatten

Broadlands abounds with historic and royal associations. Formerly the home of Lord and Lady Mountbatten, and the Victorian Prime Minister Lord Palmerston, it is now the home of Lord and Lady Romsey. Landscape and classic Palladian architecture by 'Capability' Brown. Beautiful setting overlooking the River Test. Richly decorated interiors and fine works of art.
The Mountbatten Exhibition.
Housed in the 'William and Mary' stable building, this new and enlarged exhibition and an audio-visual show, traces the eventful lives of Lord and Lady Mountbatten.
The House, Exhibition, riverside lawns and self-service restaurant are open April 1st to September 30, 10 a.m.–6 p.m. (last admissions 5 p.m.). Closed Mondays except in August, September and on Bank Holidays.
All inclusive admission charge.
Enquiries: Tel. Romsey (0794) 516878.

FURZEY GARDENS

WILL SELWOOD
ART & CRAFT GALLERY

MINSTEAD, Nr. LYNDHURST

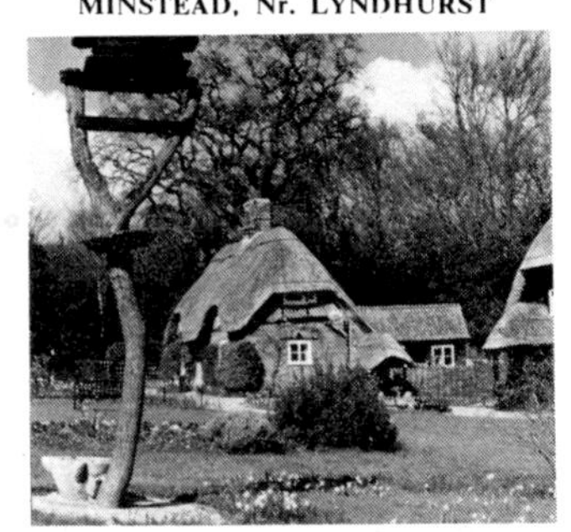

Lovely gardens in eight acres of peaceful glades, there are many main attractions including Heathers throughout the year and Azaleas, Rhododendrons, Bluebells, Peonies, Irises and Roses in season, plus many other attractive plants to extend the beauty. Summer and winter flowering trees are an important feature. Ancient cottage over 400 years old adds to the interest at all times. Gallery displays local arts and crafts of a high standard by 100 craftsmen and 50 artists. Open daily 10 a.m. to 5 p.m. Closes at dusk in winter.

PROPERTY (*showing map reference*)	LOCATION (*with nearest Rly. Stn.*)	OPENING TIMES AND ADMISSION CHARGES CATERING FACILITIES	COACH AND RAIL TOURS BUS SERVICES (*showing alighting points*)
HAMPSHIRE—*continued*			
HOUGHTON LODGE, Stockbridge *map* 3 *N* *Capt. & Mrs. M. W. Busk* From the terrace of this 18th century "cottage orne" the lawns sweep down to the River Test with fine views over the valley. Walled garden, extensive glass houses and vinery with fine displays of flowers. 18th century Folly.	1½ m S of Stockbridge off A30; W of Winchester *Stn: Dunbridge (5 m)*	GARDEN ONLY: March to July—Weds. 2–5. Open Easter Sunday & Monday 2–5. Adm. £1, Chd. 50p. *No dogs.* Plants & produce for sale.	Hampshire Bus 91 Winchester–Houghton (*alight at gates*) *no service Bk. Hols.*)
JANE AUSTEN'S HOME, Chawton *map* 3 *N* *Jane Austen Memorial Trust* Jane Austen's home with many interesting personal relics of herself and her family	1 m SW of Alton off Alton By-Pass sign post Chawton *Stn: Alton* (1 *m*)	All the year—Daily (inc. Suns. & Bank Hols.) 11–4.30. *Closed Mons. & Tues., Nov. to March also Christmas Day & Boxing Day.* Adm. 75p, Chd. (under 14) 25p.	Alder Valley 214 (*Mons. to Sats.*), 453 (*Suns. & Bk. Hols.*). Guildford–Farnham–Alton–Winchester, 259 Alton–E. Tisted–Droxford (*alight Alton*) *By-Pass singpost Chawton*) National Coach, London–Alton–Bournemouth
JENKYN PLACE, Bentley *map* 3 *P* *Mr. & Mrs. G. E. Coke* Beautifully designed garden with large collection of rare plants, including roses, double herbaceous borders	In Bentley 400 yds N of cross roads (sign to Crondall) *Stn: Bentley* (1 *m*)	GARDEN ONLY: Suns., May 6 & 20; June 3 & 17, July 1, 15 & 29; August 12 & 26: 2–6. Also by prior arrangement for organised parties any day of the year. Adm. 75p, Chd. (under 16, accompanied) free. No dogs. *In aid of National Gardens' Scheme.* Car park free. Plants for sale when available.	Alder Valley 214 (*Mons. to Sats.*), 453 (*Suns. & Bk. Hols.*), Guildford–Farnham–Alton–Winchester (*alight village*).
MACPENNY'S, Bransgore, nr Christchurch *Tim Lowndes, Esq.* *map* 3 *N* Large woodland garden. Nurseries, camellias, rhododendrons, azaleas, heathers	4 m NE of Christchurch; 1½ m W of A35 *Stn: Hinton Admiral* (3 *m*)	GARDEN ONLY—all the year daily. Mons. to Sats. 9–12.30, 1.30–5; Suns. 2–5. *Collecting box in aid of National Gardens' Scheme.*	Wilts & Dorset 115/116 Christchurch–Burley (*not Suns.*)
▲MOTTISFONT ABBEY, Mottisfont *map* 3 *N* *The National Trust* Originally a 12th cent. Augustinian Priory. South front 18th cent. Drawing room by Rex Whistler. Fine lawns and trees. Walled garden with Trust's collection of old fashioned roses	4½ m NW Romsey ¾ m W of A3057 *Stn: Dunbridge* (¾ *m*)	April to Sept.: Grounds only—Tues. to Sats. 2.30–6; Whistler Room & Cellarium—Weds. & Sats. 2.30–6. Last adm. 5. *Closed Good Friday.* Adm.: Grounds—June & July £1.20, Chd. 60p; April, May, Aug. & Sept. 90p, Chd. 45p. Whistler Room & Cellarium 30p extra, Chd. 15p extra. Special parties by appointment. All visitors to house are guided (last tour 5.15). Shop. Dogs in main grounds only, on leads. Wheelchairs grounds and cellarium only. ☎ *Lockerley* 40757	Hampshire Bus 64 Romsey–King's Somborne (*very infrequent*) (*alight Mottisfont Stn.,* ¾ *m*) Hampshire Bus connecting services from Southampton & Winchester (*change at Romsey*)
OATES MEMORIAL MUSEUM & GILBERT WHITE MUSEUM, Selborne, nr Alton *map* 3 *P* Gilbert White's home "The Wakes" with exhibitions on Gilbert White and the natural history of Selborne. The Oates Memorial Museum in "The Wakes" includes exhibits on Antarctica (Capt. L. Oates) and exploration in Africa (Frank Oates). 5 acre garden with ha-ha. Old roses bloom June—July; Annuals in August	In main street of Selborne opp. church; 4 m S of Alton on B3006 *Stns: Liss* (5 *m*); *Alton* (5 *m*)	March to Oct.—Daily (except Mons. but open Bank Hol. Mons.) 12–5.30. Last adm. 5. Adm. 80p, Chd. 40p, O.A.Ps. 65p. Reduced rates for pre-booked parties. ☎ *Selborne* (042 050) 275	Bus service (2 *hourly*) (*not Suns.*)
THE PILGRIMS' HALL, Winchester *The Dean & Chapter, Winchester Cathedral* *map* 3 *N* Late 13th century hall with fine hammer-beam roof	In the Cathedral Close *Stn: Winchester* (5 *mins. walk*)	All the year—Daily (except when booked for private meetings, functions etc.). *Parties must give notice in advance.* Adm. free	Hampshire Bus services from Andover, Fareham Petersfield, Romsey, Southampton etc. Alder Valley 214 (*weekdays*), 453 (*Suns. & B. Hols.*) from Guildford & Alton
SANDHAM MEMORIAL CHAPEL *map* 3 *J* [nr. Newbury *The National Trust* Walls covered with paintings by Stanley Spencer depicting war scenes in Salonica	In village of Burghclere 4m S of Newbury ½m E of A34 *Stn: Newbury* (4 *m*)	All the year—Daily 10.30–1, 2–6 (or sunset if earlier). *Closed Good Friday, Christmas Day & New Year's Day* Adm. 40p, Chd. half-price. No reduction for parties. No dogs. Wheelchair access. ☎ *Burghclere* 394 *or* 292	Alder Valley 123, 124 Newbury–Burghclere (*not Suns.*) (*alight Highclere station–closed*)
SPINNERS, Boldre *map* 3 *N* *Mr. & Mrs. P. G. G. Chappell* Garden entirely made by owners; azaleas, rhododendrons interplanted with primulas, blue poppies and other choice woodland and ground cover plants	1½ m N of Lymington *Stn: Lymington Town* (2 *m*)	GARDEN ONLY: April 19 to Sept. 1—Daily (except Mons.) 2–6. *Other times by appointment.* Adm. 50p. No dogs. Many rare plants for sale. ☎ *Lymington* 73347	Wilts & Dorset 112, Hythe–Lymington via Boldre (*not Suns. April & May*) (*connecting with Southampton Ferry & buses at Hythe and at Lymington for Bournemouth*)
STRATFIELD SAYE HOUSE, Reading *map* 3 *J* *The Trustees of the Duke of Wellington* 1630 house filled with the Great Duke's possessions and personality. Wellington Exhibition, State Coach, Great Duke's Funeral Carriage. Grounds, gardens, wildfowl santuary and Copenhagen's grave	1 m W of A33 between Reading & Basingstoke (turn off at Wellington Arms Hotel); signposted. Close to M3 & M4 *Stn: Bramley* (3 *m*)	HOUSE: Sat. April 21 to Sun. Sept. 30—Daily (except Fris.) 11.30–5. House closes 5.30. Wellington Country Park (3 miles from House)—nature trails, adventure playground, animals, boating, fishing etc. also National Dairy Museum: March 1 to Oct. 31—Daily 10–5.30; winter—weekends only. Adm. charges to House & Country Park not available; at time of going to press. Special rates for parties. Free parking. ☕ refreshments ☎ *Basingstoke* (0256) 882882	Stratfield Saye House—Reading Transport Express Coach Service from London & Reading (*Suns. & Bank Hols. only*) Wellington Country Park—Alder Valley services 411 & 412 Reading & Aldershot
THE VYNE, Basingstoke *map* 3 *J* *The National Trust* An important early 16th cent. house with classic portico added 1654. Tudor panelling, 18th century ornamented staircase. Extensive lawns, lake, trees, herbaceous border	4 m N of Basingstoke between Bramley & Sherborne St. John (1½ *m from each*) *Stn: Bramley* (2½ *m*)	April to Oct. 14—Tues., Weds., Thurs., Sats. & Suns. 2–6. Open Bank Hol. Mons. 11–6. Last adm. half-hour before closing. *Closed Tues. following Bank Hol. Mons.* Adm. £1.50, Chd. 75p; Grounds only 70p, Chd. 35p. *Reduced rates for pre-booked parties Tues., Weds. & Thurs. only.* Shop. Dogs in garden only, on leads. Wheelchair provided. ☎ *Basingstoke* 881337 ☕ in the Old Brewhouse (2.30–5.30)	National tour from Southampton Hampshire Bus 334, Basingstoke–Bramley (*weekdays, infrequent*), 337, 338 Basingstoke–Sherborne St. John (1½ *m walk*)
WEST GREEN GARDEN, Hartley Wintney *The National Trust* *map* 3 *K* Delightful, informal garden with lawns, flowering shrubs and herbaceous plants. *House closed for restoration after fire*	1 m W of Hartley Wintney, 1 m N of A30; 10 m Bas'stoke *Stns: Winchfield* (2 *m*); *Hook* (3 *m*)	GARDEN ONLY: April to end of Sept.—Weds., Thurs. & Suns. 2–6 (last adm. half hour before closing). Adm. 70p, Chd. 35p. No reduction for parties. No dogs.	Alder Valley 412, Reading–Hartley Wintney–Aldershot (*alight Hartley Row,* 1½ *m*) 201 Basingstoke–Hartley Wintney–Camberley–Staines (*alight Phoenix Green,* 1*m*)
HEREFORD & WORCESTER			
ABBEY DORE COURT GARDEN, *map* 2 *H* [nr. Hereford *Mrs. C. L. Ward* River and walled garden. Fern border. Herb garden. Herbaceous borders, pool and rockery	3 m off A465 Hereford – Abergavenny rd.	GARDENS ONLY: March 1 to October 31—Daily 10.30–6.30. Adm. 50p. Chd. 25p. Unusual plants & fruit for sale. ☕ refreshments	No reasonable public transport.

JANE AUSTEN'S HOME

CHAWTON, near Alton, Hants.

Jane Austen's home in Chawton, near Alton, contains many interesting personal relics of the famous authoress. It was the scene of the composition of "Mansfield Park," "Emma" and "Persuasion"; and of the revision of "Sense and Sensibility," "Pride and Prejudice" and "Northanger Abbey."

The house is one mile from Alton station and is open all the year daily, including Sundays and Bank Holidays but excluding Mondays and Tuesdays from November to March and Christmas and Boxing Days. Hours of opening: 11 a.m. to 4.30 p.m.

Entrance fee 75p Adults and 25p for Children under 14.

Originally built in the reign of Charles I, the house has been the home of the Dukes of Wellington since it was presented to the Great Duke in 1817. It contains a unique collection of paintings, prints, furniture, effects and personal belongings of this most famous soldier and statesman. Other features include: The Wellington Exhibition, an insight into the life and times of the Great Duke; 'The Last Journey', a special display featuring the Great Duke's magnificent Funeral Carriage; The State Coach; gardens, wildfowl sanctuary and Copenhagen's Grave. OPEN 1984 daily excluding Fridays from Easter Saturday to the last Sunday in September: 11.30 a.m. to 5.00 p.m. (House closes 5.30 p.m.). Just 3 miles from the House, within a peaceful rural setting, is Wellington Country Park which has been developed with many leisure facilities and includes the National Dairy Museum. OPEN daily March 1st to October 31st and at winter weekends. Both House and Park have special rates for group parties. Free parking. Refreshments.

STRATFIELD SAYE HOUSE

A personal insight into the private life of the first Duke of Wellington

Situated on the Hampshire/Berkshire borders, signposted off A33 equidistant Reading/Basingstoke, close to M4 and M3.
For further details please write to Wellington Enterprises, The Wellington Office (H84), Stratfield Saye, Reading, RG7 2BT. Tel: Basingstoke (0256) 882882.

THE VYNE

Sherborne St. John Hampshire

THE NATIONAL TRUST

A. F. Kersting photograph

Built for Lord Sandys, Henry VIII's Lord Chamberlain, of diapered red brick. The Vyne dates from the early 16th century. Both the Chapel with Renaissance glass and the Long Gallery of elaborate linenfold panelling are of this period. Extensive alterations were made in 1654 when John Webb built the earliest classical portico to a country house in England. The Palladian staircase and some of the rococo rooms date from the 1760s. The Vyne was bought after the Civil War from the Sandys family by Chaloner Chute, Speaker of the House of Commons in 1659, and remained in the Chute family until left to the Trust in 1956 by Sir Charles Chute, Bt.

OPENING TIMES OPPOSITE

History in Three Dimensions

Here's a remarkable collection of buildings spanning no less than seven centuries of social history.
You can walk around and inside all of them. You can see some in action – like the windmill and the forge.
There's fifteen acres of beautiful grounds, a free picnic area, car and coach park; a cafeteria and a shop.
School and college parties especially welcome.
For full details and latest brochure please contact:–

AVONCROFT
MUSEUM OF BUILDINGS
MG, Stoke Heath, Bromsgrove,
Worcestershire B60 4JR
Tel: Bromsgrove 31886/31363

MOTTISFONT ABBEY

NR. ROMSEY, HAMPSHIRE

THE NATIONAL TRUST

A. F. Kersting photograph

Mottisfont Abbey dates from the late years of the 12th century and was, until the Dissolution, an Augustinian Priory. It was then acquired by Lord Sandys, Henry VIII's Lord Chamberlain, who converted it to private use. The house underwent major changes in the reigns of the first two Georges. *Trompe l'oeil* painting in the "Gothick" manner by Rex Whistler in the Drawing Room. Grounds bordered by river Test.

BERRINGTON HALL

Leominster

THE NATIONAL TRUST

"Country Life" photograph

Built 1778–1781 by Henry Holland, the architect of Carlton House, London. Painted and plaster ceilings. The park was laid out by "Capability" Brown.

OPENING TIMES OPPOSITE

PROPERTY (*showing map reference*)	LOCATION (*with nearest Rly. Stn.*)	OPENING TIMES AND ADMISSION CHARGES CATERING FACILITIES	COACH AND RAIL TOURS BUS SERVICES (*showing alighting points*)
HEREFORD & WORCESTER—*continued*			
AVONCROFT MUSEUM OF BUILDINGS **Stoke Heath, Bromsgrove** *map 2 H* *Council of Management* An open-air Museum containing buildings of great interest and variety. Exhibits include a working windmill, 15th and 16th century timber-framed houses, a cockpit theatre, two great 14th century roofs, a 1946 prefab and a new exhibit—an 18th century ice house	At Stoke Heath 2 m SE of Bromsgrove off A38 (new Bromsgrove by-pass) between junctions 4 & 5 of M5	March to November—Daily 10.30–5.30 (or dusk if earler). *Closed Mons., March & Nov.* Adm. £1.20, Chd. 65p, O.A.Ps. 80p. *Parties at rates by arrangement.* Free car park & picnic site. refreshments at Museum tea room (*April to Sept., daily; Oct. weekends & by arrangement*) *Bromsgrove* 31886 *or* 31363	Midland Red 144 Birmingham–Worcester (*alight at Stoke Turn*)
BERRINGTON HALL, Leominster *map 2 H* *The National Trust* Built 1778–1781 by Henry Holland, the architect of Carlton House. Painted and plaster ceilings. "Capability" Brown laid out the park	3 m N Leominster ½ m W of A49 *Stn:Leominster* (4 *m*)	May to end of Sept.—Weds to Suns. & Bank Hol. Mons 2–6. April & Oct.—Sats., Suns. & Easter Mon. 2–5 (or sunset if earlier). Adm. £1.40, Chd. half-price. Parties of 15 or more 95p (by prior written arrangement only). Joint ticket with Croft Castle £2, Chd. half-price; Parties £1.35 (by prior written arrangement only). *Other times during these months by written arrangement only.* No dogs. Wheelchairs provided. Indoor photography by prior written arrangement only. tearoom at Hall 3–5.30 *Leominster* 5721	Midland Red X92, 292 to Luston (2 *m*)
BREDON SPRINGS, Ashton-under-Hill, nr Evesham *map 2 H* *Ronald Sidwell, Esq.* 1½-acre garden. Large plant collection in natural setting	6 m SW of Evesham, turn off A435; in Ashton turn r. then 1st l.	GARDEN ONLY: March 31 to Oct. 28—Weds., Sats., Suns., also Bank Hol. Mons. & Tues. 10–dusk. Adm. 40p (Chd. free). *In aid of National Gardens' Scheme.* Coach parties alight at church—6 mins. walk through churchyard and over 2 fields. Limited parking at house. Plants for sale. Dogs welcome	Bristol 535, Evesham–Gloucester Midland Red/Bristol 540, Evesham–Cheltenham (*alight Ashton-u-Hill* 1 *m*) (*not Suns. or B. Hols.*)
BRILLEY, CWMMAU FARMHOUSE, Whitney-on-Wye, *map 2 G* *The National Trust* Early 17th century timber-framed and stone tiled farmhouse	4 m SW of Kington between A4111 and A438. Approached by a long narrow lane	Easter, Spring & Summer Bank Hols. only—Sats., Suns. & Mons. 2–6. *At other times by prior written appointment with Mr. S. M. Joyce.* Not open May Day Bank Hol. weekend. Adm. 60p. *No reduction for parties.* No dogs. Unsuitable for wheelchairs & coaches Picnics only by prior arrangement with the tenant.	No reasonable public transport
BROBURY GARDEN & GALLERY, Brobury, nr Hereford *map 2 H* *Eugene Okarma, Esq.* 5 acres of garden around a 100 years' old house on the banks of the River Wye. Spacious lawns, rock gardens, terraces herbaceous borders; mature conifers. The Gallery specialises in old prints and 19th and 20th century watercolours.	11 m W of Hereford, off A438; signposted Brobury/Bredwardine. *Stn: Hereford* (51*m*)	GARDEN: May to Sept.—Mons. to Sats. 9–5. Adm. 75p, Chd. 40p GALLERY open all the year—Mons. to Sats. 9–5 (closes at 4 in winter). Adm. free. *Moccas* (09817) 229 The Swan Inn, Letton The Red Lion, Breadwardine	No reasonable public transport
BURTON COURT, Eardisland *map 2 H* *Lt.-Cmdr. & Mrs. R. M. Simpson* 14th century Great Hall. European and Oriental Costume. Working model fairground	5 m W of Leominster; between A44 & A4112	Whitsun to mid-Sept.—Weds., Thurs., Sats., Suns. & Bank Hol. Mons.: 2.30–6. Adm. 75p, Chd. 35p. Coach parties 60p. Coach parties catered for. Teas	Primrose Motors, Leominster–Kington (*alight Eardisland* 1 *m*) (*not Suns.*)
THE COMMANDERY Sidbury, Worcester *City of Worcester* *map 2 H* Late 15th century timber-framed hospital. Fine Great Hall, wall paintings, displays on the history of Worcester from earliest times (including the Civil War) and exhibitions. Walled gardens and canal-side terrace	In Worcester *Stns: Worcester Shrub Hill & Foregate St.*	Open all the year—Tues. to Sats. 10.30–5; Suns. (April to Sept.) 3–6. Open Bank Hol. Mons from Easter to August inc. *Closed Good Friday, Christmas & New Year.* Admission free. light refreshments available 0905 25371	City Centre services
CROFT CASTLE, nr Leominster *map 2 H* *The National Trust* Welsh Border castle mentioned in Domesday. Inhabited by the Croft family for 900 years	5 m NW of Leominster just N of B4362 signposted from Ludlow Rd (A49) *Stns: Leominster* (7 *m*); *Ludlow* (9 *m*)	April & Oct.—Sats., Suns. & Easter Mon. 2–5, May to Sept.—Weds. to Suns. & Bank Hol. Mons. 2–6. Adm. £1.30, Chd. 65p; Parties 90p. Joint ticket with Berrington Hall £2, Chd. £1; Parties £1.35. No dogs. Wheelchairs provided. *Yarpole* 246	Primrose Motors, Leominster—Presteigne (*infrequent; not Suns.*) (*alight Cock Gate crossrds.*) Midland Red West X92, 292 to Gorbett Park (3 *m*)
DINMORE MANOR, nr Hereford *map 2 H* *G. H. Murray, Esq.* 14th cent. Chapel also cloisters, "Music Room" and rock garden	6 m N of Hereford on Leominster rd (A49) *Stns : Leominster* (7 *m*); *Ludlow* (9 *m*)	All the year—Daily (except Christmas Day & Boxing Day) 2–6. Adm. 50p, Chd. & O.A.Ps. 25p. *Garden, Chapel & Music Room only open.* café at Dinmore Hill	Midland Red 434, 435, Hereford–Leominster (*alight Dinmore Manor turning,* 1 *m*)

BROBURY GARDEN & GALLERY

BROBURY, HEREFORDSHIRE

Five acres of gardens around a 100 year old house built on the banks of the River Wye. Spacious lawns, rock gardens, terraces and herbaceous borders laid out to feature splendid views and a wide variety of mature conifers. Also a nature path on the river bank.

The Gallery specialises in old prints, from simple topographical views to Rembrandt etchings. Many thousands in stock arranged for easy viewing. Also large collection of 19th and 20th century watercolours.

OPENING TIMES ABOVE

THE COMMANDERY

SIDBURY, WORCESTER

A pre-Reformation hospital converted into a house in 1540. Fine Great Hall, Solar and late 15th century wall paintings. The Royalist headquarters during the Battle of Worcester in 1651. The Commandery now contains important collections of Civil War material as well as the History of Worcester from Roman times, Craft and Industrial Displays, Furniture and Pictures.

Open all the year: for details see above

HISTORIC BISHOPS' HOUSES

AUCKLAND CASTLE

Home of the Bishops of Durham
See page 56

FARNHAM CASTLE

Former home of the Bishops of Winchester and Guildford
See page 136

HARTLEBURY CASTLE

Home of the Bishops of Worcester
See page 74

THE PALACE, WELLS

Home of the Bishops of Bath and Wells
See page 124

Church Commissioners

These properties are among several bishops' houses which have not only been in continuous Church ownership for centuries but are also buildings of great historic and architectural interest. They are now owned by the Church Commissioners.

HEREFORD & WORCESTER—*continued*

PROPERTY (*showing map reference*)	LOCATION (*with nearest Rly. Stn.*)	OPENING TIMES AND ADMISSION CHARGES CATERING FACILITIES	COACH AND RAIL TOURS BUS SERVICES (*showing alighting points*)
EASTNOR CASTLE, nr Ledbury *map 2 H* *The Hon. Mrs. Hervey-Bathurst* Excellent specimen of 19th cent. castellated architecture containing armour, pictures etc. Arboretum	5 m from M50 (exit 2) 2 m E of Ledbury on Hereford-Tewkesbury rd A438 *Stn: Ledbury 2 m*	Bank Hol. Mons.: Easter, May 7, Spring & Summer; Suns. May 20 to Sept. 23; also Weds. & Thurs. in July & Aug.: 2.15–5.30. Adm. £1, Chd. & O.A.Ps. 50p. *Parties by appointment only any day April to Sept.* ☕ at the Castle ☎ *Ledbury* 2304	
THE GREYFRIARS, Worcester *map 2 H* Δ *The National Trust* A timber-framed house built 1480 for the then adjoining Franciscan Friary	In Friar Street Worcester *Stn: Worcester Foregate Street (¼ m)*	May to end of Sept.—first Wed. in each month 2–6. Other times adult parties of 15 or more by written application only. Adm. £1, Chd. 50p; Parties, 70p. Parties of children (inc. schools) not admitted. No dogs. Unsuitable for wheelchairs. ☎ *Worcester* 23571	Midland Red from Birmingham and all parts of Worcs.
HANBURY HALL, nr Droitwich *map 2 H* *The National Trust* Wren style red brick house c. 1700. Outstanding painted ceilings and staircase by Thornhill. The Watney Collection of porcelain; contemporary Orangery	3½ m E of Droitwich, 1 m N of B4090, turn left for Hanbury Church, entrance 1 m on left *Stn: Droitwich Spa (4 m)*	April to Oct.—Sats., Suns. & Easter Mon. 2–5, May to Sept. 30—Weds. to Suns. & Bank Hol. Mons. 2–6. *Closed Good Friday.* Adm. £1.30, Chd. 65p. *Parties all the year by prior written arrangement,* 90p *per person.* Shop. No dogs. Wheelchairs provided. Braille guidebook available. ☕ teas in the house ☎ *Hanbury* 214	Midland Red 339, Bromsgrove–Hanbury; 340 Worcester–Hanbury (*alight Hanbury 1 m*) (*not Suns.*)
HARTLEBURY CASTLE, nr Kidderminster *The Bishop of Worcester* *map 2 H* Historic home of the Bishops of Worcester for over 1,000 years. Fortified in 13th century, rebuilt after sacking in the Civil War and Gothicised in 18th century. State Rooms include mediaeval Great Hall, Hurd Library and Saloon. Fine plaster-work and interesting portraits. Also County Museum in North Wing.	In village of Hartlebury. 5 m S of Kidderminster, 10 m N of Worcester off A449	STATE ROOMS: April 22 to Sept. 2—Bank Hol. Suns., Mons. & Tues. (except May 8); first Sun. in every month (also June 24) & Weds. (except May 2): 2–5. Adm. 35p, Chd. 20p. Guided tours for parties of 30 or more on weekdays by arrangement. Adm. 75p, Chd. 25p. ☎ *Hartlebury* (0299) 250410 ☕ refreshments available (except Weds.). COUNTY MUSEUM: March to Oct.—Mons. to Fris. 2–5; Suns. 2–6; Bank Hols. 11–5. *Closed Good Friday.* Adm. 40p, Chd. 20p. Family tickets (2 adults & up to 3 children) £1. School parties free. Picnic area. ☎ *Hartlebury* (0299) 250416 ☕ Café	Midland Red 315 Worcester–Kidderminster (*alight in village then 10 mins. walk*)
HELLEN'S, Much Marcle *map 2 M* Δ *The Pennington-Mellor-Munthe Trust* Manorial house lived in since 1292. Visited by Black Prince and Bloody Mary	In village of Much Marcle on Ledbury-Ross rd Entrance opp. church	Easter to Oct. 2—Weds., Sats. & Suns. 2–6 (guided tours each hour). *Other times by written appointment with the Custodian.* Adm. £1. Chd. (must be accompanied by adult) 50p. ☕ teas by prior arrangement	No reasonable public transport
HERGEST CROFT GARDENS, Kington *W. L. & R. A. Banks, Esq.* *map 2 G* 50 acres of trees, shrubs, rhododendrons and azaleas from all over the temperate world	On outskirts W of Kington off Rhayader rd. (A44) (*signposted to Hergest at W end of bypass*)	GARDENS ONLY: April 21 to Sept. 16—Daily; Oct.—Suns.; 1.30–6.30. Adm. £1, Chd. 40p. Reduced rates for pre-booked parties of over 20. ☕ home-made teas for parties of over 20 by arrangement ☎ *Kington* (0544) 230218 *or* 230160	Yeoman's Hereford–Kington Primrose Leominster–Kington
KENTCHURCH COURT, Hereford *map 2 M* *J. E. S. Lucas-Scudamore, Esq.* Fortified border manor house altered by Nash. Gateway and part of the original 14th century house still survives. Pictures and Grinling Gibbons carving. Owen Glendower's tower	Off B4347; 3 m SE of Pontrilas, 12 m Monmouth, 14 m Hereford, 14 m Abergavenny; on left bank River Monnow	May to September. *Parties only, by appointment.* Adm. £1, Chd. 50p. ☎ *Golden Valley* 240228 ☕ Temple Inn, Ewyas Harold	
LITTLE MALVERN COURT *map 2 H* *T. M. Berington, Esq.* 14th century Prior's Hall. Paintings, needlework	3 m S of Gt. Malvern on Upton-on-Severn road (A4104)	May to September—By appointment. Adm. 50p. Mrs. Berington ☎ *Malvern* (06845) 4580	No reasonable public transport.
LOWER BROCKHAMPTON, Bromyard *The National Trust* *map 2 H* Small half-timbered manor house c. 1400 with unusual detached 15th century gate house and ruins of 12th century chapel	2 m E of Bromyard N of A44 Bromyard-Worcester rd	Medieval Hall only: April to end of Oct.—Weds., Thurs., Fris. (except Good Friday), Sats. & Bank Hol. Mons. 10–1, 2–6; also Suns. 10–1. Other months by previous written appointment only. Adm. (to Medieval Hall only) 75p, Chd. 35p; Parties 50p per person by prior written arrangement only. N.B. Hall reached by rough narrow road through 1½m woods & farmland. No dogs. Wheelchair access. ☎ *Bromyard 2258*	Midland Red 420, Hereford–Bromyard–Worcester (*alight Bromyard Lodge, 1 m*)
MOCCAS COURT, Moccas *map 2 H* *R. T. G. Chester-Master, Esq.* Designed by Adam, built by Keck in 1775 and has been in the ownership of the Cornewalls, and the present owner, for three centuries. The House stands in 'Capability' Brown Parkland on the south bank of the River Wye	13 m W of Hereford by River Wye. 1 m off B4352	HOUSE & GARDENS: April to Sept.—Thurs. 2–6. Adm. 80p. Parties over 20 on other days by arrangement at special rates. Picnics in garden allowed. ✕ Red Lion Hotel, Bredwardine ☎ *Moccas* (098 17) 381	No reasonable public transport
THE PRIORY, Kemerton *map 2 H* *Mr. & the Hon. Mrs. Peter Healing* 4 acre garden; main features are long herbaceous borders planned in colour groups; stream and sunken garden; many interesting and unusual plants and shrubs.	NE of Tewkesbury; turn off A435 (Evesham-Cheltenham) at Beckford	GARDEN ONLY: May 3 to Sept. 27—Thurs.; also Suns. May 27, June 24, July 15, Aug. 5 & 26; Sept. 9: 2–7. Adm. 50p, Chd. 20p. *In aid of National Gardens' Scheme & other charities.* Plants for sale.	No reasonable public transport
SPETCHLEY PARK, Worcester *map 2 H* *Mr. & Mrs. R. J. Berkeley* 30 acres of trees, shrubs and plants. Red and fallow deer in park	3 m E of Worcester on Stratford-upon-Avon Road (A422)	Gardens & Garden Centre: April 1 to Sept. 30.—Daily (except Sats.) 11–5; Suns. 2–5.30; Bank Hol. Mons. 11–5.30. Garden Centre open also March—Mons. to Fris. 11–5. *At other times by appointment.* Adm. £1.10, Chd. 50p. Regret no dogs. ☕ in the garden (*Suns. & Bank Hols.*)	Dudley's Coaches, Worcester–Inkberrow (*alight at gates*)
STONE HOUSE COTTAGE GARDENS, Kidderminster *map 2 H* *Major & The Hon. Mrs. Arbuthnott* Sheltered wall garden. Rare wall shrubs and climbers also interesting herbaceous plants. Adjacent Nursery.	2 m SE of Kidderminster on A448 to Bromsgrove; next to Stone Church. *Stn: Kidderminster (2 m)*	GARDEN & NURSERY ONLY: March to Dec.—Weds., Thurs., Fris. & Sats. Also Sun. & Mon. May 27/28; Suns. June 24 & July 15; Sun. & Mon. Aug. 26/27. Coaches by appointment only. Adm. Suns. 50p (*for N.G.S.*); other days valuntary contribution *in aid of National Gardens' Scheme.* ☎ *Kidderminster* 69902 ✕☕ Stone Manor Hotel	
THE WEIR, Swainshill *map 2 H* *The National Trust* Spring garden with fine views of the river Wye and the Welsh and Monmouthshire hills from the cliff garden walks	5 m W of Hereford on A438 *Stn: Hereford (5 m)*	April to May 8—Daily (except Sats & Good Friday). May 9 to end of Oct.—Weds. & Bank Hol. Mons. 2–6. Adm. 50p. No reduction for parties. No coach parties. No dogs. Unsuitable for wheelchairs or visually handicapped.	No reasonable public transport

HERTFORDSHIRE

PROPERTY	LOCATION	OPENING TIMES	COACH AND RAIL TOURS
ASHRIDGE, Berkhamsted *map 3 K* *Governors of Ashridge Management College* Early Gothic revival. Begun 1808 by James Wyatt for 7th Earl of Bridgewater. 13th cent. Crypt. Tudor barn. Gardens landscaped by Repton	3½ m N of Berkhamsted (A41), 1 m S of Little Gaddesden *Stns: Berkhamsted (3 m); Tring (3 m)*	GARDENS open April to Oct.—Sats. & Suns. 2–6. Adm. 40p, Chd. 20p. House fully open some weekends & partially on others during the summer; please telephone for further information. Adm. House & Gardens 70p, Chd. 35p. ☎ *Little Gaddesden* (044 284) 3491	Green Line 706 to Berkhamsted, 708, 719 to Hemel Hempstead London Country 317, Hemel Hempstead–Berkhamsted

CROFT CASTLE

near Leominster, Herefordshire

THE NATIONAL TRUST

Edwin Smith photograph

Croft Castle has been the property of the Croft family since Domesday with an intermission of 170 years until acquired by the Trust in 1957. The House retains its ancient walls and four round corner towers of pink stone dating from the 14th or 15th century, but was modified in the 16th, 17th and again in the mid 18th century when the fine Gothic staircase and ceilings were added. Fine Chestnut, Beech and Oak Avenues.

OPENING TIMES SEE PAGE 72

The Castle from the West showing British Camp in background

EASTNOR CASTLE

LEDBURY, HEREFORDSHIRE

Built in 1814 by John, 1st Earl Somers. Contains superb collection of armour, tapestries, pictures and carved furniture. Stands in spacious grounds with specimen trees and beautiful views. The BBC series "The Pallisers" and "Little Lord Fauntleroy" were filmed here.

The Castle will be open to visitors on Bank Holiday Mondays: Easter, May 7, Spring & Summer; Sundays from May 20 to September 23 and Wednesdays & Thursdays in July & August 2.15 p.m.–5.30 p.m.

Also parties by appointment only any day April to September, inclusive. Write or phone: Ledbury 2304.

HELLEN'S

MUCH MARCLE, HEREFORDSHIRE

Ancient manorial house of brick and stone, begun 1292. Contains "Great Hall" with stone table at which Black Prince dined and bedroom prepared for Queen "Bloody Mary" in 1554. Much original furnishings and 19th century carriages.

Easter to October 3rd. Visitors are guided at each hour 2 p.m. to 6 p.m. Wed., Sat. and Sun. or by special appointment with the Custodian in writing. Admission £1, Children 50p (must be accompanied by an adult). Teas by previous arrangement.

HERGEST CROFT

GARDENS, KINGTON, HEREFORDSHIRE

"Country Life" photograph

The gardens of fifty acres contain "one of the finest and most thriving collections of exotic trees in the British Isles". Many of the trees and shrubs brought back from China in the early 1900's have grown to great size and the scope of the collection continues to expand with many recently introduced species. The wide range of maples and birches have been named as National Collections of these two genera. The trees are underplanted with rhododendrons and azaleas which include many rare species, some now more than thirty feet tall.

The gardens are a rare survival of the school of William Robinson, in addition to the woodland garden there is a traditional kitchen garden, conservatory and herbaceous borders which are at their best in the summer months. From spring bulbs to autumn colour in October the gardens have much to interest the visitor at any season.

Open daily April 21st to September 16th and Sundays in October: 1.30 p.m.–6.30 p.m. Admission £1, Children 40p. Reduced rates for pre-booked parties over 20.

Telephone: Kington (0544) 230218/230160.

SPETCHLEY PARK

WORCESTER

Home of Mr. and Mrs. R. J. Berkeley

This garden, extending over nearly 30 acres, is one of the finest in the country and it contains many fine trees and rare shrubs and plants. Particularly beautiful in April, May and June but also a show of colour throughout the summer. The park contains Red and Fallow deer. Plants and shrubs for sale at Garden Centre. Teas in garden on Sundays and Bank Holidays. House not open. Gardens and Garden Centre open April 1st to September 30th daily (except Saturdays), 11 a.m.–5 p.m. Sundays 2–5.30 p.m. Bank Holiday Mondays 11 a.m.–5.30 p.m. Garden Centre open also in March—Mondays to Fridays, 11 a.m.–5 p.m. Admission £1.10, Children 50p. Regret no dogs.

BENINGTON

LORDSHIP GARDENS

NR. STEVENAGE, HERTFORDSHIRE

These gardens were laid out in 1906 and clearly show the influence of Gertrude Jekyll. Rose gardens recently replanted for scent and soft colours, restored herbaceous borders and rockery, shrub roses, ornamental trees and unusual wall plants surround a Queen Anne manor and castle ruins overlooking parkland and lakes. A small nursery provides top quality plants propagated from the garden.

OPENING TIMES SEE PAGE 76

PROPERTY (*showing map reference*)	LOCATION (*with nearest Rly. Stn.*)	OPENING TIMES AND ADMISSION CHARGES CATERING FACILITIES	COACH AND RAIL TOURS BUS SERVICES (*showing alighting points*)
HERTFORDSHIRE—*continued*			
BENINGTON LORDSHIP GARDENS, nr Stevenage *map* 3 *K* *Mr. & Mrs. C. H. A. Bott* Terraced garden overlooking lakes, formal rose garden; Victorian folly, Norman keep and moat; Spring rock and water garden; spectacular double herbaceous borders. Small selective nursery.	4 m E of Stevenage in village of Benington ; between Walkern (B1037) & Watton - at - Stone (A602) *Stns: Watton-at-Stone* (3½ *m*); *Knebworth* (4 *m*)	GARDEN ONLY. Easter Mon. then May to first week in Aug.—Weds. & Suns. 2–5. Also Bank Hols. in May. At other times by prior arrangement May to first week in Aug. Adm. 90p. Chd. free. Parties by prior arrangement during May to July. *No dogs, please.* teas (*Suns. only*) ☎ *Benington* (043 885) 668	London Country 384, Hertford–Stevenage–Letchworth (*not Suns.*)
CAPEL MANOR INSTITUTE OF HORTICULTURE & FIELD STUDIES *map* 6 *A* *London Borough of Enfield* Comprehensive collection of hardy and glass-house plants; many fine trees including possibly the oldest copper beech in Britain; old-fashioned and species roses; shrubs and herbaceous borders; annual borders, large rock and water garden; 17th century garden of contemporary plants and herbs; culinary, aromatic and modern medicinal plants and dye plants, unusual vegetables; garden and glasshouse designed for physically handicapped gardeners; tender economic plants, banana, sugar cane etc. Grounds shared by Horses & Ponies Protection Society	2½ m NE of Enfield; ½ m W of A10 at Bullsmoor traffic lights *Stn:Turkey St.* (1½ *m*)	May to Oct.—Tues. to Fris. 10–4.30. Adm. £1, under 18 yrs. & O.A.Ps. 50p. Several Open weekends throughout the year: 2–6. Adm. £1, under 18 yrs. & O.A.Ps. 50p. Season ticket: summer £5, Winter £2.50. Further details on request from the Institute ☎ *Lea Valley* (0992) 763849	*Bus:* 217, 217B, 310 to Bullsmoor Lane
THE GARDENS OF THE ROSE, *map* 6 *A* **Chiswell Green, St Albans** *Royal National Rose Society* The Showgrounds of the R.N.R.S. where established and new roses are displayed	Off B4630 (formerly A412) St. Albans—Watford rd. *Stns: St. Albans; Watford Junction.*	June 9 to Sept. 30—Mons. to Sats. 9–5; Suns. 2–6. Adm. £1.20, Chd. (under 16) free. ANNUAL ROSE SHOW—July 7 & 8, increased admission charge. Facilities for the disabled. Licensed cafeteria ☎ *St. Albans* (0727) 50461	Local bus services (*alight "Three Hammers" Inn, Chiswell Green, approx. ¼ m walk*) *Train:* to St. Albans or Watford Junction, thence by bus or Green Line coach to Chiswell Green
GORHAMBURY HOUSE, St. Albans *The Earl of Verulam* *map* 6 *A* Mansion built 1777-84 in modified classical style by Sir Robert Taylor. 16th century enamelled glass and historic portraits	2 m W of St. Albans. Ent. off A414. *Stns: St. Albans Abbey* (4 *m*); *St. Albans City* (4½ *m*)	May to Sept.—Thurs. 2–5. Adm £1.20, Chd. & O.A.Ps. 70p. Guided tours only. Parties at special rates by prior arrangement. ☎ *St Albans* 54051	Green Line 707, 724, 727 to St. Albans London Country 330 Hemel Hempstead–St. Albans–Welwyn Garden City (*alight St. Michael's Church,* 1½ *m*)
HATFIELD HOUSE, Hatfield *map* 6 *A* *The Marquess of Salisbury* Noble Jacobean house and Tudor palace, childhood home of Queen Elizabeth I. House built by Robert Cecil, first Earl of Salisbury in 1611. Fine portraits, furniture and relics of Queen Elizabeth I. Fine gardens and large park. AN EXHIBITION FOR 1984: THE TONY DUROSE VEHICLE COLLECTION—*A splendid display of veteran, vintage, classic and specialist vehicles together with a large variety of accessories and vehicle memorabilia spanning more than 60 years. Open one hour before the House.*	In Hatfield, opposite station 21 m N of London *Stn.: Hatfield (opposite house), see top left hand corner of illustration*	HOUSE & WEST GARDENS: March 25 to Oct. 7—Daily (except Mons. but open on all Bank Hol. Mons.). *Closed Good Friday.* Hours—Weekdays 12–5 (guided tours); Suns. 2–5.30; Bank Hols. 11–5 (Suns. & Bank Hols. no guided tours—guides in each room). Adm. £2.35, Chd. £1.70. Reductions for pre-booked parties of 20 or more. Coach & car park free. A guided tour of State rooms (weekdays) takes 1 hr. Dogs not adm. to House & must be kept on leads in gardens. PARK & WEST GARDENS: March 25 to Oct. 7. Park—Daily 10.30–8; West Gardens open at House times (also Mons. 2–5). *Closed Good Friday.* PARK, EAST & WEST GARDENS: Mons. only (except Bank Hols.)—Park 10.30–8; Gardens 2–5. in adjacent restaurant—cafeteria ELIZABETHAN BANQUETING IN THE OLD PALACE THROUGHOUT THE YEAR	Pilchers Coaches from Medway towns Epsom Coaches American Express Travel Green Line 732, 797 National Tours London Country 300, 303, Hitchin-Welwyn G. C.–Hatfield–Barnet (*not Sun.*) (*alight Hatfield Town Centre,*) 341, St. Albans–Hatfield–Hertford (*not Suns*) (*alight Hatfield Station*) *Train:* Regular fast service from Kings Cross & Moorgate. Direct link, via new Moorgate/Hatfield electric train service, with *Underground:* Victoria Line at Highbury Circle Line at Moorgate Piccadilly Line at Finsbury Park *Hatfield House Lodge opposite Stn.*
KNEBWORTH HOUSE, Knebworth *map* 3 *K* *The Hon. David Lytton Cobbold* Tudor mansion started in 1492. External decoration in the Gothic style by Sir Edward Bulwer-Lytton in 1843. Gardens. Restored herb garden—designed for Knebworth by Gertrude Jekyll. Delhi Durbar Exhibition.	28 m N of London, 1 m S of Stevenage. Road access from A1(M) at Stevenage *Stn: Knebworth* (1½ *m*)	HOUSE & GARDENS: April 1 to May 31—Suns. & Bank Hols. only; June 1 to Sept. 15—Daily (except Mons.); Sept. 16 to 30—Suns only: 11.30–4.30 OPEN BANK HOL. MONDAYS For details of 1984 adm. charges & special party rates telephone The Secretary ☎ *Stevenage* 812661 N.B. Adm. charges may be adjusted on certain days for special events or at the Management's discretion at any time. in the 16th cent. Tythe Barn. Catering enquiries ☎ *Stevenage* 813825	Green Line 734, 797 (*alight Stevenage Bus Station,* 2 *m*) London Country, 300, 303, (*not Sun.*). (*alight Broadhall Way,* 1½ *m*)' Local bus to Park on peak days Taxis available in Stevenage
MOOR PARK MANSION *map* 6 *A* *Three Rivers District Council* Palladian house reconstructed in 1727 by Sir James Thornhill and Giacomo Leoni incorporating house built in 1670 for James, Duke of Monmouth. Magnificent interior decorations by Verrio, Thornhill and others. Club House of Moor Park Golf Club. Being restored by the District Council.	1 m SE of Rickmansworth. *Stns: Rickmansworth or Moor Park*	All the year—Mons. to Fris. 10–4; Sats. 10–12 noon. *Restricted viewing may be necessary on occasions.* Visitors are requested to report to reception. Adm. free. Descriptive leaflet available. Information from Information Centre. ☎ *Rickmansworth* (0923) 776611 *or Prestel page* 28800741	London Country 321, 336, W4/5/6 to town centre. Green Line 724 & 727 to Rickmansworth Station

HATFIELD HOUSE

Home of the Marquess of Salisbury

On this splendid south front Caen stone and brick were combined to create a sumptuous facade. The date 1611 forms part of the decorative carving on the great three-storied porch.

HATFIELD, HERTFORDSHIRE
21 miles from London
March 25th to October 7th

This celebrated Jacobean house, which stands in its own great park, was built between 1607 and 1611 by Robert Cecil, 1st Earl of Salisbury and Prime Minister to King James I. It has been the family home of the Cecils ever since.

The Staterooms are rich in world-famous paintings, fine furniture, rare tapestries and historic armour. The beautiful stained glass in the chapel is original. Within the delightful gardens stands the surviving wing of the Royal Palace of Hatfield (1497) where Elizabeth I spent much of her girlhood and held her first Council of State in November 1558. She appointed William Cecil, Lord Burghley as her Chief Minister. Some of her relics can be seen in the house.

25 minutes by regular fast train service from Kings Cross to Hatfield (station faces Park gates). Special party rate from British Rail. The new Moorgate to Hatfield electric train service has direct Underground links: Victoria Line at Highbury, Circle Line at Moorgate, Piccadilly Line at Finsbury Park. Hatfield House Lodge is opposite the station.

For House opening times see entry on page 76. Stamped addressed envelope for further particulars from The Curator, Hatfield House.

AN EXHIBITION FOR 1984
THE TONY DUROSE VEHICLE COLLECTION—A splendid display of veteran, vintage, classic and specialist vehicles together with a large variety of accessories and vehicle memorabilia spanning more than 60 years.
Open 1 hour before house.

ATTRACTIVE HOUSE & HARNESS ROOM SHOPS

LIVING CRAFTS EXHIBITION, MAY 10, 11, 12 & 13—11 a.m. to 6 p.m.
A FESTIVAL OF GARDENING, JUNE 23 & 24—10 a.m. to 6 p.m.
COUNTRY FARE EXHIBITION, JULY 13, 14 & 15—10 a.m. to 6 p.m.

ELIZABETHAN BANQUETS IN OLD PALACE
Tuesdays, Thursdays, Fridays & Saturdays.
Telephone 62055 or 01-837 3111 or 01-930 2377

Tel. Hatfield: Curator 62823/65159, Banqueting & Restaurant 62055/62030/72738

Not a member of the Historic Houses Association

SHAW'S CORNER

HERTFORDSHIRE

THE NATIONAL TRUST

Hidden deep in the Hertfordshire countryside, in the village of Ayot St. Lawrence, stands the home of George Bernard Shaw. Four rooms downstairs are unchanged since his death. His hats hang in the hall, his pens, dictionaries and typewriter are on his desk, his personal treasures are on view and at the bottom of the garden is the revolving summer-house where he used to retreat to work

OPENING TIMES SEE PAGE 78

CAPEL MANOR

INSTITUTE OF HORTICULTURE AND FIELD STUDIES

HERTFORDSHIRE

View of 17th century Garden at Capel Manor showing Wellhead arbour and sundial in "pleasure garden". In the foreground knot garden with spring flowers.

OPENING TIMES OPPOSITE

KNEBWORTH HOUSE and GARDENS

(just off the A1(M) at Stevenage.
OVER 250 ACRES of beautiful deer park.
Adventure Playground. Picnic Area.
Gardens by Lutyens and Jekyll.
16th Century Tithe Barns ideal for all types of functions.

DELHI DURBAR EXHIBITION

A unique Exhibition of Viceregal India and the British Raj, commemorating the great Durbar of 1877 when Queen Victoria was proclaimed Empress of India by the Viceroy, Robert 1st Earl of Lytton.

Described by *The Times* as "a staggering collection . . . fit for a museum", the Exhibition and Audio-Visual Presentation tells the story of two generations of family involvement in India's dramatic history.

Knebworth House is the romantic conception of Sir Edward Bulwer-Lytton the famous Victorian novelist and statesman. The stucco and elaborate external decoration which he added, conceal from view the red brick and simple lines of the original Tudor House. The Lytton family first came to Knebworth in 1490 and began soon afterwards to build the house. It is still lived in by the family after nearly 500 years.

OPEN: 1st April–31st May. Suns. & Bank Hols. only. 1st June–15th Sept. Daily (except Mons.). 16th Sept.–30th Sept. Suns. only. 11.30 a.m.–4.30 p.m.
(at other times for booked parties by appointment)

For all details regarding 1984 Admission Charges & Party Rates please contact: The Secretary, The Estate Office, Knebworth, Herts. Tel: Stevenage 812661
For all Catering Enquiries please telephone: Stevenage 813825

PROPERTY (*showing map reference*)	LOCATION (*with neatest Rly. Stn.*)	OPENING TIMES AND ADMISSION CHARGES CATERING FACILITIES	COACH AND RAIL TOURS BUS SERVICES (*showing alighting points*)
HERTFORDSHIRE—*continued*			
PICCOTTS END MEDIEVAL WALL PAINTINGS & MUSEUM *map 6 A* *A. C. Lindley, Esq.* Remarkable 15th century paintings in building believed to have been a Pilgrim's hospice. Medieval Well; priest's hide; fine examples of wattle and daub. A collection of early oak furniture, an impressive range of early kitchen equipment; an Elizabethan painted room. The first Cottage Hospital in England founded by Sir Astley Paston Cooper in 1826—fascinating collection of historic medical equipment.	¾ m N of Hemel Hempstead offA4146 *Stn: Hemel Hempstead (2½ m)*	GRADE I ANCIENT MONUMENT March to November—Daily 10–6. December, January & February—parties only by appointment. Admission £1, Chd. 50p ☎ *Hemel Hempstead* 56729	Green Line 708, 719 to Hemel Hempstead London Country 317 (*not Suns.*) (*buses pass the house*) United Counties 43, Dunstable–Hemel Hempstead
ST. PAUL'S WALDEN BURY, Whitwell, nr Hitchin *map 3 K* *The Hon. Lady Bowes Lyon and Mr. & Mrs. Simon Bowes Lyon* 18th century formal woodland garden with temples, statues, lake and ponds; also rhododendron and flower gardens.	5 m S of Hitchin; ½ m N of Whitwell on B651 *Stns: Knebworth (5½ m); Hitchin (6 m); Stevenage (6 m); Harpenden (7½ m)*	GARDEN ONLY: Suns.—April 29, May 13 & June 10; 2–7. Also Sat. July 14: Gardens open 2–6; Lakeside Concert at 7 p.m. Adm. 50p, Chd. 25p. *In aid of National Gardens' Scheme & other charities.* tea at the garden	No reasonable public transport
SHAW'S CORNER, Ayot St. Lawrence *The National Trust* *map 3 K* Home of George Bernard Shaw from 1906–1950. Four rooms downstairs remain as in his lifetime. (This house is of limited appeal except for those with a special interest in Shaw).	SW end of village of Ayot St. Lawrence 3 m NW Welwyn; 1 m NE of Wheathamstead *Stns: Welwyn Garden City (6 m)*	April to Oct—Mons. to Thurs. 2–6; Suns. & Bank Hol. Mons. 12–6. *Closed Fris. & Sats.* Group visits by written appointment only. March to Nov.—Suns. to Thurs. 11–6. Last adm. 5–30. Adm. £1.10, Chd. 55p, O.A.Ps. 80p (except Suns.). Parties of 20 or more 80p. *On busy days adm. may be timed ticket.* Dogs in car park only. Unsuitable for wheelchairs. ☎ *Stevenage* 820307	London Country, 304, Hitchin–St. Albans (*not Suns.*) (*alight Owen's Corner, footpath through Lamer Park 2¼ m walk*)
HUMBERSIDE			
BLAYDES HOUSE, Hull *map 5 D* *The Georgian Society for East Yorkshire* Mid-Georgian merchants house, fine staircase and panelled rooms. Restored by the Society in 1974–5	6 High Street, Hull *Stn: Hull*	Staircase, Blaydes and Partners' Rooms—all the year Mons. to Fris. (except B. Hols.) 10.30–1, 2–4. By appointment only with Blackmore Son & Co., Chartered Architects at Blaydes House. Adm. 50p. ☎ *Hull* (0482) 26406	Hull Corporation and East Yorks city services
BURNBY HALL GARDENS, Pocklington *Stewart's Burnby Hall Gardens & Museum Trust* *map 5 B* Pleasant gardens with outstanding Lily Ponds Modern museum housing Stewart Collection	13 m E of York on B1247	April to September—Mons to Fris, 10–7; Sats. & uns. 2–7. Adm. (1983 rates) 50p, Chd. 5p, O.A.Ps. & Parties 35p. Free car park. in the garden ☎ *Pocklington* 2068/2113	East Yorks/West Yorks Jt. 44, 44A, Leeds–York–Bridlington, 46, Hull–York
BURTON AGNES HALL, nr Bridlington *Trustees of Burton Agnes Hall, Preservation Trust Ltd.* *map 5 B* One of the least altered of Elizabethan country houses. Fine collection of old and French impressionist paintings, carved ceilings and overmantels	In village of Burton Agnes, 6 m SW of Bridlington on Driffield-Bridlington rd (A166)	April 20 to October 31—Daily 11–5. Hall and Gardens: Adm. £1. Chd. & O.A.Ps. 80p. teas, light lunches & refreshments ☎ *Burton Agnes* (0262 89) 324 *The management reserves the right to close the house or part thereof without prior notice; adm. charges will be adjusted on such days.*	East Yorks 121, Hull–Driffield–Bridlington–Scarborough E. Yorks/W. Yorks. Jt. 44/44A/45, Leeds–Bridlington (*alight Burton Agnes P.O., Hall 200 yds*)
BURTON CONSTABLE, nr Hull *map 5 D* *J. Chichester Constable, Esq.* Elizabethan House built 1570. Interior by R. Adam, Wyatt, Carr and Lightoler. Beautiful grounds, lakes, parkland by 'Capability' Brown	At Burton Constable; 1½ m N of Sproatley; 7½ m NE of Hull (A165): 10 m SE of Beverley (A1035)	Easter Sat. & Weekends until last Sun. in Sept.; open Bank Hol. Mons.: 1–5. Adm. charges not available at time of going to press. Open by arrangement for parties booked in advance. *Further enquiries to the Comptroller*: ☎ *Skirlaugh* 62400 Cafeteria	East Yorks. 220 & 221, Hull–Hornsea (*alight Sproatley, 1½ m*)
ELSHAM HALL COUNTRY PARK, Brigg *Capt. J. Elwes, D.L.* *map 5 D* Beautiful English park with lakes and wild gardens. Waterfowl and fish that can be fed by hand. Domestic animals and Bird Garden. Nature trails. Adventure playground. Pony trekking (by appointment). Arts and Craft Centre including Craftcentre, Blacksmith, Pottery and Gallery. Caravan Club site. Fishing (by appointment).	4 m from Brigg on Barton-on-Humber rd. A15 *Stns: Elsham (1½ m) (not Suns.); Barnetby (2½ m)*	PARK: April 16 to Sept. 30–Mons to Sats. 11–5.30; Suns. & Bank Hols. 11–6.30. *Park closes 8 p.m. or dusk.* Sept. 30 to April 15—Suns. & Bank Hols. only 11–4 or dusk. *Park closes early in bad weather. Closed Good Friday & Christmas Day.* Adm.: Easter to Oct. £1.20, Chd. 60p. Oct. to Easter £1, Chd. 50p. *The Hall is not open to the public.* The Granary Tea Room—lunches & fresh teas daily in summer & Suns. & Bank Hols. in winter. Parties by arrangement. Special menus available. Coach parties welcome by arrangement with Administrator. ☎ *Barnetby* 688698	
EPWORTH—The Old Rectory *map 5 D* *Trustees of the World Methodist Council* Built 1709. Restored 1957. Childhood home of John & Charles Wesley, oldest Methodist shrine	In Epworth, 3 m N of Haxey on A161, 18 m E of Doncaster M180 exit 2	March to Oct.—Weekdays 10–12, 2–4; Suns. 2–4. *Donations welcomed. Other times by previous arrangement with the Warden. Coaches by arrangement only. Accommodation by arrangement.* ☎ *Epworth* (0427) 872268 at the House *by arrangement only*	Lincs. 399 Scunthorpe–Haxey–Doncaster

PROPERTY (*showing map reference*)	LOCATION (*with nearest Rly. Stn.*)	OPENING TIMES AND ADMISSION CHARGES CATERING FACILITIES	COACH AND RAIL TOURS BUS SERVICES (*showing alighting points*)

HUMBERSIDE—*continued*

PROPERTY	LOCATION	OPENING TIMES	TOURS
MAISTER HOUSE, Hull *map 5 D* *The National Trust* Rebuilt 1744 with a superb staircase-hall designed in the Palladian manner	160 High St., Hull *Stn: Hull (1½ m)*	Staircase a[illegible] ntrance hall only: all the year—Mons. to Fris., 10–4. *Closed Bank Hols.* Adm. by guide book 50p. No dogs. Unsuitable for wheelchairs & parties. ☎ *Hull* (0482) 24112	East Yorks. services from all parts of N. Humberside
NORMANBY HALL, Scunthorpe *map 5 D* *Scunthorpe Corporation* Regency mansion by Sir Robert Smirke, furnished and decorated in period. Costume displays. Spacious gardens and deer pa[illegible]. Riding School. Stable complex comprising Craft Pottery and Countryside Centre	4 m N of Scunthorpe on B1430, turn right at Normanby village. Car Park off Thealby Lane	Nov. to March—Mons. to Fris. 10–12.30, 2–5; Suns. 2–5. *Closed Sats.* April October—Mons., Weds., Thurs., Fris. 10–12.30, 2–5.30; Suns. 2–5.30. *Closed Tues.* Adm. 40p. Chd 20p. *N.B. Liable to close for private functions without prior notice; please telephone in advance* ☕ café in grounds ☎ *Scunthorpe* (0724) 720215	Lincolnshire, 360, Scunthorpe–Burton Stather–Whitton (*alight Normanby*)
SEWERBY HALL, Bridlington *map 5 B* *Borough of East Yorkshire* Built 1714–20 by John Greame with additions 1803. Gardens of great botanical interest	In Bridlington on the cliffs, 2 m NE from centre town ***Stn: Bridlington (2m)*** *(not Suns. except June–Aug.)*	Park open all year: Daily 9–dusk. Art Gallery open Easter to Sept.—Suns. to Fris. 10–12.30, 1.30–6; Sats. 1.30–6. Adm. (1983 rates) 40p, Chd. 20p. ☕ at the Hall (summer only). *Parties by arrangement*	Tours from Derby, Leeds, Nottingham etc. E. Yorks. buses Bridlington–Flamborough
SLEDMERE HOUSE, Driffield *map 5 B* *Sir Tatton Sykes, Bart.* Georgian house built in 1787. Ceilings by Joseph Rose, fine collection of furniture and paintings, famous library 100ft. long. Gardens and Park by 'Capability' Brown	24 m E of York on main York–Bridlington rd; 8 m NW of Driffield at junction of B1251 & B1253	Good Friday, Easter Sat., Sun. & Mon. (April 20–23 then all Suns. to May 27; May 29 to Sept. 30—Daily (except Mons. & Fris.); open all Bank Hols.; 1.30–5.30 (last adm. 5). Adm. £1.20, Chd. 70p, O.A.Ps. £1; Grounds only 60p, Chd. 30p. Private parties arranged by appointment only on Weds. evenings. Free car & coach parks. Illustrated brochure from:—The House Secretary, Sledmere House, Driffield, East Yorkshire. ✕ ☕ Self-service restaurant. Licensed restaurant for booked meals. ☎ *Driffield* (0377) 86208	Boddy's tour from Bridlington and Hull National tour from Hull and district Pullman Coaches tour from York Pyne's tour from Harrogate Wallace Arnold tour from Scarborough National tours from Harrogate East Yorks. 34, Driffield–Malton
WILBERFORCE HOUSE, Hull *map 5 D* *Hull City Council* 17th century mansion. Birthplace of William Wilberforce, the slave emancipator	25 High Street, Hull *Stn: Hull*	All the year—Weekdays 10–5; Suns. 2.30–4.30. *Closed Good Friday, Christmas Day, Boxing Day & New Year's Day.* Adm. free. ☎ *Hull* (0482) 223111, *Ext.* 2737	City Transport

ISLE OF WIGHT

PROPERTY	LOCATION	OPENING TIMES	TOURS
CARISBROOKE CASTLE, Newport *map 3 N* *Dept. of the Environment* Very fine medieval castle	1¼ m SW of Newport on the Isle of Wight	All the year: March 15 to Oct. 15—Weekdays 9.30–6.30; Suns. 2–6.30. Oct. 16 to March 14—Weekdays 9.30–4; Suns. 2–4. *Closed Dec. 24, 25, 26 & Jan. 1.* Adm: summer—£1.40, Chd. (under 16) & O.A.Ps. 70p; winter—70p, Chd. (under 16) & O.A.Ps. 40p. ☕ at Castle (*summer months*)	Southern Vectis, 49 East Cowes–Carisbrooke Castle (*Mons.–Fris., May–Sept. plus regular service all year to village, ½ m*) Tours from Ryde, Shanklin & Ventnor Red Funnel services sail frequently between Southampton & West & East Cowes
NEWTOWN OLD TOWN HALL, Newtown *map 3 N* *The National Trust* 18th century building of brick and stone. One of the buildings surviving from the island's former ancient borough	In Newtown, midway between Newport and Yarmouth	April to end of May—Weds., Suns. & Bank Hol. Mons. 2.30–5.30. June, July & Sept.—Wed., Thurs., Sats. & Suns. 2.30–5.30. August—Daily 2.30–5.30. Adm. 30p, Chd. 15p. No reduction for parties. Shop. No dogs. Unsuitable for wheelchairs.	Southern Vectis 12, Sandown–Newport–Freshwater Bay (*alight Winchester Corner 1 m*).
NUNWELL HOUSE, Brading *map 3 N* *Colonel & Mrs. J. A. Aylmer* A house in which King Charles I stayed before his imprisonment and which shows architectural development from Jacobean to Edwardian periods. Interesting furniture, pictures and military collections. Large gardens	1 m from Brading, turning off A3055; 3 m S of Ryde *Stn: Brading*	April 22 (Easter) to Sept. 21—Suns. to Thurs. 12.30–5.30. *Closed Fris. & Sats.* Visits by parties at other times by appointment. Adm. £1, Chd. 50p. No dogs ✕ ☎ teas & light refreshments in House; large parties book in advance ☎ *Brading* (098 372) 240	Vectis 13 & 36 (*alight Brading, 1 m*)
OSBORNE HOUSE, East Cowes *map 3 N* *Dept. of the Environment* Queen Victoria's favourite residence	1 m SE of East Cowes on the I.o.W. *Stn: Ryde Esplanade (3 m)*	April 2 to Oct. 13—Weekdays 11–5 (July & Aug. 10–5). *Closed Suns.* Adm. £2, Chd. (under 16 yrs.) & O.A.Ps. £1. ☕ in the Grounds	Southern Vectis tours from Ryde, Shanklin & Ventnor Southern Vectis 4, Ryde–East Cowes; 19/49 Ventnor–Newport–East Cowes (*alight gates*) Red Funnel services, sail frequently between Southampton & East Cowes

KENT

PROPERTY	LOCATION	OPENING TIMES	TOURS
BLACK CHARLES, nr. Sevenoaks *map 6 D* *Mr. & Mrs. Hugh Gamon* Charming 14th cent. home of John de Blakecherl and his family from 1317 to 1746. A hall house with beautiful panelling, fireplaces and many other interesting features.	3 m S of Sevenoaks off A21: 1 m E in the village of Underriver *Stns: Hildenborough (3 m); Sevenoaks (5 m)*	Open to groups by appointment. ☎ *Hildenborough* (0732) 833036	Maidstone 204 Tonbridge–Underriver

PROPERTY (*showing map reference*)	LOCATION (*with nearest Rly. Stn.*)	OPENING TIMES AND ADMISSION CHARGES CATERING FACILITIES	COACH AND RAIL TOURS BUS SERVICES (*showing alighting points*)
KENT–*continued*			
△ **BOUGHTON MONCHELSEA PLACE, nr Maidstone** *map 6 D* *M. B. Winch, Esq.* Grey stone, battlemented Elizabethan manor house with breathtaking views over the 18th century landscaped park with fallow deer	**In village of Boughton Monchelsea 5 m S of Maidstone. Turn off Maidstone-Hastings road (A229) at Linton** *Stns: Marden; Staplehurst; Maidstone W & E (all 5 m)*	Easter to Oct. 7—Sats., Suns. & Bank Hols. (also Weds. during July & August) 2.15–6. House & Grounds £1.25, Chd. 60p. Grounds only 55p, Chd. 30p. *Parties welcome any day, at special rates, but only by previous engagement* ☕ at the House ☎ *Maidstone* (0622) 43120	**Maidstone 59, Maidstone–Boughton-Chart Sutton** *weekdays hourly (alight gates)* **National tours from Thanet and Hastings** Epsom Coaches, East Kent—Folkestone
CHARTWELL, Westerham *map 6 C* *The National Trust* The home for many years of Sir Winston Churchill	2 m S of Westerham off B2026 *Stns : Edenbridge (4 m); Edenbridge Town (4½ m) (not Suns.); Oxted (5½ m); Hurst Green (6 m); Sevenoaks (6½ m)*	HOUSE: March to November. GARDEN & STUDIO: April to mid-October. Weekdays (except Mons. & Fris.) 2–6 or sunset if earlier; Sats. & Suns. 11–6. Last admission half-hour before closing (*closes 4 p.m. in Nov.*) Also open Weds. & Thurs. from 11 during July & Aug. *Closed Good Friday & Tues. after Bank Hol. Mons.* Adm. House & Garden £2.20, Chd. £1.10; Gardens only £1, Chd. 50p; Studio 40p extra. *Pre-booked parties of 15 or more Tues. mornings only (except Tues. following Bank Hol. Mons.)* £1.70, *Chd.* 90p. *Enquiries to the Administrator. No other visitors Tues. mornings.* Dogs admitted to grounds on lead. Shop. Wheelchairs provided. ✕ ☕ at Restaurant in grounds ☎ *Edenbridge* 866368	Frames' tours from London National tours from Bournemouth & Kent Rickards tour from London—(*Weds., May to Sept.*) Green Line 705 to Chartwell (*Tues., Weds., Thurs., Sats. & Suns. in summer*)
CHIDDINGSTONE CASTLE, nr Edenbridge *The late Denys E. Bower, Esq.* *map 6 D* Interesting pictures and furnishings. Royal Stuart & Jacobite collection; Ancient Egyptian collection; Japanese lacquer, swords, netsuke; Georgian Barrel Organs	In Chiddingstone 5 m E of Edenbridge via Bough Beech and Hever (off B2027) *Stns: Penshurst (2½ m); Hever (3 m) (not Suns.)*	March 24 to Oct. 31—Tues. to Sats. 2–5.30; Suns. & Bank Hol., Sats. & Mons. 11.30–5.30. *Closed Mons. except Bank Hols.* Sunday winter opening times on enquiry. Adm. £1.10, Chd. under 5 free, 5–11 years 50p. Fishing £5 daily—bookable in advance. Special rates for advance bookings of 20. ☎ *Penhurst* 870347 ☕ teas availabe in High season or by arrangement (organised by Friends of Chiddingstone Castle).	National tours from South Coast resorts Green Line 704 to Tunbridge Wells, then Maidstone & District 233. Tunbridge Wells–Edenbridge (daily) (*alight Chequers Garage, Bough Beech, 1 m*) 288 to Chiddingstone (*Sats. only*)
CHILHAM CASTLE GARDENS, nr. Canterbury *map 6 D* *Viscount Massereene & Ferrard D.L.* Attractive Jacobean house set in 25 acres of gardens originally laid out by Tradescant and later reputedly landscaped by "Capability" Brown; terraces, rose garden, lake. Old trees, spring bulbs, magnificent views, Autumn colour	In Chilham village, 6 m W of Canterbury (A252), 8 m NE of Ashford (A28), 22 m NW of Dover, Faversham turn off M2 *Stn: Chilham (1 m)*	End of March—Daily (inc. Bank Hols.). Open from 11 a.m. Adm. £1.70, Chd. 80p. Free parking. Coaches welcome. Special rates for parties on application. Medieval Banquets & entertainment by arrangement. Falconry demonstrations. Petland and Gift Shop—daily. Jousting display Suns. & Bank Hol. Mons. ☕ Jacobean tearoom ☎ *Canterbury* 730319	
COBHAM HALL, nr Rochester *map 6 D* *Westwood Educational Trust Ltd.* Charming mixture of Gothic and Renaissance architecture. Fine example of work of James Wyatt. Now a girls' public school	4 m W of Rochester on Watling St & Rochester Way (B2009 off A2). 27 m from London *Stn: Sole Street (1½m)*	April 19 to 24—Daily; then July 29 to Aug. 30—Weds., Thurs. & Suns.; also Summer Bank Hol. Mon. (Aug. 27): 2–6. Last tour starts 5.30. Adm. House and Gardens 80p, Chd. & O.A.Ps. 40p. *Reduced rates for parties* ☕ available ☎ *Shorne* 3371	Maidstone 311 Gravesend–Cobham
CRITTENDEN HOUSE, Matfield *map 6 D* *B. P. Tompsett, Esq.* Garden completely planned and planted during last 22 years on labour-saving lines. Spring shrubs, roses, lilies, foliage, waterside planting of ponds in old iron workings	5 m SE of Tonbridge off B2160 *Stn: Paddock Wood (3 m)*	GARDENS ONLY: Sun. April 1; Easter Sun. & Mon. April 22/23; Spring Bank Hol. Mon. May 28; Sun. July 1: 2–6.30. Adm. 50p, Chd. 20p. *In aid of National Gardens Scheme & other charities.* Also Sun. June 3: 2–6.30 *for R.S.P.C.A.* and Fri. & Sat. May 25/26 Illuminations 7.30–11.30 *for C.P.R.E.* Cars free.	Maidstone 6, Maidstone–Tunbridge Wells–Tenterden–Goudhurst–Tunbridge Wells (*alight Standings Cross, Matfield, 1 m*)
DEAL CASTLE, Deal *map 3 S* *Dept. of the Environment* 16th century coastal fortification	On the sea front *Stn: Deal (¼ m)*	All the year: March 15 to Oct. 15—Weekdays 9.30–6.30; Suns. 2–6.30. Oct. 16 to March 14—Weekdays 9.30–4; Suns. 2–4. *Closed Dec:* 24, 25, 26 & *Jan.* 1. Adm. 50p. (under 16) & O.A.Ps. 25p.	East Kent 13, 14 from Canterbury, 80 80A, from Dover, 66X from Margate & Ramsgate, 87 from Ramsgate (changing at Sandwich). National Coach 007 from London Victoria
△ **DOVER CASTLE, Dover** *map 3 S* *Dept. of the Environment* The Keep was built by Henry II in 1180-6. Outer curtain built in the 13th century	E end of Dover *Stn: Dover Priory (1½ m)*	KEEP & UNDERGROUND WORKS—all year: March 15 to Oct. 15—Weekdays 9.30–6.30; Suns: 2–6.30. Oct. 16 to March 14—Weekdays 9.30–4; Suns. 2–4. *Closed Dec.* 24, 25, 26 & *Jan.* 1. Adm.—KEEP: summer—£1.20, Chd. (under 16) & O.A.Ps. 60p; winter—70p, Chd. (under 16) & O.A.Ps. 40p. UNDERGROUND WORKS: 50p, Chd. (under 16) & O.A.Ps. 25p. GROUNDS open free (same hours as Keep). ☕ in Castle (summer months)	Tours from all parts of Kent and Sussex East Kent 80, 80A, Dover–Deal; 93, Dover–Guston–E/W Langdon; (*alight Castle*) and other services from all parts to Dover
DOWN HOUSE, Downe *map 6 D* *Royal College of Surgeons of England* The home of Charles Darwin for 40 years	In Downe, 5½ m S of Bromley off A233 *Stns: Orpington (3 m) & Bromley Sth (5 m)*	March 1 to following Jan. 31—Daily (except Mons. & Fris. but open Bank Hol. Mons.) 1–6. Last admission 5.30. Adm. £1, Chd. 20p. *Closed Dec.* 24, 25, 26 & *Feb.* ☎ *Farnborough* (0689) 59119	London Transport 146, Bromley–Hayes–Downe (*not Suns.*) Crystals 858, Orpington–Biggin Hill (*not Sats. or Suns.*)
EMMETTS GARDEN, nr Brasted *map 6 C* *The National Trust* Hillside shrub garden of 4 acres. Lovely spring and autumn colours	1½ m S of A25 on Sundridge–Ide Hill Rd *Stn: Sevenoaks (4½m); Penshurst (5½ m)*	SHRUB GARDEN ONLY. April & July to end of Oct.—Suns. (inc. Easter) & Weds. 2–6. Last adm. 5. *Closed Bank Hols. except Easter.* May & June—Suns., Tues., Weds. & Thurs. 2–6. Adm. 70p. *No reduction for parties or children.* Dogs admitted. Wheelchair access to level parts of garden only.	London Country 404, 418 (*summer Suns.*) Sevenoaks–Ide Hill (*alight Ide Hill ½ m*) Green Line 705 (*Suns. only*) and London Country 483 to Sundridge (*2 m*) Maidstone E3 (*Weds. & Fris. only, alight Toys Hill*).
EYHORNE MANOR, Hollingbourne *Mr. & Mrs. Derek Simmons* *map 6 D* Early 15th century timber-framed house, galleried chimney. Laundry museum. Whole house shown. Herbs and old-fashioned roses	5 m E of Maidstone. 400 yds N of A20 on B2163 *Stn: Hollingbourne (½ m)*	Good Friday to Sept. 25: Sats. & Suns., 2–6. Also Spring & Summer Bank Hols. & in August Tues., Weds., Thurs., Sats. & Suns. 2–6. Adm. 90p, Chd. 45p. ☕ home made teas	Maidstone & District East/Kent 10, 710 Sevenoaks-Maidstone–Ashford–Folkestone (*alight Hollingbourne, Great Danes*)
FINCHCOCKS, Goudhurst *map 6 D* *Mr. & Mrs. Richard Burnett* Early 18th century house containing historic keyboard instruments.	1½ m W of Goudhurst 10 m E of Tunbridge Wells off A262 *Stns: Marden (7m) Paddock Wood (8m)*	April 22 (Easter) to Sept. 30—Suns.; also Bank Hol. Mons. & Weds. to Sats. in Aug.: 2–6. Demonstrations & music on instruments of the collection on Open Days. Adm. £2, Chd. £1.20. Free parking. ☕ teas available ☎ *Goudhurst* (0580) 211702	
GADS HILL PLACE, Rochester *map 6 B* *Gads Hill Place School Ltd.* Grade 1 listed building, built 1780. Home of Charles Dickens from 1858 to 1870.	On A226; 3 m from Rochester; 4 m from Gravesend; *Stn: Higham (1 m)*	By prior appointment only. Apply to the Bursar, Gads Hill Place School, Higham, Rochester. Adm. free. ✕ ☕ Sir John Falstaff Hotel opposite House.	Local service (*frequent, passes House*)
△ **GODINTON PARK, Ashford** *map 6 D* *Alan Wyndham Green, Esq.* House belongs mostly to Jacobean times, interior contains wealth of panelling and carving, portraits, furniture and china. Formal gardens	1½ m W of Ashford off Maidstone rd at Potter's Cnr. (A20) *Stn: Ashford (2 m)*	Easter Sat., Sun. & Mon.; then June to September—Suns. & Bank Hols. only 2–5. Adm. House & Gardens £1, Chd. (under 16 yrs) 50p. Weekdays by appointment only. Parties of 20 or more 80p per person.	Frames Tours from London (*Fris.*) Maidstone & District and East Kent from Maidstone (*alight Hare & Hounds, Potters Corner*) (*½ hourly service to Maidstone, Ashford, Hythe & Folkestone*); connections in Ashford for Canterbury & the Weald
GOODESTONE PARK, nr Canterbury *The Lord & Lady FitzWalter* *map 3 S* Large garden. Old walled rose garden. Fine trees; good views. Connections with Jane Austen.	8 m SE of Canterbury; 4 m E of A2; ½ m SE of B2046; S of A257	GARDEN ONLY: Suns. April 15, 22, 29 & from May 27 to July 1 inclusive. April 16 to June 28—Mons., Weds. & Thurs. 2–6. Adm. 80p, Chd. (under 12) 10p. *No dogs* ☕ teas—Suns. only	No reasonable public transport

CHARTWELL

WESTERHAM, KENT

THE NATIONAL TRUST

Home of Sir Winston Churchill for 40 years. The house is left much as it was during his lifetime, with many souvenirs of his life and times Two rooms contain the uniforms and hats he wore, and gifts received from all over the world. Beautiful garden with lakes and terraces: studio where Churchill painted. On busy days a timed ticket system operates. Restaurant and shop.

OPENING TIMES SEE PAGE 80

COBHAM HALL

COBHAM, Kent
Mid-way between London and Canterbury

" Country Life " photograph

AN INDEPENDENT PUBLIC SCHOOL FOR GIRLS

A combination of a spacious house, dating from 1587 and magnificent grounds. Interior by James Wyatt. Family gilded State Coach built in 1715.

The 50 acres of grounds with giant cedars, other specimen trees and 100-year-old lawns provide a good example of landscape gardening.

Teas are available for visitors.

Further particulars from The Bursar, Cobham Hall, Cobham. Telephone Shorne 3371.

For times of opening see opposite

EYHORNE MANOR

HOLLINGBOURNE

Outstanding early 15th century manor house with 17th century additions. The home of Mr. and Mrs. Derek Simmons. Rare smoking bay in which visitors may walk. House completely restored and furnished by the family. Models showing original construction and evolution of the house to present day. A unique laundry museum in one of the fourteen rooms shown. Domestic aromatic herbs in all the rooms. Intimate garden, specialising in herbs and old-fashioned roses.

CHIDDINGSTONE CASTLE

NEAR EDENBRIDGE, KENT

Wet or fine Chiddingstone Castle is enthralling. Set in 30 acres of parkland with lake and caves and glorious views over the Weald, it is an important example of romantic late Georgian passion for the Middle Ages. In 1805 the former 17th century mansion (of which some internal features remain) was remodelled by William Atkinson in the 'Castle Style' which he was then also employing at Scone Palace. It was the home of the late Denys Eyre Bower who left it to the Nation. It is now administered by a private charitable trust and its sole support is the income from visitors.

Inside the Castle is a treasure house. Royal Stuart and Jacobite relics bring history to life (Lely's "Nell Gwyn", Samuel Cooper's "Charles II"), Japanese swords and lacquer enchant the eye; Egyptian antiquities, fine furniture, Georgian barrel organs playing 18th century dance music. All this and more were the life time collections of that remarkable connoisseur Denys Bower whose last wish was that others should continue to enjoy them as he had.

Opening times & admission charges opposite.

FINCHCOCKS **Goudhurst Kent**

Finchcocks, dated 1725, is a fine example of Georgian baroque architecture, noted for its fine brickwork, with a front elevation attributed to Thomas Archer. It is set in beautiful parkland near the village of Goudhurst. The house contains a magnificent collection of historic keyboard instruments which are restored to full playing condition, and provides a unique setting where visitors can hear music performed on the instruments for which it was written. Demonstration tours and music whenever the house is open.

Open Days: Easter to end of September, Sundays only; Bank Holiday Mondays and daily in August except for Mondays and Tuesdays. 2-6 p.m. Teas.

Open by appointment for groups on other days from April to October, with musical tours and special catering. Fully licensed restaurant.

Festival of concerts in September; Fair in October. Also lectures, courses, master classes and children's events. Full details send s.a.e.

GODINTON PARK

ASHFORD, KENT

The existing house belongs mostly to Jacobean times though there are records of another house being here in the 15th century. The interior of Godinton contains a wealth of very fine panelling and carving, particularly in the Hall and on the Staircase.

The house contains interesting portraits and much fine furniture and china.

The gardens were originally laid out in the 18th century and were further extended and improved in the 19th century by Sir Reginald Blomfield with topiary work and formal gardens giving a spacious setting to the house.

The house is open to visitors by permission of Mr. Alan Wyndham Green, the present owner.

PROPERTY (*showing map reference*)	LOCATION (*with nearest Rly. Stn.*)	OPENING TIMES AND ADMISSION CHARGES CATERING FACILITIES	COACH AND RAIL TOURS BUS SERVICES (*showing alighting points*)
KENT—*continued*			
GREAT COMP, nr Borough Green *map 6 D* *The Great Comp Charitable Trust* *(Mr. & Mrs. R. Cameron)* Outstanding garden of seven acres, very wide variety of trees, shrubs, heathers and herbaceous plants. Old brick walls, much new stone work, paving and ornaments.	2 m E of Borough Green B2016 off A20. First Right at Comp crossrds ½ m on left *Stn: Bor. Green & Wrotham* (1½ *m*)	GARDEN ONLY. April 1 to October 31—Daily 11–6. *Parties by prior arrangement.* Adm. £1, Chd. 50p. *No dogs.* ☕tea in the Old Dairy 3.30–5; Suns. & Bank Hols. and for parties by arrangement ☎ *Borough Green* 882669	Maidstone 9, Sevenoaks–Maidstone (*alight Platt Mill ½ m*)
GREAT MAYTHAM HALL, Rolvenden *Mutual Households Association map 6 D* Built in 1910 by Sir Edwin Lutyens	½ m W of Rolvenden village *Stn: Rye* (9 *m*)	May to September—Weds. & Thurs. 2–5. Adm. 50p, Chd. 25p. Free car park. No dogs admitted.	Maidstone 297 Tenterden-Tunbridge Wells, 12 Maidstone–Tenterden–Hastings (*alight Rolvenden Bull*)
HALL PLACE GARDENS, Leigh *map 6 D* *The Lord Hollenden* Large outstanding garden with 11 acre lake; lakeside walk over picturesque bridges; many interesting trees and shrubs, well labelled.	4 m W of Tonbridge; leave A21 at Hildenborough via B2027 to Leigh *Stn: Leigh* (½ *m*)	GARDEN ONLY: May 20 to June 24—Suns. 2.30–6.30. Adm. 60p. Chd. (under 14) 20p. Free car park. Dogs on leads only. *May 27 & June 10 in aid of National Gardens' Scheme.* ☕ teas at garden.	Rail service Tonbridge–Redhill–Guildford
HEVER CASTLE, nr Edenbridge *map 6 C* Formal Italian Garden with statuary and sculpture, lake and 13th century moated Castle	Midway between London & S coast: 3 m SE Edenbridge off B2026 *Stn: Hever* (1 *m*) (*not Suns.*); *Edenbridge* (3½ *m*); *Penshurst* (4 *m*)	April 1 to Sept. 30: Gardens & Castle—Daily (except Thurs.) 12–6. Last adm. 5. Special PRE-BOOKED party visits of 15 or more ANY EVENING & ANY THURSDAY throughout the year. Adm. charges on application. Souvenir shops, Children's adventure playground, radio-controlled model boats. Garden produce. Special one-day events. ✕☕ luncheons, light refreshments (licensed) ☎ *Edenbridge* (0732) 865224	Frames' tours from London National tours from Kent & Sussex Maidstone 234, Tunbridge Wells–Hever–Edenbridge (*not Suns.*) Pilchers Coaches from Chatham
HOLE PARK, Rolvenden *map 6 D* *D. G. W. Barham, Esq.* Formal and natural gardens, rhododendrons and azaleas. Fine lawns, trees and yew hedges. Dell and water garden. Bluebell glades, spring bulbs. Autumn colours.	Between Rolvenden & Benenden; 3½ m SW of Tenterden (B2086)	GARDENS ONLY: Suns. April 15 & 29; May 13 & 27: 2–7. Weds. April 25; May 2, 9, 16, 23 & 30; June 6: 2–7. Suns. Oct. 7 & 14: 2–6. Adm. 50p. Chd. (under 12) 20p. *In aid of National Gardens' Scheme & Gardeners' Charities.* No dogs.	Maidstone 12, Maidstone—Tenterden—Hastings 297 Tunbridge Wells—Goudhurst—Tenterden (*alight gates*)
IGHTHAM MOTE, Ivy Hatch *map 6 D* *C. H. Robinson, Esq.* One of the most complete remaining specimens of an ancient moated manor house	2½ m S of Ightham, off A227, 6 m E of Sevenoaks off A25	March to Oct.—Fris. 2–5. Nov. to Feb.—Fris. 2–4. April to Sept.—Suns. 2–5. Adm. £1.30. Chd. 80p. *Guided tours for parties of 20 or more by prior arrangement with Agent. Mons. to Thurs. morning or afternoon. Adm.* £1.10. *Chd.* 70*p.* ☎ *Sevenoaks* 62235	Maidstone 9, Sevenoaks–Maidstone (*alight Seven Wents, 2 m*); 322, Gravesend–Tunbridge Wells (*alight High Cross, 1 m*)
KNOLE, Sevenoaks (1456) *map 6 D* △ *The National Trust* One of the largest private houses in England, dating mainly from 15th century, with splendid Jacobean interior and fine collection of 17th and 18th century furniture	At the Tonbridge end of Sevenoaks, just E of A225; 25 m from London *Stn: Sevenoaks* (1½ *m*)	April to end of Nov.—Weds. to Sats. (inc. Good Friday) & Bank Hol. Mons. 11–5; Suns. 1–5. Last adm. 1 hr. before closing. *Closed Dec. to March.* Adm. £2, Chd. £1. Connoisseurs' Day—Fris. (except Good Friday) when extra rooms shown. Adm. £2.50, no reductions for children. Visitors guided Oct. (except Weekends) & Nov. (except Suns.). *Parties of 25 or more by prior arrangement with the Administrator on Tues. only (except Tues. following Bank Hols.). Adm.* £1.50, *Schoolchd, (all ages) accompanied by Staff* 80*p.* Garden open May to Sept.—first Weds. only each month. Adm. 50p. Car park £1. Shop. ☎ *Sevenoaks* 453006	Rickards tours from London—(*Weds., May to Sept.*) Green Line 704, 705 (*Suns. only*) National Coach 034 from Rye; Maidstone 9, from Maidstone London Country 402, Bromley–Sevenoaks; 483, Croydon–Tonbridge (*alight gates*); 404 Sevenoaks–Ide Hill; 454, 454A Tonbridge–Sevenoaks–Dunton Green National tours from East Kent
LADHAM HOUSE, Goudhurst *map 6 D* *Betty, Lady Jessel* Spring and summer flowering shrubs, mixed borders, bog garden, spring and autumn heather garden	11 m E of Tunbridge Wells off A262 *Stn: Marden* (4½ *m*)	GARDEN ONLY—Suns., April 15, 11–6; May 20 & July 15, 11–7; Oct. 7, 11–6. *Open other times by appointment:* Adm. £1, Chd. (under 12) 20p. *In aid of National, Gardens' Scheme.* Free parking.	No reasonable public transport.
LEEDS CASTLE, nr Maidstone *map 6 D* *Leeds Castle Foundation* Castle of the medieval Queens of England. Fairytale castle built in the middle of a lake in romantic setting of landscaped parkland. Lovingly restored and beautifully furnished by the late Lady Baillie. Museum of Medieval Dog Collars. Water and Woodland gardens. Culpeper Garden, Greenhouses, Vineyard. Duckery and Aviary—regret no dogs. 9 hole golf course open every day of the year. Castle gift shop	4 m E of Maidstone; access London to Folkestone rd, junc. A20 & M20 *Stn: Hollingbourne* (2 *m*)	April 1 to Oct. 31—Daily (except Mons. in April, May & Oct. but open Bank Hol. Mons.) 12–5. Nov. 1 to March 31—Sats. & Suns. only 12–4. Winter—Sunday lunches with tours of Castle. Kentish Dinner every Saturday throughout year. Parties by arrangement. Reduced prices for Chd. (under 16) Students & O.A.Ps. Picnic area, Car park. Passenger trailer takes elderly visitors from car park to Castle. Facilities for the disabled. N.B. *The Trustees reserve the right to change days and hours of opening and to close all or parts of the Castle for seminars and special events.* ☕✕ Lunch & refreshments available in licensed restaurants ☎ *Maidstone* 65400; *Telex* 965737	Britainshrinkers Road 'n rail tours from London (*Tues.*) Evan Evans Tours from London (*Tues. & Thurs. afternoons*) Invictaway direct from London (Victoria Coach Station) combined coach/admission ticket, once daily all year on open days London Transport coach tours from London (*Sats.*) Orient-Express rail and coach inclusive tours (*Weds. & Fris.*) National Travel tours from London (*Sats.*) National Travel tours from Kent & Sussex Park Lane Sightseeing from London (*Weds. & Fris.*) British Rail from London (Victoria) or Bromley, combined rail/admission ticket available from Victoria Travel Centre or SR London Travel Centres, April-Oct twice daily on open days Maidstone & District local bus routes, 10, 710 from Maidstone (20 *mins.*); (*alight Hollingbourne corner ½m*)

IGHTHAM MOTE

IVY HATCH, SEVENOAKS

A late mediaeval moated manor house extensively remodelled in the early 16th century. Features include the Great Hall, Old Chapel and Crypt circa 1340, Tudor Chapel with painted ceiling circa 1520, Drawing Room with Jacobean fireplace and frieze, 18th century Palladian window and hand painted Chinese wallpaper.

OPENING TIMES ABOVE

KNOLE KENT

THE NATIONAL TRUST

Edwin Smith photograph

Begun by Thomas Bourchier, Archbishop of Canterbury, in 1456 and greatly extended c. 1603 by Thomas Sackville, to whom it was granted by Queen Elizabeth I, Knole is one of the largest private houses in England. The State Rooms contain a large collection of family portraits on loan from Lord Sackville, rare furniture, rugs and tapestries dating from the 17th to 18th century.

OPENING TIMES ABOVE

GREAT COMP GARDEN

NR. BOROUGH GREEN, KENT

Colorline Photographic photographs

The garden of seven acres made, and until 1982 maintained, by Mr. & Mrs. R. Cameron, with virtually no assistance is now, after 27 years, fully developed. In a setting of well maintained lawns the design contains paving, old brick walls, new stone walls, "ruins", terraces, ornaments and a Chilstone temple, informal woodland glades and winding paths and one of the best heather gardens in the country. A wide variety of trees, shrubs and herbaceous plants includes many which are rarely seen. Good autumn colour. Unusual plants for sale.

HEVER CASTLE & GARDENS near EDENBRIDGE KENT

One of the most charming castles in Britain. Dating back 600 years, Hever Castle was once the childhood home of Anne Boleyn, where Henry VIII courted her for 6 years until she became his second wife and the Mother of Elizabeth I. Since 1903, and until recently, Hever Castle was the home of the Astor family and is filled with arts and treasures collected over the years and stunning flowers grown in the Hever Grounds. Some of the rooms in the gorgeous 'Tudor Village' connected to the Castle and built for the Astor's guests are now open for accommodation and entertainment. Spectacular Italian gardens, picturesque lake and licenced pavilion wine bar for excellent meals and refreshments.

Castle open every day except Thursdays, 12.00–6.00 (last entry 5.00). Private tours every evening and Thursdays for pre-booked parties. Regular one-day shows.

All enquiries to the Booking Office, Hever Castle, Edenbridge, Kent.
Telephone (0732) 865224.

Set on two islands in the middle of a lake and surrounded by 500 acres of parkland, Leeds Castle really is the loveliest Castle in the world.

Built in AD857, it was named after Led, Chief Minister of Ethelbert IV, King of Kent.

Converted to a Royal palace by Henry VIII it was lovingly restored in the thirties by the late Lady Baillie. On display there are fine paintings, antique furniture, Flemish tapestries, and a unique collection of ornamental dog collars.

In the grounds there's a duckery with all kinds of waterfowl, an aviary with exotic tropical birds, the Culpeper Garden, and the Vineyard.

Other attractions include a nine hole golf course, greenhouses, Garden Shop and Gift Shop.

Telephone: (0622) 65400.

FOR TIMES OF OPENING SEE UNDER KENT.

LEEDS CASTLE MAIDSTONE KENT

PROPERTY (*showing map reference*)	LOCATION (*with neatest Rly. Stn.*)	OPENING TIMES AND ADMISSION CHARGES CATERING FACILITIES	COACH AND RAIL TOURS BUS SERVICES (*showing alighting points*)
KENT—*continued*			
LULLINGSTONE CASTLE, Eynsford *Guy Hart Dyke, Esq.* *map 6 D* Family portraits, armour, Henry VII gateway. Church.	In the Darenth valley via Eynsford on A225 *Stn: Eynsford (¼ m)*	April to October. CASTLE & GROUNDS—Sats., Suns. & Bank Hol. Mons. 2–6. Adm. £1.50, Chd. 75p, O.A.Ps. £1. GROUNDS ONLY—Weds., Thurs. & Fris. 2–6. Adm. £1, Chd. & O.A.Ps. 50p. No dogs. Enquires & bookings ☎ *Farningham* (0322) 862114	All cars & coaches via Roman Villa
LYMPNE CASTLE, nr Hythe *map 6 D* *Harry Margary, Esq.* 14th century building restored in 1905. Once owned by the Archdeacons of Canterbury. Terraced gardens with magnificent views out to sea and across Romney Marshes to Fairlight	3 m NW of Hythe off B2067 8 m W of Folkestone *Stn: Sandling (2½ m)*	June to September & Bank Hol. weekends—Daily 10.30–6. *Open other days when possible & to parties by appointment.* Adm. 75p, Chd. 20p. at nearby tea room ☎ *Hythe* (0303) 67571	East Kent/Maidstone 10, 10X, Maidstone–Ashford–Folkestone (*alight Newingreen* 1 *m*)
MOUNT EPHRAIM, Hernhill, nr Faversham *Mrs. M. N. Dawes & Mr. E. S. Dawes* *map 6 D* Terraced garden, with beautiful views, leading to small lake. Herbaceous border, topiary, extensive Japanese rock garden. Small woodland area with rhododendrons. Wide variety of plants and shrubs. Fine trees.	6 m W of Canterbury, 3 m E of Faversham; ½ m N of A2 at Boughton. *Stns: Canterbury* (6 *m*); *Faversham* (3 *m*)	GARDENS ONLY: April 15 to Sept. 30—Suns. & Bank Hols. only 2–6. Adm. £1, Chd. 20p. Parties by prior arrangement. ☎ *Canterbury* (0227) 751310 *or* 751496	East Kent/Maidstone 333, Canterbury–Faversham (*alight Woodmans Hall*, ½ *m*)
NEW COLLEGE OF COBHAM, Cobham *Presidents of the New College of Cobham* *map 6 D* Almshouses based on medieval chantry built 1362, part rebuilt 1598. Originally endowed by Sir John de Cobham and descendants	4 m W of Rochester; 4 m SE of Gravesend; 1½ m from jct Shorne / Cobham (A2). In Cobham rear of Church of Mary Magdalene *Stn: Sole St (1 m)*	April to Sept.—Daily (except Thurs.) 10–7. Oct. to March—Mons., Tues., Weds., Sats. & Suns. 10–4. ☎ *Meopham* (0474) 814280	*B.R.*, London (*Victoria*) Maidstone & District 310, 311 Gravesend–Cobham–Meopham
OLD SOAR MANOR, nr Borough Green *The National Trust (under the guardianship of Dept. of the Environment)* *map 6 D* Solar block of a late 13th c. knight's dwelling	2 m S of Borough Green (A25) appr'd via A227 and Plaxtol *Stn: Bor. Green & Wrotham (2½ m)*	April to mid Sept.—Weekdays 9.30–6.30; Suns. 2–6.30. *Closed May* 2. Adm. 30p, Chd. (under 16 yrs.) & O.A.Ps. 15p (charges subject to revision without notice).	Maidstone 222 Tunbridge Wells–Borough Green connections from Gravesend (*alight Plaxtol*, 1 *m*)
OWLETTS, Cobham *map 6 D* *The National Trust* A red-brick Carolean house with contemporary staircase and plasterwork ceiling. Small gardens	1 m S of A2 at W end of village, at junct. of rds from Dartford & Sole st *Stn: Sole St. (1 m)*	April to end of Sept.—Weds. & Thurs. 2–5. Adm. 50p. *No reduction for parties or children. No indoor photography. No dogs.* Wheelchair access to ground floor only.	Maidstone 310 Gravesend–Longfield (*not Suns.*)
THE OWL HOUSE, Lamberhurst *map 6 D* *Maureen, Marchioness of Dufferin & Ava* 16th cent. half-timbered, tile-hung wool smuggler's cottage. Beautiful gardens, magnificent roses, woodland walks.	8 m SE of Tunbridge Wells; 1 m from Lamberhurst off A21 *Stn: Wadhurst (4 m)*	GARDENS ONLY. All the year—Mons., Weds., Fris., Sats., Suns. & Bank Hol. weekends 11–6. Adm. £1, Chd. 50p.	National Coach 034, 037 London–Hastings Maidstone 78, 280, Tunbridge Wells–Lamberhurst (*alight village*, 1½ *m*)
PATTYNDENNE MANOR, Goudhurst *Mr & Mrs. D. C. Spearing* *map 6 D* Magnificent 15th century timbered house, once the home of Henry VIII's and Elizabeth I's standard bearer. Pattyndenne is still lived in as a family home.	1 m S of Goudhurst on W side of B2079 between Goudhurst & Bedgebury Pinetum nr humpback bridge *Stn: Marden (5½ m)*	Sundays—Aug. 5, 12, 19, 26; Sept. 2, 9, 16: 2.15–5.30, also Bank Hol. Mon. (August 27). Adm. (approx.) £1.30, Chd. 65p. All enquiries ☎ *Goudhurst* 211361	Maidstone 26, Maidstone–Goudhurst; 297 Tunbridge Wells–Goudhurst–Tenterden (*alight Goudhurst*, 1 *m*)

LYMPNE CASTLE

KENT

Romantic mediaeval castle with an earlier Roman, Saxon and Norman history. It was rebuilt about 1360. 300 feet above the well known Roman Shore Fort—Stutfall Castle. Four miles from the ancient Cinque Port of Hythe, it commands a tremendous view across Romney Marshes to Fairlight over the great sweep of the coast from Dover to Dungeness and across the sea to France.

OPENING TIMES OPPOSITE

MOUNT EPHRAIM GARDENS

HERNHILL, Nr. FAVERSHAM, KENT

These gardens were laid out in 1912 on land belonging to the Dawes family for 300 years but two World Wars virtually reduced them to a wilderness. When Mr. & Mrs. Bill Dawes took over in 1951 they tackled the problem without knowledge but with energy and enthusiasm, gradually restoring the old serenity and beauty. There is a herbaceous border with adjacent topiary, rose terraces leading to a small lake and woodland area, an extensive Japanese rock garden and a diversity of shurbs and plants throughout. Mature trees frame fine views over the surrounding countryside.

PENSHURST PLACE KENT

The Family Home of William Philip Sidney, Viscount De L'Isle, VC, KG

Penshurst Place is one of the outstanding Stately Homes in Britain. The core of the house is the breathtaking Great Hall of a crenellated 14th century manor, extended down the centuries into a fascinating amalgam of period gothic which exemplifies the maxim of unity within diversity. Here can be traced the development of the English Country House from medieval to modern times. The pageant of history is thronged with residents of Penshurst, including King Henry VIII and Sir Philip Sidney, the flower of Elizabethan chivalry. The present owner, William Sidney, Viscount De L'Isle, VC, KG, is the eighteenth in succession of his family to make his home here since 1552. Penshurst is situated in a picturesque Kentish valley at the confluence of the infant Medway with the river Eden. In these tranquil and rural surroundings it is difficult to realise that the centre of London is little more than 30 miles away. Penshurst is the ideal setting for a family outing with much to enjoy by adults and children alike. The fine State Rooms contain a notable collection of early portraits, tapestry and splendid furniture. The great walled garden offers many surprises with its diverse enclosures, formal parterre and an orchard made famous through the poetry of Edmund Spenser. Children love the Toy Museum and Venture Playground. There are pleasant walks and picnic areas, a free car park for visitors to Penhurst Place and a restaurant for light refreshments and afternoon teas. Limited access for wheelchairs. No dogs admitted except Guide Dogs for the Blind.

FOR OPENING DETAILS SEE ENTRY UNDER KENT. For all enquiries and for Party Bookings please contact:- The Comptroller, Penshurst Place, Penshurst, Tonbridge, Kent. TN11 8DG. Telephone: Penshurst (0892) 870307.

LULLINGSTONE CASTLE

EYNSFORD, KENT

Lullingstone Castle, historic family mansion, frequented by Henry VIII and Queen Anne, still lived in by descendants of the original owners who built it nearly 500 years ago.

OPENING TIMES OPPOSITE

Property of Maureen, Marchioness of Dufferin and Ava

THE OWL HOUSE

LAMBERHURST, KENT

13 acres of Romantic Walks, Spring flowers, Azaleas, Roses, Rhododendrons, Rare Shrubs, Woodland Lakes.

The setting of Marchioness Dufferin and Ava's 16th century "Owlers" or Smugglers' Haunt.

Gardens open all the year daily (except Tuesdays and Thursdays) and weekends including all Bank Holiday weekends 11 a.m.–6 p.m. Admission: Adults £1.00, Children 50p. Dogs on lead.

PATTYNDENNE MANOR

GOUDHURST, KENT

Pattyndenne is one of the great ancient timber houses of England. Built of oak in 1470 before bricks, chimneys, and Columbus's discovery of the Americas. In Tudor times the home of the personal standard bearer to Henry VIII and Elizabeth I. Features include the Banqueting Hall, King Post, Dragon Beams, oak trees at each corner, enormous fireplaces. Pattyndenne is still lived in as a family home.

KENT—*continued*

PROPERTY (*showing map reference*)	LOCATION (*with nearest Rly. Stn.*)	OPENING TIMES AND ADMISSION CHARGES CATERING FACILITIES	COACH AND RAIL TOURS BUS SERVICES (*showing alighting points*)
PENSHURST PLACE, *map 6 D* **Tunbridge Wells** *The Rt. Hon. Viscount De L'Isle, V.C., K.G.* The early house, including the Great Hall, dates from 1340. There were later additions but the whole house conforms to the English Gothic style in which it was begun	In Penshurst village on B2176. W of Tonbridge & Tunbridge Wells *Stn: Penshurst (2 m)*	April 1 to Oct. 7—Daily (except Mons.). Open Good Friday & Bank Hol. Mons. GROUNDS (Gardens, Home Park, Venture Playground, Nature Trial) 12.30–6. HOUSE (Great Hall, Staterooms, Toy Museum, & Shop) 1–5.30. Adm. inclusive £2.35, Chd. £1, O.A.Ps. £2. Free car Car park & picnic area for use of visitors to Penhurst Place only. No dogs (except Guide Dogs). Restaurant (self-service; refreshment & afternoon teas ☎ *Penshurst* (0892) 870307	National Coach tours from Essex, Medway towns & South Coast resorts Green Line 704 from London (Victoria) to Sevenoa Tonbridge and Tunbridge Wells. Maidstone and District 231, 232, 233, 287 fr Tunbridge Wells Rail to Hildenborough, Tonbridge or Tunbridge W from Charing Cross. *(Taxis usually available Tonbridge & Tunbridge We*
PORT LYMPNE *map 6 D* **ZOO PARK, MANSION & GARDENS** **Lympne, Hythe** *John Aspinall, Esq.* Early 20th cent. house in Dutch colonial style with Moorish patio, Rex Whistler Tent Room, Wildlife Art Gallery, Wildlife Photographic Exhibition etc. Gardens. Woodlands. Zoo Trek	3 m W of Hythe; 6 m W of Folkestone; 7 m SE of Ashford; off A20 *Stn: Sandling (4 m)*	All the year—Daily. *Closed Christmas Day.* Adm. charges not available at time of going to press. Free car park. cafeteria ☎ *Hythe* (0303) 60618/9	Nat. Bus
QUEBEC HOUSE, Westerham *map 6 C* *The National Trust* Probably early 16th century in origin, now mainly 17th century. Relics of General Wolfe.	At junct. of Edenbridge & Sevenoaks rds (A25 & B2026) *Stns: Sevenoaks (4m); Oxted (4 m)*	March—Suns. only 2–6. April to October—Daily (except Thurs. & Sats.), inc. Good Friday, 2–6. Last adm. 5.30. Adm. £1.10, Chd. 55p. *Pre-booked parties* 80p. No dogs. Unsuitable for wheelchairs. ☎ *Westerham* 62206	Green Line 705 London Country 410, Bromley–Reigate; 483 Croyd –Sevenoaks *(alight Westerham)*
QUEX PARK, Birchington *map 3 M* *Powell Cotton Museum Trustees* Furnished rooms in Regency and Victorian house adjoining museum of natural history and ethnography. Fine dioramas of African and Asian mammals. Set amidst parkland and woods with grounds, extensive lawns and many beautiful specimen trees.	In Birchington, ½ m S of B'ton Sq (signposted). SW of Margate; 13 m E. of Canterbury *Stn: Birchington (1m)*	April & May—Thurs. & Suns.; June to Sept.—Weds., Thurs. & Suns. (also Fris. during Aug.): 2.15–6. Open Bank Hols. in summer. Adm. 80p, Chd. 50p. Parties on other days by arrangement. Ground floor rooms & museum only suitable for disabled. tea room, light refreshments. ☎ *Thanet* (0843) 42168	East Kent 53, 70 to Park Lane
RIVERHILL HOUSE, Sevenoaks *map 6 D* *Major David Rogers* Small country house, home of the Rogers family since 1840. Panelled rooms, portraits and interesting memorabilia. Fine collection of mature trees. Sheltered terraces with shrubs and roses. Azaleas and rhododendrons in woodland setting. Ancient trackway known as "Harold's Road". A display of family treasures —450 years of CHRISTIAN HERITAGE on view in the house during Exhibition.	2 m S of Sevenoaks on rd to Tonbridge (A225) *Stn: Sevenoaks (2 m)*	April 1 to Aug. 31. GARDEN open Suns. & Mons. 12–6. Adm. 75p, Chd. 30p. Picnics allowed. Free car park. *No dogs.* Exhibition "Smithfield to Sevenoaks" July 15 to Aug. 5 daily 2–5.30. Adm. £2.25. No children. VI Form students & Friends of H.H.A. £1.50. House open only for group bookings except for period of Exhibition. Adm. £1. House & Garden £1.50. No children. No party bookings Suns. or Bank Hols. All group visits please contact Mrs. Rogers in writing or tel. Sevenoaks (0732) 452557/ 458802 catering for 20–60 in Old Stable; morning coffee, Ploughman's lunches, home made teas, refreshments	No local bus service Frequent main line trains from London (Chari Cross) to Sevenoaks (½ *hr*) then by taxi
ROYDON HALL, nr. Maidstone *map 6 D* *The World Government of the Age of Enlightenment—Great Britain* Manor House of 16th century origin. Rare wood panelled interiors. A residential academy for Transcendental Meditation and TM-Sidhi programme, founded by His Holiness Maharishi Mahesh Yogi. Beautiful views.	10 m SW of Maidstone. 35 m London. Off Seven Mile Lane (B2016) just S of crossing A26 *Stn: Yalding (2½ m)*	March 21 to October 17—Weds., Suns. & Bank Hols. 1.30–4.30 (guided tours between 1.30 & 4). *Parties throughout the year by arrangement.* Adm. (1983 rates) £1.30, O.A.Ps. £1, Chd. (under 14) 60p, (under 8, free). Reduced rates for parties by prior arrangement any day except Suns. *Closed Good Friday & Christmas week.* N.B. The right is reserved to close without prior notice. Free car park. teas (inc. in adm. charge except Chd. under 8, tea 30p) ☎ *Maidstone* (0622) 812121	British Rail from Charing Cross to Paddock Wo *(taxis usually available)*
ST. JOHN'S JERUSALEM GARDEN, **Dartford** *map 6 D* *The National Trust* Large garden, moated by River Darent. The House, the main walls of which formed the church of a Commandery of the Knights Hospitallers, was altered in later centuries. Only the former chapel and garden are open to the public.	3 m S of Dartford at Sutton-at-Hone on E side of A225 *Stn: Farningham Rd (¾ m)*	GARDEN & FORMER CHAPEL ONLY. April to end October—Weds. 2–6. Adm. 30p. *No reduction for parties or children. No dogs.* Wheelchair access to garden only.	London Country 492, from Dartford or Sidcup *(alight Sutton-at-Hone)*
SALTWOOD CASTLE, nr Hythe *map 3 S* *The Hon. Alan Clark, M.P. & Mrs. Clark* Norman castle, subject of quarrel between Thomas à Becket and Henry II. Grounds and parts of Castle including battlement walk, undercroft, armoury	2 m NW of Hythe; from A20 turn S at sign to Saltwood *Stn: Sandling (1½ m)*	*Saltwood Castle is closed to the general public in* 1984. Private parties of 20 or more can be accommodated following an *appointment confirmed in writing.* ☎ *Hythe* (0303) 67190 (*Secretary*)	E. Kent 110 Hythe–Sandling, 113 Hythe–Saltwood
SANDLING PARK, nr Hythe *map 3 S* *Major A. E. Hardy* Large garden with good views and fine trees; rhododendrons, azaleas, magnolias and big collection of primulas in woodland setting	½ m from M20, exit 11; ent. off A20 only; 2 m NW of Hythe *Stn: Sandling (¼ m)*	GARDEN ONLY—Suns.: May 6, 13, 20, 27 & June 3: 10–5. Adm. £1, Chd. (under 16) 20p. Plants for sale. No dogs. *In aid of National Gardens' Scheme.*	Maidstone/E. Kent Jt. 10, 10A, 10B, Maidstone Ashford–Folkestone *(alight Newingreen, 1 m)* East Kent 99, Folkestone–Hythe–Ashford *(alight Newingreen, 1 m)* 110, Hythe–Sandling Junct. *(alight S. Junct., ¼ m*
SCOTNEY CASTLE GARDEN, *map 6 D* **Lamberhurst** *The National Trust* Romantic landscape garden framing moated castle, 14th century and later.	1½ m SE of Lamberhurst (A21) *Stn: Wadhurst (5½ m)*	GARDEN ONLY: April to end of Oct.—Weds. to Fris. 11–6 or sunset if earlier (*closed Good Friday*); Sats., Suns. & Bank Hol. Mons. 2–6 or sunset if earlier. Last adm. half-hour before closing. OLD CASTLE: May 2 to Aug. 27—days & times as for Garden. Adm. April, Sept. & Oct. £1.50, Chd. 75p (£1.60 & 80p respectively when Old Castle open). Parties by prior appointment £1 (£1.20 when Old Castle open). *No reduction on Sats., Suns. or Bank Hol. Mons. No dogs.* Shop. Wheelchairs provided (garden only, not exhibition. ☎ *Lamberhurst* (0892) 890651	National tours from Medway towns & East Kent National Coach 034, 037, London–Hastings *(alight Chequers Inn, Lamberhurst)* Maidstone 250, 256, 260, Tunbridge Wells–Wadhur connections for Hawkhurst *(alight Spray Hill or Lamberhurst)* Pilchers Coaches from Chatham
SISSINGHURST CASTLE GARDEN, **Sissinghurst** *map 6 D* *The National Trust* A famous garden created by the late V. Sackville-West and Sir Harold Nicolson between the surviving parts of an Elizabethan mansion	2 m NE of Cranbrook; 1 m E of Sissinghurst village (A262) *Stn: Staplehurst (5½ m)*	April to Oct. 14—Tues. to Fris. 1–6.30; Sats., Suns. & Good Friday 10–6.30. *Closed Mons. in Bank Hols.* Adm. Tues. to Sats. £2.20; Suns. £2.60, Chd. half-price. Pre-booked parties £1.70, Chd. £1.10. No dogs. Shop. No picnics in garden. Adm. to wheelchair visitors is restricted to 2 at any one time. *Liable to serious overcrowding Suns.* in the Oast House Restaurant. *Good Friday to Oct. 14–Tues. to Suns. (inc. Good Friday)* 10–6. *Closed Mons.*. ☎ *Cranbrook* 712850	Maidstone 4, 5 from Medway towns, Maidstone Hastings *(alight Sissinghurst Village, 1 m)*

QUEBEC HOUSE

WESTERHAM, Kent

THE NATIONAL TRUST

A. F. Kersting photograph

In this house, which is almost square with three pointed gables on each side, and of typical Kent red brick, General Wolfe spent his early boyhood. The house contains relics of Wolfe and there is a new exhibition about the Battle of Quebec in the Tudor stable block behind the house.

OPENING TIMES OPPOSITE

RIVERHILL HOUSE

SEVENOAKS, KENT

between Sevenoaks and Tonbridge on A225

Riverhill is known for its interesting garden and fine views across the Kentish countryside.

GARDEN open every SUNDAY and MONDAY from April 1st to August 31st, 12 noon–6 p.m. Booked parties throughout the week.

HOUSE open ONLY to booked parties during above period. CHRISTIAN HERITAGE EXHIBITION "Smithfield to Sevenoaks". See opposite.

SALTWOOD CASTLE **KENT**

One of the finest Norman Castles in private ownership. Famous 'Battlement Walk' rings the Inner Bailey. Mediaeval Undercroft, torture chamber. Dungeon where Thorpe the Lollard was imprisoned for sixteen years. Ruined 13th century chapel.

Formerly lived in by the wicked Sir Ralph de Broc, murderer of Thomas à Becket and more recently by Lord Clark of *Civilisation* fame, part of whose art collection is housed in the Keep which is open to private parties by appointment.

Special V.I.P. tours conducted by members of the family, including sherry in the Great Library, for pre-booked parties at extra charge.

Tea-shop exclusively home-made with produce from the estate.

N.B. Saltwood Castle is closed to the general public in 1984. Private parties of 20 or more can be accommodated following an appointment confirmed in writing.

"Aerofilms Ltd" photograph

"B.T.A." photograph

SCOTNEY CASTLE GARDEN

LAMBERHURST, KENT

THE NATIONAL TRUST

This romantic castle, started in 1379, is hidden in a deep wooded valley where a wide moat reflects the grey ruined mansion, and rust-stained tower. Its setting is the picturesque landscape garden belonging to Scotney Castle, the home of Mrs. Christopher Hussey. Its great trees, massed daffodils and azaleas, quarry garden and lush waterside vegetation afford a beauty and peace at all seasons.

The house is not open to the public. Garden open April to October inclusive; the Old Castle open May 2nd to August 27th.

OPENING TIMES OPPOSITE

ROYDON HALL **Nr. MAIDSTONE, KENT**

Set in the heart of the Garden of England, Roydon Hall has a delightful view over the Weald of Kent. Over a period of 400 years this beautiful English manor house has been the cherished home of 3 families; the Roydons, the Twysdens and the Cooks. Originally called "Fortune", the house was acquired in the early 16th century by Thomas Roydon who added the gardens and fortified towers.

Subsequent owners have been good country squires, doing their duty to their God, King, and country. The atmosphere of stability, contentment, and serenity is greatly enhanced by its present use as an academy of the World Government of the Age of Enlightenment—Great Britain, the organisation dedicated to improving the quality of life through the Transcendental Meditation and TM-Sidhi programme, founded by His Holiness Maharishi Mahesh Yogi.

Come to Roydon Hall and enjoy the peaceful atmosphere of this great historic house.

Outstanding features include the Elizabethan wood panelling; the 16th century Tudor brick entrance with 4-centred arch and octagonal towers; fine examples of decorated chimney stacks; garden clock tower.

Beautiful views. Exhibitions on the Transcendental Meditation and TM-Sidhi Programme. Parties and lectures catered for. Teas available. ☎ Maidstone (0622) 812121.
(Approximately 1 hour from London by the M20 and 20 minutes from Maidstone or Tonbridge.)

OPENING TIMES OPPOSITE

KENT—*continued*

PROPERTY (*showing map reference*)	LOCATION (*with nearest Rly. Stn.*)	OPENING TIMES AND ADMISSION CHARGES CATERING FACILITIES	COACH AND RAIL TOURS BUS SERVICES (*showing alighting points*)
SMALLHYTHE PLACE, Tenterden *map 6 D* *The National Trust* The Ellen Terry Memorial Museum. Timbered 16th century yeoman's home. Relics of Dame Ellen Terry, Mrs. Siddons etc.	2 m S of Tenterden on E side of Rye Rd (B2082) *Stns. Rye (8 m); Appledore (8 m)*	March—Sats. & Suns. only; April to end of Oct.—Daily (except Tues. & Fris.) 2–6 or dusk if earlier. *Closed Good Friday.* Last adm. half-hour before closing. Adm. £1, Chd 50p. *Parties should give advance notice—no reduction. No parties in August.* No indoor photography. No dogs. Unsuitable for wheelchairs. ☎ *Tenterden* 2334 ☕ The Spinning Wheel & The Tudor Rose. Tenterden.	Maidstone 12, Tenterden–Rye (*not Suns.*) (*alight Smallhythe*)
SPRIVERS GARDEN, Horsmonden *map 6 D* *Mr. & Mrs. Michael Dibben* *(The National Trust)* Gardens within gardens, having some unusual plants and shrubs, herbaceous borders, architectural temples and ornaments. Parts of the garden under restoration and replanting. Small collection of Waterfowl. Woodland walks and avenues being re-opened and planted	3 m N of Lamberhurst on B2162; 10 m SE of Tonbridge *Stn: Paddock Wood (4 m)*	April to end of Sept.—Weds. only 2–5.30. Adm. 50p, Chd. 25p. No reductions for parties. No dogs. Wheelchair access.	Maidstone 297 Tenterden–Tunbridge Wells (*not Suns.*)
SQUERRYES COURT, Westerham *map 6 D* *J. St. A. Warde, Esq.* ✿ William and Mary manor house. Period furniture, paintings, tapestries and china. Objects of interest connected with General Wolfe. Attractive grounds with lake, fine display of spring bulbs, rhododendrons and azaleas.	Western outskirts of Westerham on A25 *Stn: Oxted (3½ m)*	March to Oct.—Sats., Suns. & Bank Hol. Mons.; also Weds., May to Sept.: 2–6 (last adm. 5.30). *Closed Good Friday.* Adm. House & Grounds £1.20, Chd. (under 14 yrs.) 60p; Grounds only 60p, Chd. (under 14 yrs.) 30p. Parties over 20 (any day except Suns.) by arrangement at reduced rates. Dogs on leads in grounds only. Free parking at house ☎ *Westerham* (0959) 62345 *or* 63118 ☕ homemade teas at weekends & for booked parties	London Country 410, Bromley–Reigate (*alight near entrance*)
Δ **STONEACRE, Otham** *map 6 D* *The National Trust* A half-timbered small manor house, c. 1480	In Otham, 3 m SE of Maidstone; 1 m S of A20 *Stn: Bearsted (2 m)*	April to September—Weds. & Sats. 2–6. Adm. 90p, Chd. 45p. No reduction for parties No dogs. Unsuitable for wheelchairs.	Maidstone 12B, Maidstone–Leeds (*alight The White Horse, Otham, ¼ m*)
SWANTON MILL, Mersham *map 6 D* *Mrs. G. Christiansen* ✿ Working water mill. 3 acre garden	2 m from A20 *Stn: Ashford (5 m)*	GARDENS: April to Sept.—Sats. & Suns. 3–6. At other times by appointment. Adm. £1, Chd. 50p ☎ *Aldington* 223 *or* 01-937 0931	East Kent 99, Folkestone–Mersham–Ashford (*alight Broad Oak*) (*not Suns.*)
TEMPLE MANOR, Rochester *map 6 D* *Dept. of the Environment* Surviving building comprises 13th cent. stone hall with a vaulted undercroft, 17th cent. extensions	¾ m S of Strood High St. near A2 *Stn: Strood (1 m)*	April to Sept.—Weekdays 9.30–6.30; Suns. 2–6.30 Adm. 30p, Chd. (under 16 yrs.) & O.A.Ps. 15p.	Local services 140, 141 (*alight Priory Rd*) Maidstone 150, 152, Gillingham–West Malling–Maidstone (*alight Strood Cemetery*) National Coach 031 from London
TONBRIDGE CASTLE, Tonbridge *map 6 D* *Tonbridge & Malling District Council* ✿ Built by Richard de Fitzgilbert and mentioned in the Domesday Book the remains of the castle overlook the River Medway. Only orthodox large motte-and-bailey in Kent. Adjoining mansion dates from mid 18th cent. Gardens.	In town centre off High St. *Stn: Tonbridge*	April 20 to July 20—Weekends & Bank Hols. only. *Parties of 30 or more at other times by arrangement.* July 21 to Sept. 9—Daily 11.30–1, 2–5.30. Adm. 55p, Chd. & O.A.Ps. 30p. School parties 25p per Chd. (minimum charge £9.50—1 adult per 10 Chd. free) ☎ *West Malling* (0732) 844522 *Ext.* 432	Local buses stop in High Street, opposite (near Castle).
WALMER CASTLE, (1540) Walmer *map 3 S* *Dept. of the Environment* ✿ Built for coastal defence. The residence of the Lord Warden of the Cinque Ports	On coast at Walmer 2 m S of Deal off the Dover–Deal rd *Stn: Walmer (1¼ m)*	All the year: March 15 to Oct. 15—Weekdays (except Mons.) 9.30–6.30; Suns. 2–6.30. Oct. 16 to March 14—Weekdays (except Mons.) 9.30–4; Suns. 2–4. Open Bank Hol. Mons. *Closed Dec. 24, 25 & 26; Jan. 1; also when Lord Warden of the Cinque Ports is in residence. Gardens closed during winter.* Adm.: summer—90p, Chd. (under 16) & O.A.Ps. 50p; winter—50p, Chd. (under 16) & O.A.Ps. 25p.	Valliant Cronshaw tours from London East Kent–local service 385 Deal–Kingsdown (*alight gates*); 80, 80A Dover–Deal (*alight Granville Rd*)

LANCASHIRE

PROPERTY (*showing map reference*)	LOCATION (*with nearest Rly. Stn.*)	OPENING TIMES AND ADMISSION CHARGES CATERING FACILITIES	COACH AND RAIL TOURS BUS SERVICES (*showing alighting points*)
ASTLEY HALL, Chorley *map 5 C* *Chorley Borough Council* (1922) Elizabethan house reconstructed in 1666. Furniture, pottery, tapestries, pictures	2 m NW town centre on A6 (ftpath access only to Hall ¾ m) or A581 (car access, turn r. after 1½ m—signposted)	All the year: April to September—Daily 12–5.30; October to March—Mons. to Fris. 12–3.30; Sats. 10–3.30; Suns. 11–3.30. Adm. 55p, Chd. (accompanied by adult) 15p; Chd. (unaccompanied) 35p, O.A.Ps. & registered unemployed 15p. (prices subject to review in April 1984). Large free car park. ☕ at the Hall (*summer months*)	Local services (*alight rear of Hall*) Express Services Manchester–Preston–Blackpool–*frequent* (*alight Chorley*) Ribble services from Wigan, Blackburn, Bolton & Preston *frequent* (*stop at park gate ¾ m*)
BROWSHOLME HALL, nr Clitheroe *map 5 A* Δ Home of the Parker family, Bowbearers of the Forest of Bowland. Tudor with Elizabethan front, Queen Anne Wing and Regency additions. Portraits, furniture and antiquities. Guided tours by members of the family	5 m NW of Clitheroe; off B6243; Bashall Eaves — Whitewell signposted	Easter week (April 21–29); Spring Bank Hol. Weekend (May 26–28); every Sat. in June, July & Aug. and daily Aug. 18–27; 2–5. Adm. House, Grounds & Picnic site £1.20, Chd. 60p. Reductions for booked parties at other times by arrangement with Mrs. Parker. ☎ *Stoneyhurst* 330	No reasonable public transport.
GAWTHORPE HALL, Padiham *map 5 C* *The National Trust* Early 17th century manor house restored in 1850s. Fine panelling and moulded ceilings. Houses Kay-Shuttleworth collection of lace and embroidery and Ryder Collection of early European furniture	On E outskirts of Padiham (¾ m drive to house is on N of A671 E of Padiham Adult Centre) *Stn: Rose Grove (2m)*	March 16 to October 31—Weds., Sats., Suns. & Bank Hol. Mons.; also Tues. in July & Aug.: 2–6. Adm. (subject to alteration) 80p, Chd. 40p Pre-booked conducted parties—details from the Warden. Craft Gallery open daily (except Mons. & Good Friday) 2–5. Adm. free. Shop. No dogs. Wheelchairs in garden only. *N.B. Hall is only partly on view as it is let to Lancashire County Council* ☕ Tea-room open to all at weekends, 3–5. ☎ *Padiham* 78511	Ribble, 150, Preston–Blackburn–Burnley (*alight near gates in Victoria rd*)
HOGHTON TOWER, nr Preston *map 5 C* *Sir Bernard de Hoghton, Bt.* ✿ Dramatic 16th century fortified hill-top mansion with the magnificent Banqueting Hall where James I knighted the 'Loin of Beef 'in 1617. Permanent collection of antique dolls and dolls' houses. Walled gardens and Old English Rose Garden.	5 m E of Preston on A675	Easter Sat., Sun. & Mon., then Suns. to end of Oct., also Sats. in July & Aug. & all Bank Hols.: 2–5. Adm. £1, Chd. 50p. School parties—Chd. 25p. Private visits welcome (minimum 25 persons) at any time throughout week. Apply Secretary, Hoghton Tower, Preston PR5 0SH. Souvenir & Craft Shop. ☕ Tea rooms ☎ *Hoghton* (025-485) 2986	Ribble from Preston & Blackburn (*half hourly*) (*alight entrance to drive*)
LEIGHTON HALL, Carnforth *map 5 A* Δ *Mr. & Mrs. R. G. Reynolds* Mid 12th century House rebuilt in the late 18th century with a neo Gothic facade added in 1800. Home of the Gillow family containing early and prototype Gillow furniture. Extensive grounds and gardens. Displays with trained eagles and falcons at 3.30 p.m. Largest antique Doll House in the north.	2 m W of A6 thro' Yealand Conyers; signposted from M6, exit 35 jct. with A6. *Stns: Silverdale (1½ m, bridlepath only); Carnforth (2½ m)*	May to Sept.—Suns., Bank Hol. Mons. & Tues. to Fris.: 2–5 (last tour of House, 4.30). Other times by appointment for parties of 25 or more. Special Educational Programme for Schools—mornings from 10 a.m. Adm. House & Grounds £1.20. Chd. 80p. Teachers with schools, free. Antique Dolls' House 40p. Chd. 30p. Enquiries: Mr. or Mrs. Reynolds, at the Hall. ☎ 0524 734474 Schools Programme—Mr. A. Oswald ☎ 0524 701353 ☕ teas at the Hall. Salad lunches/high teas for booked parties. ✕ Bar meals & Restaurant—Warton Grange (1 *m*)	Ribble 554, Kendal–Lancaster & Carnforth (*alight Warton Village stores or Friends' Meeting House, Yealand*) B.R. Lancaster–Barrow (*alight Silverdale public footpath over Leighton Moss R.S.P.B. Reserve*)

SMALLHYTHE PLACE

The Ellen Terry Memorial Museum

TENTERDEN, KENT

THE NATIONAL TRUST

G. Douglas Bolton photograph

A yeoman's timbered house dating from the 16th century which was owned by Dame Ellen Terry from 1899 until she died there in 1928. The house contains personal and theatrical relics of Dame Ellen, Sir Henry Irving, Mrs. Siddons and others.

OPENING TIMES OPPOSITE

SQUERRYES COURT

Westerham, Kent

The House, built in 1681, is a typical William and Mary period Manor House which has been owned and occupied by the Warde family for 250 years. The interior contains a fine collection of paintings by Old Masters—tapestries—period furniture and china. The Wolfe Room has pictures and other objects of interest connected with General Wolfe—a friend of the family—who received his first commission in the grounds where a Cenotaph commemorates the occasion.

The grounds, with woodland walks, formal garden and an attractive lake, contain many fine trees and a notable display of spring bulbs, azaleas and rhododendrons.

Home-made teas at weekends and for booked parties.

Jeremy Whitaker photograph

Open March to end of October—Saturdays, Sundays and Bank Holiday Mondays; also Wednesdays from May to end of September: 2—6 p.m. (last adm. to House 5.30 p.m.)

TONBRIDGE CASTLE

TONBRIDGE, KENT

The remains of the Norman castle overlook the River Medway. Built by Richard de FitzGilbert the castle is mentioned in Domesday Book. Only orthodox large motte-and-bailey in Kent, the gatehouse is a fine example of 13th c. fortification with four massive towers and a dungeon. The Fitzgilberts were the owners for 250 years during which time the castle was linked with many events of national history. The adjoining mansion dates from mid 18th c. and the castle grounds are now laid out as attractive public gardens.

SPRIVERS

HORSMONDEN, KENT

Tranquil garden, unusual plants mixed with old favourites, set on sloping land on the outskirts of Horsmonden. Approached by an old Chestnut Avenue with new planting. Gardens within gardens, lawns and paths, fountains, ornaments and temples. Woodland walks and avenues being opened up and replanted.

OPENING TIMES OPPOSITE

Leighton Hall

CARNFORTH

Signposted from Junct. 35 M6 & A6 north of Carnforth

One of Britain's most beautifully sited houses with the Lakeland Fells as a backcloth. Home of the Gillow family it contains much of their early and prototype work.

DAILY, WEATHER PERMITTING, FLYING DISPLAYS WITH TRAIND BIRDS OF PREY.

A comprehensive morning educational programme for schools. 1983 SANDFORD AWARD WINNER.

Antique American Doll House, 12 ft. long 1 in. to 1ft. scale. Adm. charge extra.

HOGHTON TOWER

Lancashire

5 miles east of Preston on A675; M6 Exit 28, M61 Exit 8

Historic Hoghton Tower. Dramatic 16th century Fortified Hilltop Mansion. The seat of Sir Bernard de Hoghton, Bt. As seen in 'The Roots of England' and 'Lancashire Witches' on B.B.C. TV. Spend a few hours in this delightful historic mansion where, in the magnificent

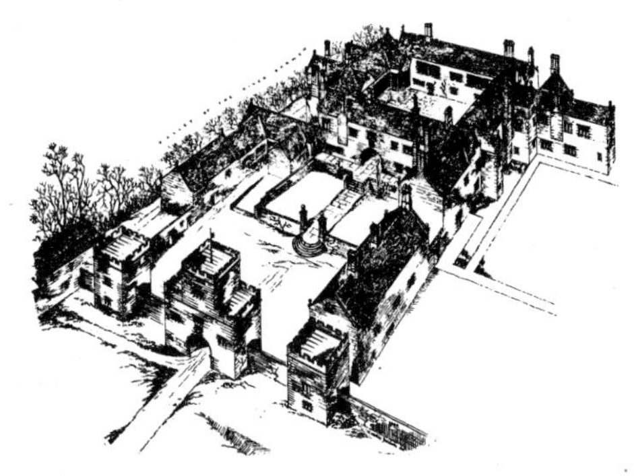

Banqueting Hall James I knighted the loin of beef in 1617. Permanent exhibition of Dolls and Dolls Houses and historic Hoghton Documents. Gift Shop. Tea Rooms. Special catering for private parties and functions. Exciting events throughout the year. Open Easter Saturday, Sunday and Monday; every Sunday until the end of October; Saturdays and Sundays July and August; all Bank Holidays. Admission £1. Children 50p. School parties, children 25p. Private visits welcome, minimum 25 at any time throughout the week. Apply Secretary, Hoghton Tower, Preston PR5 0SH. Tel. (0254) 852986.

RUFFORD OLD HALL

ORMSKIRK, LANCASHIRE

THE NATIONAL TRUST

G. Douglas Bolton photograph

Thought by many to be the finest timber-framed house in Lancashire the magnificent mediaeval Great Hall at Rufford is noted for its unique, movable screen. There are collections of arms and armour, fine 17th century oak furniture and costumes. The domestic life of cottage and farmstead in Lancashire during the 18th and 19th centuries is brought to life through the many fascinating relics to be seen here.

OPENING TIMES SEE PAGE 90

PROPERTY (*showing map reference*)	LOCATION (*with nearest Rly. Stn.*)	OPENING TIMES AND ADMISSION CHARGES CATERING FACILITIES	COACH AND RAIL TOURS BUS SERVICES (*showing alighting points*)
LANCASHIRE—*continued*			
MEOLS HALL, Southport *map* 1 *V* *Colonel R. F. Hesketh* A 17th century house, with subsequent additions, containing an interesting collection of pictures, furniture, china, etc.	1 m N of Southport; 16 m SW of Preston; 20 m N of Liverpool; near A565 & A570. *Stn: Southport*	April to Sept.—Thurs. & Bank Hol. Mons. 2–5. Adm. £1, Chd. (accompanied by an adult) free.	Local bus services stop at Gate every 15 mins., short walk to Hall
RUFFORD OLD HALL, Rufford, nr Ormskirk *The National Trust* *map* 5 *C* One of the finest buildings of the 15th century this is remarkable for its ornate hammer-beam roof and unique screen. Fine collections of 17th century oak furniture and 16th century arms and armour and tapestries. Also museum of Lancashire life	**7 m N of Ormskirk, at N end of Rufford** village on E side of A59 *Stns: Rufford (½ m) (not Suns.); Burscough Bridge (2½ m)*	April to end of Oct.—Daily (except Fris. but open Good Friday) 2–6. Last adm. 5.30. Adm.: Hall & Garden £1.30, Chd. 65p; Garden only 50p, Chd. 25p. at the Hall (parties should book) *Rufford* (0704) 821254	National tours from Lancashire towns Ribble X61, Liverpool–Ormskirk–Preston Ribble 337, 347 Southport–Chorley (two hourly) *(alight Hesketh Arms approx 600 yds)*
SAMLESBURY HALL, nr Preston *map* 5 *C* *Samlesbury Hall Trust* 14th century Manor House owned and administered by private trust.	On A677; 6 m E of Preston; 7 m W of Blackburn	All the year—Tues. to Suns. 11.30–5 (summer), 11.30–4 (winter). *Closed Mons.* Adm. 80p, Chd. (under 16) 40p. Coach & organised parties by appointment Tues. to Fris. only. Tea room open 12 noon (coffee, lunch, teas)	Local buses from Preston & Blackburn *(half-hourly)*
Δ **THURNHAM HALL, Thurnham, nr Lancaster** *map* 5 *A* *Mr. & Mrs. S. H. Crabtree* House dates from the 13th century. Major portion 16th cent. with 19th cent. facade and chapel. Beautiful panelling, fine Elizabethan plasterwork; Jacobean staircase. Exhibition on the Shroud of Turin. Tour of Great Hall by Robot guide; as seen on 'Blue Peter' and other T.V. programmes.	6 m S of Lancaster on A588; 2 m from M6 jct 33 (follow Glasson Dock sign)	Easter Hols. 11–5.30. April, May, Sept. & Oct.—Mons. to Thurs. 2–5; Suns. 11–5.30. *Closed Fris. & Sats.* June, July & Aug.—Mons. to Fris. 2–5; Suns. 11–5.30. *Closed Sats.* Adm. £1, Chd. 50p, O.A.Ps. 90p. For party prices please tel. Mrs. O. Crabtree. Souvenir shop. teas at the Hall *Lancaster* 751766	Battersby's Coaches, Morecambe National Bus Co. from Heysham, Morecambe & Lancaster *(Suns. only)*
TOWNELEY HALL ART GALLERY & MUSEUM and MUSEUM OF LOCAL CRAFTS & INDUSTRIES, Burnley *Burnley Borough Council* *map* 5 *C* House dates from 14th century with 16th, 17th and 19th century modifications. Fine entrance hall	½m SE of Burnley on the Burnley–Todmorden rd (A646)	All the year—Mons. to Fris. 10–5.30 (closes 5.15 in winter); Suns. 12–5. *Closed Sats. throughout year.* Adm. free *Closed Christmas Day, Boxing Day & New Year's Day* at café in grounds *Burnley* 24213	Ribble Services, X14, X43 & X53 from Manchester Ribble 150, Preston–Burnley ; 236, Bolton–Rawtenstall–Burnley *(alight gates)* *(Corporation Bus terminus 10 mins walk)*
TURTON TOWER, Blackburn *map* 5 *C* *Borough of Blackburn* 15th century pele tower with Elizabethan farmhouse attached, standing in 8 acres of grounds. Owned by Humphrey Chetham of Manchester in the Civil War. Period furnishings, paintings, weaponry and local history room.	Chapeltown Rd., Turton. 5 m N of Bolton on B6391. *Stn: Bromley Cross*	Gardens open throughout the year—Adm. free. Tower open Saturday to Wednesday 12–6. *Closed Thurs., Fris. & Christmas Day, Boxing Day & New Year's Day.* Adm. 25p, Chd. 10p. *Bolton* (0204) 852203	Greater Manchester Transport 565 *(alight main gates)*
WHALLEY ABBEY, nr Blackburn *map* 5 *C* *Blackburn Diocesan Board of Finance Ltd.* Ancient Cistercian Abbey (now in ruins) amongst which is set a 16th century manor house now used as a Retreat and Conference House. Ribble Valley countryside	3 m S of Clitheroe; 7 m N of Blackburn & Accrington; 7 m NW of Burnley	GROUNDS ONLY: Open all year. Adm. 50p. Catering for parties only booked with the Manager, Whalley Abbey *Whalley* (0254-82) 2268	
WINDLE HALL, St. Helens *map* 5 *C* *The Lord & Lady Pilkington* Three acre walled garden, surrounded by lawns and woodland, herbaceous borders rockery, greenhouses and roses	5 m W of M6, only approach is by bridge over East Lancs. rd.	GARDEN ONLY—Suns. July 1 & Sept. 2: 2–6. Adm. 40p. Chd. (5-14 yrs. & accompanied) 30p, O.A.Ps. 30p. *In aid of National Gardens' Scheme.* in the garden	Merseyside 6, from St. Helens to Abbey rd, (½ m)
LEICESTERSHIRE			
BATTLEFIELD OF BOSWORTH PROJECT, Market Bosworth *map* 3 *E* *Leicestershire County Council* Site of the famous Battle of Bosworth Field (1485) featuring a Visitor Centre and outdoor interpretation of the Battle.	15 m W of Leicester; 2 m S of Mkt. Bosworth *Stns: Hinckley (6½m); Nuneaton (8 m)*	BATTLEFIELD CENTRE: April to Oct.—Mons. to Chd. 40p (Special Event Days excepted). Parties at any time by appointment—reduced rates. BATTLE TRAIL: All the year during daylight hours refreshments at Bosworth Buttery (April to Oct.) *Market Bosworth* (0455) 290429	Buses from Leicester (Horsefair St.) to Market Bosworth
BELGRAVE HALL, Leicester (1709-13) *Leicestershire Museums, Art Galleries & Record Service* *map* 3 *E* A small Queen Anne house and garden with furniture of 18th and early 19th century.	Off Thurcaston rd, Belgrave, 2 m from City centre on Loughboro' rd (A6) *Stn: Leicester (2½ m)*	All the year—Weekdays (except Fris.), 10–5.30, Suns. 2–5.30. Adm. free. *Closed Good Friday, Christmas Day & Boxing Day. This Museum will be closed until Easter 1984 due to major structural repairs.* *Leicester* (0533) 554100	Leicester Corp. 40 from Haymarket *(alight few yards from Hall)* Midland Red 624, from St. Margaret's Bus Stn. *(alight few yards from Hall)*
BELVOIR CASTLE, nr Grantham *map* 3 *F* *His Grace the Duke of Rutland* Seat of the Dukes of Rutland since Henry VIII's time, rebuilt by Wyatt 1816. Notable pictures, furniture, objets d'art. Special Events most Sundays. **(SEE ALSO PAGE 16)**	7 m WSW of Grantham, between A607 (to Melton Mowbray) & A52 (to Nottingham) *Stn: Bottesford (4½m)*	March 27 to Sept. 30—Tues., Weds., Thurs. & Sats. 12–6; Suns. 12–7; Bank Hol. Mons. only 11–7; Good Friday 12–6; also Suns. only in Oct. 2–6. Last adm. 40 mins. before closing. Adm. £1.80, Chd. £1. *No extra charges in Castle.* Parties of 30 or more O.A.Ps. £1; 30 or more adults £1.30; 30 or more School children £1 (accompanying teachers free). All Coach Excursion passengers £1.30. No dogs. Café at Castle *Grantham* (0476) 870262	Coach tours from Birmingham, Leics., Cambs., Lincs. Northants., Derbys., London, etc. Lincs. 31 from Grantham *(alight Woolsthorpe crossroad, 1½ m)* B.R. Merrymaker from Euston
GUILDHALL, Leicester *map* 3 *E* *Leicestershire Museums, Art Galleries & Records Service* A medieval timber building dating from 14th to 17th centuries. Mayor's Parlour, Library and old police cells	Guildhall Lane *Stn: Leicester*	All the year—Weekdays (except Fris.) 10–5.30; Sundays 2–5.30 Adm. free. *Closed Good Friday, Christmas Day & Boxing Day* *Leicester* (0533) 554100	Midland Red services from all parts of Leicestershire & adjoining counties
Δ **LANGTON HALL, nr Market Harborough** *G. R. Spencer, Esq.* *map* 3 *E* Small English country house set in beautiful parkland. Gardens laid out in the French style. Exhibition of dolls and art	In village of W. Langton 4½ m N of Mkt. Harborough, 12 m S of Leicester	Easter to Oct.—Thurs., Sats. & Suns. & Bank Hols. 2–5. Adm. £1.30, Chd. & O.A.Ps. 65p. *Other days for parties by appointment.* Souvenir shop. Garden shop. home-made cream teas, snacks *East Langton* (085 884) 240	Midland Red 613, Leicester–Market Harborough *(alight Church Langton)*
MANOR HOUSE, Donington le Heath *Leicestershire Museums, Art Galleries & Record Service* *map* 3 *E* 13th century Manor house with furniture. Herb garden	1 m SW of Coalville 13 m NW of Leicester off A50; 4 m from M1 at exit 22	April 18 to September 30—Weds., Thurs., Fris., Sats., & Suns. 2–6. Bank Hol. Mons. & Tues. 2–6 Adm. free in the Barn *Coalville* (0530) 31259	Midland Red 664, 677, 687, 688, 689 from Coalville *(alight Hugglescote ½ m)* 694 from Coalville *(alight Standard Hill ½ m)* 664 from Leicester The Newarke *(alight Hugglescote ½ m)*

THURNHAM HALL

THURNHAM, LANCASTER

Home of Mr and Mrs S. H. Crabtree

House dates from 13th century, major portion 16th century, with 19th century facade and chapel. The house contains beautiful panelling and fine Elizabethan plaster work. Jacobean staircase. Period furniture and family portraits. Tour of Great Hall by Robot guide (as seen on 'Blue Peter' and other T.V. programmes.

SITUATED: between Darwen and Bolton on the Chapeltown Road B6391

OPEN: Saturday to Wednesday 12am - 6pm including Bank Holidays

ADMISSION: Adults 25p Children 10p
Free admission to car park & grounds

TOWNELEY HALL

ART GALLERY AND MUSEUM

Burnley, Lancashire

The house contains furnished rooms including an Elizabethan Long Gallery, an Entrance Hall with plasterwork by Vassali completed in 1729. Collections include oak furniture, 18th and 19th century paintings and Zoffany's painting of Charles Towneley. Loan exhibitions are held throughout the summer. A Museum of local Crafts and Industries was opened in the Brew House in 1971.

LEICESTERSHIRE'S HERITAGE

Five historic buildings forming an important part of the architectural heritage of the country and containing complementary collections. Administered by the Leicestershire Museums, Art Galleries and Records Service.

BELGRAVE HALL Leicester. A furnished Queen Anne house and gardens on the outskirts of the town. A dairy, agricultural collection and the Beaumanor Coach c. 1740 are to be found in the stables.

THE GUILDHALL Leicester. This medieval building was once the Town Hall; it contains a notable Mayor's Parlour, an intriguing collection of exhibits relating to Law and Order and an ancient library.

THE MANOR HOUSE Donington-le-Heath. A superb example of a 13th century Manor House with some later alterations. The magnificent oak roof trusses were inserted circa 1280.

OAKHAM CASTLE Oakham. The Norman Hall of the late 12th century with its display of horseshoes given by Peers of the Realm provides an interesting link with the customs of the past.

WYGSTON'S HOUSE Leicester. A medieval house with Georgian additions forms the setting for a Museum of Costume from 1769 to 1924; in addition there are reconstructions of clothing shops of the '20s.

See the main text for opening times.

Oakham Castle.
Horseshoes from visiting Peers of the Realm.

LANGTON HALL

WEST LANGTON

near MARKET HARBOROUGH, Leics.

Langton Hall, a private home dating from mediaeval times, contains a magnificent collection of classical Chinese furniture. The drawing room walls are covered in 18th century Venetian lace and the rooms upstairs have splendid views over the beautiful Leicestershire countryside. The spacious gardens lead to a nature trail and animal paddock with exotic birds.

PRESTWOLD HALL

LOUGHBOROUGH

"Country Life" photograph

Prestwold Hall stands on the site of many earlier houses including the Priory of the Gilbertine Order. Since then it had been occupied by the Skipwith family who sold it to Sir Christopher Packe, Lord Mayor of London, during the time of Cromwell. In 1843 William Burn remodelled the house for Charles William Packe in which state it remains virtually unaltered. The house contains a considerable amount of marbled plasterwork and fine collections of English and European 18th century furniture.

Open by appointment only for parties of 20 or more.

For details see page 92

PROPERTY (*showing map reference*)	LOCATION (*with nearest Rly. Stn.*)	OPENING TIMES AND ADMISSION CHARGES CATERING FACILITIES	COACH AND RAIL TOURS BUS SERVICES (*showing alighting points*)
LEICESTERSHIRE—*continued*			
OAKHAM CASTLE, Oakham *map* 3 F *Leicestershire Museums, Art Galleries & Records Service* Late 12th century Norman hall with collection of horseshoes given by peers of the realm	N of Market Place nr town centre. Off A605 *Stn: Oakham (5 mins. walk)*	GROUNDS: April to Oct.—Daily 10–5.30. Nov. to March—Daily 10–4. CASTLE, etc.: April to Oct.—Suns. & Mons. 2–5.30; Tues. to Sats. & Bank Hols. 10–1, 5.30 Nov. to March—as above but closing at 4 p.m. Adm. free. *Closed Good Friday, Christmas Day & Boxing Day* ☎ *Oakham* (0572) 3654	United Counties 242, Stamford–Oakham–Uppingham Lincolnshire 23, Grantham–Oakham National Coach 488 from Grimsby, Lincoln, Newark, Grantham Barton 125, Melton Mowbray–Oakham 117 Nottingham–Peterborough Midland Red 623, Leicester–Oakham (*Sats. only*)
PRESTWOLD HALL, Loughborough *map* 3 A *Mr. S. Packe-Drury-Lowe* Fine early 19th century house set in large gardens. Home of the Packe family for over 300 years	2½ m NE of Loughborough	By appointment only for parties of 20 or more throughout the year. Apply in writing to the Curator. Adm. £1. The church will also be open to visitors (a voluntary donation would be appreciated)	No reasonable public transport
STANFORD HALL, Lutterworth *map* 3 E *The Lord & Lady Braye* William and Mary house dating from the 1690s. Furniture, pictures, Replica 1898 Flying Machine. Motor cycle and Car Museum. Walled rose garden leading to Old Forge. Nature Trail. Display of family costumes. Sunday Craft Centre	7½ m NE of Rugby, 3½ m from A5. 6 m from M1 at Exit 18, 4 m from M1 at exit 20. 6 m from M6 at exit 1. 1½ m from B5414 at Swinford	Easter Sun. to end of Sept.—Thurs., Sats. & Suns. also Bank Hol. Mons. & Tues. following 2.30–6. Adm. House & Grounds etc. £1.50, Chd. 70p. Grounds, Rose Garden, Flying Machine, Old Forge, Sunday Craft Centre 60p, Chd. 30p Parties of 20 or more (min. £24) £1.20, Chd. 60p; O.A.P. parties of 20 or more £1.10; School parties of 20 or more (one teacher adm. free) £1.20, Chd. 60p. Adm. prices subject to increase on Special Show days. Motor-cycle & Car Museum 60p, Chd. 30p. **N.B. On Bank Hols. the Grounds, Cafeteria, Museum, Craft Centre & Souvenir Shop open 12-6.** (pre-booked) ☎ *Rugby* (0788) 860250	Barton tours from Nottingham National tours from Derby, Alfreton, Belper, Stockport and the Midlands
WYGSTON'S HOUSE, Leicester *map* 3 E *Leicestershire Museums, Art Galleries & Records Service* Museum of Costume (1769–1924) in a medieval house with Georgian additions. Shop reconstructions	Applegate St., St. Nicholas Circle nr City centre. *Stn: Leicester*	All the year—Weekdays (except Fris.) 10–5.30; Sundays 2–5.30 Adm. free. *Closed Good Friday, Christmas Day & Boxing Day* ☎ *Leicester* (0533) 554100	Midland Red services from all parts of Leicestershire & adjoining counties
LINCOLNSHIRE			
AUBOURN HALL, nr. Lincoln *map* 3 B *H. N. Nevile, Esq.* Late 16th century house attributed to J. Smythson (Jnr.). Important carved staircase and panelled rooms	In Aubourn village 7 m S of Lincoln	July & August—Weds. 2–6; also open Suns. June 24 & July 8 or by appointment. Adm. 80p, Chd. 50p	Lincs. 7A, Lincoln–Newark (via Bassingham) (*alight Royal Oak, Aubourn*)
BELTON HOUSE, Belton *map* 3 B *The National Trust* The crowning achievement of Restoration country house architecture, built 1684–1688 for Sir John Brownlow, heir to the fortunes of a successful Elizabethan lawyer; alterations by James Wyatt 1777, plasterwork ceilings by Edward Goudge, fine wood carvings of the Grinling Gibbons school. Family portraits, furniture, tapestries, Speaker Cust's silver and siver-gilt, celebrated paintings in the Hondecoeter Room. Formal gardens, orangery by Jeffrey Wyattville, 17th century stables, magnificent landscape park.	3 m NE of Grantham on A607 Grantham–Lincoln rd; easily accessible from A1. *Stn: Grantham (3 m)*	April to end of Oct.—Weds. to Suns. & Bank Hol. Mons. 1–5.30. Park & Restaurant (due for completion mid-summer) opens at 12 noon. Adm. House £2. No reduction for parties. School parties contact the Administrator for details. 1984 Events—details from the Administrator. Kiosk provides teas, ice-creams (until new Restaurant opens when light lunches then available) ☎ *Grantham* (0476) 66116	Lincolnshire 601 Grantham–Lincoln; 609 Grantham–Sleaford
BELVOIR CASTLE—SEE UNDER LEICESTERSHIRE			
DODDINGTON HALL, Doddington *map* 3 B *Mr. & Mrs. A. G. Jarvis* Elizabethan manor house, furniture. Spring bulbs, rose garden; Schools project	In Doddington 5 m W of Lincoln	Easter Mon. then May to September—Weds., Suns. & Bank Hol. Mons. 2–6. Adm. £1.60, Chd. 80p. Gardens half-price. *Parties at other times by arrangement* ☎ *Lincoln* (0522) 694308	No reasonable public transport

STANFORD HALL

LUTTERWORTH, Leicestershire

Seat of the Cave family, ancestors of Lord Braye, since 1430

The present house was started by William Smith the Elder and finished by the famous Smith of Warwick. It contains a fine collection of Stuart pictures and relics, antique furniture and family costumes dating from Queen Elizabeth's time. Also a full size replica of the 1898 Flying Machine of Percy Pilcher, officially recognised as England's Pioneer Aviator who experimented at Stanford. He was killed flying at Stanford in 1899. There is also a fine collection of vintage Motor Cycles and several historic Motor Cars to be seen in the Museum. Nature Trail. Sunday Craft Centre.

OPENING TIMES ABOVE

THE OLD HALL

GAINSBOROUGH, Lincolnshire

15th and 16th century Manor House with fine medieval kitchen, great hall and other Rooms, Royal Visitors: Richard III 1484; Henry VIII 1509 and 1540. Manor House sold to William Hickman 1597 whose mother Rose Hickman befriended John Smyth, the Separatist. The Hall was the first meeting place of early Dissenters, later known as Pilgrim Fathers. John Wesley often preached in the Hall. Collections of Bygones. Furniture, Paintings etc.

Open weekdays 10 a.m. to 5 p.m.; also Sundays 2 to 5 p.m. from Easter to October. Closed Christmas Day, Boxing Day and New Year's Day.

PROPERTY (*showing map reference*)	LOCATION (*with nearest Rly. Stn.*)	OPENING TIMES AND ADMISSION CHARGES CATERING FACILITIES	COACH AND RAIL TOURS BUS SERVICES (*showing alighting points*)
LINCOLNSHIRE—*continued*			
FULBECK HALL, nr Grantham *map 3 B* *Mrs. D. M. Fane* Mainly 18th century house set in 11 acres garden. Home of the Fane family for 350 years. Interesting collection of furniture and pictures	On A607 Lincoln—Grantham rd, 1 m S of jct. with Newark–Sleaford rd (A17)	Bank Hol. Mons.: Easter (April 23), May 7 & 28; then August—Daily (except 6, 13 & 20) 2–6. Adm. £1, Chd. 30p, O.A.Ps. 70p. Free parking cream teas *Loveden* (0400) 72205	601, Lincoln—Grantham (*alight Fulbeck*)
FYDELL HOUSE, Boston *map 3 B* *The Boston Preservation Trust* Built 1726 by William Fydell, three times Mayor of Boston. Now houses Pilgrim College	In South Square, next door to Guildhall *Stn: Boston (¼ m)*	All the year—Mons. to Fris. only 9–12, 2.30–4.30. Adm. free *At other times by appointment with the Secretary of the Preservation Trust.*	Lincs. services from Louth, Skegness, Spalding etc Premier Travel 3, Cambridge–Boston–Skegness 34, Bedford–Boston–Skegness (*summer Sats. only*)
GRANTHAM HOUSE, Grantham *map 3 B* *The National Trust* Dating from 1380 but extensively altered and added to throughout the centuries. The grounds run down to the river.	In Castlegate, immediately E of Grantham Church *Stn: Grantham (1 m)*	April to end of Sept.—Weds. & Thurs. 2–5. Adm. 80p, Chd. half-price. No reduction for parties. No dogs. Unsuitable for wheelchairs.	Lincs. 601, Lincoln–Grantham
GRIMSTHORPE CASTLE, Bourne *map 3 B* *Grimsthorpe & Drummond Trust* The home of the Willough by de Eresby family since 1516. Examples of early 13th century architecture, the Tudor period of the reign of Henry VIII and work by Sir John Vanbrugh. State Rooms and Picture Galleries open to the Public	4 m NW of Bourne on A151 Colsterworth / Bourne rd. SE of Grantham	Castle, Garden & Grounds: July 29 to Sept. 9—Daily 2–6. Adm. £1, O.A.Ps. & Students 50p; Chd. under school-age free.	No reasonable puclic transport
GUNBY HALL, Burgh-le-Marsh (1700) *The National Trust* *map 3 B* Built by Sir William Massingberd in 1700. Reynolds' portraits, contemporary wainscoting. Walled gardens full of flowers and roses	2½ m NW of Burgh-le-Marsh, 7 m W of Skegness on S side of A158 *Stn: Skegness (7 m)*	House & Garden: April to end of Sept.—Thurs. 2–6; Tues., Weds. & Fris. by prior written appointment only to J. D. Wrisdale, Esq., Gunby Hall, nr. Spilsby, Lincs. Adm. House & Gardens £1.10, Chd. 55p. Garden only 80p, Chd. 45p. No reduction for parties. No dogs. Wheelchairs in garden only. *Scremby* 212	Lincs. 6, Lincoln–Skegness (*alight at main gates*)
HARRINGTON HALL, Spilsby *map 3 B* *Lady Maitland* Mentioned in the Domesday Book, Harrington is a Caroline Manor House standing on a medieval stone base. Panelled rooms, 17th and 18th century furniture, pictures and china. The terrace is the "High Hall Garden" of Tennyson's Maud, who lived at the Hall with her guardian	5 m E of Horncastle (A158 Lincoln/ Skegness rd); turn left on leaving Hagworthingham, signposted Harrington 2 m	House, Gardens & Garden Centre: Easter to Sept. 30—Thurs. 2–5 also Suns. April 22 (Easter), May 6, 13, 27 & July 18. Gardens & Garden Centre: April to Oct. 30—Weds. & Thurs. 12 noon–8 (or dusk if earlier) also Easter Mon. (April 23) & Suns. June 3, 17 & July 22; 2–6. Adm. (1983 rates): House, Gardens & Centre £1. Chd. 50p, O.A.Ps. 75p. Gardens & Centre only 50p, Chd. 25p, O.A.Ps. 40p.	No reasonable public transport
MARSTON HALL, Grantham *map 3 B* *Rev. Henry Thorold, F.S.A.* 16th century manor house. Interesting pictures and furniture. Held by Thorolds since 14th century. Ancient garden with notable trees. Gothick gazebo	6 m NW of Grantham 1½ m off A1	Open on certain Sundays for local charities (details to be announced in local press) and at other times by appointment. Adm. House & Garden £1. *Loveden* (0400) 50225	No reasonable public transport facilities
THE OLD HALL, Gainsborough *map 5 D* *Lincolnshire County Council* 15th century brick and timber manor house	In centre of Gainsborough *Stn: Gainsborough*	All the year—Mons to Sats. 10–5; Suns. (Easter to Oct.) 2–5. *Closed Christmas Day, Boxing Day & New Year's Day.* Adm. charge. Reductions for organised parties who may visit outside normal opening times by prior arrangement with Mrs. D. Musson, 0427 2669 (afternoons) or 3349 (evenings). at the Hall (*by previous arrangement*)	Buses to Gainsborough from Doncaster, Scunthorpe, Lincoln, Newark, Retford, Sheffield etc.
SPRINGFIELD GARDENS, Spalding *Springfields Horticultural Society* *map 3 B* Centre of the British Bulb Industry. 25 acres of landscaped gardens with over 1,000,000 spring flowers in bloom. In summer over 12,000 roses in bloom together with other displays. SPECIAL ATTRACTIONS — FLOWER PARADE DAY, MAY 5 GARDENERS' DAY OUT, JULY 15 & AUG. 19	1½ m from centre of Spalding on A151 *Stn: Spalding (2 m) (not Suns.)*	April 1 to Sept. 30—Daily 10–6. Adm.: April to mid May (except May 5, 6 & 7) £1.20. Flower Parade weekend (May 5, 6 & 7) £1.50; summer season £1. Reduction of 15% for pre-booked parties over 30. Shops etc. Licensed restaurant open all year *Spalding* (0775) 4843	Bus 505 Spalding—King's Lynn (*hourly*) (*alight entrance*) National tours. Regular coach service from Victoria, London (*Springtime only*)

PROPERTY (*showing map reference*)	LOCATION (*with nearest Rly. Stn.*)	OPENING TIMES AND ADMISSION CHARGES CATERING FACILITIES	COACH AND RAIL TOURS BUS SERVICES (*showing alighting points*)
LINCOLNSHIRE—*continued*			
TATTERSHALL CASTLE (1440) *map 3 B* *The National Trust* The Keep is one of the finest survivals of a fortified brick dwelling	12 m NE of Sleaford on Louth rd (A153); 3½ m SE of Woodhall Spa	All the year—Daily 11–6.30 (Suns. 1–6.30 or sunset if earlier). Oct. to March closed 1–2. *Closed Christmas Day & Boxing Day.* Adm. £1.10. Chd. 60p. Parties of 20 or more £1, Chd. 50p. Dogs in grounds only, on leads. Wheelchair access. ✕ Fortescue Arms Hotel, Tattersall	**Barton X9, Long Eaton–Nottingham–Skegness** (*summer only*) **Lincs. 502 Boston–Tattershall, 503 Boston–Martin** (*connections from Lincoln*)
WOOLSTHORPE MANOR, nr Grantham *The National Trust* *map 3 F* 17th century farm house, birthplace of Sir Isaac Newton	7 m S of Grantham, ½ m NW of Colsterworth; 1 m W of A1 (not to be confused with Woolsthorpe, nr. Belvoir) *Stn: Grantham (7 m)*	April to end of Oct.—Suns. to Thurs. 1.30–6. *Closed Fris. & Sats.* Adm. £1.30, Chd. half-price. No reduction for parties. *Closed Good Friday.* No dogs. Wheelchair access to garden & ground floor only. Parking for coaches limited to one at a time—please book. *N.B. In the interests of preservation numbers admitted to rooms at any one time must be limited; liable to affect peak weekends & Bank Hols.* ☎ *Grantham* (0476) 860338	Lincs. 607/8, Grantham South Witham (*not Suns.*) (*5-10 mins. walk*)
LONDON			
APSLEY HOUSE, Wellington Museum *Victoria & Albert Museum* *map 6 A* Built 1771–8. Fine paintings, porcelain, silver-plate and personal relics of first Duke of Wellington	At 149 Piccadilly, Hyde Park Corner	All the year—Tues., Weds., Thurs. & Sats. 10–6; Suns. 2.30–6. Adm. 60p, Chd. (under 16) & O.A.Ps. 30p *Closed Mons. & Fris. also Christmas Eve, Christmas Day, Boxing Day, New Year's Day & May 7.* ☎ 01-499 5676	*Und.:* Hyde Park Corner (*Piccadilly Line*) *Bus:* 2, 2B, 9, 9A, 14, 16, 16A, 19, 22, 25, 26, 30, 36, 36A, 36B, 38, 52, 73, 74, 137, 500, 506
ASHBURNHAM HOUSE, Westminster *Westminster School* *map 6 A* Formerly the home of the Earls of Ashburnham	Little Dean's Yard, SW1 *Stns: Victoria & St. James Pk.*	During school Easter holidays (*but closed Good Friday and Easter Monday*)—Mons. to Fris. 10–4. Adm. 50p, Chd 25p ☎ 01-222 3116	*Train:* Victoria *Und.:* Victoria and St. James's Park *Bus:* 11, 24, 29, 39, 88, 503
100 BAYSWATER ROAD, W2 *map 6 A* Small Regency house where Sir James Barrie wrote "Peter Pan".	On N side of Kensington Gdns.	Open January to March and October to December by written appointment only. *Unsuitable for parties of more than four.*	*Underground:* Central Line in Queensway *Bus:* 12, 88
BOSTON MANOR, Brentford *map 6 A* *London Borough of Hounslow* Jacobean house (1622) with elaborate plaster ceiling in the State Room which also contains a fireplace and mantelpiece dating from 1623. Original oak staircase. The house is set in a small park	In Boston Manor Rd.	May 26 to Sept. 29—Saturday afternoons only 2–4.30.	Local bus services
BURGH HOUSE, Hampstead *map 6 A* *Burgh House Trust* Queen Anne House (1703) with original staircase. Now a community meeting place, art gallery and local history museum. Changing exhibitions	New End Sq., 200 yds. down Flask Walk, E of Und. stn. *Stn: Hampstead (Und.)*	All the year—Weds. to Suns. 12–5; Bank Hol. Mons. 2–5. *Closed Good Friday, Christmas Eve, Christmas Day & Boxing Day.* ☎ 01-431 0144 ✕ Licensed Buttery (for bookings ☎ 01-431 2516)	*Train:* Hampstead Heath (Broad St./Richmond) *Und:* Hampstead (*Northern Line*) *Bus:* 24, 46, C11 (*alight Sth. End Green, ¼ m*) 210 (*alight Jack Straw's Castle*); 268 (*alight High St.*)
CARLYLE'S HOUSE, Chelsea (1708) *The National Trust* *map 5 A* Home of Thomas and Jane Carlyle 1834/1881 *Note: Certain rooms have no electric light, visitors wishing to make a close study of the Interior should avoid dull days.*	At 24 Cheyne Row, Chelsea, SW3 (off Cheyne Walk on Chelsea Embankm't *Stns: Sloane Sq. (Und. 1 m); Clapham Jct. (B.R. 1½ m)*	April to end of Oct.—Weds. to Suns. & Bank Hol. Mons. 11–5. Last adm. 4.30. *Closed Good Friday.* Adm. £1, Chd. half-price; O.A.Ps. 70p. No reduction for parties, which should not exceed 20. No dogs. Unsuitable for wheelchairs. ☎ 01-352 7087	*Und.:* Sloane Square then 11, 19 & 22 (*alight Old Church St.*) *Und.:* to S. Kensington then 49 to King's Rd. *Bus:* 11, 19, 22 to Old Church St., 39 to Albert Bridge
CHELSEA PHYSIC GARDEN, SW3 *map 6 A* The second oldest Botanic garden in the country, founded 1673, and only recently opened to the public, comprises 4 acres tightly packed with some 5,000 fascinating plants	66 Royal Hospital Rd., Chelsea: at jct. of Royal Hosp. Rd., Swan Walk & Chelsea Embankment; adjacent to Chelsea Flower Show site. *Stn: Sloan Sq. (Und.)*	April 22 (Easter) to Oct. 21—Suns. & Weds. 2–5. Also Bank Hols. & Tues., Weds., Thurs. & Fris. of Chelsea Flower Show week 12–5. Open at all times for groups by appointment. Adm. £1, Chd. & Students (with cards) 50p. *No dogs.* Garden accessible for disabled & wheelchairs. Parking in street Suns., *other days across Albert Bridge in Battersea Park,* free.	*Bus:* 39 from Victoria Stn. to Clapham Junction
CHISWICK HOUSE *map 6 A* *Dept. of the Environment* Villa designed by the Earl of Burlington 1725, and derived from Palladio's Villa Capra. William Kent decorated the rooms	In Burlington Lane, Chiswick, W.4 *Stn: Chiswick (½ m)*	All the year: March 15 to Oct. 15—Daily 9.30–6.30. Oct. 16 to March 14—Weds. to Suns. 9.30–4. *Closed Mons. & Tues.; also Dec. 24, 25 & 26, Jan. 1.* Adm. 50p, Chd. (under 16) & O.A.Ps. 25p. ☕ in the grounds.	*Und.:* Hammersmith (*District, Met. & Piccadilly Lines*), then bus 290 *Bus:* E3, 290 (*alight gates*)

TATTERSHALL CASTLE

LINCOLNSHIRE

THE NATIONAL TRUST

This moated castle was built about 1440 by Ralph Cromwell, Treasurer of England, but only the massive five-storey keep, 100 feet high, now remains. Museum, with model of Castle and other exhibits in the Guard House.

OPENING TIMES ABOVE

CARLYLE'S HOUSE

24, CHEYNE ROW, CHELSEA S.W.3

THE NATIONAL TRUST

Eric de Mare photograph

Carlyle's house is in the centre of old Chelsea, once the haunt of famous artists and writers. 'Eminent, antique' was Carlyle's first impression of this Queen Anne house where he was to live and work for nearly fifty years. Dickens, Chopin, Leigh Hunt, Tennyson and Emerson were among the many illustrious Victorians who came here to visit Mr. and Mrs. Carlyle. An atmosphere of past greatness lingers in this quiet old house which still contains its original furnishings and many of the books and personal possessions of the Carlyles. Jane Carlyle's bedroom and the kitchen are now open and the small garden has recently been replanted.

HISTORIC HOUSES ADMINISTERED BY THE

VICTORIA & ALBERT MUSEUM

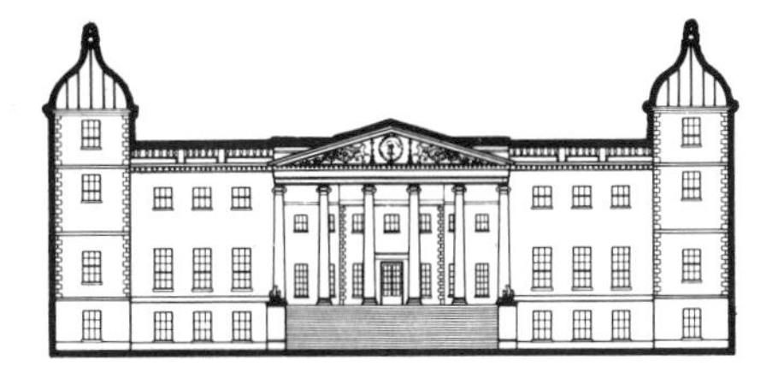

Osterley Park House

Osterley, Middlesex

An Elizabethan mansion transformed into an 18th century villa. Elegant neo-classical interior decoration designed by Robert Adam for the banker Robert Child. The state apartment comprises a Gobelins tapestry ante-room, a bedroom with embroidered velvet bed, and a dressing room decorated in the "Etruscan" style.

The house is set in a landscaped park with an Elizabethan stable block.

Apsley House

London W1

Sometimes called "Number 1, London," Apsley House was the home of the first Duke of Wellington, famous for his success in the Peninsular War and at the Battle of Waterloo (1815). Apsley House, designed by Robert Adam from 1771 to 1778, was bought by the Duke from his brother Marquis Wellesley in 1817. In 1818 the architect Benjamin Dean Wyatt was employed to alter the house and from 1828 to 1830 he added the Waterloo Gallery. Apsley House contains many Wellington relics, porcelain from Sèvres, Berlin and Meissen, magnificent silver such as the Portuguese centrepiece and the Waterloo shield.

The house is the most splendid surviving London palace of the early 19th century. Its culmination is the Waterloo Gallery, the supreme example of the revived Louis XIV style, hung with Wellington's superb paintings, many from the Spanish royal collection and including works by Velasquez, Van Dyck, Correggio, Murillo and Goya.

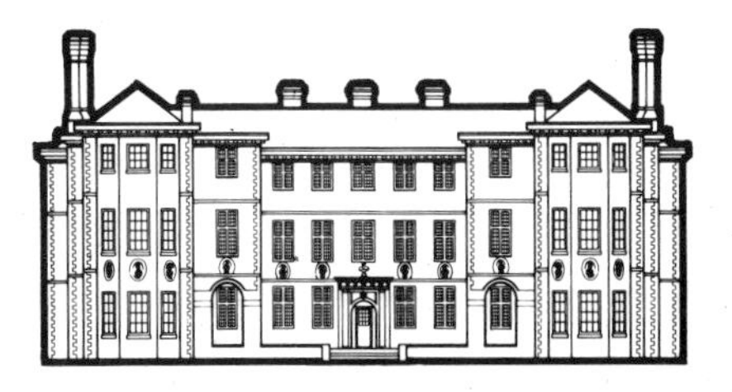

Ham House

Richmond

Ham House dates from the early 17th century but was enlarged and enriched by the Duke and Duchess of Lauderdale in the 1670s. The house contains most of the paintings and furniture which so impressed John Evelyn 300 years ago, as well as fine Georgian furnishings introduced by the Earls of Dysart.

The formal gardens have recently been returned to their 17th century plan.

PROPERTY (*showing map reference*)	LOCATION (*with nearest Rly. Stn.*)	OPENING TIMES AND ADMISSION CHARGES CATERING FACILITIES	COACH AND RAIL TOURS BUS SERVICES (*showing alighting points*)
LONDON—*continued*			
Δ **COLLEGE OF ARMS, City of London EC4V 4BT** *The Corporation of Kings Heralds & Pursuivants of Arms* *map 6 A* Mansion built in 1670s to house the English Officers of Arms and their records, and the panelled Earl Marshal's Court	On N side of Queen Victoria St.; S of St. Paul's Cathedral	EARL MARSHAL'S COURT ONLY open—All the year (except on Public holidays & on State & special occasions) Mons. to Fris. 10–4. Group visits (up to 10) by arrangement only. RECORD ROOM open for tours (groups of up to 20) by special arrangement in advance with the Registrar. Adm. free (parties by negotiation). *No coaches, parking, indoor photography or dogs.* Shop—books, souvenirs ☎ 01-248 2762	*Und:* Blackfriars, St. Paul's, Bank *Bus:* all services for St. Paul's Cathedral
THE DICKENS HOUSE, WC1N 2LF *map 6 A* *The Trustees of the Dickens House* ♿ House occupied by Dickens and his family 1837-39. Relics displayed include manuscripts, furniture, autographs, portraits, letters and first editions	48 Doughty St; nr Grays Inn Rd/Guilford St	All the year—Mons. to Sats. 10–5. *Closed Suns. & Bank & Public Hols.* Adm. £1, Students 75p, Chd. 50p; Families £2 (subject to alteration). Parties by appointment. Ground floor only (2 rooms) suitable for disabled—reduced adm. charge. ☎ 01-405 2127	*Und:* Russell Sq, Holborn, Chancery Lane, Kings Cross *Bus:* 17, 18, 46 to *Guildford St;* 19, 38, 55, 172 *to John St.*
FENTON HOUSE, Hampstead (1693) *The National Trust* *map 6 A* Collection of porcelain, pottery and Benton Fletcher collection of early keyboard musical instruments	On W side of Hampstead Grove, 300 yds N of Hampstead *Stns: Hampstead (Und. 300 yds.); Hampstead Heath (B.R. 1 m)*	March—Sats. & Suns. 2–sunset. April to Oct.—Sats. to Tues. (inc. Bank Hol. Mons.) 2–6; Weds. 2–sunset. Last adm. half-hour before closing. *Closed Good Friday.* Adm. £1.50, Chd. 75p, O.A.Ps. £1 (except Suns.). *No reduction for parties.* No dogs. Unsuitable for wheelchairs. ☎ 01-435 3471 *Closed all January, December and Good Friday.* ☎ 01-435 3471	*Und.:* Hampstead Station (*Northern Line*) *Bus:* 210 from Archway or Golders Green Stns. 268 Finchley Road Station–Golders Green (*alight Jack Straw's Castle, 200 yds.*)
GUNNERSBURY PARK, Acton W3 8LQ *map 6A* *London Boroughs of Ealing & Hounslow* Large mansion built 1802 by architect owner Alexander Copeland. Fine rooms by Sydney Smirke for N. M. Rothschild c. 1836. Now a local history museum. Large park and other buildings of interest	Mansion at NE corner of Park; alongside Nth Circular (A406); N of Gt. West Rd. & M4; Kew Bridge 1½ m; Chiswick Rndabout ½ m. *Stn: Acton Town (Und., ¼ m)*	March to Oct. (end B.S.T.)—Mons. to Fris. 1–5; Sats., Suns. & Bank Hols. 2–6. Oct. (end B.S.T.) to Feb.—Mons. to Fris. 1–4; Sats., Suns. & Bank Hols. 2–4. *Closed Christmas Eve (variable), Christmas Day, Boxing Day & Good Friday.* Vehicle access Popes Lane. Pedestrians—many entries to Park. ☕ Cafeteria in Park (daily April–Sept.; weekends only in winter)	*Und:* Acton Town (¼ *m*); Gunnersbury (1 *m*); Ealing Broadway (1¾ *m*) *B.R.* Gunnersbury (1*m*); Kew Bridge (1½ *m*); Ealing Broadway (1½ *m*) *Bus:* E37 (*Suns.*)
HALL PLACE, Bexley *map 6 A* *Bexley London Borough Council* Historic mansion (1540). Outstanding Rose, Rock, Water, Herb, Peat gardens and Floral bedding displays, Conservatories, Parkland, Topiary designed in the form of the Queen's Beasts.	Near the junction of A2 and A223 *Stn: Bexley (½ m)*	MANSION: Weekdays 10–5; Suns. 2–6 (except from Nov. to March). Museum & other exhibitions. PARK & GROUNDS: daily during daylight throughout the year. Adm. free. ☕ at café (*weekends only during winter*)	*Train:* Bexley Green Line: 725, 726 London Country: 400, 401, 421, 492 (*alight Gravel Hill*) London Transport: 132 (*alight Gravel Hill*)
HAM HOUSE, Richmond *map 6 A* *The National Trust (administered by the Victoria & Albert Museum)* ♿ 17th century house with superb Charles II and Early Georgian furnishings. Portrait gallery	On S bank of River Thames opposite Twickenham 1 m S of Richmond *Stns: Kingston (2 m); Richmond (2 m)*	All the year—Daily (except Mons.): April to Sept. 2–6; Oct. to Mar. 12–4. Open Bank Hol. Mons. (except May 7). Adm. £1.50, Chd. (under 16) & O.A.Ps. 75p, Children under 12 must be accompanied by an adult. Grounds free. *Closed Good Friday, Christmas Eve, Christmas Day, Boxing Day, New Year's Day & May 7.* ☕ in Tea Pavilion (*summer months*) ☎ 01-940 1950	*Bus:* 65 from Ealing; 65, 71, 265 (*Suns. only*) from Kingston and Richmond (*alight Fox & Duck*)
HAMPTON COURT PALACE *map 6 A* *Dept. of the Environment* Royal palace built in 1514 by Wolsey, additions by Henry VIII and later by Wren for William III. State rooms, tapestries, pictures. Famous gardens are at their best in mid-May	On N bank of River Thames at Hampton Court *Stn: Hampton Court*	State Apartments & Great Hall: May to Sept.—Weekdays 9.30–6; Suns. 11–6. March, April & Oct.—Weekdays 9.30–5; Suns. 2–5. Nov. to Feb.—Weekdays 9.30–4; Suns. 2–4. Last adm. half hour before closing. *Closed Dec. 24, 25 & 26; Jan. 1 & Good Friday.* Adm.: summer £2, Chd. (under 16 yrs.) & O.A.Ps. £1; winter—£1, Chd. (under 16 yrs.) & O.A.Ps. 60p. ✕ ☕ refreshments in the Grounds	Rail & Steamer tour from London—Daily (*summer*) National tours from Essex Frames' tours from London Keith Tours from Aylesbury Pilchers tours from Medway towns Green Line: 715, 716, 718, 726
Δ **HOGARTH'S HOUSE, Chiswick** *map 6 A* *London Borough of Hounslow* The artist's country house for 15 years	In Hogarth Lane, Great West Road, Chiswick, W4 2QN (*200 yds. Chis. Hse.*) *Stn: Chiswick (½ m)*	April to Sept.—Mons. to Sats. 11–6; Suns. 2–6. Oct. to March–Mons. to Sats. 11–4; Suns. 2–4. *Closed Tuesdays, Good Friday, first 2 weeks in Sept. (3–16), last 3 weeks in Dec. & New Year's Day.*	*Und:* Hammersmith, then bus 290 *Bus:* 27, 91 (*not Suns.*), 117, 267 (*alight Duke's Avenue*) 290, E3 (*alight Chiswick House*)
KEATS HOUSE, Hampstead *map 6 A* *London Borough of Camden* Built in 1815-16 and completely restored in 1974-75. Poet John Keats wrote his famous odes here	S end of Hampstead Heath nr South End Green *Stn: (BR) Hampstead Heath*	All the year—Weekdays 10–1, 2–6; Suns., Easter, Spring & Summer Bank Hols., 2–5. Adm. free. *Closed Christmas Day, Boxing Day, New Year's Day Good Friday, Easter Eve & May 7.*	*Und:* Belsize Park or Hampstead *Bus:* 24, 46, C11 (*alight South End Grn.*) 268 (*alight Downshire Hill*)
KENSINGTON PALACE, Kensington *Dept. of the Environment* *map 6 A* Bought by William III, 1689. Altered and added to by Wren and later alterations	W side of Kensington Gardens	State Apartments open all the year—Weekdays 9–5; Suns. 1–5. *Closed Dec. 14, 25, 26 & Jan. 1.* Adm.: summer—£1, Chd. (under 16 yrs.) & O.A.Ps. 50p; winter—50p, Chd. (under 16 yrs.) & O.A.Ps. 30p.	*Bus:* 9, 49, 52, 73, *to Palace Gate* 12, 88 *to Queensway* 27, 28, 31, 52 *to Kensington High St.*
KENWOOD, The Iveagh Bequest, Hampstead *Greater London Council* *map 6 A* Once the seat of Lord Mansfield. Adam decoration. Fine paintings and furniture	Hampstead, NW3 5 m Charing Cross	All the year—Daily. April to Sept. 10–7. Oct. to March 10–5 (or dusk if earlier). *Closed Christmas Eve, Christmas Day & Good Friday.* Adm. free. ✕ ☕ **at the House**	*Bus:* **210 from Archway or Golders Green Stns.** (*alight 200 yds from House*)
KEW GARDENS, Kew *map 6 A* *Royal Botanic Gardens* 300 acres in extent containing living collection of over 25,000 different plant species and ♿ varieties. Greenhouses. Herbarium. Museums	On south bank of Thames at Kew 1 m from Richmond *Stn: Kew Gardens (¼ m)*	All the year—Daily, open at 10. *Closed Christmas Day & New Year's Day.* Houses open from 11; Museums open from 10. Closing times vary according to season but not later than 4.50 Mons. to Sats. & 5.50 Suns. Adm. 15p (adults, Chd. 10 yrs. & over, prams & invalid vehicles). Invalid chairs may be hired (15p) at the Main Gate. Accompanied children under 10 yrs. adm. free. Organised school parties issued with free entry vouchers on prior application. ☕ at Pavilion (*summer months*); at Kiosk (*all year*).	District Line or L.M.R. to Kew Gardens Southern Region to Kew Bridge *Bus:* 7 (*summer Suns. only*). 27, 65, 90B, 117, 267 Steamers from Westminster Bridge or Charing Cross to Kew Pier (*summer months*)
KEW PALACE (Dutch House) Kew *Dept. of the Environment* *map 6 A* Built 1631, Dutch style. Souvenirs of George III	In Kew Gardens on S bank of Thames *Stn: Kew Bridge (¾ m)*	April to Sept.—Daily 11–5.30. Adm. 60p, Chd. (under 16) & O.A.Ps. 30p. ☕ in Kew Gardens (*summer months*)	District Line or LMR to Kew Gardens *Bus:* 15 (*summer Suns. only*) 27, 65, 90B Steamers from Westminster Bridge to Kew Pier (*summer months*)
LANCASTER HOUSE, nr St. James's *Dept. of the Environment* *map 6 A* Finest surviving example in London of a great town mansion of the early Victorian period	Stable Yard, St. James's, SW1	State Apartments—Easter Eve to mid-December, Sats. Suns. & Bank Hols. 2–6. *Closed at times for Government functions.* Adm. 60p, Chd. (under 16) & O.A.Ps. 30p.	*Und.:* Green Park or Piccadilly Circus *Bus:* 9, 14, 19, 22, 25, 38, 506 (*alight Green Park*)
LINLEY SAMBOURNE HOUSE, W8 *The Victorian Society* *map 6 A* The home of Linley Sambourne (1845-1910), chief political cartoonist at '*Punch*'. Collection of works by artists and cartoonists of the period.	18 Stafford Terrace	March to October—Weds. 10–4 & Suns. 2–5. Parties by appointment only. Adm. £1.50. Apply to The Victorian Society, 1 Priory Gardens, Bedford Park, London W4. ☎ 01-994 1019	
LITTLE HOLLAND HOUSE, Carshalton *London Borough of Sutton* *map 6 C* The home of Frank Dickinson (1874-1961), follower of the Arts and Crafts movement; artist, designer and craftsman in wood and metal who built the house himself to his own design and in his pursuance of his philosophy and theories. Features his interior design, and painting, hand-made furniture and other craft objects.	40 Beeches Ave., Carshalton. On B278 (off A232). *Stn.: Carshalton Beeches*	March to Oct.—first Sunday in the month plus Bank Hol. Suns. & Mons. in that period 12–6. Adm. free.	London Transport 154 London Country 403, 408 (*alight "Windsor Castle" P.H.*) Green Line 716, 726 (*alight "Windsor Castle" P.H.*)

THE DICKENS HOUSE MUSEUM & LIBRARY

48 DOUGHTY STREET, LONDON, WC1N 2LF

Whilst living at 48, Doughty Street, Dickens finished *Pickwick Papers* and wrote *Oliver Twist* and *Nicholas Nickleby*. Here may be seen the study in which this young man, in his early twenties, wrote these books and created such immortal characters as Fagin, Bill Sikes, the Artful Dodger, the Squeers and Crummles families and wrote the famous Fanny Squeers letter. Pages of the original manuscripts of his early books and others are on view, together with valuable first editions in the original paper parts of most of his works. Here also is a collection of several hundreds of his letters; his special marriage licence; his family Bible with his personal record of his sons and daughters, two of whom were born in this house; the reading desk he used on all his Reading Tours and many personal relics. It was here, too, that Dickens entertained, in the dining room and drawing room, many of the literary and artistic celebrities of his time and where his lifelong friendship with his biographer, John Forster started. Entrance to the House includes the Suzannet Rooms containing the unique Suzannet collection.

Open to the public on weekdays 10–5. Closed Suns. & Bank Hols. Adm. (subject to alteration) £1, Students 75p, Children 50p; Families £2. Groups by arrangement. Tel. 01-405 2127.

FENTON HOUSE

HAMPSTEAD

THE NATIONAL TRUST

A late seventeenth century house of great charm, standing by itself in a fine walled garden, with beautiful wrought iron gates. The panelled rooms contain a fascinating collection of porcelain, early keyboard instruments and needlework pictures.

HOGARTH'S HOUSE

CHISWICK

LONDON BOROUGH OF HOUNSLOW

The artist's country house for 15 years.
Hogarth Lane, Great West Road, Chiswick W4 2QN
(200 yards from Chiswick House)
Telephone: 01-994 6757

LINLEY SAMBOURNE HOUSE

18 STAFFORD TERRACE, LONDON W.8

The home of Linley Sambourne (1845-1910), chief political cartoonist at PUNCH. Unique interior reflecting artistic taste of 1870-1910. Collection of works by artists and cartoonists of the period, including Kate Greenaway, Tenniel and Walter Crane. Open March 1st to October 31st—Wednesday 10–4, Sunday 2–5; parties by appointment only. Admission £1.50. Apply to The Victorian Society, 1 Priory Gardens, Bedford Park, London W4. Tel. 01-994 1019.

LITTLE HOLLAND HOUSE

40 BEECHES AVENUE, CARSHALTON, SURREY

The Living Room and part of the Sitting Room

The home of Frank Dickinson (1874–1961), follower of the Arts and Crafts movement; artist, designer and craftsman in wood and metal who built the house himself to his own design and in pursuance of his philosophy and theories. Features his interior design, painting, hand-made furniture and other craft objects. Admission free.
Guide book and other publications available.

KEATS HOUSE

KEATS GROVE, LONDON

London Borough of Camden

Keats House was built in 1815–1816 as Wentworth Place, a pair of semi-detached houses. John Keats, the poet, lived here from 1818 to 1820; here he wrote "*Ode to a Nightingale*" and met Fanny Brawne, to whom he became engaged. Keats' early death in Italy prevented the marriage.
Keats House was completely restored in 1974–1975. It houses letters, books and other personal relics of the poet and his fiancée.

PROPERTY (*showing map reference*)	LOCATION (*with nearest Rly. Stn.*)	OPENING TIMES AND ADMISSION CHARGES CATERING FACILITIES	COACH AND RAIL TOURS BUS SERVICES (*showing alighting points*)
LONDON—*continued*			
MARBLE HILL HOUSE, Twickenham *Greater London Council* *map 6 A* A complete example of an English Palladian villa. Early Georgian paintings and furniture.	**Twickenham, Middx. 11 m from Charing Cross** *Stns: St. Margaret's (½ m) (not Suns.); Twickenham (1 m)*	All the year—Daily (except Fris.). Feb. to Oct. 10–5; Nov. to Jan. 10–4. Adm. free. *Closed Christmas Eve and Christmas Day.* Car park in Marble Hill Park. ✕☕ in Stable Block.	*Bus:* **27, 33 (*not Suns.*), 73, 90, 90B, 202, 270 (*Mons.–Fris.*)**
MARLBOROUGH HOUSE, Pall Mall Δ *Foreign & Commonwealth Office* *map 6 A* Built by Wren for Sarah, Duchess of Marlborough, subsequently a Royal residence and now a Commonwealth Centre	**Pall Mall, SW1 (almost adjacent to St. James's Palace)**	HOUSE ONLY—Conducted tours by arrangement with with the Administration Officer, weekdays only when not in use for conferences. Adm. 50p. ☎ 01-930 9249 QUEEN'S CHAPEL—Mon. to Fri. throughout the year by arrangement with the Administration Officer. *Closed Good Friday, Christmas Day & Bank Holidays*	*Und.:* **Green Park, Piccadilly, St. James's Park** *Bus:* **9, 14, 19, 22, 25, 38, 506**
MUSEUM OF GARDEN HISTORY, Lambeth *map 6 A* *The Tradescant Trust* The former church of St. Mary-at-Lambeth is being converted into the first museum of its kind in the world. The tomb of John Tradescant, gardener to Charles I, lies in the churchyard where the Tradescant Garden is being created, planted with species shrubs and flowers of the period	At the gates of Lambeth Palace.	Mons. to Fris. 11–3; Suns. 10.30–5. At other times by appointment. *Closed from second Sunday in Dec. to first Sunday in March.* Shop. Further information from: The Tradescant Trust, 7 The Little Boltons, London SW10 9LJ. ☎ 01-373 4030 (between 7–9 a.m.) ☕ Parties catered for if pre-booked	Local bus & Und. services
Δ**THE OLD PALACE, Croydon** *map 6 C* *Old Palace School (Croydon) Ltd.* Seat of Archbishops of Canterbury since 871. 15th century Banqueting Hall and Guardroom. Tudor Chapel. Norman undercroft.	**In central Croydon** *Stns: East Croydon or West Croydon (few mins. walk)*	CONDUCTED TOURS ONLY 2–30 p.m.—April 9, 10, 11, 12, 13 & 14; May 29, 30 & 31; June 1 & 2; July 16–21 & 23–28. Adm. £1.50 (inc. tea); Chd. & O.A.Ps. 75p. Car park. Parties catered for, apply Bursar. Unsuitable for wheelchairs. ☎ 01-680 5877	**Green Line 716, 725, 726, 755 London Transport 154, 157 and all routes serving Croydon centre London Country 403, 405, 409, 411, 414, 455, 725, 726**
OLD ROYAL OBSERVATORY, Greenwich *National Maritime Museum* *map 6 A* **Now part of the National Maritime Museum it includes Flamsteed House, designed by Sir Christopher Wren, the Meridian Building and the Greenwich Planetarium**	**In Greenwich Park, N side of Blackheath** *Stn: Maze Hill (short walk)*	Weekdays—summer 10–6; winter 10–5. Sundays—summer 2–5.30; winter 2–5. Open Bank Hol. Mons. *but closed Tues. following. Closed Mons. (except Bank Hols.), Good Friday, Christmas Eve, Christmas Day, Boxing Day, New Year's Day & May* 7. Adm. free ☕ in Park cafeteria	*Bus:* **53 (*alight Chesterfield Walk*) 1A (*Suns.*), 70, (*Mons–Fris.*), 108B, 177, 180 185, 188 (*alight King William Walk, 350 yds.*)**
ORLEANS HOUSE GALLERY, Riverside Twickenham *map 6 A* *London Borough of Richmond upon Thames* ♿ **The magnificent Octagon built by James Gibbs in 1720. An outstanding example of the baroque, with adjacent art gallery is situated in attractive woodland garden.**	**Access from Richmond Road (A305)** *Stns: St. Margaret's (½ mile) (not Suns); Twickenham (½ m)*	Tues. to Sats. 1–5.30 (Oct. to Mar. 1–4.30); Suns. 2–5.30 (Oct. to Mar. 2–4.30). Easter, Spring, Summer Bank Hols. 2–5.30 *Closed Christmas* Adm. free	**Any bus from Richmond Station to Twickenham (*alight at Crown Hotel and proceed down Orleans Rd.*)**
OSTERLEY PARK HOUSE, Osterley *The National Trust (administered by the Victoria & Albert Museum)* *map 6 A* ♿ **Splendid State Rooms furnished by Robert Adam, including a Gobelins Tapestry Room.** Garden houses and Tudor stable block	½ m N of Great West road (turn off at traffic lights, Thornbury road, near Osterley Station) *Stns: Syon Lane (½ m) (not Suns.); Brentford (1½ m)*	HOUSE: Daily (exc. Mons.): April to Sept. 2–6; Oct. to Mar. 12–4. Open Bank Hol. Mons. (except May 7). Adm. £1.50, Chd. (under 16) & O.A.Ps. 75p. Chd. under 12 must be accompanied by an adult. *Closed Good Friday, Christmas Eve, Christmas Day, Boxing Day, New Year's Day & May 7* **GARDENS: Open all year.** Adm. free ☎ **01-560 3918** ☕ **in the Stables (summer months)**	*Und:* **Osterley (*Piccadilly Line*)** Green Line: 704, *Bus:* 91 (*not Suns*) & 116 (*peak hours*)
THE QUEEN'S HOUSE, Greenwich *map 6 A* *National Maritime Museum* Designed by Inigo Jones for Anne of Denmark, wife of James I. Completed 1635 for Henrietta Maria wife of Charles I	**On S bank of Thames at Greenwich** *Stn: Maze Hill (½ m)*	Weekdays—summer 10–6; winter 10–5. Sundays—summer 2–5.30; winter 2–5. Open Bank Hol. Mons. *but closed Tues. following. Closed Mons. (except Bank Hols.), Good Friday, Christmas Eve, Christmas Day, Boxing Day, New Year's Day & May* 7. Adm. free ✕☕ licensed restaurant.	*Train:* Maze Hill *Bus:* 1A Suns., 70 Mons. to Fris. 108B, 177, 180, 185, 188 (*alight King William Walk 350 yds*)
RANGER'S HOUSE, Blackheath *map 6 A* *Greater London Council* Ⓔ A long Gallery of English Portraits in the 4th Earl of Chesterfield's house, from the Elizabethan to the Georgian period	**Chesterfield Walk Blackheath SE 10** *Stns: Greenwich or Blackheath* **(15 *mins. walk*)**	All the year—Daily. Feb. to Oct. 10–5; Nov. to Jan. 10–4. *Closed Christmas Eve, Christmas Day & Good Friday.* Adm. free. ☎ 01-853 0035	*Bus:* 53, 54. 75
ROYAL NAVAL COLLEGE, Greenwich Δ *The Admiralty* *map 6 A* Begun by Webb, finished by Wren, Hawksmoor & Vanbrugh. Painted Hall and Chapel	**On S bank of Thames at Greenwich** *Stns: Greenwich (½ m); Maze Hill (½ m)*	All the year—Daily (except Thurs.), 2.30–5 (last admission 4.45). *Closed Thurs. Other occasions necessitate closure on some open days—these are publicised in daily newspapers.* Adm. free. ✕☕ at National Maritime Museum	*Train:* Greenwich or Maze Hill *Bus:* 1A Suns; 70, Mons. to Fris. 53, 54, 75, 177, 180, 185, 188 *By River:* to Greenwich Pier

ORLEANS HOUSE

RIVERSIDE, TWICKENHAM

LONDON BOROUGH OF RICHMOND UPON THAMES

Russells photograph

The magnificent Octagon built by James Gibbs in 1720 for James Johnston, Joint Secretary of State for Scotland under William III. An outstanding example of baroque architecture. The adjacent wing has been converted into an art gallery and the whole is situated in an attractive woodland garden.

OPENING TIMES ABOVE

ST. JOHN'S GATE

The Museum & Library of the Order of St. John

CLERKENWELL, LONDON EC1M 4DA

Tidnam Photographic photograph

St. John's Gate, formerly the southern entrance to the Priory of the Knights of St. John, houses the most comprehensive collection of items relating to the Order of St. John outside Malta. Together with the nearby Priory Church and 12th century Crypt it now forms the headquarters of the modern Order of St. John, whose charitable foundations include St. John Ambulance and the Opthalmic Hospital in Jerusalem. The collection includes Maltese silver, Italian furniture, coins and pharmacy jars.

OPENING TIMES SEE PAGE 101

"You feel as if you're almost in the middle of a jewel box"—Basil Taylor, BBC4

SYON HOUSE

BRENTFORD, Middlesex

Set on the bank of the Thames and on the road to Hampton Court this historic seat of the Duke of Northumberland is noted not only for its association with some of the fascinating characters and stirring historical events of the last five-and-a-half centuries, but also for its elegant furniture and interesting pictures within the magnificent setting of one of Robert Adam's masterpieces of decoration.

Pedestrian entrances: Brent Lea, London Road, Brentford and Park Road, Isleworth. Motorists: Park Road, Isleworth, only. Free Car Park. Restaurant.
For opening times see opposite page.

Enquiries to the Supervisor, Syon House, Brentford. Telephone 01-560 0884.

WHITEHALL

CHEAM, SURREY

This unique timber-framed, continuous-jettied house dates back to about 1500. Originally built as a farmhouse, Whitehall, with its many additions, has associations with Henry VIII's Nonsuch Palace, the English Civil War and Cheam School. The latter, which started life in this house, became famous for its many royal, aristocratic and otherwise distinguished pupils. Whitehall now features revealed sections of original fabric and displays including Medieval Cheam Pottery, Nonsuch Palace, Timber-framed Buildings and Cheam School.

Refreshments and appropriate publications available.

SOUTHSIDE HOUSE

WIMBLEDON COMMON

The Kemeys — Pennington — Mellor — Munthe family

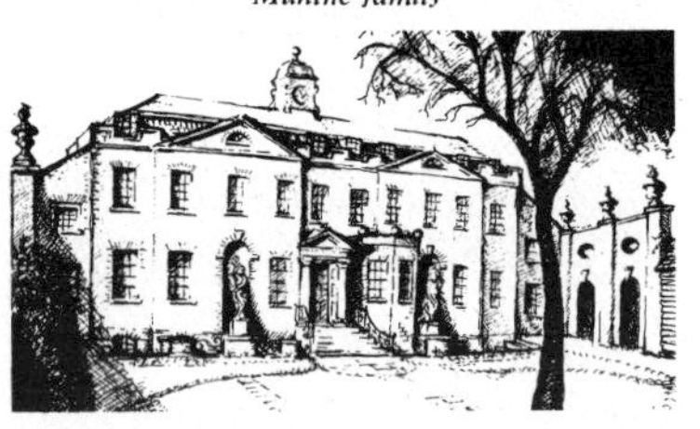

Built by Robert Pennington as a refuge from the plague in London after his small son perished in 1665, the facade and entrance hall show Dutch baroque influence—admired by Pennington during exile in Holland with Charles II.

Contents include family portraits from 1580 onwards; relics of the Pennington-Mellor's "dear infamous relative" Philip, the last Duke of Wharton (member of the 'Hell Fire Club') and of the family's "Scarlet Pimpernel" son, John Pennington, from the French Revolution; also the vanity case of Anne Boleyn (whose sister married into the family). A music room was created mid-18th century for Frederick, Prince of Wales and a bed in 1900 for Edward, Prince of Wales (the silver box with comfits for his sore throat is still on view).

Past visitors include Nelson, Lady Hamilton, Byron and Axel Munthe who wrote part of his "Story of San Michele" here.

CROXTETH HALL & COUNTRY PARK

(Merseyside County Museums)

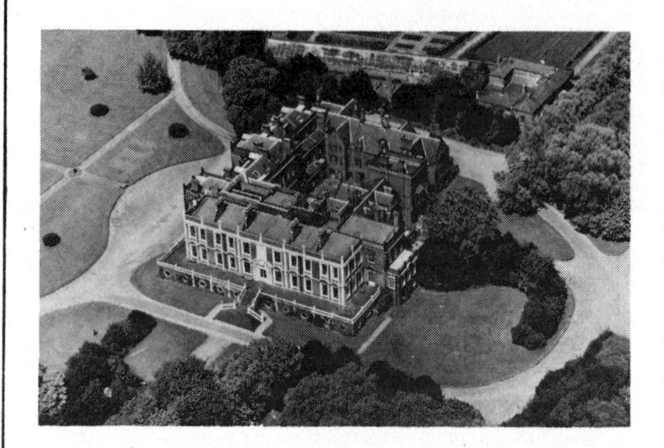

Croxteth Hall is the centrepiece of a beautiful wooded estate where you can enjoy the pleasures of real countryside only a few miles from the amenities of Liverpool City Centre. Former home of the Earls of Sefton, the Hall is set in a 500-acre Country Park with gardens, woods, pasture and a working farm.

Principal Rooms with exhibitions, furniture and paintings. Permanent display of "The Croxteth Heritage". Superb walled garden with old fruit trees, flue wall etc. Carriage and craft displays. Rare Breeds Farm with Victorian farmyard and Farm Shop. Miniature Railway. Country walks and picnic places. Ranger service. Gift shop, garden shop and café. Full programme of events and attractions. Free car park. Award-winning education service.

Telephone 051–228 5311 for details.

SPEKE HALL

MERSEYSIDE

SEVEN MILES FROM
THE CENTRE OF LIVERPOOL

This magnificent timber-framed building, set in its own grounds on the outskirts of Liverpool, is an outstanding example of a Tudor manor house. It is built around a cobbled courtyard which is dominated by two ancient yew trees and was formerly moated. It is noted for its Great Hall with fine panelling, the Great Parlour with Jacobean stucco ceiling, its priest holes and ghost. The house is fully furnished, from the bedrooms to the Kitchen, and still retains an intimate atmosphere. There are Victorian gardens.

PROPERTY (showing map reference)	LOCATION (with nearest Rly. Stn.)	OPENING TIMES AND ADMISSION CHARGES CATERING FACILITIES	COACH AND RAIL TOURS BUS SERVICES (showing alighting points)
LONDON—*continued*			
△ **ST. JOHN'S GATE, Clerkenwell** *map 6 A* *The Order of St. John* Headquarters of the Order in England the 16th gatehouse contains the most comprehensive items relating to the Order of St. John outside Malta.	In St. John's Lane, Clerkenwell EC1M 4DA *Stn: Farringdon (Und.)*	MUSEUM open Tues., Fris. & Sats. 10–6. Tours of the building, including the Grand Priory Church and Norman crypt, 11 & 2.30 on these days. ☎ 01-253 6644, Ext. 35	*Buses:* 5, 55, 243 to Clerkenwell Road; 4 to Aldersgate St., Goswell Rd.; 277, 279 to St. John Street
△ **SOUTHSIDE HOUSE, Wimbledon Common, S.W.19** *map 6 A* *Pennington—Mellor—Munthe Trust* The Kemeys-Pennington-Mellor-Munthe family built the house after the great plague of London in 1665 and still live here. Furniture and pictures of the 17th to 19th centuries; vanity case of Anne Boleyn; sword used in a fatal duel of 1608. Home of Hilda Pennington-Mellor, English wife of Axel Munthe, the Swedish doctor and philanthropist	On S side of Wimbledon Common, opp. 'Crooked Billet' Inn *Stns: Wimbledon (1 m); Raynes Park (1 m)*	Oct. 1 to March 31—Tues., Thurs. & Fris. 2–5. Guided tours each hour. Adm. £1, Chd. 50p (must be accompanied by adult). Other times by written appointment only to the Curator. *The house is closed for Christmas & Easter.*	*Train:* Waterloo to Wimbledon then L.T. bus 93 *(alight "Rose & Crown" Inn, 6 mins. walk to house)*
△ **SYON HOUSE, Brentford** *map 6 A* *His Grace the Duke of Northumberland, K.G., P.C., G.C.V.O.* Noted for its magnificent Adam interior and furnishings, famous picture collection, and historical associations dating back to 1415. "Capability" Brown landscape	On N bank of Thames between Brentford & Isleworth *Stns: Brentford (B.R. 1 m.); Syon Lane (B.R. 1 m) (not Suns.)*	Good Friday to September 26—Daily (except Fris. & Sats) 12–5. Last adm. 4.15. Also Suns. in October, 12–5. Adm. charges not available at time of going to press. ☎ 01-560 0881/4	*Bus:* 237, Shepherd's Bush–Brentford–Sunbury; 267, Hammersmith–Brentford–Hampton Court *(passes Gunnersbury & Kew Bridge Stns.)*; E1, E2 from Greenford & Ealing *(Suns. only)*; 117 *(Mons. to Fris.)*; 203 *(Mons. to Sats.)*; from Staines or Hounslow *(alight Brent Lea entrance, London Road, Brentford)*; 37 from Peckham, Clapham Jun., Putney, Richmond *(alight Isleworth Square for Park Road entrance)* *Und.:* Gunnersbury Stn. *(District Line)*
SYON PARK GARDENS, Brentford *map 6 A* *His Grace the Duke of Northumberland, K.G., P.C., G.C.V.O.* Includes the Great Conservatory, by Dr Fowler, containing the Aviary and Aquarium. Within the Estate is the London Butterfly House and the British Motor Industry Heritage Trust (telephone details in column 3); also the Syon Art Centre.	On N bank of Thames between Brentford & Isleworth *Stns: Brentford (B.R. 1 m.); Syon Lane (B.R. 1 m) (not Suns.)*	All the year: March 1 to Oct. 24—Daily 10–6. Oct. 25 to Feb. 28—Daily 10–dusk; *(aviary & aquarium closed during winter months)*. Last adm. 1 hour before closing. *Closed Christmas Day & Boxing Day.* Adm. charges not available at time of going to press. Winter—reduced rates. Free car park. Bars & Restaurant ☎ 01-560 0881/4 London Butterfly House—opening times & adm. charges ☎ 01-560 7272 British Motor Industry Heritage Trust—opening times & adm. charges ☎ 01-560 1378	**As for Syon House—see above**
TOWER OF LONDON, Tower Bridge *Dept. of the Environment* *map 6 A* Dating from Norman times. Historical relics, armouries, dungeons. Crown jewels	On N bank of Thames above Tower Bridge *Stns: (B.R.) London Bridge (¾ m); Fenchurch St. (¼ m); Cannon St. (¼ m) (Mons.-Fris.); Liverpool St. (¾ m); Moorgate (1 m)*	All the year: March to October—Weekdays 9.30–5, Sundays 2–5; November to February—Weekdays 9.30–4. *Closed Suns. Nov. to Feb. also Good Friday Dec. 24, 25, 26 & Jan. 1.* Adm. Oct. to March £2, Chd. (under 16) & O.A.Ps. £1; April to Sept. £3, Chd. (under 16) & O.A.Ps. £1.50. Jewel House 80p, Chd. (under 16) & O.A.Ps. 40p. refreshments in grounds	London Trans. tours—summer Frames' tours—daily Rickards tours—daily *Und.:* Tower Hill *Bus:* 9A (Suns.) 42, 78 *(to Minories)*: 47, 70, 188, *(to Tooley st.)*: 8A, 10, 10A, 21, 35, 40, 40A, 43, 44, 47, 48, 133, 501, 513 *(to Monument)*
WHITEHALL, Cheam *map 6 C* *London Borough of Sutton* Timber-framed house built c.1500. Sections of original fabric; medieval Cheam pottery; Nonsuch Palace; timber-framed buildings and Cheam School.	No. 1, Malden Rd.; on A2043 nr. Cheam village crossrds., just N of junc. with A232 *Stn: Cheam (¼ m)*	April to Sept.—Tues. to Fris. 2–5.30, Sats. 10–5.30, Suns. 2–5.30. Oct. to March—Weds. & Thurs. 2–5.30. Sats. 10–5.30, Suns. 2–5.30. Also Bank Hol. Mons. (as for Suns.). *Closed Dec. 24 to Jan. 2 inclusive.* Adm. 40p (under 18 years, 15p). Party bookings & guided tour facilities. light refreshments ☎ 01-643 1236	London Transport 213A London Country 403, 408 Green Line 716, 726
△ **WHITE LODGE, Richmond Park** *map 6 A* *Governors of the Royal Ballet School* A former Royal residence, built early 18th cent.	In Richmond Park *Stn: Richmond (2 m)*	Open throughout August—Daily 2–6. Adm. 75p. ☎ 01-748 7306	Green Line 714, 715, 718 to Kingston Vale *Bus:* 72, 85 to Kingston Vale; 27, 33, 37, 65, 71, 73, 90B, 202, 270, 290 to Richmond
MERSEYSIDE			
BLUECOAT CHAMBERS, Liverpool L1 3BX *The Bluecoat Society of Arts* *map 2 D* Fine Queen Anne building, cobbled quadrangle, garden courtyard, gallery, concert hall, artists studios.	School Lane, in the City centre. *Stn: Liverpool Lime Street.*	Mons. to Sats. 10–5. For further details telephone Adm. free. ☎ 051-709-5297 Coffee shop & restaurant	
CROXTETH HALL & COUNTRY PARK, Liverpool 12 *map 5 C* *Merseyside County Museums* 500 acre Country Park centred on the ancestral home of the Molyneux family, Earls of Sefton. Principal rooms with paintings and displays Heritage Exhibition; rare breeds farm and fine walled garden; miniature railway. Events programme	5 m NE of Liverpool City Centre; signposted from A580 & A5088 (ring rd)	Parkland open daily throughout the year, adm. free. Hall, Farm & Garden: Good Friday to Sept. 30—Daily 11–5. Winter months Heritage Exhibition & Farm only, hours on request. Pre-booked parties at other times by arrangement—reduced rates. Adm. charges not available at time of going to press. Free car park. Picnic areas. *Wheelchair access to Exhibition, Farm & Gardens but not to Principal Rooms.* Café during season ☎ 051-228 5311	Merseyside P.T.E. 12, 12A, 12C, 18C, 18D from City Centre
△ **SPEKE HALL, Liverpool** *map 5 C* *The National Trust (administered by Merseyside County Museums Dept.)* Richly half-timbered house dating from c. 1490–1612. Great Hall. Elaborate plasterwork. Priest holes. Fully furnished.	**On N bank of Mersey, 7 m from City centre** *Stn: Garston (2 m)*	All the year—April 1 to Sept. 30—Weekdays 10–5, Suns. 2–7. Bank Hols. 10–7. Oct. 1 to Mar. 31—Weekdays 10–5, Suns. 2–5. Adm. (subject to revision) 60p, Chd. 30p. *Pre-booked party rates from the Warden. Last admission 1 hr. before closing time. Closed Good Friday, Christmas Eve, Christmas Day, Boxing Day & New Year's Day.* Free car park. ☎ 051-427 7231 Tea room April–September & at other times for parties by prior arrangement.	Merseyside Transport 80, 82C from Liverpool; 81/81D from Bootle; 62 from Kirkby; 89 from St. Helens; 84 from Garston Stn. *(connects with Merseyrail)* Crosville H1 Liverpool—Warrington; H25 Liverpool — Runcorn *(alight Speke Hall traffic lights, 1 m)*
NORFOLK			
BEESTON HALL, Beeston St. Lawrence *Sir Ronald & Lady Preston* *map 3 H* 18th cent. "Gothick" country house with Georgian interiors in picturesque setting.	2½ m NE of Wroxham on S side of A1151; 11 m NE of Norwich	Principal Rooms & Garden: April 22 to Sept. 16—Fris. & Suns. also Bank Hols.: 2–5.30. Adm. £1, Chd. (accompanied by adult) 50p. O.A.Ps. 80p. Parties by arrangement. Free car park. teas in the Orangery	Eastern Counties 722, 723, 724 Norwich–Wroxham–Stalham *(alight at turning, ½ m from gates)* Also accessible from The Broads at Neatishead
BLICKLING HALL, Aylsham *map 3 D* *The National Trust* Great Jacobean house, altered 1765-70. State rooms include Peter the Great Room with fine Russian tapestry, Long Gallery with exceptional ceiling and State bedroom. The Formal Garden design dates from 1729. Temple and Orangery, park and lake	1½ m NW of Aylsham on N side of B1354 (which is 15 m N of Norwich on A140) *Stn: Nth. Walsham (8 m)*	Hall & Gardens—March 31 to Nov. 3.—Daily (except Mons. & Thurs. but open Bank Hol. Mons. 2–6; also open from 11 a.m.—April 21 to Sept. 29). Adm. £1.70, Chd. (with adult) 60p. Pre-booked parties £1.40. Free car park. Shop (closed Mons. & Thurs.). Dogs in Park & picnic area only, on leads. Wheelchair access—2 provided. teas in East Wing (coffee and light lunches April 21 –Sept. 29); *(large parties by arrangement;* table licence). Picnic area in walled orchard. ☎ *Aylsham* 733084	National tour from Norwich Norfolk Motors tours from Yarmouth and Lowestoft, every Sun. E. Counties to Aylsham (1½ *m*)

PROPERTY (*showing map reference*)	LOCATION (*with nearest Rly. Stn.*)	OPENING TIMES AND ADMISSION CHARGES CATERING FACILITIES	COACH AND RAIL TOURS BUS SERVICES (*showing alighting points*)

NORFOLK—*continued*

PROPERTY	LOCATION	OPENING TIMES	TRANSPORT
FELBRIGG HALL, nr Cromer *map 3 D* *The National Trust* 17th century country house with Georgian interiors set in a fine wooded park. Important 18th century Library and Orangery. Traditional walled garden. Woodland and Lakeside walks.	2 m SW of Cromer on S side of A148 *Stn: Cromer* (3 *m*)	Principal Rooms & Gardens: March 31 to Nov. 4—Tues., Weds., Thurs., Sats., Suns. & Bank Hol. Mons. 2–6. Adm. £1.70, Chd. (*with adult*) 85p. Pre-booked parties of 15 or more £1.10, Tues., Weds. & Thurs. only. Shop. No dogs. Wheelchair access, 2 provided. in old kitchen. Picnic area. *West Runton* 444	Eastern Counties from Norwich, King's Lynn Sheringham, Yarmouth etc. to Cromer (2 *m*)
FRITTON LAKE & GARDENS *map 3 H* *Lord & Lady Somerleyton* Beautiful 2 mile long lake and gardens with spring bulbs, herbaceous borders and ornamental trees. Wooded walks, fishing, boating, adventure playground and putting green.	Off A143, 5 m SW of Gt. Yarmouth, 5 m NW of Lowestoft *Stn: Haddiscoe* (1½ *m*)	April 1 to Oct. 1—Daily 11–6. Adm. 80p, Chd. 60p. Free Car & Coach Park Fritton Old Hall	Eastern Counties 615/6 Yarmouth–Beccles (*not Suns.*); 614 Yarmouth–Loddon–Norwich (*Weds. & Sats. only*)
HALES HALL, Loddon *map 3 H* *Mr. & Mrs. Terence Read* Medieval fortified manor house and 'Great Barn'. Restored from dereliction. Excavated ruins and moated gardens. Guided tours of this small family home.	12 m SE of Norwich; 12 m NE of Lowestoft; off A146	House, Barn & Garden: Easter to Sept. 30—Suns.; also Fris. in June, July & Aug. 2.30–5.30. Open Bank Hol. Mons. 2.30–5.30. Adm. 85p, Chd. 50p. Parties by arrangement all year. Free car park. Spinning & weaving demonstrations (Suns.). teas	No reasonable public transport
HOLKHAM HALL, Wells (1734) *map 3 C* Fine Palladian mansion. Pictures, tapestries, statuary, furnishings. Nessfield laid out the formal garden	2m W of Wells; S of the Wells–Hunstanton rd (A149)	June to Sept.—Suns., Mons. & Thurs. 1.30–5; also Weds. in July & Aug. 1.30–5 and Spring & Summer Bank Hol. Mons. 11.30–5. Adm. £1, Chd. (5–15) 50p. O.A.Ps. 75p. Adm. to Park: Cars 50p, Motorcycles 25p; Coaches & Pedestrians free. Pre-paid coach parties of 20 or more—10% reduction. served in tea rooms *Fakenham* (0328) 710227	National tours from Norwich Norfolk Motors tours from Yarmouth and Lowestoft every Thursday E. Counties 417, Hunstanton–Wells (*not Suns.*)
HOUGHTON HALL, Kings Lynn *map 3 C* *The Marquess of Cholmondeley* 18th century mansion built for Sir Robert Walpole. State rooms, pictures and china. Pleasure grounds. Various breeds of heavy horses on show in the stables. Private collection of model soldiers and militaria	13 m E of King's Lynn; 10 m W of Fakenham	Easter Sun. (April 22) to Sept. 30—Suns., Thurs. & Bank Hols. HOUSE opens 12–5.30 (Suns. 1.30–5.30). Last adm. 5. Gates, Picnic Area, Children's Playground, stables and Model Soldier & Militaria Collection opens Suns., Thurs. & Bank Hols. 12–noon. Last adm. 5. Adm. £1.50, O.A.Ps. £1, Chd. 50p (under 5 free). Season tickets £5 per adult. Family ticket (2 parents & children of school age) £10. These tickets provide adm. any day Houghton is open to the public in 1984. No additional charges except for special events which will be advertised. Reduction of 10% for pre-booked parties of 20 or more. Car park near House, toilets & lift to State floor for the disabled. Free parking for coaches & cars. tea room. *East Rudham* 569	Eastern Counties 468, King's Lynn–Fakenham–Holt–Sheringham–Cromer (*alight Harpley* 1 *m*)
MANNINGTON HALL GARDENS, Saxthorpe, Norfolk *map 3 C* *Hon. Robin & Mrs. Walpole* 15th century moated house and Saxon church ruin set in attractive gardens	2 m N of Saxthorpe, nr B1149; 18 m NW of Norwich. 9 m from coast	GARDEN ONLY: June 1 to Aug. 31—Weds., Thurs. & Fris. 11–8; Suns. 2–5. Adm. 80p, Chd. (under 16, accompanied) free, O.A.Ps. 60p. House open only by prior appointment. Adm. £2 (inc. Garden entrance). Charity Sundays: April 15, May 6, May 27, Sept. 9, Oct. 7. Also Sat. Aug. 11 for Itteringham Village Hall. Rose Festival Thurs., Fri. & Sat., June 29, 30 & July 1 teas *Saxthorpe* (026 387) 284	Local transport to Saxthorpe (2 *m*)
MEDIEVAL MERCHANT'S HOUSE, King's Lynn *map 3 G* *Mrs. M. H. Kelly* Georgian fronted brick town house containing its 14th century "Hall" core. Panelled rooms, beams and fireplaces of 17th, 18th and 19th centuries. Guided tours are given by the owners who are restoring the entire site.	9 King St. (in the centre of King's Lynn) *Stn: King's Lynn* (10 *mins. walk*)	April 20–23; May 5–7 & 26–29; July 20–29 and July 31 then Aug. 1–31: Tues., Fris., Sats. & Suns. 11–1, 2.15–5.30. Other times by appointment. Adm. £1. Chd. (accompanied) 50p, O.A.Ps. 70p. Pre-booked parties at other times of more than 10 people, 70p per person. Hotels, restaurants in King's Lynn.	B.R. Trains from London (Liverpool St.) via Cambridge & Ely to King's Lynn (10 *mins. walk*) Eastern Counties & National buses to King's Lynn bus station (5 *mins. walk*)
OAKLEIGH HOUSE, Swaffham *map 3 G* *William J. Holliday, Esq.* Elizabethan house with Georgian facade. Reception rooms, bedrooms, servants quarters and gardens	In Market Place opposite 'Pedlar' sign. On A47, 15 m from King's Lynn, 28 m from Norwich	April 5 to Sept. 30—Suns., Thurs. & Bank Hols. 2–5.30 (last adm. 5). Adm. £1, Chd. 50p. Parties at any time by arrangement. teas in the Old Coachhouse	Eastern Counties 434, 438 (*alight opposite house*)

BLICKLING HALL

NORFOLK

THE NATIONAL TRUST

A. F. Kersting photograph

This great Jacobean house, built in 1616–24 for Sir Henry Hobart, has been said "to satisfy the most romantic conception of an English Country House". The largely Georgian staterooms contain collections of furniture, tapestries and pictures and the long gallery has an elaborate Jacobean ceiling. The formal garden and beautiful grounds display a succession of colour and interests throughout the year.

OPENING TIMES SEE PAGE 101

FELBRIGG HALL

NORFOLK

THE NATIONAL TRUST

Fine 17th century House with Jacobean South Front and William & Mary West Wing. Important interiors by James Paine including The Cabinet hung with William Windham's Grand Tour picture collection. 18th century Library on first floor contains books from Dr. Johnson's own collection. Early 18th century Orangery with fine camellias. The landscaped park and woods have many mature Sweet Chestnut, Oak and Beech. Walled garden and lake.

OPENING TIMES ABOVE

MEDIEVAL MERCHANT'S HOUSE

KING'S LYNN, NORFOLK

Behind the Georgian facade lies a merchant's house which is a unique example of a medieval brick town house, still a family home with its 14th century "Hall" core and panelled rooms, beams and fireplaces from the 17th, 18th and 19th centuries.

Guided tours are given by the owners who are restoring the entire site as a private venture.

Print collections include an Isadore Kaufman memorial set, 17th century maps and Nelson memorabilia.

OPENING TIMES OPPOSITE

FRITTON LAKE AND GARDENS

NEAR GREAT YARMOUTH, NORFOLK

Peter Calvert photograph

The two mile long lake, probably the most beautiful in East Anglia, formed by peat cutting in the 12th century, is surrounded by woodland, ornamental trees and attractive gardens through which pathways meander. The 18th century lakeside garden is set with spectacular and colourful borders. Spring and early Summer are particularly enchanting with an array of tulips, rhododendrons, bluebell woods and wintering wildfowl on the lake.

While most of Fritton is managed so as to retain its peace and tranquility, there is an area which children (and parents) find enormous fun. The adventure play area is one of the best of its kind. Also there are boats for hire, putting, fishing, pony rides, wind surfing, a visitor centre explaining the wildlife and history of Fritton and a resident basket-maker who can be watched at work. Refreshments are available.

Open 1st April to 1st October—daily 11–6.

HOUGHTON HALL **KINGS LYNN, NORFOLK**

The home of the Marquess and Marchioness of Cholmondeley

Houghton Hall, one of the finest examples of Palladian architecture in England, was built in the 18th century for Sir Robert Walpole by Colen Campbell and Thomas Ripley, with interior decoration by William Kent.

Later, Houghton was inherited by the 1st Marquess of Cholmondeley through his grandmother, Sir Robert's daughter.

Situated in beautiful parkland, the house contains magnificent furniture, pictures and china.

Private collection of 20,000 Model Soldiers and Militaria.

Gift Shop. Tea Room. Picnic Area.

Open every Sunday, Thursdays and Bank Holiday from:—
Easter Sunday, April 22nd to Sunday, September 30th.

House opens: Thursday and Bank Holidays 12 noon–5.30 p.m. Sundays 1.30 p.m.–5.30 p.m. Last admission to House and Soldier Museum 5.00 p.m.

Gates and Picnic Area and Children's Playground, Stables and Model Soldier & Militaria Collection open Sundays, Thursdays and Bank Holidays at 12-noon. Last admission at 5.00 p.m.

Admission: Adults £1.50, O.A.Ps. £1, Children 50p. Children under 5 years free. Season tickets £5 per adult. Family tickets for two parents and children of school age—£10 These tickets provide for admission on any day that Houghton is open to the public throughout the 1984 Season.

There will be no additional charges except for special events which will be specifically advertised and for which we reserve the right to adjust admission charges.

A reduction of 10% for pre-booked parties of 20 and over. Facilities for the disabled include Invalid car park near House, toilets and lift to State floor.

Ample free parking for cars and coaches is available.

HOLKHAM HALL

WELLS, Norfolk

18th century Palladian Home of Coke of Norfolk was erected in 1734. Open to visitors Spring and Summer Bank Holiday Mondays. 11.30 a.m.-5 p.m.; Sundays, Mondays and Thursdays, June to September (also Wednesdays, July and August) 1.30 p.m.–5 p.m. On view, the Marble Hall and State Rooms containing the extensive collection of Pictures. Tapestries, Statuary and Furnishings. Only entry to park. Almshouses gates. Holkham Village.
Charge for admission to view Hall: Adults £1, Children (5–15) 50p, O.A.Ps. 75p.
Admission to Park: Cars 50p, Motor-cycles 25p. Coaches and Pedestrians free.
Pre-paid Coach parties of 20 or more—10% reduction.

Also on View
The Holkham Studio Pottery

Bygones at Holkham. Agricultural and Domestic Bygones incorporating Craft Demonstrations, Steam Days and Engineerium. Garden centre.

OAKLEIGH HOUSE

SWAFFHAM, NORFOLK

Oakleigh House is a good example of a late 16th century house with a mid 18th century facade (1755). The present house is built on the site of the former home of John Chapman, the Swaffham Pedlar. The interior is of a comfortable mid Georgian flavour with a notable 17th century staircase. The entire house has recently been completely and tastefully restored. The Victorian Garden contains exotic pheasants.

A LIVED IN HOME — NOT A MUSEUM

WALSINGHAM ABBEY

NORFOLK

East Window (Priory Church)

The Grounds contain the remains of the Augustinian Priory, founded in 1153 on a site next to the Holy House, the shrine of Our Lady, built in 1061. The Grounds are open to the public from 2–5 p.m. April: Weds.; May, June, July & Sept.: Weds., Sats. & Suns.; Aug.: Mons., Weds., Fris., Sats. & Suns. Also Bank Holidays from Easter to Sept.

Walsingham is a picturesque village containing fine examples of 15th–18th century architecture with half-timbered houses and medieval pump-house. Ruins of Franciscan Friary, Court House Museum, Anglican Shrine, Pottery. R.C. Slipper Chapel and new Chapel 1m. to the south.
Accommodation and Catering—Black Lion Hotel; Knight's Gate Hotel.

BOUGHTON HOUSE

NR. KETTERING, NORTHAMPTONSHIRE

Home of The Duke of Buccleuch and Queensberry K.T.

A 500 year old Tudor monastic building gradually enlarged around 7 courtyards until the French style addition of 1695. Outstanding collection of 17/18th century French and English furniture, tapestries, 16th century carpets porcelain, painted ceilings—notable works by El Greco, Murillo, Caracci and 40 Van Dyck sketches—celebrated Armoury. Teas in newly restored Stable Block. Virtually entire ground floor open but limited access to State Rooms on 1st floor at extra charge.

Beautiful parkland with avenues and lakes—picnic area—gift shop—exciting adventure woodland play area.

OPEN: April 1st, 7th/8th, 14th/15th & 20th–23rd (Easter). May 5th–7th & 26th–28th. *Closed May 29th to July 27th.* Reopen July 28th–September 16th—Daily (except Fridays). September 19th–October 31st—Wednesday, Thursday, Saturday & Sunday. GROUNDS 12.30–6 p.m. HOUSE 2–6 p.m. (Bank Hol. Sundays & Mondays and all Sundays in August 1–6 p.m.). Last entry 5 p.m.
Admission charges see entry.

Off A43 through Geddington, 3m. North of Kettering. Northampton 17 miles, Leicester 26, Peterborough 32, Coventry 44, Cambridge 45. London 70 minutes by train.

Parties welcome (special terms, extended hours and dates for pre-booked groups over 20). Telephone Kettering (0536) 82248.

"A vision of Louis XIV's Versailles transported to England"

ALTHORP NORTHAMPTONSHIRE

Magnificent picture collection of English and European Masters – Reynolds, Gainsborough, Rubens, Van Dyck, Lely, Lotto, Lucidel, Maratti. French furniture by Weisweiler, Saunier, Boulle. Rare porcelain from the Bow, Chelsea, Sèvres and Meissen factories.

Built by Sir John Spencer in 1508, altered by Henry Holland in 1790 and entirely redecorated in 1982. Rooms open in rotation. Maintained as a private home where visitors are welcome.

Presents shop for jewellery, china, glass and separate wine shop in the historic Georgian Stables. Tea-room with home-made cakes and scones all year.

Home of the Spencer family since 1508

OPEN ALL YEAR

Gates 2.20. House 2.30–5.30 (August 2.30–6). Bank Hols. 11.30–6. Suns., Tues., Weds., Thurs. and Sats.—open all year. Mons.—closed (except August and Bank Hols.). Weds.—Connoisseurs' Day. Fris.—closed (except August).

Admission: £2.50 (inc. parties—no special reductions); Children £1.25. Connoisseurs' Day £3.50. Gardens 50p. Children 25p. Coach parking fees £10 paid in advance (booking essential); cars free. Wine shop, Gift shop and Tea room—Free entry.

Prices subject to fluctuation as details submitted well in advance of printing.

For parties and special times or booking write (enclosing s.a.e.) to: The Countess Spencer, Althorp, Northampton NN7 4HG.

N.B.—*For security reasons House and Grounds may be closed without notice. Coaches will be informed.* House unsuitable for small children and frail and disabled people.

OXBURGH HALL NORFOLK

THE NATIONAL TRUST

"Aerofilms Ltd." photograph

Built in 1482 by Sir Edmund Bedingfeld, a favourite of Richard III, the house has come down in direct male descent in the Bedingfeld family for over 450 years. It was given to the National Trust by the Dowager Lady Bedingfeld in 1952. Of mellow red brick and surrounded by a wide moat, the house, with its magnificent gate tower, is one of the most romantic of its period to have survived. This great tower, which is comparable with that at Layer Marney, is flanked by octagonal turrets and rises sheer from the moat to a height of 80 feet. Panels of needlework by Mary Queen of Scots and Bess of Hardwick are displayed here.

OPENING TIMES OPPOSITE

CASTLE ASHBY

Near NORTHAMPTON

SIXTEENTH CENTURY ANCESTRAL HOME OF THE MARQUESS AND MARCHIONESS OF NORTHAMPTON

The House has been extensively refurbished in the last 2 years. Interior contains 1600–1635 ceilings, oak panelling, staircase and chimney pieces and 1600–1700 tapestries and furniture. The valuable collection of pictures includes many of the Italian Renaissance period (1480–1520) as well as examples of the English 18th century School and the Dutch 17th century School.

Televised by the B.B.C. as a typical Elizabethan House. Built in 1574 with Inigo Jones (1635) front.

200 Acres of Capability Brown Parkland and Terraced Gardens by Sir Digby Wyatt together with Italian Garden, Orangery and Arboretum.

OPENING TIMES SEE PAGE 106

PROPERTY (*showing map reference*)	LOCATION (*with nearest Rly. Stn.*)	OPENING TIMES AND ADMISSION CHARGES CATERING FACILITIES	COACH AND RAIL TOURS BUS SERVICES (*showing alighting points*)
NORFOLK—*continued*			
OXBURGH HALL, Swaffham *map 3 G* *The National Trust* Late 15th century moated house. Outstanding gatehouse tower. Needlework by Mary Queen of Scots. Unique French parterre laid out circa 1845. Woodland walk, if dry weather.	7 m SW of Swaffham on S side of Stoke Ferry Rd *Stn: Downham Market (10m)*	Gatehouse, Principal Rooms & Gardens: March 31 to Oct. 14—Mons., Tues., Weds., Sats. & Suns. 2–6. Bank Hol. Mons. 11–6. Oct. 15 to 28—Weekends only 2–5.30. Adm. £1.60, Chd. (with adult) 80p. Pre-booked parties of 15 or more £1.20 (Mons., Tues. & Weds. only). Shop. No dogs. Wheelchair access, 2 provided. in Old Kitchen ☎ *Gooderstone* 258	National tours from Norwich, King's Lynn, Wisbech & Ely Norfolk Motors tours from Yarmouth and Lowestoft on Sundays E. Counties 404, Downham Marke–Swaffham (*Sats. only*); also C. S. Pegg Ltd. (*alight village*)
RAINTHORPE HALL & GARDENS, Flordon, nr Norwich *map 3 H* *George Hastings, Esq.* Elizabethan Manor House set in large gardens	1 m SSW of Newton Flotman (A140) on Flordon Rd., 8 m S of Norwich	GARDENS: May to Sept.—Suns. & Bank Hol. Mons. 2.30–6. Adm. 60p, Chd. 25p, O.A.Ps. 50p. Car park free. Plants on sale. House open by appointment. Gardens only suitable for disabled.	Bus to Newton Flotman (1 *m*)
SANDRINGHAM HOUSE & GROUNDS, Sandringham *map 3 C* *Her Majesty the Queen* House, Grounds and Museum open *House, Grounds and Museum are NOT open when H.M. The Queen or any member of the Royal Family is in residence.*	8 m NE of King's Lynn (off A149)	House & Grounds: April 22 to Sept. 27—Mons., Tues., Weds. & Thurs. 11–4.45 (Grounds 10.30–5); Suns. 12–4.45 (Grounds 11.30–5). *House only closed July* 16 to *Aug.* 4 *inc. House & Grounds closed July* 20 *to Aug.* 1 *inc.* Adm. House & Grounds £1.50, Chd. 80p, O.A.Ps. £1.20. Grounds only £1.20. Chd. 70p, O.A.Ps. 90p. *No reduction for parties.* Free coach & car park. ☎ *King's Lynn* (0553) 2675	National tours from all parts of East Anglia (summer) Norfolk Motors tours from Yarmouth and Lowestoft on Weds. and Thurs. National and Venture tours from London (summer) E. Counties 411, King's Lynn–Sandringham–Hunstanton
TRINITY HOSPITAL, Castle Rising *Trustees* *map 3 C* Nine 17th century brick and tile Almshouses with court, chapel and treasury	4 m NE of King's Lynn on A149 *Stn: King's Lynn (5 m)*	All the year—Tues., Thurs. & Sats. Summer: 10–12, 2–6. Winter: 10–12, 2–4. Adm. free	E. Counties 410, 411, 412, 413, King's Lynn–Hunstanton (*alight Black Horse, Castle Rising*)
WALSINGHAM ABBEY, Walsingham *Walsingham Estate Company* *map 3 C* Augustinian Priory and crypt	On B1105 midway between Wells and Fakenham	Grounds open 2–5: April—Weds.; May to July & Sept.—Weds., Sats. & Suns.; August—Mons., Weds., Fris., Sats. & Suns. Also Bank Hols. Easter to Sept. *Other times by arrangement with Estate Office.* Adm. 40p, Chd. & O.A.Ps. 25p. ☎ *Walsingham* 259 Black Lion Hotel; Knight's Gate Hotel	Norfolk Motors tours from Yarmouth & Lowestoft every Sunday E. Counties 450, 454, Norwich–Fakenham–Wells (*not Suns.*) (*alight Little Walsingham Market Place*)
NORTHAMPTONSHIRE			
ALTHORP, Northampton *map 3 E* *The Earl Spencer* Built by Sir John Spencer in 1508, altered by Henry Holland in 1790 and entirely redecorated in 1982. Splendid interior containing pictures of many European schools; French furniture; large collection of porcelain. Rooms open in rotation. N.B.—*Please respect times when house and grounds are closed. No early arrivals except by appointment.*	6 m NW of Northampton on Northampton – Rugby rd (A428) 6 m from M1 exit 16 *Stns: Long Buckby (5½ m); Northampton (6½ m)*	Gates open 2.20. House 2.30–5.30 (Aug. 2.30–6). Bank Hols. 11.30–6. Suns., Tues., Weds., Thurs. & Sats.—Open all year. Mons.—*closed except during August & Bank Hols.* Weds.—Connoisseurs' Day. Fris.—*closed except Aug.* Adm. £2.50 (inc. parties—no special reductions). Chd. £1.25; Connoisseurs' Day £3.50. (extra rooms—longer tour).Gardens 50p, Chd. 25p. Coach parking fees £10; paid in advance—booking essential; cars free. Wine shop & Gift shop. Free entry to shop & tea room. For parties & special times or booking write (enclosing s.a.e.) to: The Countess Spencer, Althorp, Northampton NN7. *Information & prices are subject to alteration without notice as details submitted well in advance of printing.* tea room; home-made cakes & scones available at counter. Functions welcomed in the house. N.B.—*For security reasons House & Grounds may be closed without notice; Coach parties will be informed.* House unsuitable for small children and frail & disabled people.	Mid. Red 595, Coventry–Northampton (*alight main gates, ¾ m*) United Counties 346, Northampton–Long Buckby–West Haddon (*alight main gates, ¾ m.*)
AYNHOE PARK, Aynho *map 3 J* *Mutual Households Association* 17th century mansion. Alterations by Soane	6m SE of Banbury on main London —Birmingham Rd	May to September—Weds. & Thurs. 2–5. Adm. 50p, Chd. 25p Free car park. No dogs admitted	Midland Red 491, Banbury–Croughton. Midland Red/Oxford 499, Banbury–Aynho–Bicester (*not Suns.*) (*alight Cartwright Arms*)
BOUGHTON HOUSE, Kettering *map 3 F* *His Grace the Duke of Buccleuch & Queensberry K.T.* 15th century monastic building enlarged between 1530 and 1695 around 7 courtyards. Celebrated art treasures; lovely grounds, exciting adventure woodland play area and nature trail.	3 m N of Kettering on A43 at Geddington; 75 m from London on A1 or M1	April 1, 7/8, 14/15 & 20–23; May 5–7 & 26–28. *Closed May* 29 *to July* 27. Re-open July 28 to Sept.16 —Daily (except Fris.) & Sept. 19 to Oct. 31—Weds., Thurs., Sats. & Suns. Grounds open 12.30–6. House open 2–6 except Bank Hol. Sun. & Mons. and all Suns. in Aug.: 1–6. Last adm. 5. Adm. House & Grounds £2, Chd. £1, O.A.Ps. £1.50. Grounds only £1, Chd. & O.A.Ps. 50p. Pre-booked parties £1.50. State Room supplement £1.50. Party rates for schools on application. Surcharge of 50% per head for parties over 20 on non-regular open dates. Wheelchairs adm. free, ground floor only. Gift, craft & garden shops. Picnic area & lakeside walks. teas in restored Stables ☎ *Kettering* (0536) 82248	United Counties 253, 254, 256, Northampton–Kettering–Corby, 257 Kettering–Thrapston (*alight gates*) Hourly trains London–Kettering (70 *mins*) (taxis at Stn.)

DEENE PARK

NORTHAMPTONSHIRE

Deene, which has belonged to the Brudenell family since 1514, is a 16th and 17th century transformation of a mediaeval manor house with extensive 19th century additions.

It is still the "elegant habitation of the Brudenells" as William Camden described it in the 16th century and was the home of the Earl of Cardigan who led the Charge of the Light Brigade.

Its special appeal lies in its indefinable atmosphere of a home cherished by the same family for over four centuries.

OPENING TIMES SEE PAGE 106

PROPERTY (*showing map reference*)	LOCATION (*with nearest Rly. Stn.*)	OPENING TIMES AND ADMISSION CHARGES CATERING FACILITIES	COACH AND RAIL TOURS BUS SERVICES (*showing alighting points*)
NORTHAMPTONSHIRE—*continued*			
BURGHLEY HOUSE, Stamford *map 3 F* △ *Burghley House Trustees* Finest example of later Elizabethan architecture. State Apartments, pictures, furniture, silver fireplaces, painted ceilings, tapestries	1 m SE of Stamford (Lincs.), just off A1 *Stn: Stamford (1 m)*	April 1 to October 7—Daily 11–5 (Good Friday & Suns. 2–5). Closed Sept. 8. Adm. charges not available at time of going to press. tea in the Orangery. Enquiries for party rates & menus telephone *Stamford* (0780) 52451	**Barton & Skills tours from Nottingham** **National tours from the Midlands and East Anglia, Derby, Nottingham and Stockport** **Norfolk Motors tours from East Anglian towns** **Barton bus, Stamford–Peterborough** **United Counties 244, 245 Corby–Stamford**
CANON'S ASHBY HOUSE, *map 3 E* **Canon's Ashby** *The National Trust* An exceptional small manor house, restored garden, small park and church. Part of original Augustinian Priory.	On B4525 Northampton–Banbury rd.	April to end of Oct.—Weds. to Suns. & Bank Hol. Mons. 1–6 (timed ticket system in operation in house & garden). *Closed Good Friday.* Adm. £2, Chd. £1. Parking for cars; Coaches must pre-book. Dogs, on leads, in Home Paddock only. *Blakesley* (0327) 86004	No reasonable public transport
CASTLE ASHBY, Northampton *map 3 F* △ *The Marquess of Northampton* Elizabethan with Inigo Jones (1635) front, 17th cent. ceilings, staircases and panelling. Valuable collection of pictures. Gardens	6 m E of Northampton; 1½ m N of the Northampton—Bedford rd (A428)	Parties admitted at all times of the year by prior arrangement—full catering available. Gift shop. For any open days contact Administration Office: *Yardley Hastings* (060 129) 234 Gardens & Nature Trail open Suns., April to Oct.	**Tours from Bedford, Nottingham, Peterborough, & c.** **National tours from the Midlands** **United Counties 363 from Northampton**
COTON MANOR GARDENS *map 3 F* *Commander & Mrs. H. Pasley-Tyler* An outstanding old English Garden of exceptional charm and beauty. Enchanted by flamingoes, wildfowl and tropical birds at large in the water gardens	10 m N of Northampton & 11 m SE of Rugby off A428; also 2 m from A50	April to Oct.—Thurs., Suns., Bank Hol. Mons. & Tues. following 2–6; also Weds. in July & August. Oct.—Suns. only. Adm. £1.20, Chd. 60p. *Parties any day by arrangement.* Unusual plants for sale. home-made teas at house *Northampton* (0604) 740219	**No reasonable public transport.**
DEENE PARK, nr Corby *map 3 F* △ *Edmund Brudenell, Esq.* Mainly 16th century house of great architectural importance and historical interest. Large lake, park, extensive gardens with old fashioned roses, rare trees and shrubs.	8 m NW of Oundle; 6 m NE of Corby on Kettering–Stamford rd (A43)	Easter, Spring & Summer Bank Hol. Suns. & Mons. also every Sun. in June, July & Aug. 2–5. Adm. charges not available at time of going to press. *Special guided tours showing more of the house to parties of 20 or more may be arranged on application to the House Keeper.* *Bulwick* 278 *or* 361 (*office hours*)	No reasonable public transport
DELAPRE ABBEY, nr Northampton *Northamptonshire Borough Council* *map 3 E* House rebuilt or added to 16th to 19th centuries Converted for use as The County Record Office	On London rd (A508) 1 m due S of centre of Northampton	All the year—Thurs. 2.30–5 (closes 4.30 October to April) Adm. free 'public rooms and passages only'.	**Frequent services from town centre**
GUILSBOROUGH GRANGE WILDLIFE PARK, Guilsborough *map 3 E* *Major & Mrs S. J. Symington* Birds and wildlife in country house and garden setting in beautiful natural surroundings with fine views	10 m NW of Northampton; 10 m SE of Rugby; on outskirts of Guilsboro' on West Haddon rd. 6 m from M1, jct 18.	All the year—Daily 10–7 (or dusk if earlier). Adm. £1.80, Chd. & O.A.Ps. 90p. Special party rates. Free car park. Picnic area. Gift shop. Dogs allowed, on leads refreshment room	**United Counties 326 Northampton–Guilsborough–Market Harborough**
HINWICK HOUSE, nr Wellingborough △ *R. M. Orlebar* *map 3 F* A Queen Anne house of excellent architecture. Pictures by Van Dyck; Lely, Kneller etc. Lace, tapestries and needlework. Furniture, china, objets d'art. "A Century of Fashion" clothes from 1840 to 1940 on permanent display	3½ m S of Rushden, 6 m SE of Wellingborough, 3 m from A6 at Wymington	Easter; May 7; Spring & Summer Bank Hol. Suns., Mons. & Tues. also daily May 19 to 26: 2–5. Otherwise by appointment. Adm. £1. Parties welcome throughout year. by arrangement *Rushden* 53624	
HOLDENBY HOUSE GARDENS, Northampton *map 3 E* *James Lowther, Esq.* Once the largest house in Elizabethan England, subsequently the prison of Charles I in the Civil War. Original garden remains. Elizabethan garden, fragrant and silver borders. Rare farm animals. Donkeys and train rides. Museum.	7 m NW of Northampton, off A428 & A50; 7 m from M1, exit 18	GARDENS: April to Sept.—Suns. & Bank Hol. Mons. 2–6; also Thurs., July & Aug., 2–6. Adm. £1, Chd. 50p. HOUSE: Open by arrangement to pre-booked parties Mons. to Fris. Adm. £1.50, Chd. 75p. Enquire for special rates for school parties. Plant & Souvenir shop. home-made teas in Victorian Kitchen. *Northampton* (0604) 770786 *or* 770241	No reasonable public transport
KIRBY HALL, Gretton *map 3 F* *Dept. of the Environment* Built 1570 (partly roofed). 17th cent. gardens	2 m SE of Gretton	All the year: March 15 to Oct. 15—Weekdays 9.30–6.30; Suns. 2–6.30. Oct. 16 to March 14—Weekdays 9.30–4; Suns. 2–4. *Closed Dec. 24, 25, 26 & Jan. 1.* Adm. 40p, Chd. (under 16) & O.A.Ps. 20p.	**United Counties 263, Corby–Gretton**

Burghley House

Stamford

THE LARGEST AND GRANDEST HOUSE OF THE ELIZABETHAN AGE

Home of the Cecils for over 400 years.

Built in 1587 by William Cecil, first Lord Burghley, and Lord High Treasurer to Queen Elizabeth I and occupied by his descendants ever since. Eighteen treasure filled State Rooms are on view including the Heaven Room — the finest painted room in England. Of special interest are the silver fireplaces, needlework, painted ceilings, medieval kitchen with over 260 copper utensils, and one of the largest private art collections in Britain. The house is set in a Deer Park landscaped by "Capability" Brown. Home of the famous Burghley Horse Trials.

Refreshments available in the Orangery.

Open daily from April 1st until October 7th (not 8th of September). Weekdays 11 a.m.-5 p.m.; Sundays and Good Friday 2-5 p.m.

For further information and details of special party rates and menus contact The Manager, telephone Stamford (0780) 52451.

PROPERTY (showing map reference)	LOCATION (with nearest Rly. Stn.)	OPENING TIMES AND ADMISSION CHARGES CATERING FACILITIES	COACH AND RAIL TOURS BUS SERVICES (showing alighting points)
NORTHAMPTONSHIRE—*continued*			
LAMPORT HALL, Northampton *map 3 E* *Lamport Hall Trust* The home of the Isham family from 1560 to 1976. Present house mainly 17th and 18th century.	8 m N of Northampton on A508 to Mkt. Harborough	Easter to end of Sept.—Suns. & Bank Hol. Mons. 2.15–5.15. Also Thurs. in July & Aug., 2.15–5.15. School & private parties any time by appointment. Adm. £1.25, Chd. 65p. Free car park. No dogs please. ☕ teas at the house	United Counties X61 Northampton–Market Harborough–Leicester–Nottingham *(daily) (alight Lamport, Swan)*
LYVEDEN NEW BIELD, Oundle *map 3 F* *The National Trust* The shell of an unusual Renaissance building erected about 1600 by Sir Thomas Tresham to symbolize the Passion. He died before the building could be completed and his son was then imprisoned in connection with the Gunpowder Plot. A new view platform allows visitors to look from the East Window.	4 m SW of Oundle via A427. 3 m E of Brigstock (A6116) (½ m walk from car park)	All the year—Daily. *Property approached via two fields. Parties by arrangement with Custodian, Lyveden New Bield Cottage, nr. Oundle, Northants.* Adm. 50p, Chd. 25p. *No parking for coaches but which may drop & return to pick up passengers.* Dogs admitted, on leads. Unsuitable for disabled or visually handicapped. ☎ *Benefield* 358	United Counties/Eastern Counties 265, Kettering—Corby—Oundle—Peterborough *(alight Brigstock, 3 m)*
PRIEST'S HOUSE, Easton-on-the-Hill *The National Trust* *map 3 F* Pre-Reformation priest's house given to the National Trust by The Peterborough Society. Contains a small museum of village bygones	2 m SW of Stamford off A43 *Stn: Stamford (2 m)*	Access only by prior appointment with the Rector, Easton-on-the-Hill, nr. Stamford (*Stamford* 2616). Key can be collected from key holders listed at building. Adm. free. No dogs. Unsuitable for disabled or visually handicapped & Coaches.	United Counties 240, 245 Stamford–Corby (*½ m*) *(not Suns.)*
ROCKINGHAM CASTLE, nr Corby *map 3 F* Δ *Commander Michael Saunders Watson* Royal Castle till 1530, since then home of the Watson family. Spans 900 years of English life and culture set amid lovely gardens and fine views	2 m N of Corby 9 m from Market Harborough, 14 m from Stamford on A427. 8 m from Kettering on A6003	Easter Sun. to Sept. 30—Suns. & Thurs. also Bank Hol. Mons. & Tues. following and Tues. during Aug.: 2–6. Adm. £1.50, Chd. 80p. Gardens. only 80p. *Any other day by previous appointment for parties.* ☕ teas—home-made at Castle. ☎ *Corby* (0536) 770240	Tours from Derby, Nottingham, Birmingham, Luton, &c. United Counties 263, Corby–Gretton Hourly trains London to Kettering (taxis at Station)
RUSHTON HALL, Rushton, nr Kettering *Royal National Institute for the Blind* *map 3 F* Dates from c. 1500, with later additions	4 m NW of Kettering, off A6003	Grounds & exterior of premises only (with a limited inspection of the interior) by prior appointment August—Daily 10–4.	No reasonable public transport
SOUTHWICK HALL nr Oundle *Christopher Capron, Esq.* *map 3 F* Manor house, retaining mediaeval building dating from 1300, with Tudor re-building and 18th cent. additions. Victorian and Edwardian Exhibition; Bygones of Agricultural and Carpentry tools; Archaeological finds and fossils, collection of named bricks.	3 m N of Oundle 4 m E of Bulwick	Suns. April 15 & May 13; Bank Hol. Suns. to Tues. following: April 22–24, May 6–8 & 27–29, Aug. 26–28; also Weds. June 6 to Sept. 12: 2.30–5. Adm. £1, Chd. 50p. Parties at other times by arrangement with The Secretary, Southwick Hall, Peterborough PE8 5BL. ☕ teas ☎ *Oundle* (0832) 74013 *or* 74064	No reasonable public transport
STOKE PARK PAVILIONS, Towcester *R. D. Chancellor, Esq.* *map 3 E* Two pavilions and colonnade. Built 1630 by Inigo Jones	Stoke Bruerne village 7 m S of Northampton just W of Stony –N'pton rd A508	June—Suns. only, 2–6. July & Aug.—Sats., Suns. & Bank Hols. 2–6. *Exterior only on view* Adm. 50p	United Counties 330 Northampton–Stony Stratford *(alight Stoke Bruerne village)*
SULGRAVE MANOR, Banbury *map 3 E* Δ *The Sulgrave Manor Board* English home of ancestors of George Washington. The house was completed in 1558 and was lived in by descendants of the Washington family for 120 years.	Sulgrave Village is off Banbury–Northampton rd. (B4525); 7 m NE of Banbury; 28 m SE of Stratford-u-Avon; 30 m N of Oxford; 70 m NW of London.	Feb. 1 to Dec. 31—Daily (except Weds.). April to Sept. (inc.) 10.30–1, 2–5.30. Other months 10.30–, 2–4. *Closed Christmas Day & all January.* Adm. 80p. Schoolchildren 40p. Free car & coach parking Special opening WED. JULY 4. *Closed June 10 for private function.* ☎ *Sulgrave* (029 576) 205 ☕ refreshments at Thatched House Hotel opposite ☎ *Sulgrave* (029 576) 232	No reasonable public transport
NORTHUMBERLAND			
ALNWICK CASTLE, Alnwick *map 1 R* *His Grace the Duke of Northumberland K.G.* Important example of medieval fortification restored by Salvin, dating to 12th century	In the town of Alnwick, 30 m N of Newcastle off the A1 *Stn: Alnwick (4 m)*	May 6 to Sept. 28—Daily (except Sats.) 1–5. No admission after 4.30. Adm. £1.30, Chd. 60p. *Party rates Adults £1, Chd. 50p. No dogs* ☎ *Alnwick* (0665) 602722 *or* 602207	United 505, 506, Newcastle–Alnwick–Berwick-upon-Tweed; X18, 418 Newcastle–Alnwick
BAMBURGH CASTLE, Bamburgh *map 1 L* Δ *The Lord Armstrong* Fine 12th century Norman Keep. Remainder of castle considerably restored	16 m N of Alnwick 6 m from Belford 3 m from Seahouses *Stn: Chathill (6 m) (not Suns.)*	Easter to end of Oct.—Daily (incl. Suns.) open at 1; Adm. £1.30, Chd. 60p. *Subject to amendment.* For closing times enquire The Custodian ☕ Clock Tower tea rooms ☎ *Bamburgh* 208	National tours from Northumberland United 460, 466, 501, 502, X51, Alnwick–Bamburgh–Belford–Berwick *(alight Castle gates)*
CALLALY CASTLE, Whittingham *map 1 R* Δ *Major A. S. C. Browne, D.L.* 17th cent. mansion incorporating 13th cent. Pele tower with Georgian and Victorian additions. Exceptional fine salon with 18th cent. plasterwork. Only three families have owned Callaly since Saxon times. A fascinating house in a delightful environment. Televised by the B.B.C. Tyne-Tees and W.A.G.A. (U.S.A.)	2 m W of Whittingham 10 m W of Alnwick	May 5 to June 17 & July 7 to Sept. 16—Sats., Suns. & Bank Hol. Mons. 2.15–5.30. Last guided party 5 p.m. Adm. £1, Chd. 50p *(prices—subject to alteration). No dogs. Closed Easter week & June 6 to July 8. On other days on application to the Agent, Callaly Castle, Alnwick* ☎ *Whittingham* (066 574) 663	United 464 Morpeth–Berwick-upon-Tweed; 473 Alnwick–Whittingham–Wooler; 474 Morpeth–Coldstream *(not Suns. for all buses) (alight Whittingham, 2 m)*

ROCKINGHAM CASTLE

'Armscote' as in B.B.C. TV's "By the Sword Divided'

The castelle of Rockingham standeth upon the toppee of an hill right stately'

The house itself is memorable not so much as representing any particular period, but rather a procession of periods. The dominant influence in the building is Tudor within the Norman walls, but practically every century since the 11th has left its mark in the form of architecture, furniture, or works of art. There is a particularly fine collection of English 18th, 19th and 20th century paintings, and Charles Dickens, a frequent visitor, was so captivated by Rockingham that he used it as a model for Chesney Wold in Bleak House.

2 miles from Corby, Northamptonshire.

'A royal residence for 500 years'.

Rockingham Castle was built by William the Conqueror on the site of an earlier fortification and was used by the early Kings of England until the 16th century when it was granted by Henry VIII to Edward Watson whose family still live there today.

The Castle stands in 12 acres of formal and wild garden and commands a splendid view of five counties. Particular features are the 400 years old elephant hedge and the rose garden marking the foundations of the old keep.

See also
THE NAVAL CONNECTION
a colourful exhibition linking 500 years of Naval history with the Castle.

OPENING TIMES SEE PAGE 104

Home of Commander and Mrs. Michael Saunders Watson

SULGRAVE MANOR

Open to the public
Every day except Wednesday
from 1st February to 31st December
April to September inclusive
10.30 a.m.–1 p.m. & 2 p.m.–5.30 p.m.
Other months
10.30 a.m.–1 p.m. & 2 p.m.–4 p.m.
Special opening WEDNESDAY 4th JULY
(usual summer times)
CLOSED 10th JUNE for private function

ADMISSION: Adults 80p. Schoolchildren 40p includes access to House & Gardens, Guided Tour
Free parking for Cars & Coaches

Refreshments at 'Thatched House Hotel' (opposite the Manor House)

Telephones:
Manor House — Sulgrave (029576) 205
Hotel — Sulgrave (029576) 232

SULGRAVE MANOR

BANBURY, OXON OX17 2SD

THE WASHINGTON ANCESTRAL HOME

The Washington ownership dates from 1539 when Lawrence Washington purchased the land upon the Dissolution, by Henry VIII, of St. Andrew's Priory, Northampton. The House was completed in 1558 (the year Elizabeth I came to the throne of England) and was lived in by descendants of the Washington family for 120 years.

Today it is an excellent example of a small Manor House, typical of a wealthy man's home and gardens in Elizabethan times, restored and refurbished with scholarly care and attention to detail which makes a visit both a delight and an education.

"A perfect illustration of how a house should be shown to the public" is how Nigel Nicholson describes it in his "Great Houses of Britain"

SULGRAVE MANOR has been open to the public since 1921 when it was established as a 'Token of Friendship' between the people of Britain and the United States. It is now held in trust for the peoples of both nations, the trustees being the American Ambassador in London, the British Ambassador in Washington and the Regent of Mount Vernon, Virginia.

The village of Sulgrave is situated 1 mile off the Northampton road (B4525), 7 miles N.E. of Banbury, 28 miles S.E. of Stratford upon Avon, 30 miles N. of Oxford and 70 miles N.W. of London.

" Country Life " photograph

The Home of the Duke of Northumberland K.G.

ALNWICK CASTLE

NORTHUMBERLAND

The rugged appearance of this famous Border fortress, which has been the seat o the Percy family since Norman times, belies the rich elegance of the interior.

The Keep, Armoury, Guard Chamber, Library and other Principal Apartments are on view in addition to the Dungeon, State Coach and Museum of British and Roman Antiquities. There are pictures by Titian, Canaletto, Van Dyck and other famous artists, fine furniture, Meissen china and various historical heirlooms.

Parties catered for in hotels and cafés in the town. Free parking. Enquiries to Supervisor, Estate Office, Alnwick Castle, Northumberland. Tel.: Alnwick (0665) 602722 or 602207.

CALLALY CASTLE

WHITTINGHAM, NORTHUMBERLAND

17th century mansion incorporating 13th century Pele tower with Georgian and Victorian additions. Exceptional fine salon with 18th century plasterwork. Televised by the B.B.C., Tyne-Tees and W.A.G.A. (USA). Only three families have owned Callaly since Saxon times. A fascinating house in a delightful environment.

Open May 5th to June 17th and July 7th to September 16th on Saturdays, Sundays and Bank Holidays 2.15 p.m.–5.30 p.m. Last guided party 5 p.m. Closed Easter Week and June 18th to July 6th.

PROPERTY (*showing map reference*)	LOCATION (*with nearest Rly. Stn.*)	OPENING TIMES AND ADMISSION CHARGES CATERING FACILITIES	COACH AND RAIL TOURS BUS SERVICES (*showing alighting points*)
NORTHUMBERLAND—*continued*			
CRAGSIDE HOUSE & COUNTRY PARK, Rothbury *map 1 R* *The National Trust* The House designed by Richard Norman Shaw for the first Lord Armstrong and built between 1864–95. It contains much of its original furniture and Pre-Raphaelite paintings. It was the first house in the world to be lit by electricity generated by water power. The Country Park is famous for its rhododendrons, magnificent trees and the beauty of the lakes.	½ m E of Rothbury, 30 m N of Newcastle-u-Tyne. Entrance off Rothbury/Alnwick rd B6341; 1 m N of R'bury at Debdon Burn Gate	COUNTRY PARK: April to Sept.—Daily 10.30–6; Oct.—Daily 10.30–5; Nov. to March—Sats. & Suns. 10.30–4. Adm. 90p; parties of 15 or more 60p. HOUSE: April to end of Sept.—Daily (except Mons. but open Bank Hol. Mons. 1–6; Oct.—Weds., Sats. & Suns. 2–5. Last adm. half-hour before closing. Adm. House & Country park £2.10; parties of 15 or more £1.50. Parties by prior arrangement only with the administrators. Displays & shop in Visitor centre. Dogs in Country Park only. Wheelchair access to House—lift available (wheelchairs provided). Toilets for disabled. ☎ *Rothbury* (0669) 20333 refreshments in café; meals in Visitor centre	Tower Transit 716, Newcastle (Haymarket)–Wallington–Cragside; United 416, Newcastle–Morpeth–Rothbury–Thropton (*alight Reiverswell*); 475, Alnwick–Rothbury
GEORGE STEPHENSON'S COTTAGE, Wylam-on-Tyne *map 1 R* *The National Trust* A small stone cottage built c. 1750. The birthplace, in 1781, of the inventor.	8 m W of Newcastle; 1½ m S of A69 at Wylam-on-Tyne *Stn: Wylam (½ m)*	April to end of Oct.—Weds., Sats. & Suns. 2–5. Other times of the year by appointment only with the tenant. Adm. 30p, Chd. 15p. Parking facilities 500 yds. from cottage by War Memorial in village. No dogs. Wheelchair access. N.B. Access to cottage by foot only. ☎ *Wylam* 3457	United 686 from Newcastle (*alight bus stop, ¼ m*)
HOWICK GARDENS, Alnwick *map 1 R* *Howick Trustees Ltd.* Lovely flower, shrub and rhododendron gardens	6 m NE of Alnwick, nr Howick village *Stn: Alnmouth (5 m)*	April to September—Daily 2–7. Adm. 40p, Chd. 20p.	United 501, X51 Alnwick–Craster–Embleton–Belford–Berwick (*alight Howick Hall*)
LINDISFARNE CASTLE, Holy Island *The National Trust* *map 1 L* Built about 1550. Sympathetically restored as a comfortable house by Lutyens in 1903.	5 m E of Beal across causeway *Stn: Berwick-upon-Tweed (10 m—to start of causeway)*	April to end of Sept.—Daily (except Fris. but open Good Friday) 11–5. Oct.—Sats & Suns. 11–5. Last adm. half-hour before closing. Adm. £2 June to Aug.; £1.40 at other times. Parties of 15 or more £1.40 by prior arrangement only with the Administrator. No dogs in Castle. Unsuitable for wheelchairs. ☎ *Berwick* (0289) 89244	National tours from Tyneside and Durham; United 505/6, Newcastle–Berwick-upon-Tweed (*alight Beal for Holy Island*); United 477, Berwick–Holy Island (*daily July to end Aug. Enquire for days of operation remainder of year*)
MELDON PARK, Morpeth *map 1 R* *M. J. B. Cookson, Esq.* Built in 1832 for the Cookson family and occupied by them up to the present time. Main ground floor rooms only open to the public. Different coloured rhododendrons, especially in the wild garden.	7 m W of Morpeth on B6343 Morpeth–Hartburn rd.; NW of Newcastle-on-Tyne *Stn: Morpeth (7 m)*	House & Grounds: May 26 to June 24—Daily 2–5; also open Summer Bank Hol. weekend (Aug. 25/26/27). Adm. £1, Chd. 50p. Car park free. light refreshments	
PRESTON TOWER, Chathill *map 1 L* *Major T. H. Baker-Cresswell* One of the few survivors of 78 Pele Towers listed in 1415. The tunnel vaulted rooms remain unaltered and provide a realistic picture of the grim way of life under the constant threat of 'Border Reivers'. One room is furnished in contemporary style and there are displays of historic and local information.	7 m N of Alnwick; 1 m E from A1. Follow Historic Property signs. *Stn: Chathill (1 m)*	April to Sept.—Daily 10–6. Adm. 50p, Chd. 25p. Free car park. No dogs (except those left in car).	Bus services via A1 (*1 m*)
WALLINGTON HOUSE, GARDEN and GROUNDS, Cambo *map 1 R* *The National Trust* Built 1688, altered 18th century. Central Hall added in 19th century, decorated by William Bell Scott, Ruskin and others. Fine porcelain, furniture and pictures in series of rooms including a late Victorian nursery and dolls' houses. Museum. Coach display in West Coach House. Woodlands, lakes, walled terraced garden and conservatory with magnificent fuchsias.	Access from N, 12 m W of Morpeth on B6343; Access from S, A696 from Newcastle, 6m NW of Belsay, B6342 to Cambo	GROUNDS: All the year. Adm. £1. Parties of 15 or more 70p. Please keep to footpaths in the woods. HOUSE: April to end of Sept.—Daily (except Tues.) 1–6; Oct.—Weds., Sats. & Suns. 2–5. Last adm. half-hour before closing. Adm. House & Grounds £2.20. Parties of 15 or more £1.50. No dogs in house; on leads in walled garden. Shop & Information Centre. Wheelchairs provided. *Parties by prior arrangement with the administrators: No bookings on Bank Hols. & Suns. in July & Aug.* ☎ *Scots Gap* (067 074) 283 (House) refreshments available at Clock Tower Resaurant ☎ *Scots Gap* (067 074) 274	National Express 372, 374, 375, 378 and Vasey's 808 from Newcastle (*alight Shielhill crossroads, 1½ m*); Vasey/Snaith 909, 919 Morpeth–Wallington (*Mons.–Fris. only*) (*alight gates*); Tower Transit 716 Newcastle (Haymarket)–Rothbury (*peak Suns. only*)
NORTH YORKSHIRE (*see also West & South Yorkshire*)			
BEDALE HALL, Bedale *map 5 A* *Hambleton District Council* Georgian mansion with fine ballroom wing and museum room. Domestic and craft exhibits	7½ m SW of Northallerton on A684, 1½ m W of A1 at Leeming Bar	March to September—Tues. 2–4.30 or by appointment at other times. Adm. free	United Auto. 72, Darlington–Leyburn; 147, Ripon–Bedale
BENINGBROUGH HALL, nr York *The National Trust* *map 5 B* This Baroque house has been completely restored and in the principal rooms are 100 famous portraits on permanent loan from the National Portrait Gallery. Victorian laundry and exhibitions. Gardens and Adventure Playground.	8 m NW of York; 3 m W of Shipton (A19); 2 m SE Linton-on-Ouse; follow signposted route *Stn: York (8 m)*	April to end of Oct.—Tues., Weds., Thurs., Sats. & Suns. 12–6. Bank Hol. Mons. 11–6. Garden open from 11 a.m. Adm. House & Garden £1.70; special for 1984 Chd. (accompanied) free. Pre-booked parties of 15 or more £1.30. Chd. 50p. Garden & Exhibitions £1.20, Chd. (accompanied) free. Picnic area. Shop. No dogs. Wheelchairs provided. Lunches, teas ☎ *York* (0904) 470715 (Restaurant open from 11 a.m.)	York Pullman, York–Linton-on-Ouse (*alight Newton-on-Ouse 1 m*)
BROUGHTON HALL, Skipton *map 5 A* *H. R. Tempest, Esq.* Georgian front. Built 1597 and altered in 1756, 1810 and 1840. Private Chapel. Extensive grounds, with Italian garden laid out by W. A. Nesfield	3½ m W of Skipton on S side of A59	June—Weekdays 2–5. Also Spring & Summer Bank Hols. 11–5. *Other times by prior appointment.* Adm. £2. No reductions. ☎ *Skipton* 2267 Chapel open for Mass 9.30 on Suns., Tues. & Weds. throughout year. Bull Inn, Broughton	Ribble X27 Liverpool–Preston–Skipton, X43 Manchester–Skipton (*alight Broughton ½ m*)
CASTLE HOWARD, York *map 5 B* *Lord Howard of Henderskelfe* Designed by Vanbrugh 1699–1726 for the 3rd Earl of Carlisle, assisted by Hawksmoor, who designed the Mausoleum. Fine collection of pictures, statuary and furniture. Beautiful park and grounds. Costume Galleries covering 18th to 20th centuries in the Stable Court. Displays changed every year.	15 m NE of York, 3 m off A64; 6 m W of Malton; 38 m Leeds, 36 m Harrogate, 22 m Scarborough, 50 m Hull *Stn: Malton (6 m)*	March 25 to Oct. 31—Daily. Grounds open 10.30, Cafeteria 11, House & Costume Galleries 11.30–5 (last adm. 4.45). Adm. charges not available at time of going to press. *Special terms for adult booked parties.* Cafeteria. Licensed restaurant available for advance bookings. ☎ *Coneysthorpe* (065 384) 333	For information on bus services telephone West Yorkshire Road Car Co. ☎ *York* (0904) 24161
CONSTABLE BURTON HALL, Leyburn *map 5 A* *M. C. A. Wyvill, Esq.* Extensive borders, interesting alpines, large informal garden. John Carr house completed in 1768	On A684, between Leyburn (3 m) & Bedale; A1 (7 m)	Gardens: May 1 to August 1—Daily 9–6. Adm. 50p, collecting box. House: opening dates & adm. charges not available at time of going to press. Party rates by arrangement ☎ *Bedale* 50428	No reasonable public transport
DUNCOMBE PARK, Helmsley *map 5 B* *Trustees of Duncombe Park* Two 18th cent. Temples. Formal gardens	1 m W of Helmsley	Gardens only: May to August—Weds., 10–4. Adm. 10p, Chd. 5p. *Call at Estate Office for admission*	Tours from York; Nearest bus service Helmsley (*1 m to Park*)

CRAGSIDE
HOUSE & COUNTRY PARK

ROTHBURY, NORTHUMBERLAND

THE NATIONAL TRUST

Designed by Richard Norman Shaw for the first Lord Armstrong and built between 1864 and 1895. It contains much of its original furniture and pre-Raphaelite pictures. It was the first house in the world to be lit by electricity generated by water power. The Country Park is famous for its rhododendrons, magnificent trees and the beauty of the lakes.

LINDISFARNE CASTLE

HOLY ISLAND

THE NATIONAL TRUST

"Philipson Studios" photograph

Lindisfarne Castle was built about 1550 in a romantic situation on a high rock overlooking the sea. It was made habitable by Sir Edwin Lutyens after 1900.

MELDON PARK

MORPETH, NORTHUMBERLAND

Meldon Park was built by John Dobson, the famous North East architect, in 1832 for the Cookson family and since that date it has been occupied by them up to the present time except for the duration of the last war. The house and grounds are open from 2 p.m.–5 p.m. from Saturday, 26th May to Sunday, 24th June and the August Bank Holiday week-end 25th, 26th and 27th August.

The public are admitted to the main ground floor rooms which are renowned for the spacious view of the local rolling countryside. At this time of year the grounds are highlighted by the many different coloured flowering rhododendrons, especially those in the wild garden. Light refreshments are on sale; car park—free; and there are facilities for the disabled.

CASTLE HOWARD

This magnificent 18th Century palace was the first major work of Sir John Vanbrugh, and contains a unique collection of famous pictures, furniture, tapestries and porcelain. Features of particular interest are the Long Gallery, the Chapel, and the Great Hall surmounted by a painted and gilded dome. Castle Howard is set in extensive grounds which include lakes, a fountain, Vanbrugh's beautiful Temple of the Four Winds and the Mausoleum designed by Hawksmoor.

The Costume Galleries in the stable court contain the largest private collection in Britain of 18th-20th century dress, selections of which are exhibited in period settings changed every year.

Enquiries to the Comptroller, Castle Howard, York.
Tel. Coneysthorpe (065 384) 333

WALLINGTON
HOUSE, GARDEN & GROUNDS

CAMBO, NORTHUMBERLAND

THE NATIONAL TRUST

Wallington, which was built in 1688, has interiors mainly dating from the mid-18th century. There is good rococo plasterwork, fine porcelain and needlework exhibits. The central hall, which was added in the 19th century, was decorated by William Bell Scott, Ruskin and others. The home of the Trevelyan family since 1777, Wallington was given to the National Trust with porcelain, pictures and furniture in 1942 by the late Sir Charles Trevelyan. Walled Garden with Conservatory containing magnificent fuchsias.

BENINGBROUGH HALL

Near YORK, N. YORKSHIRE

THE NATIONAL TRUST

Built about 1716, this attractive house stands in a wooded park and was reopened in 1979 after a major restoration programme. In the principal rooms are nearly 100 pictures from the National Portrait Gallery representing many of the notable personalities of the period 1688-1760. The Victorian laundry is open and exhibitions describe domestic life of the period at all levels through the portraits, sound and visual displays. Gardens. Adventure Playground.

PROPERTY (*showing map reference*)	LOCATION (*with nearest Rly. Stn.*)	OPENING TIMES AND ADMISSION CHARGES CATERING FACILITIES	COACH AND RAIL TOURS BUS SERVICES (*showing alighting points*)
NORTH YORKSHIRE—*continued*			
EBBERSTON HALL, Scarborough *map 5 B* *W. de Wend Fenton, Esq.* Palladian Villa of 1718 designed by the architect Colin Campbell. Water gardens attributed to William Benson and Switzer. Elaborate woodwork and cornices comparable to Castle Howard and Beningbrough	11 m SW of Scarborough on A10 Scarborough – Pickering rd	Easter to mid Sept.—Daily 10–6. Adm. 90p Gapes Inn, Ebberston	United bus passes house
FOUNTAINS ABBEY, Ripon *map 5 A* *The National Trust* Ruins of Cistercian monastery. Ornamental gardens laid out by John Aislabie, 1720	4 m SW of Ripon; 9 m N of Harrogate; W of A61	DEER PARK: open all year during daylight hours. ABBEY & GARDEN: Jan. 1 to March 31—Mons. to Sats. 9.30–4; Suns. 2–4. April 1 to Oct. 15—Daily 9.30–8. Oct. 16 to Dec. 31—Daily 9.30–4. *Closed Christmas Eve, Christmas Day, Boxing Day & Good Friday.* Adm. (until March 31) 50p, Chd. & O.A.Ps. 25p; April 1 to Dec. 31: £1.30, Chd. 50p. Party rates available. N.T. members free. Car park: Coaches £3, cars 60p. Café & Kiosk in the grounds	National tours from Blackpool, Chesterfield, Sheffield & Stockport, etc. West Yorks. & United 36, Leeds–Harrogate–Ripon then: United 145, Ripon–Fountains Abbey (*alight Abbey*) Excursions & tours from all parts
GEORGIAN THEATRE, Richmond *map 5 A* *The Georgian Theatre (Richmond) Trust Ltd.* Built in 1788. Historically very important being country's oldest theatre in original form. Beautiful intimate interior; also Theatre Museum	Friars Wynd, off Market Place	Easter weekend, then May 1 to September 30—Daily 2.30–5; also Sats. & Bank Hol. Mons.10.30–1. Adm. 40p, Chd. (under 16) 30p. Party rates on application. Intermittent season of Plays, Recitals etc. *Theatre may be viewed during winter months; apply in writing to the Manager. Party rates available*	United services serving Richmond
GILLING CASTLE, Helmsley *map 5 B* *Ampleforth Abbey Trustees* Original Norman keep with 16th and 18th century additions	In Gilling East, 18 m N of York	All the year—Monday to Friday 10–12, 2–4. Adm. free to Hall and Great Chamber only Gardens—July to September. Adm. 50p	No reasonable public transport
HOVINGHAM HALL, York *map 5 B* *Sir Marcus & Lady Worsley* Palladian house, designed c. 1760 by Thomas Worsley. Unique Riding School, magnificent yew hedges, dovecot, private cricket ground. Family portraits.	20 m N of York on Malton–Helmsley rd (B1257)	By written appointment for parties of 15 or more. May 8 to Sept. 13—Tues., Weds. & Thurs. 11–7. Adm. £1.20, Chd. 60p. refreshments at the Hall by arrangement The Worsley Arms, Hovingham	West Yorks. from & to Malton
MARKENFIELD HALL, Ripon *map 5 A* *The Lord Grantley, MC.* Fine example of English manor house. 14th, 15th & 16th c. buildings surrounded by moat	3 m S of Ripon off the Ripon-Harrogate rd (A61)	April to Oct.—Mons. 10–12.30, 2.15–5. Adm. 50p, Chd. (accompanied by adult) free. Exterior only all other days in *May*—times as above. Adm. free.	West Yorks. & United 36, Leeds–Harrogate–Ripon (*alight 3 m S. of Ripon, 1 m walk*)
NEWBURGH PRIORY, Coxwold *map 5 B* *Capt. V. M. Wombwell* Originally 12th cent. Augustinian Priory with 16th, 17th and 18th cent. alterations and additions. Wild water garden and collection of rock plants. Walled garden	5 m from Easingwold off A19 9 m from Thirsk	May 16 to Aug. 29—Weds. House open 2–5, Grounds 2–6. Adm. House & Grounds £1, Chd. 50p. Grounds only 50p, Chd. 20p. *Other days for parties of 20 or more by appointment with the Administrator.* in the Old Priory Kitchens *Coxwold* (034 76) 435	United 128, Scarborough–Ripon (*alight Coxwold 1¼ m*)
NEWBY HALL, Ripon *map 5 B* *R. E. J. Compton, Esq.* One of the most famous Adam houses beautifully redecorated, contains superb Gobelins tapestries, fine collection of antique sculpture and furniture. Miniature Railway through the Gardens and Adventure Gardens for children.	4 m SE of Ripon on Boroughbridge Rd. (B6265). 3 m W of A1; 14 m Harrogate, 20 m York, 35 m Leeds	HOUSE: April & Sept.—Weds., Thurs., Sats., Suns., & Bank Hol. Mons.; May to Aug.—Daily (except Mons. but open Bank Hol. Mon.): 1–5 GARDENS: April 1 to Sept. 30—Daily (except Mons. but open Bank Hol. Mons.) 11–5.30. Last adm. 5. Adm. charges not available at time of going to press. Enquiries to: Opening Administrator. Newby Hall, Ripon HG4 5AE. Licensed Restaurant for lunches & teas in the "Garden Restaurant" *Boroughbridge* (090 12) 2583	National tours from Harrogate, Leeds, Keighley, Hull, Scarborough, Teeside, Co. Durham & Tyneside United 143, Ripon–York (2 *hourly*)
NORTON CONYERS, Ripon *map 5 A* *Sir J. Graham, Bt.* This Jacobean manor house has belonged to the Grahams, who still live in it, since 1624. Family pictures, furniture and wedding dresses. Visited by Charlotte Bronte, the house is one of the originals of Thornfield Hall in "Jane Eyre".	3½ m N of Ripon nr Wath; 1½ m from A1	June to Sept. 2—Suns.: also Bank Hol. Suns. & Mons. and daily July 23 to Aug. 4: 2–5.30. Pre-booked parties all year. Adm. £1, Chd. 60p, O.A.Ps. 90p. Interesting Garden Centre in the 18th century walled garden, specialising in unusual hardy plants. Open all year Mons. to Fris. 9–5; Sats. & Suns. April 1 to Sept. 30: 2–5.30. refreshments for parties by arrangement *Melmerby* (076 584) 333	United 147 Ripon–Bedale (*infrequent*)
NUNNINGTON HALL, nr Helmsley *map 5 B* *The National Trust* Sixteenth century manor house with fine panelled hall and staircase. Carlisle Collection of Miniature Rooms on display.	In Rydeale; 4½ m SE of Helmsley, 1½ m N of B1257	April to end of Oct.—Tues., Weds., Thurs., Sats. & Suns. 2–6. Bank Hol. Mons. 11–6. Adm. £1.20, Chd. 60p. Pre-booked parties of 15 or more 90p, Chd. 50p. No dogs. Unsuitable for disabled or wheelchairs. N.B. The Carlisle Collection is now at Nunnington Hall. teas *Nunnington* 283	United 128 Scarborough—Helmsley—Ampleforth, connections from Ripon. West Yorks 94 Malton–Hovingham (*alight Hovingham, 2 m*)
OSGODBY HALL, nr Thirsk *map 5 B* *Colonel C. d'A. P. Consett, D.S.O., M.C.* Small Jacobean Grade I Hall. Outstanding 17th century forecourt and staircase. Fully lived-in. Conducted tours by the owners.	4 m E of Thirsk on A170; turn S at sign ½ m thro' Sutton-under-Whitestonecliff	Easter weekend to Sept.—Sats., Suns. & Bank Hols. 2–5.30. Adm. 75p, Chd. 35p. Coaches by arrangement teas by arrangement	No reasonable public transport

OPENING TIMES SEE PAGE 114

FOUNTAINS ABBEY & STUDLEY ROYAL

RIPON, NORTH YORKSHIRE

THE NATIONAL TRUST

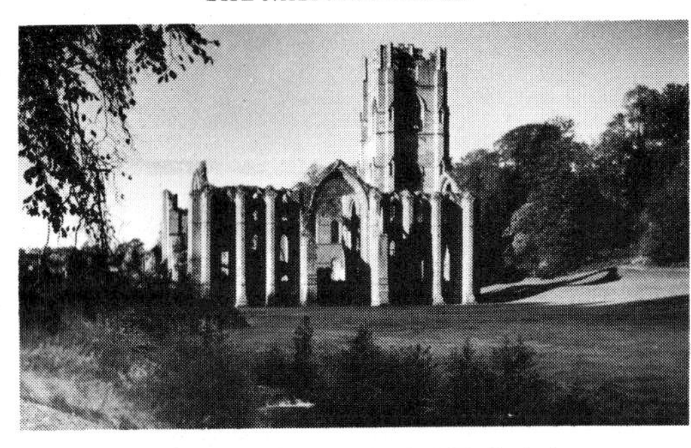

Fountains Abbey, founded by Cistercian monks in 1132, is the largest monastic ruin in Britain. Situated on the banks of the River Skell, the Abbey ruins provide the dramatic focal point of the landscape garden laid out by John Aislabie between 1720 and 1740. Famous for its water gardens, ornamental temples, follies and magnificent vistas, the garden is bounded at its western edge by a lake and 400 acres of deer park. Other features of interest include Fountains Hall, a late Elizabethan style house built between 1598-1611, and St Mary's Church (owned by the DOE) and built by William Burges 1871-8.

GEORGIAN THEATRE

Richmond, North Yorkshire

From a Bowers-Brittain original, Copyright reserved

Built by actor-manager Samuel Butler in 1788 it is the oldest theatre in Britain in its original form. Many famous artists past and present have played here—Edmund Kean, Macready, Yehudi Menuhin among them. It has an exceptionally attractive intimate interior. Theatre Museum contains the oldest and largest set of scenery in the U.K. (1836). Visiting the Georgian Theatre is a unique experience and a must for everyone interested in theatre.

Open daily May 1st to September 30th and Easter weekend 2.30–5 p.m.; also Saturday and Bank Holiday Monday mornings 10.30 a.m.–1 p.m. Admission 40p, Children (under 16) 30p. Party rates on application. Spring, Summer Concerts, Autumn and Christmas seasons. Telephone Richmond (0748) 3021 (afternoons).

Newby Hall

Ripon, North Yorkshire

This famous Adam House is one of the most intimate of stately homes in Yorkshire—it is still a lived in family house. Set in 25 acres of glorious gardens, the house with its elegant state apartments and gracious rooms—all recently redecorated and refurbished—provides the perfect setting for the treasures on view. The Adam Sculpture Gallery of Imperial Roman Sculpture; the Gobelins Tapestries—one of only five complete sets in the world; Chippendale furniture; 18th century porcelain; and many more priceless works of art.

The gardens too, have much to offer—throughout the 25 acres are many rare trees and shrubs as well as individually designed rose and sunken gardens. The miniature riverside railway has been extended to wind through the gardens—now a journey of over a mile. There is an Adventure Garden for the children with dare-devil cable ride, island fort and boats.

- **Woodland car park and picnic area**
- **Licensed Garden Restaurant for lunches and teas**
- **Miniature railway and Adventure Gardens for Children**
- **Information Pavilion and Shop**

For further enquiries please contact: The Opening Administrator, The Estate Office, Newby Hall, Ripon HG4 5AE.

For opening times see page opposite.

NEWBURGH PRIORY

COXWOLD, YORK

One of the North's most interesting Historic Houses. Originally built in 1145 with alterations in 1568 and 1720-1760, the Priory has been the home of one family and its descendants since 1538. The house contains the tomb of Oliver Cromwell (his third daughter, Mary, was married to Viscount Fauconberg—owner 1647-1700). In the grounds there is a really beautiful Water Garden full of rare alpines, plants and rhododendrons. Afternoon tea is served in the original kitchen.

OPENING TIMES OPPOSITE

NUNNINGTON HALL

HELMSLEY
NORTH YORKSHIRE

THE NATIONAL TRUST

A large sixteenth century manor house situated on the banks of the River Rye. In addition to the principal reception rooms, including the magnificent Hall with its fine carved chimney-piece, visitors will see panelled bedrooms, fine tapestries and china in an interior which fully justifies the expectations aroused by the outside view of this charming old hall. The Carlisle Collection of Miniature Rooms fully furnished in different periods are on display. Garden.

PROPERTY (*showing map reference*)	LOCATION (*with nearest Rly. Stn.*)	OPENING TIMES AND ADMISSION CHARGES CATERING FACILITIES	COACH AND RAIL TOURS BUS SERVICES (*showing alighting points*)
NORTH YORKSHIRE—*continued*			
RIEVAULX TERRACE, Helmsley *map 5 B* *The National Trust* Grass terrace with views of Rievaulx Abbey. Two 18th century Temples and permanent exhibition.	**2½ m NW of Helmsley on Stokesley rd. (B1257)**	April to Oct.—Daily 10.30–6 (last adm. 5.30). *Closed Good Friday.* Ionic Temple closed 1–2 p.m. Adm.: Fris. to Mons. £1.10. Tues. to Thurs. £1; Chd. 50p. Pre-booked parties of 15 or more 90p/80p each adult. Chd. 40p. Dogs admitted. Wheelchairs provided. ☎ *Bilsdale* 340	United 298. Stokesley–Helmsley, connections from Scarborough & Pickering (*Fris. & Sats. only*) (*alight Lane end, ½ m*)
RIPLEY CASTLE, Ripley *map 5 A* *Sir Thomas Ingilby, Bt.* Has been the home of the Ingilby family since early 14th cent. Main gateway dates from reign of Edward IV. Extensive gardens.	In Ripley 3½ m N Harrogate, 7½ m from Ripon	Easter weekend to May 31—Sats. & Suns.; June to Sept.—Tues., Weds., Thurs., Sats. & Suns.: 2–6. Open Good Friday & Bank Hol. Mons. 11–6. Pre-booked parties any day by arrangement from Good Friday to end of Sept. Gardens only open from Good Friday to end of Sept.—Daily 11–6. Adm. £1.50, Chd. 80p. Parties of 25 or more £1.50, 45 or more £1; Chd. in party of 25 or more 60p. Reduced rates for O.A.Ps. & unemployed with UB40. Gardens only 80p, Chd. 40p ☕ at the Castle ☎ *Harrogate* (0423) 770152	West Yorks. & United Jt. 36, Leeds–Harrogate–Ripon West Yorks. 23, 25, Harrogate–Pateley Bridge or Markington (*Sats. only*)
SHANDY HALL, Coxwold *map 5 B* *The Laurence Sterne Trust* Exceptional medieval house altered and added to in 17th and 18th centuries but little changed since Laurence Sterne wrote '*A Sentimental Journey*' and most of '*Tristram Shandy*' there. Walled garden	6 m from A19 at Easingwold; 13 m from A1 at Dishforth	June to Sept.—Weds. 2–5; Suns. 2.30–4.30. *At all other times by previous appointment with Hon. Curator* Adm. (1983 rates) 80p. Chd. (accompanied) half price. Book & handicrafts shop. ☕ in village ☎ *Coxwold* 465	United 128 Ripon–Thirsk–Scarborough (*passes gate*)
SKIPTON CASTLE, Skipton *map 5 A* Fully roofed medieval fortress. Attractive 15th century courtyard. Massive Gatehouse.	Centre of Skipton *Stn: Skipton (¼ m)*	All the year—Mons. to Sats. 10–6; Suns. 2–6 (or sunset if earlier). *Closed Good Friday & Christmas Day.* Adm. 80p; under 18 yrs. 40p; under 5 yrs. free. Charge inc. illustrated tour sheet. Pre-booked guided school parties 40p per person, including accompanying adults	National tours from N. Lancashire towns Frequent bus service from all parts (*bus station in centre of town*)
STOCKELD PARK, Wetherby *map 5 B* *Mrs. R. E. F. Gough* Small country mansion, one of the finest examples of the work of James Paine, built in the Palladian style 1758-63. Main feature is the central hall and staircase. Attractive grounds and gardens.	3m N of Wetherby, 7 m SE of Harrogate on A661	July 17 to August 19—Daily (except Mons.) 2.30–5.30. Other times by appointment. Adm. charges not available at time of going to press ☕ home-made teas ☎ *Wetherby* (0937) 66101 *or Harrogate* (0423) 61274	Buses stop outside main gate.
SUTTON PARK, Sutton-on-the-Forest *Mrs. Sheffield* *map 5 B* Early Georgian house built in 1730. Historical contents include Chippendale, Sheraton and French furniture; plasterwork by Cortese, paintings and porcelain. Beautiful gardens, Georgian Ice House in the grounds, Temple/Woodland/Daffodil walks and Nature Trail.	8 m from York, m from Easingwold on B1363 York–Helmsley rd. Look for the Sutton Park signs on A19 in Easingwold area	Suns. April 1, 8 & 15; Good Friday, Easter Sun. & Mon. (April 20, 22, 23); May 1 to Sept. 30—Suns., Tues., Weds., Thurs. & Bank Hol. Mons.: 2–6. Last adm. to House 5.30. Adm. House & Gardens £1.30, Chd. 60p, O.A.Ps. £1; Coaches £1 per person; Families (2 adults & 2 Chd. under 14) £2.60. Gardens only 75p, Chd. 30p, O.A.Ps. 75p. Special openings by arrangement. *Dogs adm. to Grounds only (not Gardens)* on a lead. Gift shop & Plant & Garden produce. ✕☕ Tea room/restaurant	Reliance Motor Bus Service from York, (*passes gates*)
THORP PERROW ARBORETUM, nr Snape *Sir John & Lady Ropner* *map 5 A* 60 acres of landscaped grounds containing an arboretum of over 2,000 species of trees and shrubs, including some of the largest and rarest in England.	N of Ripon on the Well-Bedale rd	End of March to end of October. Adm. £1, Chd. under 12 & O.A.Ps. 50p. Free car park. Picnic area.	No reasonable public transport
TREASURER'S HOUSE, York *map 5 B* *The National Trust* Large 17th century house of great interest. Fine furniture and paintings. Exhibition	Behind York Minster *Stn: York (½ m)*	April to Oct.—Daily, 10.30–6. *Closed Good Friday.* Adm. £1.20, Chd. 60p (if accompanied). *Pre-arranged parties of 15 or more 90p each adult, chd. 50p. Party rates do not apply Suns. & Bank Hols.* No car parking facilities. No dogs. Wheelchair access—part of ground floor only. ☎ *York* (0904) 24247	Services by West Yorkshire, East Yorkshire and United from all parts of Yorkshire National tours to York.
NOTTINGHAMSHIRE			
CARLTON HALL, Carlton-on-Trent *map 3 B* *Executors of the late Lt. Col. G. H. Vere-Laurie* Georgian house by Carr of York. Beautiful drawing room. Magnificent ancient cedar in grounds.	7 m N of Newark just off A1	April to October—By appointment any day in writing. Adm. House and Garden £1	No reasonable public transport
CLIFTON HALL, Clifton Village, nr Nottingham *map 3 A* *Trent Polytechnic* This recently restored Georgian mansion forms part of Trent Polytechnic and houses the School of Education.	Just outside the village, 5 m SW from Nottingham on A453	Open by appointment only. Applications to visit the Hall should be made to The Assistant Director (Administration), Trent Polytechnic, Burton Street, Nottingham.	Buses from Nottingham (*alight in village* **10** *mins. walk*).
CLUMBER CHAPEL, Clumber *map 5 D* *The National Trust* Built 1886–1889 as a private chapel for the Seventh Duke of Newcastle and recently restored. Also large park with lake and 18th century bridge and temples	In Clumber Park 4½ m SE of Worksop, 6½ m SW of East Retford *Stns: Worksop (4½ m); Retford (6½ m)*	April to end of Sept.—Mons. to Fris. 12–6.30; Sats., Suns. & Bank Hol. Mons. 12–7. Oct. to end of March—Daily 12–3.30. At other times by application to The National Trust, The Estate Office, Gardens Cottage, Clumber Park, Worksop, Notts, S80 3AZ. Adm. free. Vehicle parking charges. Park open all year; dogs admitted. Shop. Tricycles, tandems, wheelchairs & special fishing platform for disabled. ☎ *Worksop* 476592 *or* 476653 ☕ Licensed restaurant for lunches & teas (daily; dinners April—end of Sept., Thurs.–Sats. from 7.15) ☎ *Worksop* 484122	East Midland 33 (*not Suns.*), 150 (*Sats.*), 133 (*Suns. in summer only*) (*alight Clumber Park*)
HOLME PIERREPONT HALL, Radcliffe-on-Trent, nr Nottingham *map 3 A* *Mr & Mrs Robin Brackenbury* Medieval brick manor house. Historic Courtyard garden with box parterre, 1875. Oak furniture. Concerts and Operas—s.a.e. for programme.	5 m SE from centre of Nottingham off A52 approach past Nat. Water Sports Centre	Easter Sun., Mon. & Tues., May 7 & Spring & Summer Bank Hol. Mons. & Tues.; June, July & Aug.—Suns., Tues., Thurs. & Fris.; Sept.—Suns: 2–6. Adm. charges not available at time of going to press. *Parties by appointment throughout year* ✕ buffet lunches for parties by appointment. ☕ home-made teas	Buses 78 & 79 Nottingham to Radcliffe-on-Trent (*thence 1 m walk*)
NEWARK TOWN HALL, Newark *map 3 B* *Newark Town Council* Designed by the architect John Carr, in 1773, the Newark Town Hall is perhaps one of the finest Georgian town halls in the country. Currently undergoing refurbishment it remains open to the public. On display is the Town's collection of silver gilt and silver plate, generally of the 17th and 18th century and including the "Newark Monteith" and the Newark Siege Pieces, silver coins struck during the last siege of Newark (1645–6) in the Civil War. Other items of interest are early historical records and various paintings including a collection by the artist Joseph Paul	Market Place, Newark; located on A1 & A46 *Stn: Newark*	All the year—Mons. to Fris. 10–12, 2–4. Open at other times by appointment. *Closed Sats., Suns., Bank Hols. & Christmas. Adm. free* Administrator ☎ *Newark* (0636) 700200	Local bus services B.R. Services—London to Edinburgh; Crewe to Lincoln
NEWSTEAD ABBEY, Linby *map 3 A* *Nottingham City Council* Part of original priory survives, bought by Sir John Byron, 1540, and converted to a house. Byron relics, pictures, furniture. Extensive beautiful gardens	11 m N of Nottingham on the Mansfield rd (A60) *Stn: Nottingham, then by Trent bus*	Abbey open Good Friday to Sept. 30.—Daily 2–6 (last adm. 5.15). Adm. 50p, Chd. 10p. Also October 1 to Easter by arrangement. Gardens open all year—Daily 10–dusk. Grounds & Gardens Adm. (1983 rates) 60p, Chd. 20p. Charges subject to revision. ☕ at tearoom in the grounds ☎ *Mansfield* (0623) 797392	Trent 63, Nottingham–Chesterfield (*frequent*) (*alight at Abbey gates*)

THE LAURENCE STERNE TRUST

SHANDY HALL

COXWOLD, NORTH YORKSHIRE

The medieval house where the modern novel was born

Here in 1760–68 the witty and eccentric local parson Laurence Sterne wrote *Tristram Shandy* and *A Sentimental Journey*, books that 'jump clean out of the 18th century into the 20th', influencing Dickens, Goethe, Tolstoy, Balzac, Proust, Melville, Joyce, Virginia Woolf and other great writers. Little changed today, Shandy Hall is not a museum but a welcoming, lived-in house full of relevant books, pictures, memorabilia—and surprises! Five centuries old, timber-framed and architecturally fascinating too.

OPENING TIMES OPPOSITE

Stockeld Park

WETHERBY, YORKSHIRE

The finest example of the work of James Paine

The House and Gardens will be open from 17th July to 19th August

SUPERB HOME-MADE TEAS

OPENING TIMES:
2.30 p.m.–5.30 p.m.
Every Day Except Monday

THORP PERROW

Near SNAPE, NORTH YORKSHIRE

Thorpe Perrow, the North Country home of Sir John and Lady Ropner, contains within its 60 acres of landscaped grounds an arboretum—a fine collection of over 2,000 species of trees and shrubs, including some of the largest and rarest in England. The grounds are now open to the general public, and have rapidly become a popular focal point in the North of England.

Thorp Perrow is open from the end of March until the end of October. This is a pleasant outing that may be enjoyed by all members of the family, who may wander at will amidst these magnificent surroundings. There is a free car park and picnic area, and the entrance to Thorp Perrow Arboretum can be found on the Well to Bedale Road (near Snape) north of Ripon.

TREASURER'S HOUSE

YORK

in Chapter House Street, behind York Minster

THE NATIONAL TRUST

The home of the Treasurers of York Minster from the time of William the Conqueror until the reign of Henry VIII.

Like many of the great historic buildings of York, the Treasurer's House has a front which disguises a history much more fascinating than you might think from a first glance. All the principal rooms are open to visitors and it is worth the most careful and detailed exploration.

An exhibition and tape/slide show in the basement illustrates some of the personalities and traditions with which the house is associated.

RIPLEY CASTLE

near HARROGATE

"Country Life" photograph

RIPLEY CASTLE, near HARROGATE, still the home of the Ingilby family for more than 600 years, certainly gives variety to its visitors.

After passing Cromwell's bullet marks on the walls of the early 15th century gatehouse, they go through the Adams part of the Castle with its lovely pictures, chandeliers, furniture and mantlepieces, into the historical Tudor part, to see the armour and old weapons of the Civil Wars and a floor made from the deck of a British man-o-war. Your guide will show you the Priest's hole, rediscovered a few years ago. Then out on to the Terrace to admire the lovely view over the lakes and up the Thornton Valley and on to the Pleasure Grounds and Gardens laid out by "Capability" Brown and planted with specimen trees from many parts of the world.

SKIPTON CASTLE

SKIPTON, NORTH YORKSHIRE

Sheer rock high above the moat makes Skipton Castle unassailable from the North. The flanks and front of the enchanting 15th century Courtyard, sited on the motte of the original Norman Castle, are defended by a semi-circle of six massive 14th century round towers. In the grounds the shell of the baronial Chapel. Withstood three years of siege in the Civil War. Today it stands fully roofed and dominant with its sturdy Gatehouse at the head of Skipton High Street.

Open all year except Good Friday and Christmas Day. Admission charge includes 40 sketch illustrated tour sheet in English, French or German. *Guided party tours by previous booking:*

Car park behind nearby Town Hall.

HOLME PIERREPONT HALL

near NOTTINGHAM

c. 1510

"Country Life" photograph

An early Tudor house with medieval lodgings with regional oak and other manorhouse furniture and family pictures. All the rooms shown are in constant daily use and the tours are usually guided by the family. The Charles II staircase and rooms undergoing restoration are usually on view.

Parties by appointment throughout the year. Formal Victorian courtyard garden. Jacob sheep etc. Fine church with family monuments. Home-made teas.

Holme Pierrepont Opera Trust programme of Early Music concerts and operas on request.

PROPERTY (*showing map reference*)	LOCATION (*with nearest Rly. Stn.*)	OPENING TIMES AND ADMISSION CHARGES CATERING FACILITIES	COACH AND RAIL TOURS BUS SERVICES (*showing alighting points*)
NOTTINGHAMSHIRE—*continued*			
THRUMPTON HALL, Nottingham *map 3 E* Δ *George FitzRoy Seymour, Esq.* Jacobean. Magnificent carved staircase. Fine pictures and furniture. Lived in and shown by owners	7 m S of Nottingham & 3 m E of M1 at Junction 24; 1 m from A453	By appointment for parties of 20 or more persons. Adm. House & Gardens £1.50, Chd. 75p. Minimum charge of £30 per party of 20. Open all year including evenings. ✕☕ by prior arrangement ☎ *Nottingham* 830333	No reasonable public transport
WOLLATON HALL, Nottingham *map 3 A* *City of Nottingham* ⓔ Fine example of late Elizabethan Renaissance architecture. Natural History Museum	2¼m W of City centre *Stn.: Nottingham (2 m)*	All the year: April to Sept.—Weekdays 10–7, Suns. 2–5. Oct. to March—Weekdays 10–dusk, Suns. 1.30–4.30. Adm. free (small charge Suns. & Bank Hols.). *Conducted tours by arrangement.* 35p; *Chd.* 10p *(subject to alteration). Closed Christmas Day* ☎ *Nottingham* 281333 ☕ at refreshment pavilion *(April to Sept.)*	Nottingham City Transport 21, 23; 45 to Lime Tree Ave.: 11, 35 (34 & 36 off Peak times) to Derby Road Gates (¼ *m*)
OXFORDSHIRE			
ARDINGTON HOUSE, nr Wantage *map 3 J* *D. C. N. Baring, Esq.* Early 18th century of grey brick with red brick facings. Hall with Imperial staircase, panelled dining room with painted ceiling. Magnificent cedar trees.	12 m S of Oxford; 12 m N of Newbury; 2½ m E of Wantage *Stn: Didcot (8 m)*	May to Sept.—Thurs., Fris. & all Bank Hols. 2–5. Parties of 10 or more welcomed any day by appointment. Adm. House & Grounds £1. ☕ teas by arrangement ☎ *East Hendred* (023-588) 244	*Bus:* Oxford–Didcot–Wantage *(hourly)* *B.R.* to Didcot, then by bus
ASHDOWN HOUSE, nr Lambourn *map 3 J* Δ *The National Trust* Built late 17th cent. by first Lord Craven for Elizabeth of Bohemia. Mansard roof crowned by a cupola with a golden ball. Contains the Craven Family portraits associated with Elizabeth of Bohemia. Box parterre and lawns	2½ m S o Ashbury, 3½ m N of Lambourn on W side of B4000	Hall, stairway & roof only. April—Weds. only; May to Sept.—Weds., also first & third Sats. each month: 2–6. Courtyard and grounds open & access to roof of house *(fine views)*. No access to rooms. Conducted tours to roof 2.30, 3.30, 4.30 & 5.30. Adm. Grounds, hall, stairway & roof £1, Chd. half-price. No reduction for parties (which should pre-book in writing). Dogs in grounds only, on leads. Wheelchair access to garden only.	Alder Valley 108 Newbury–Upper Lambourn *(thence 2½ m walk) (not Suns.)* Thamesdown Transport 47, 48 from Swindon *(Weds., alight entrance; Sats. alight Ashbury 2½ m walk)*
BLENHEIM PALACE, Woodstock *map 3 J* Δ *His Grace the Duke of Marlborough* Masterpiece of Sir John Vanbrugh in the classical style. Fine collection of pictures and tapestries. Gardens and park designed by Vanbrugh and Queen Anne's gardener, Henry Wise. Later construction was carried out by "Capability" Brown, who also created the famous Blenheim lake. Exhibition of Churchilliana and Sir Winston Churchill's birth room. Churchill paintings on exhibition	SW end of Woodstock which lies 8 m N of Oxford (A34)	March 12 to October 31—Daily 11–6 (last adm. 5). Special prices & times apply on May 27 & 28 when the Lord Taverners Charity Cricket Match & the Woodstock Horse Show take place. *Reduced rates for parties.* Educational service for school parties—Palace, Farm, Forestry, Horticulture & Nature Tail. Adm. charges not available at time of going to press ✕☕ Licensed Restaurant & self service cafeteria at the Palace. ☎ *Woodstock* (0993) 811325 (24 *hrs*)	Rail, road & steamer tours from London *(Waterloo)* —*(July to September every Wed. & Thurs.)* National tours from most areas Grey Green tours from London Rickards tours from London—*(Thurs., May to Sept.)* Valliant Cronshaw tours from London Worth's Service, Oxford–Enstone Oxford–South Midland 420, 422 Oxford–Woodstock; 442 Oxford–Woodstock–Witney; Oxford 190 London–Oxford–Woodstock–Stratford *(2 direct services daily)*; Oxford–South Midland/Midland Red West 191 Oxford–Chipping Norton–Evesham–Worcester Midland Red/Oxford X50 Oxford–Stratford–Birmingham X59 Coventry–Banbury–Oxford *(Suns. only)* Britainshrinkers Road 'n Rail Tours from London
BOTANIC GARDENS, Oxford *map 3 J* *University of Oxford* Oldest botanic garden in Britain, founded 1621	High Street *Stn: Oxford*	All the year—Weekdays 8.30–5; Suns. 10–12, 2–6 (closes 4.30 winter). Adm. free. *Closed Good Friday and Christmas Day*	All City Services
BROOK COTTAGE, Alkerton *map 3 E* *Mr. & Mrs. David Hodges* 4 acre landscaped garden, mostly formed since 1964, surrounding 17th cent. house. Wide variety of young trees, shrubs and plants of all kinds; water garden; one-colour borders; collection of shrub roses. Interesting throughout season.	6 m NW of Banbury; ½ m A422 (Banbury–Stratford-u-Avon). In Alkerton take lane opp. war memorial, then right fork. *Stn: Banbury (5½ m)*	GARDEN ONLY: Sats. & Suns.—June 9 & 10; July 7 & 8: 2–7; Oct. 20 & 21: 11–6. Also April 1 to Oct. 31 by appointment. Adm. 60p, Chd. (accompanied) free. *In aid of National Gardens' Scheme.* ☕ on above dates & for parties by prior arrangement. Oct. 20 & 21 Ploughman's lunch available. ☎*Edge Hill* (029 587) 303 or 445	Midland Red 210 Banbury–Stratford upon Avon *(not Suns.) alight Alkerton War Memorial 2 min. walk)*
BROUGHTON CASTLE, Banbury *map 3 E* *The Lord Saye & Sele* A moated Tudor mansion with early 14th cent. nucleus. Beautiful plasterwork ceilings and chimney pieces	2 m SW of Banbury on the Shipston-on-Stour rd (B4035) *Stn: Banbury (3 m)*	May 18 to Sept. 14—Weds. & Suns.; also Thurs. in July & Aug.: 2–5. Bank Hol. Suns. & Bank Hol. Mons. 2–5. Adm. £1.50, Chd. 80p, O.A.Ps. £1.10. *Parties on other days throughout the year by appointment—reduced rates.* ☕ home made teas ☎ *Banbury* 62624	Midland Red South 487, 488 Banbury–Chipping Norton *(alight Bloxham Grove Turn, 1½ m walk)*
BUSCOT OLD PARSONAGE, nr Lechlade *The National Trust* *map 3 J* Built in 1703 of Cotswold stone and stone tiles. On the banks of the Thames. Small garden	2 m SE of Lechlade; 4 m NW of Faringdon on A417	All the year—Weds. 2–6, by appointment in writing with the tenant. Adm. 50p. *No reduction for children or parties.* No dogs. Unsuitable for wheelchairs.	
BUSCOT PARK, nr Faringdon *map 3 J* Δ *The National Trust* Built 1780. Fine paintings and furniture. Burne-Jones room. Attractive garden walks, lake	3 m NW Faringdon on Lechlade–Faringdon rd (A417)	April to September—Weds., Thurs. & Fris. (inc. Good Friday) 2–6, 2nd & 4th Sats. & immediately following Suns. in each month, 2–6. *Last admission to house* 5.30. Adm. House & Ground £1.50, Chd. 75p. Grounds only 75p, Chd. 40p. *No dogs. No indoor photography.* Unsuitable for wheelchairs.	
THE CHANTRY HOUSE, Henley-on-Thames *St. Mary's Church P.C.C.* *map 3 J* Church Hall, formerly school, dating back to 1400 A.D.	Next to church, by bridge over R. Thames; A423 *Stn: Henley-on-Th.*	All year—Thurs. & Sats. 10–12. At other times by appointment. ☎ *Henley* (0491) 577340	Bus service from London, Oxford, Reading, High Wycombe *B.R.* Western Region
CHASTLETON HOUSE, Moreton-in-Marsh *Mrs. A. Clutton Brock* *map 3 J* Built 1603. Fine plasterwork and panelling. Original furniture and tapestries. Topiary garden designed 1700	4 m SE of Moreton-in-Marsh, 5 m NW of Chipping Norton. Oxford 26 m, Stratford-on-Avon 20 m *Stn: Moreton-in-Marsh (4½ m)*	All the year—Mons., Tues., Thurs. & Fris. 10.30–1, 2–5.30: Sats. & Suns. 2–5. *Closes at dusk in winter. Closed Weds.* Adm. £1, Chd. 50p. Special rates for parties ☕ Brewhouse Tearoom: in grounds (closed in winter) Afternoon teas. ☎ *Barton-on-the-Heath* 355	Tours from West of England and South Wales
DITCHLEY PARK, Enstone *Ditchley Foundation* *map 3 J* Third in size and date amongst the great 18th cent. mansions of Oxfordshire. Designed by Gibbs, decoration of Great Hall by Kent	1½ m W of A34 at Kiddington; 2 m from Charlbury (B4437) *Stn: Charlbury (2 m)*	July 23 to August 3—Daily 2–5 Adm. £1, Chd. 50p Free car park ☎ *Enstone* 346	No local transport nearer than Kiddington (1½ *m*) or Charlbury (2 *m*)
DIVINE MERCY COLLEGE & MUSEUM, FAWLEY COURT, Henley-on-Thames *Marian Fathers* *map 3 J* Designed by Sir Christopher Wren, built 1684 as a family residence. The house, decorated by Grinling Gibbons, is situated in a beautiful park designed by "Capability" Brown. The Museum contains documents of Polish kings and memorabilia of the Polish Army.	1 m N of H-on-T via A4155 to Marlow *Stn : Henley-on-Thames (1½ m)*	All the year (except Easter, Whitsuntide & Christmas weeks and June)—Weds. & Suns. 2–5. Also Thurs. in July & Aug. *Closed Easter, Whitsuntide & Christmas weeks and June.* Adm. £1.20, Chd. 50p., O.A.Ps. £1 Car park. No dogs. ☕ teas, coffee & home-made cakes available July & Aug.	Alder Valley 328, 329 Reading–Henley–High Wycombe *(alight entrance)*
THE GREAT BARN, Great Coxwell *The National Trust* *map 3 J* 13th century, stone built, stone tiled roof, exceptionally interesting timber roof construction. Magnificent proportions	2 m SW of Faringdon between A420 & B4019	Daily at reasonable hours. Adm. free. Dogs on leads admitted. Wheelchair access.	Swindon & District/Oxford & South Midland Joint 66, 67, 68 Oxford–Faringdon–Swindon *(approx. 2 hourly) (alight Great Coxwell Turn)*

THRUMPTON HALL
NOTTINGHAMSHIRE

OPEN FOR PARTIES OF TWENTY OR MORE ANY DAY OR EVENIN G OF THE YEAR — BY ARRANGEMENT

Please contact The Hon. Mrs. George Seymour: Tel. No. 0602 830333 or write to her at Thrumpton Hall, Nottingham NG11 0AX

Fine Jacobean house, built 1607, incorporating earlier manor house. Priest's hiding hole, magnificent Charles II carved staircase, carved and panelled saloon and other fine rooms containing beautiful 17th and 18th century furniture and many fine portraits. Large lawns separated from landscaped park by ha-ha and by lake. This house retains the atmosphere of a home, being lived in by owners who will show parties round.

Teas or more substantial meals available. For admission charges see opposite.

ARDINGTON HOUSE
Nr. WANTAGE, Oxfordshire

Eighteenth century (circa 1720) house of grey brick with red brick dressings. Magnificent Cedar trees adjoining.

Hall of outstanding beauty with interesting Imperial staircase. Panelled dining room with painted ceiling.

All rooms are lived in and shown by the family.

OPENING TIMES OPPOSITE

BROUGHTON CASTLE OXFORDSHIRE
The home of Lord and Lady Saye & Sele and owned by the family for 600 years

Approached through parkland, Broughton Castle stands on an island surrounded by its broad moat. Much of the mediaeval house of 1300 remains; it was greatly enlarged between 1550 and 1600.

The Castle contains fine panelling and fireplaces, splendid plaster ceilings and good period furniture

Broughton is essentially a family home and not a museum.

Broughton has interesting Civil War connections. Secret meetings of the Parliamentary leaders among whom William, 8th Lord Saye and Sele was prominent, took place here before the Civil War.

After the battle of Edge Hill in 1642, the Castle was besieged and captured by the Royalists.

Arms and armour of the period are displayed in the Great Hall.

Open: May 18th—September 14th Wednesdays and Sundays; also Thursdays in July and August 2.00–5.00 pm. Bank Holiday, Sundays and Bank Holiday Mondays 2.00–5.00 pm.

PARTIES ON OTHER DAYS THROUGHOUT THE YEAR BY APPOINTMENT

DITCHLEY PARK
OXFORDSHIRE

Property of the Ditchley Foundation Ltd.

"Country Life" photograph

Third in size and date of the great 18th century houses of Oxfordshire. Ditchley is famous for its splendid interior decoration (William Kent and Henry Flitcroft).

For three and a half centuries the home of the Lee family and their descendants —with whom Robert E. Lee was directly connected—Ditchley was the weekend Headquarters of Sir Winston Churchill during the last War.

It has now been restored, furnished and equipped as an Anglo - American Conference Centre.

Open daily July 23rd to August 3rd: 2 to 5 p.m.

DIVINE MERCY COLLEGE & MUSEUM, FAWLEY COURT
HENLEY-ON-THAMES, OXON

Fawley Court, designed by Sir Christopher Wren, was built in 1684 for Colonel William Freeman as a family residence.

The Mansion House, decorated by Grinling Gibbons and later by James Wyatt, is situated in a beautiful park designed by Lancelot "Capability" Brown.

The museum consists of the library, the Polish kings' various documents, very rare and well preserved collection of historical sabre and many memorable military objects of the Polish Army. Paintings and sculptures illustrate the ancient history and the Middle Ages.

PROPERTY *(showing map reference)*	LOCATION *(with nearest Rly. Stn.)*	OPENING TIMES AND ADMISSION CHARGES CATERING FACILITIES	COACH AND RAIL TOURS BUS SERVICES *(showing alighting points)*
OXFORDSHIRE—*continued*			
GREYS COURT, Henley-on-Thames *map* 3 *J* *The National Trust* Beautiful gardens, medieval ruins, a Tudor donkey wheel for raising well water and a 16th cent. house containing interesting 18th cent. plasterwork and furniture. The newly created "Archbishop's" Maze was open for the first time in 1982.	At Rotherfield Greys NW of Henley-on-Thames on the road to Peppard *Stn: Henley-on-Thames* (3 *m*)	House: April to Sept.—Mons., Weds., Fris. 2–6. Garden: April to end of Sept.—Mons. to Sats., 2–6. Last admissions half—hour before closing Adm.: House & Garden £1.50, O.A.Ps. £1. Garden only £1, O.A.Ps. 70p, Chd. half-price. Parties must book in advance. No reduction for parties. *Closed Good Friday*. Dogs in car park only. Wheelchairs provided. tea & biscuits (April to June—Weds., & Sats.; July to Sept.—Mons., Weds., Fris. & Sats.); also for booked parties at all times	Oxford 390, London–Henley–Abingdon–Oxford *(2 hourly) (alight Bix then 1½ m walk)*
KINGSTON HOUSE, Kingston Bagpuize *Lady Tweedsmuir* *map* 3 *J* Flowering shrubs and bulbs; woodland garden; herbaceous plants and hydrangeas. Charles II Manor House.	5½ m W of Abingdon at jct of A415 & A420 *Stn: Oxford* (9 *m*)	April, May & June—Sats., Suns. & Bank Hol. Mons 2.30–5.30. Adm.: Gardens 60p, Chd. & O.A.Ps. 40p. House (extra) 80p, Chd. & O.A.Ps. 50p (children under 5 not admitted to House). Groups welcome by appointment. No dogs. Gifts, books, plants for sale. teas	Bristol–Swindon & District/Oxford–South Midland 66, 67, 68 *(approx. 2-hourly) (alight Kingston Bagpuize, "Hind's Head" P.H.)*
KINGSTONE LISLE PARK, nr Wantage *Capt. & Mrs. Leopold Lonsdale* *map* 3 *J* Handsome house with dramatic flying staircase. Fine furnishings and beautiful gardens.	5 m W of Wantage on B4507	Bank Hol. weekends (Sats., Suns. & Mons.) May 5/6/7, May 26/27/28 & Aug. 25/26/27; also during Aug.—Tues., Thurs. & Suns.; during Oct.—Thurs. & Suns.: 2–5. Adm. £1.40, Chd. 80p. *Parties at other times by appointment.* *Uffington* (036 782) 223	No reasonable public transport
MAPLEDURHAM HOUSE, Mapledurham *J. J. Eyston, Esq.* *map* 3 *J* Late 16th cent. Elizabethan home of the Blount Family. Original moulded ceilings, great oak staircase, fine collection of paintings and private chapel. Unique setting in grounds running down to the Thames. 15th cent. Watermill nearby is now restored and operating	4 m NW of Reading off Caversham–Woodcote rd A4074 *Stns: Pangbourne* (4 *m*); *Reading* (4 *m*) *(bridleways)*	House: Easter Sun. to end of Sept.—Sats., Suns. & Bank Hols. 2.30–5.30. Last admission 5 p.m. *Mid-week & weekend parties of not less than* 30 *by arrangement.* Watermill—see advertisement for details. Adm. House £1.40, Chd. 70p; Watermill 70p, Chd. 40p. cream teas, refreshments. Party catering *Reading* (0734) 723350 *(House)*	River service from the Promenade Car Park Caversham Bridge, Reading (D.&T. Scenics Ltd.) at weekends & Public Hols. *(the promenade is ½ m from Reading station & on bus route* 20, 29) Chiltern Queen bus services from Reading Station *(not Suns.) (alight Trench Green, 1½ m)* **Red Car Services tours from Norwich** Coliseum Coaches Ltd.—tours from Southampton Windsorian Coaches from Windsor
MILTON MANOR HOUSE, nr Abingdon *map* 3 *J* *Mrs. Marjorie Mockler* 17th cent. house with Georgian wings. Traditionally designed by Inigo Jones. Walled garden & pleasure grounds	In Milton village 4 m S of Abingdon, 1 m from Sutton Courtney on B4016. A34, signpost Milton *Stn: Didcot* (3 *m*)	Easter Sat. (April 21) to October 21—Sats. & Suns. and all Bank Hols.: 2–5.30. Adm. £1. Chd. 50p. Free car park. *Coach parties welcome by arrangement at reduced rates. Candlelight tours in the evening by arrangement* by arrangement *Abingden* (0235) 831287 *or* 831871	Oxford–South Midland 302, 304, 306 Oxford–Abingdon–Didcot–Wantage *(alight Milton Rd., Sutton Courtenay,* 1 *m walk)*
NUNEHAM PARK, Nuneham Courtenay, nr Oxford *map* 3 *J* *The University of Oxford* Thames-side Palladian villa designed by Stiff Leadbetter (additions by "Capability" Brown and Smirke) in picturesque landscape setting created by Brown. and William Mason Renovated by Rothmans International as Conference Centre. Temple by "Athenian" Stuart. Disputed site of Goldsmith's "deserted village". No original furniture or paintings.	7 m SE of Oxford 1 m from A423 at Nuneham Courtenay (turn off A423 to SW in centre of village) *Stn: Culham* (4½ *m*)	August 18, 19 & 25, 26, 27; Sept. 1 & 2: 2–5.30. Gates close at 5. Adm. to house & gardens £1.50, Chd. 50p, O.A.Ps. 90p. Art & Furniture Exhibition with part adm. fee being donated to N.S.P.C.C. in its Centenary Year. Picnic area provided. Access to Carfax Conduit. Gardens under restoration. light refreshments	Oxford/Alder Valley 5 Oxford–Reading–Oxford; Oxford 510. Oxford–Wallingford *(alight Nuneham Post Office,* 1 *m)*
PUSEY HOUSE GARDENS, nr Faringdon *Michael Hornby, Esq.* *map* 3 *J* Herbaceous borders, walled gardens, water garden, large collection of shrubs and roses. Many fine trees.	5 m E of Faringdon, ½ m S off A420, 12 m W of Oxford	April 1 to May 31—Weds., Thurs. & Suns. 2–6. June 2 to Oct. 21—Daily (except Mons. & Fris.) 2–6. Also Bank Hol. weekends (Sats., Suns. & Mons.) 2–6.Adm. £1.20,Chd. under 11 years free.Pre-booked parties £1 per person. Car park free. Plants for sale. teas available *Buckland* 222	Swindon & District/Oxford & South Midland Joint 66, 67, 68 Oxford–Swindon *(alight Pusey Turn, ½ m)*
ROUSHAM HOUSE, Steeple Aston *map* 3 *J* *C. Cottrell-Dormer, Esq.* 17th cent. country house with landscape garden by William Kent. Portraits, miniatures	12 m N of Oxford off Banbury rd (A423) at Hopcrofts Holt Hotel (1 *m*) *Stn: Heyford* (1 *m*) *(not Suns)*	April to Sept.—Weds., Suns. & Bank Hols. 2–5.30. Gardens only 10–6 every day. Adm. House £1.50. Chd. (under 14) 50p; Garden £1. *Parties of 25 or more by arrangement on other days.*	Midland, Red/Oxford X59, Coventry–Banbury–Oxford *(alight Rousham; Hopcroft's Holt Inn, Suns.)*

GREYS COURT

HENLEY-ON-THAMES

THE NATIONAL TRUST

Greys Court, 2½ miles from Henley-on-Thames, the home of Sir Felix and Lady Brunner was donated by Sir Felix to the National Trust together with the 286 acres of gardens, wood and farmland and an endowment for its upkeep. The 16th century house, stands within the ruined 14th century fortifications of the original 13th century house of Robert de Grey.

PUSEY HOUSE GARDENS

near **FARINGDON, OXFORDSHIRE**

"Amateur Gardening" photograph

The garden at Pusey House affords a wide variety of attractions. The herbaceous borders and the rose gardens are outstanding in midsummer, the shrubberies are full of interesting and unusual plants and the lake is fringed with a water garden filled with many varieties of primula and other waterside plants. There are exceptionally fine trees, many of which are particularly effective with their autumn colouring.

OPENING TIMES ABOVE

KINGSTON HOUSE

KINGSTON BAGPUIZE, OXFORDSHIRE

The home of Lord and Lady Tweedsmuir

A superb Charles II manor house surrounded by parkland, a large garden and attractive 17th century stable buildings. The house has a magnificent cantilevered staircase and well-proportioned panelled rooms with fine furniture and pictures. The large and interesting garden contains beautiful trees, lawns, a woodland garden, herbaceous and shrub borders and many lovely bulbs.

OPENING TIMES ABOVE

KINGSTONE LISLE PARK

Nr. Wantage, Oxon

The central part of this house was built in 1677 but most of the ingenious and dramatic interior dates from 1812. A notable feature is the fascinating procession of spaces comprising the hall, in part of which the renowned staircase rises. This staircase, two flights of which are flying, is such that it can connect the most unexpected levels.

The house is furnished with good furniture, pictures, glass and needlework. The extensive gardens have outstanding charm and beauty, displaying a succession of colour and interest throughout the year.

MILTON MANOR HOUSE

near ABINGDON, OXFORDSHIRE

Peter Kingsland photograph

Sir John Betjeman writes:
" Like all the best things in England this is hidden. Milton village street is true 'Berkshire.' The Manor House is splendid. Inside are handsome rooms and an exciting contrast—a Chapel and Library in Strawberry Hill Gothick. Do go and see it."

Elisabeth de Stroumillo, writing in the 'Daily Telegraph' says:
"Milton Manor, a perfect gem of an historic house, is small and perfectly proportioned – the interior is a delight. Milton Manor is not to be missed."

ROUSHAM HOUSE

Steeple Aston, Oxon

Rousham House was built by Sir Robert Dormer in 1635 and the shooting holes were put in the doors while it was a Royalist garrison in the Civil War. Sir Robert's successors were Masters of Ceremonies at Court during eight reigns and employed Court artists and architects to embellish Rousham. The house stands above the River Cherwell one mile from Hopcrofts Holt, near the road from Chipping Norton to Bicester. It contains 150 portraits and other pictures and much fine contemporary furniture. Rooms were decorated by William Kent (1738) and Roberts of Oxford (1765). The garden is Kent's only surviving landscape design with classic buildings, cascades, statues and vistas in thirty acres of hanging woods above the Cherwell.

Gardens open daily 10 a.m. to 6 p.m. House: Wednesdays, Sundays and Bank Holidays, April to September, 2 p.m. to 5.30 p.m. Parties of 25 and over by arrangement.

MAPLEDURHAM

HOUSE, WATERMILL and COUNTRY PARK

4 miles west of Reading on the banks of the River Thames

Historic Home of the Blount family since Elizabethan times.

OPEN: Easter Sunday to 30th September
Saturdays, Sundays and Bank Holidays.
HOUSE: 2.30 p.m.–5.30 p.m.
COUNTRY PARK & PICNIC AREA: 12.00–7.00 p.m.
WATERMILL: 12.30 p.m.–5.00 p.m.

Also open 2–4 p.m. on Sundays in winter.

GUIDED PARTY VISITS of House and Watermill
Tuesday, Wednesday & Thursday afternoons by appointment only.

Shop for gifts, flour and other watermill produce. Home-made afternoon and cream teas.

Visit Mapledurham by river; A launch runs from Caversham Promenade to Mapledurham & back each day the House is open and can also be hired for party visits.

For all enquiries and details of prices please contact:
The Estate Office, Mapledurham House, Reading RG4 7TR. Telephone (0734) 723350

PROPERTY (showing map reference)	LOCATION (with nearest Rly. Stn.)	OPENING TIMES AND ADMISSION CHARGES CATERING FACILITIES	COACH AND RAIL TOURS BUS SERVICES (showing alighting points)
OXFORDSHIRE—*continued*			
STANTON HARCOURT MANOR, Stanton Harcourt *map* 3 J *Mr. Crispin & The Hon. Mrs. Gascoigne* Unique medieval buildings in tranquil surroundings—Old Kitchen, Pope's Tower and Domestic Chapel. House contains fine collection of pictures, furniture, silver and porcelain	9 m W of Oxford; 5 m SE of Witney; on B4449, between Eynsham & Standlake *Stn: Oxford (8 m)*	Bank Hol. Suns. & Mons.: April 22/23, May 6/7, 27/8, Aug. 26/27; also Suns. April 8, June 10 & 24, July 8 & 22, Aug. 12, Sept. 9 & 23 and Thurs. May 3 & 24, June 7 & 21, July 5 & 19, Aug. 9 & 23, Sept. 6 & 20: 2–6. Adm.: House & Garden £1, Chd. (12 & under) 50p; Garden only 75p, Chd. (12 & under) 25p. Home container-grown shrubs & pot plants for sale.	Oxford–South Midland 471, 472 from Witney (*Thurs. only, infrequent*) (*alight entrance*)
STONOR PARK, nr Henley on Thames *Lord & Lady Camoys* *map* 3 J Ancient home of the Stonor family and centre of Catholicism. Fine furniture and important sculpture. Magnificent setting.	On B480; 5 m N of Henley-on-Thames 5 m S of Watlington; *Stn. Henley-on-Thames (5 m) (not Suns in April*	April 1 to Sept. 30—Weds., Thurs. & Suns. (also Sats. in Aug.) 2–5.30. Open Bank Hol. Mons. 11–5.30. Adm. £1.50, Chd. (under 14) in family parties FREE. For details of party rates telephone. ☎ *Turville Heath* (049 163) 587	Oxford 390 London–Henley–Abingdon–Oxford (2 *hourly*) (*alight Smiths Hospital, Henley, 3 m walk*)
UNIVERSITY OF OXFORD—SEE PAGE 184			
WATERPERRY HORTICULTURAL CENTRE, nr Wheatley *map* 3 J Church of Saxon origin and historical interest in grounds. Famous old glass, brasses and woodwork. Many interesting plants. Shrub, Herbaceous and Alpine Nurseries. Glasshouses and comprehensive Fruit Section.	8 m E of Oxford. 2 m from Wheatley off old A40. 20 mins. walk (footpath only) from Waterstock turn on A418. *Stn: Oxford (9 m)*	All the year—Daily. Summer 10–6; Winter 10–4. *Closed Dec. 24 to Jan. 3 & between July 17 to 22 for preparations & event of* ART IN ACTION 84. Adm. to Gardens & Nurseries 70p. Party bookings at all times by arrangement only. Garden Shop. *In aid of National Garden's Scheme Aug. 12. Gardeners' Sunday on June 10.* Teashop ☎ *Ickford* (084 47) 226	Oxford 280 Oxford–Aylesbury (*alight Waterstock Turn, 20 mins. walk*)
WROXTON ABBEY, Wroxton, nr Banbury *Wroxton College of Fairleigh Dickinson University* *map* 3 E 17th century manor house surrounded by 56 acres of lawns, woodlands and restored 18th century garden features	3 m W of Banbury on A422 *Stn: Banbury (4 m)*	Bank Hol. Mon. May 7; Spring Bank Hol. Sun. & Mon. (May 27/28); Summer Bank Hol. Mon. (Aug. 27). Other days by appointment. Grounds open April to Sept.—Mons. to Fris. 12–dusk. ☎ *Wroxton St. Mary* (029 573) 551	Midland Red South 210 from Banbury (*infrequent, not Bank Hols.*)
SHROPSHIRE			
ACTON ROUND HALL, Bridgnorth *H. L. Kennedy, Esq.* *map* 2 H Built in 1714 for Sir Whitmore Acton by the Smith Brothers of Warwick and abandoned from 1717–1918, the house remains little altered from its original state	6 m W of Bridgnorth; 15 m SE of Shrewsbury	May 10 to September 27—Thurs. 2.30–5.30 Adm. £1, Chd. 50p	Midland Red 962, 964, Shrewsbury–Bridgnorth–Stourbridge (*alight Muckley Cross, ¾ m*); 971, 972, Bridgnorth–Ludlow (*alight Monkhopton Council Houses, 1 m*)
ADCOTE, Little Ness, nr Shrewsbury *map* 2 D *Adcote School Educational Trust Ltd.* 'Adcote is the most controlled, coherent and masterly of the big country houses designed by Norman Shaw" (Mark Girovard, 'Country Life' Oct. 1970)	7 m NW of Shrewsbury off A5 *Stn: Shrewsbury (7½ m)*	April 25 to July 12 (except May 25–29) then Sept. 10 to 30—Daily 2–5. Other days throughout the year by prior appointment. Adm. free but the Governors reserve the right to make a charge.	No reasonable public transport

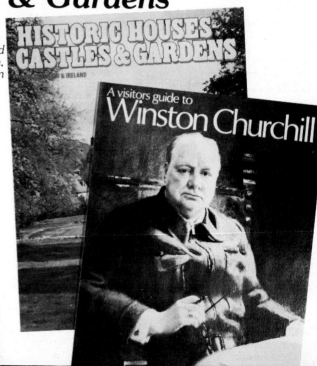

STONOR

Nr. HENLEY ON THAMES, OXFORDSHIRE

Stonor is the home of Lord and Lady Camoys and the Stonor family. The family have been at Stonor for over 800 years.

Set in a wooded deer park in a fold of the Chiltern hills Stonor has one of the most beautiful situations of any house in England. Built over many centuries from c. 1190–1930 the house contains many examples of some of the earliest domestic architecture in Oxfordshire.

Fine family portraits and furniture, tapestries and important Italian sculptures, paintings and drawings. Beautiful stained glass and heraldic shields.

A centre of Catholicism throughout the Recusancy period, with its own Chapel where Mass has been and is celebrated today, still using the pre-Reformation licences to do so. The room called 'Mount Pleasant' where St. Edmund Campion and his companions had their secret Printing Press in 1581—which led to arrests, imprisonment in the Tower and executions—will be on view with an exhibition on Campion's life and work. It was in this room that John Stonor and others were arrested and taken to the Tower of London on 10th August, 1581.
Gift Shop and Tea Room.

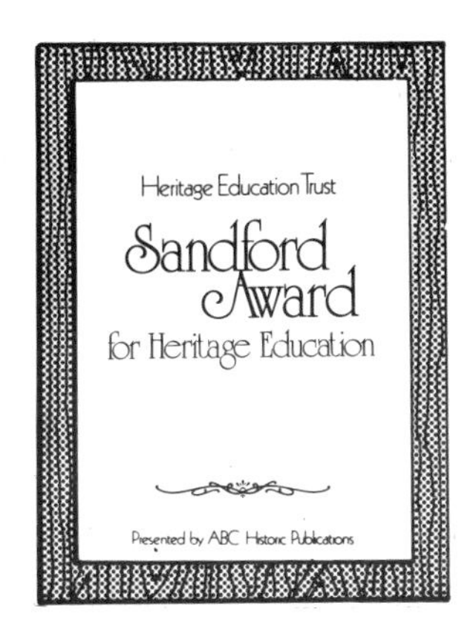

For information on

EDUCATIONAL SERVICES

SEE PAGE 8

STANTON HARCOURT MANOR

OXFORDSHIRE

The Old Kitchen

Unique Mediaeval Buildings. House contains fine collection of pictures, furniture, silver and porcelain.

OPENING TIMES OPPOSITE

WATERPERRY
GARDENS
NR. WHEATLEY, OXON.

Ornamental Gardens—Fine trees, herbaceous and shrub borders, alpines and bulbs.

Saxon village church in grounds.

Working Nurseries—All year interest

Teashop.

OPENING TIMES OPPOSITE

PROPERTY (*showing map reference*)	LOCATION (*with nearest Rly. Stn.*)	OPENING TIMES AND ADMISSION CHARGES CATERING FACILITIES	COACH AND RAIL TOURS BUS SERVICES (*showing alighting points*)
SHROPSHIRE—*continued*			
ATTINGHAM PARK, nr Shrewsbury *The National Trust* *map 2 H* Designed in 1785 by George Steuart for the 1st Lord Berwick. Remarkable for its interior decoration. Famous painted boudoir	At Atcham; 4 m SE of Shrewsbury, on N side of Wellington rd (A5) *Stn: Shrewsbury (5m)*	April to end of Sept.—Mons., Weds., Sats. & Suns. 2–5.30; Bank Hol. Mons. 11.30–5.30. Last adm. 5. *Closed Good Friday.* Oct.—Sats. & Suns. 2–5.30. Adm. House & Grounds £1.40, Chd. 70p. Grounds only 30p. Reduced rates for parties which must book in advance. (*No parties Tues.*). Dogs in park only, on leads. Wheelchairs provided. home-made teas (parties must pre-book) *Upton Magna* 203	Midland Red X96, Birmingham–Shrewsbury 893. Shrewsbury–Wolverhampton (*alight Atcham*)
BENTHALL HALL, Much Wenlock *map 2 H* *The National Trust* 16th cent. stone house with mullion windows. Interior improved in 17th cent. Fine oak staircase and plaster ceilings. Interesting small garden	4 m NE of Much Wenlock, 8 m S of Wellington, 1 m NW of Broseley (B4375) *Stns: Wellington (8 m); Shifnal (8 m)*	Easter Sat. to September—Tues., Weds. & Sats. 2–6 (last adm. 5.30). Also Bank Holiday Mons. (Ground floor only) 2–6 (last adm. 5.30). Adm. £1.20, Chd. 60p. Garden only 60p. *No reduction for parties.* No dogs. No stiletto heels. Wheelchair access. *Telford* (0952) 882254	Midland Red 906 Telford–Much Wenlock (*Tues. only alight Benthall Pipe Works, ½ m*) 909 Wellington–Bridgnorth (*alight Broseley Sq.*)
BOSCOBEL HOUSE, Shifnal *map 2 H* *Dept. of the Environment* 17th cent. house. Charles II took refuge here after the Battle of Worcester	4 m E of Tong; 4½ m N of Albrighton (off A41) *Stn: Cosford (3½ m)*	All the year: March 15 to Oct. 15—Weekdays 9.30–6.30; Suns. 2–6.30. Oct. 16 to March 14—Weekdays 9.30–4; Suns. 2–4. *Closed Dec. 24, 25, 26 & Jan. 1.* Adm. 50p, Chd. (under 16) & O.A.Ps. 25p.	Midland Red 879 passes house (*Weds., Sats. & Suns.*)
BROSELEY HALL, Broseley *map 2 H* *Mrs. V. West* A small 18th century house updated by the architect of the Ironbridge, T. F. Pritchard, in 1767 by the addition of fine carved chimneypieces and a small garden temple. Also includes the collection of the Wilkinson Society, a tribute to John Wilkinson the great Ironmaster.	4 m NE of Much Wenlock; between Wellington & Bridgnorth on B4375 *Stn: Wellington (9m)*	May to Sept.—Thurs. & Bank Hol. Mons. 2.30–5. Adm. 60p. Parties by arrangement. teas by arrangement *Telford* (0952) 882748	*Bus:* 909 Wellington–Bridgnorth via centre of Broseley (*hourly*) (*alight Lady Forester Hospital*)
CARDING MILL VALLEY & LONG MYND, nr Shrewsbury *map 2 H* *The National Trust* Chalet Pavilion in the magnificent scenery of Carding Mill Valley.	15 m S of Shrewsbury; W of Church Stretton valley & A49 *Stn: Church Stretton (1 m)*	Information Centre, Shop & Café: April to end of Sept.—Mons., Tues., Weds., Thurs. & Sats. 12.30–6, Suns. & Bank Hol. Mons. 10.30–6. Also open first 2 weekends in Oct. *Closed Fris. but open Good Friday.* Open for booked parties & special functions throughout year. Adm. free. Car park 50p; coaches free. Dogs allowed if kept under control. Enquiries to Mrs. L. Michael. *Church Stretton* 722631 snacks, light lunches, teas etc. at Chalet Pavilion (Dogs not allowed in Pavilion)	Midland Red North services from Shrewsbury or Ludlow to Church Stretton (½ m)
CONDOVER HALL, Condover, nr Shrewsbury *map 2 H* *Royal National Institute for the Blind* "E" shaped building, an excellent example of masons' craft of the late 16th century	5 m S of Shrewsbury; 1½ m from A49	Grounds & exterior of premises by prior appointment only (with a limited inspection of the interior) August—Daily 10–4.	Midland Red Shrewsbury–Ryton; Shrewsbury–Church Stretton; Shrewsbury–Church Stretton–Hereford (*alight Condover Church*)
DUDMASTON, Quatt, Bridgnorth *map 2 H* *The National Trust* Late 17th century house; fine furniture, Dutch flower paintings previously owned by Francis Darby of Coalbrookdale. Modern pictures.	4 m SE of Bridgnorth on A442 *Stn: Bridgnorth (Severn Valley Rly.) (4 m)*	April to end of Sept.—Weds. & Suns. 2.30–6 (last adm. 5.30); also Thurs. for pre-booked parties only 2–6 (last adm. 5.30). *Closed all other days inc. Bank Hols.* Adm. House & Garden £1.40; Garden only 70p. Parties must book in advance (no reductions). Dogs in garden only, on leads. Shop. refreshments; teas.	Midland Red 297 Bridgnorth–Kidderminster (*passes gates*)
HODNET HALL GARDENS, nr Market Drayton *map 2 D* *Mr. & the Hon. Mrs. Heber Percy* Garden extends over 60 acres	12 m NE of Shrewsbury 5½ m SW of Market Drayton, at jct of A53 to A442. M6 18½ m (jct 15) leading to A53.	April 1 to September 30—Weekdays 2–5; Suns. & Bank Hols. 12–6. Adm. £1, Chd. 50p. *Reduced rates for organised parties of 25 or over.* Free car & coach Park. Dogs allowed, but must be kept on leads Suns., Bank Hols. & daily May to Aug. *Parties to pre-book (menu on request)* (063-084) 202	National tours from Birmingham & the Midlands, the Potteries, Birkenhead & Hoylake Salopia, Whitchurch–Hodnet–Market Drayton (*Weds. & Sats.*) Midland Red 928/9, Shrewsbury–Hodnet–Market Drayton (*alight crossroads*)
MAWLEY HALL, Cleobury Mortimer *Galliers Trustees* *map 2 H* 18th c. house attributed to Smith of Warwick. Notable contemporary plasterwork & panelling	1 m S of Cleobury Mortimer (A4117); 7 m W of Bewdley	By written appointment to Administrator. Admission £1	Midland Red X92, Birmingham–Kidderminster–Ludlow 292, Kidderminster–Ludlow
SHIPTON HALL, Much Wenlock *map 2 H* *J.N.R.N. Bishop, Esq.* Elizabethan stone manor house. Georgian Stable Block; interior designs and plasterwork by T. F. Pritchard. Stone walled garden, medieval dovecote and Parish Church.	In Shipton, 6 m SW of Much Wenlock junc. B4376 & B4368	May to September—Thurs. also Suns. in July & Aug. and Bank Hols.: 2.30–5.30. Other times by appointment. Adm. 90p, Chd. 50p. Special rate for parties of 20 or more. teas/buffets by prior arrangement	Midland Red 971/2, Ludlow–Shipton–Bridgnorth (*alight Shipton*)

HODNET HALL GARDENS

HODNET, MARKET DRAYTON, SHROPSHIRE

Home of Mr. and the Hon. Mrs. A. Heber Percy

These beautiful landscape gardens with their series of lakes and pools occupy some 60 acres and rank among the finest in the country. Magnificent forest trees, flowers and shrubs in endless variety provide an exciting show of colour throughout the seasons. Featured on television and radio. Picturesque 17th-century tearooms contain unique collection of Big Game Trophies. Gift Shop. Plants, flowers and vegetables are on sale at the garden centre.

The main lake and tearooms in Springtime

A warm welcome from The National Trust in SHROPSHIRE

ATTINGHAM PARK Near SHREWSBURY

The house, built for the 1st Lord Berwick in 1785, contains a series of richly decorated state rooms.
In 1805 John Nash added his dramatic picture gallery and circular staircase, using cast iron from Coalbrookdale.
The park is an outstanding example of the work of Humphry Repton and, apart from the addition of an attractive shrub walk along the River Tern, has survived virtually unaltered.
A small exhibition devoted to the work of Repton is on display in the house.

DUDMASTON BRIDGNORTH

Dudmaston is one of the most beautiful Shropshire estates and has not changed ownership, except by inheritance, since the 12th century. The house, the home of Sir George and Lady Labouchere, is mainly 18th century and contains fine furniture and pictures. Notable is the collection of modern paintings and sculpture including works by Matisse, Ben Nicholson, Barbara Hepworth and Henry Moore. Two further galleries contain water colours and an interesting series of botanical pictures. Dudmaston also has connections with the Darby family of Coalbrookdale.
Attractive shrub garden and superb views over Dudmaston Pool and the surrounding country.

BENTHALL HALL

MUCH WENLOCK, Shropshire

David Cockroft photograph

Built of ashlar stone with brick chimneys, the exterior of Benthall provides a romantic example of late 16th century architecture. Inside there are panelled rooms, a moulded plaster ceiling of the period and a remarkable carved oak staircase c. 1610.

CARDING MILL VALLEY AND LONG MYND

Location: 15m S of Shrewsbury and W of Church Stretton valley and A49. The Chalet Pavilion, in the magnificent scenery of Carding Mill Valley, has a licensed restaurant open for lunches and teas.

Opening times etc:

Open: All year. Café, shop and information centre: April to end of Sept. and first two weekends in Oct., Mon. to Sat. (closed Fridays, except Good Friday) 12.30-6 p.m. Sun. and Bank Holidays 10.30-6. Open for booked parties and special functions throughtout year; please telephone Mrs. L. Michael (Church Stretton 722631). Dogs allowed if kept under control.

Admission: Free. Car park 50p. Coaches free.

Refreshments: Snacks, light lunches, salads, teas and high teas at the Chalet Pavilion. Dogs not allowed in the Chalet Pavilion.

For further information and membership details write to the Regional Information Officer, The National Trust, Attingham Park, Shrewsbury SY4 4TP. Tel: Upton Magna 649.

PROPERTY (*showing map reference*)	LOCATION (*with nearest Rly. Stn.*)	OPENING TIMES AND ADMISSION CHARGES CATERING FACILITIES	COACH AND RAIL TOURS BUS SERVICES (*showing alighting points*)
SHROPSHIRE–*continued*			
STOKESAY CASTLE, Craven Arms *map 2 H* *Sir Philip & Lady Magnus-Allcroft* Finest example of a moated and fortified manor house, dating from the 13th century	8 m from Ludlow; ½ m S of Craven Arms on 3rd class rd off A49 *Stn: Craven Arms* (1 *m*)	March 7 to 31—Daily (except Tues.) 10–5; April to Sept.—Daily (except Tues.) 10–6; Oct.—Daily (except Tues.) 10–5; Nov.—Daily (except Mons. & Tues.) 10–5. Last adm. half an hour before closing. *Closed Dec., Jan. & Feb.* Adm. 80p, Chd. (under 15 yrs.) 40p. Party bookings in advance. Toilets. Free car park. Enquiries to The Custodian, Stokesay Castle, Craven Arms, Shropshire SY7 9AH ☎ *Craven Arms* (058 82) 2544	Midland Red 434, 435, Shrewsbury–Hereford (*alight Stokesay Bridge*)
△**TYN-Y-RHOS HALL nr Oswestry** *map 2 D* *Chevalier M. Thompson–Butler–Lloyd* Mansion with historic Welsh Royal connections. Park only. Featured on H.T.V. Dec. 1982	2¼ m from Weston Rhyn, near Bron-y-Garth (off A5)	May to end of Sept.—Weds., Thurs., Sats., Suns. & Bank Hol. Mons. 2.30–6. Adm. 80p teas at the Hall ☎ *Chirk* (0691) 777898	B.R. Liverpool–Chirk Llangollen–Glynceiriog; Crosville, Oswestry–Llanarmon, D2 Oswestry–Wrexham
UPTON CRESSETT HALL, Bridgnorth *William Cash, Esq.* *map 2 H* Elizabethan Manor House and magnificent Gatehouse in beautiful countryside by Norman church. Unusually fine medieval timber work and interesting brick and plaster work; 14th century Great Hall	4 m W of Bridgnorth, 18 m SE of Shrewsbury off A458	May to Sept.—Thurs. 2.30–5. Adm. £1, Chd. 50p. *Parties at other times throughout the year by appointment* teas & light refreshments by prior arrangement ☎ *Morville* 307	No reasonable public transport
WENLOCK PRIORY, Much Wenlock *Dept. of the Environment* *map 2 H* 7th century Saxon foundation refounded in the 12th century as Cluniac priory	In Much Wenlock, 12 m SE of Shrewsbury on the Bridgnorth rd	All the year: March 15 to Oct. 15—Weekdays 9.30–6.30; Suns. 2–6.30. Oct. 16 to March 14—Weekdays 9.30–4; Suns. 2–4. *Closed Dec.* 24, 25, 26 & *Jan.* 1. Adm. 40p, Chd. (under 16) & O.A.Ps. 20p. ✕ Storks Hotel or Gaskell Arms, Much Wenlock	Midland Red 904, Wellington–Much Wenlock; 962/964, Shrewsbury–Much Wenlock–Bridgnorth–Stourbridge
WESTON PARK, nr Shifnal *map 2 H* *The Earl of Bradford* Built 1671 by Lady Wilbraham, one of the finest examples of the Restoration period. Magnificent gardens and vast parklands designed by "Capability Brown" Ⓔ	Entrance from A5 at Weston – under – Lizard, 5 m Shifnal, 12 m Wolverhampton, 15 m Stafford, 6 m W of Junction 12 M6 (Gailey), 3m N. of Junction 3 M54 (Tong)	House & Park: April 21–29. May—Weekends & Bank Hol. Mons. May 29 to July 22—Daily (except Mons. & Fris.) then July 23 to Aug. 31—Daily. Sept.—Weekends only. Last admission 5 p.m. Adm. Grounds, Aquarium, Museums £1.50, Chd. & O.A.Ps. £1. House 60p, Chd. & O.A.Ps. 40p *Special rates for parties, educational visits by schools, etc. booked in advance.* Dogs (on leads) admitted to Park but not into House. ✕ Cafeteria & licensed restaurant; special facilities for handicapped & wheelchairs. ☎ *Weston-under-Lizard* 207 *or* 385	National tours from the Midlands & Potteries Midland Red 893 Wolverhampton–Ironbridge–Shrewsbury (*alight Tong 2 m*) Midland Red X96 Birmingham–Shrewsbury (*not Suns.*) (*alight Weston-under-Lizard*) Happy Days, Wolverhamptpn–Donnington (*Sats. & Weds. only*)
WILDERHOPE MANOR, Wenlock Edge *The National Trust* *map 2 H* Built in 1586. Limestone house, with 17th century plaster ceilings	7 m SW of Much Wenlock, ½ m S of B4371 *Stn: Church Stretton* (8 *m*)	April to end of Sept.—Weds. & Sats. 2–4.30. Oct. to March—Sats. only 2–4.30. *Closed Dec.* 24. Adm. 80p, Chd. 40p. *No reduction for parties. No dogs.* ☎ *Longville* 363	Midland Red 950, 951, Ludlow–Bridgnorth (*infrequent*) *alight Shipton,* 1½ *m by footpath*
SOMERSET			
BARFORD PARK, Enmore *map 2 R* *Mr. & Mrs. Michael Stancomb* Queen Anne house set in park with fine trees; formal garden, water garden and woodland garden.	5 m W of Bridgewater *Stn: Bridgwater* (6½ *m*)	May to September—Weds., Thurs. & Bank Hol. weekends 2–6, or other times by appointment. Adm. charges not available at the time of going to press. ☎ *Spaxton* (027 867) 269	No reasonable public transport
BARRINGTON COURT, Ilminster *map 2 S* △ *The National Trust* 16th century house and extensive garden laid out in 1920s by Gertrude Jekyll. Late 17th cent. stable block.	3 m NE of Ilminster at E end of Barrington, ½ m E of B3168 *Stn: Crewkerne* (7 *m*)	GARDEN: April 22 to Sept. 26—Suns. to Weds. 2–5.30. COURT: April 25 to Sept. 26—Weds. only 2–5. Adm. Garden £1 (parties of 15 or more 70p); Court 50p (no reduction for parties). Chd. half-price. Coaches by appointment only. No picnics. No dogs. Wheelchair access. teas ☎ *Ilminster* (046 05) 2242	Southern National 261, 263 Taunton–Sth. Petherton (*not Suns.*) (*alight Barrington, near school*)
THE BISHOP'S PALACE, Wells *map 2 S* *The Bishop of Bath & Wells* The fortified and moated Palace comprises the Bishop's Residence (15th century, Jocelin's Hall (early 13th century), the Bishop's Chapel and the ruins of the Banqueting Hall (both late 13th century). The gardens have interesting trees, the new Jubilee Arboretum and the wells from which Wells derives its name. On the Moat are the swans which ring for food	In Wells	Palace, Chapel and Grounds: Easter Sat. then April 22 to October 28—Suns., Bank Hol. Mons. & Thurs. (& daily in August) 2–6. Last adm. 5.30. Adm. 80p, Chd. 30p, O.A.Ps. 50p. Reduction for parties. refreshments available in the Undercroft.	Bristol buses from Bath, Bristol, Burnham-on-Sea, Cheddar, Glastonbury, Shepton Mallet, Weston-super-Mare etc.
BRYMPTON d'EVERCY, nr Yeovil *map 2 S* *Charles E. B. Clive-Ponsonby-Fane, J.P.* Mansion house with late 17th cent. South front and Tudor West front. State Rooms, extensive gardens and Vineyard. Priest House. Museum. Painting and photographic exhibitions. Estate produce, wine and cider. 14th century Parish Church alongside.	2 m W of Yeovil. Follow signs from A30 (Exeter rd) or A3088 (Montacute rd.) *Stns: Yeovil Pen Mill* (4 *m*) *or Yeovil Jct.* (5½ *m*)	Easter weekend (Fri. to Mon. inc.) then May 1 to Sept. 30—Daily (except Thurs. & Fris.) 2–6. *Further details of party rates from Brympton Estate Office, Yeovil.* GENEROUS DISCOUNT RATES FOR O.A.Ps., FELLOWS OF R.H.S. & NATIONAL TRUST MEMBERS—EVERY MONDAY, TUESDAY & WEDNESDAY. ☎ *West Coker* (093-586) 2528 cream teas in Old Stables.	Safeways 466, Yeovil–South Petherton (*alight end of drive*)
THE CHURCH HOUSE, Crowcombe *The Charity Commissioners* *map 2 R* Historic 15th century stone building with graceful open timber roof.	Opposite Crowcombe Church; off A358 Taunton–Minehead rd. *Stn: Crowcombe* (*West Somerset Rly.*) (2 *m*)	May 28 to Sept. 28—Mons. to Fris. 2.30–4.30. Adm. free. light refreshements	Southern National 218, Taunton—Minehead (*alights at village or at house, depending on bus route*)

STOKESAY CASTLE

CRAVEN ARMS SHROPSHIRE

Sir Philip and Lady Magnus-Allcroft

The name Stokesay meant originally the Stoke, or dairy farm, of the Norman family of Say which lived there from 1105 until 1255. Although dubbed a castle Stokesay is, in fact, a fortified manor house of the 13th century. It is the best preserved as well as the oldest surviving example of its kind in England and its romantic setting is marvellously attractive.

Stokesay was bought in 1280 and rebuilt by Lawrence of Ludlow, the richest wool merchant of his day who, like countless subsequent tradesmen, was eager to enter the ruling gentry class by acquiring land. Lawrence fortified Stokesay under licence from King Edward I before dying in 1296 and his descendants lived there happily for three hundred years.

In 1620 the Craven family bought Stokesay which fell, at the start of the 19th century into neglect and decay. But in 1869 it was bought from Lord Craven and restored and repaired by John Darby Allcroft M.P. of Worcester, the greatest glove manufacturer of his day, who was the grandfather of its present owner Lady Magnus-Allcroft. She, like previous members of her family, has cherished Stokesay Castle which she feels she holds in trust for posterity.

A Unique Example of a Fortified Manor House of the 13th Century

OPEN

From first Wednesday in March: Daily (except Tuesday) 10 a.m.–5 p.m.

April to September: Daily (except Tuesday) 10 a.m.–6 p.m.

October: Daily (except Tuesday) 10 a.m.–5 p.m.

November: Daily (except Monday & Tuesday) 10 a.m.–5 p.m.

Last admissions half an hour before closing time.

CLOSED

December, January and February.

ADMISSION

Adults 80p. Children under 15 years 40p. Party bookings in advance. Toilets. Free car park.

All communications to:
The Custodian, Stokesay Castle, Craven Arms, Shropshire SY7 9AH. Telephone: Craven Arms (058 82) 2544.

WESTON PARK

SHIFNAL, SHROPSHIRE

Access is from the A5 at Weston under Lizard, 6 miles west of Junction 12 on M6, 3 miles north of Junction 3 on M54.

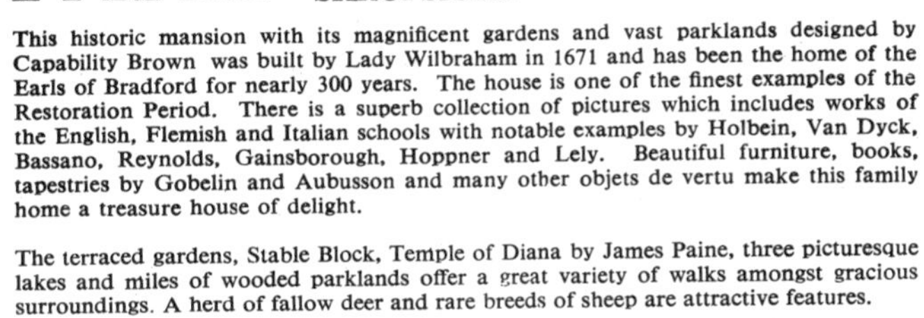

This historic mansion with its magnificent gardens and vast parklands designed by Capability Brown was built by Lady Wilbraham in 1671 and has been the home of the Earls of Bradford for nearly 300 years. The house is one of the finest examples of the Restoration Period. There is a superb collection of pictures which includes works of the English, Flemish and Italian schools with notable examples by Holbein, Van Dyck, Bassano, Reynolds, Gainsborough, Hoppner and Lely. Beautiful furniture, books, tapestries by Gobelin and Aubusson and many other objets de vertu make this family home a treasure house of delight.

The terraced gardens, Stable Block, Temple of Diana by James Paine, three picturesque lakes and miles of wooded parklands offer a great variety of walks amongst gracious surroundings. A herd of fallow deer and rare breeds of sheep are attractive features.

OPEN EASTER to end of SEPTEMBER (for details see entry on page 120).

WOODLAND ADVENTURE PLAYGROUND – AQUARIUM – STUDIO POTTERY – ARCHITECTURAL & NATURE TRAILS – MINIATURE RAILWAY – MUSEUM OF COUNTRY BYGONES – GARDEN SHOP – CAFETERIA AND LICENSED RESTAURANT

Excellent facilities available for private functions—Dinners, Wedding Receptions, Candlelight Evenings, promotional events, conferences, shooting parties.

All enquiries and bookings to: The Administrator, Weston Park, Shifnal, Shropshire TF11 8LE.
Tel. No. Weston-under-Lizard (095 276) 207 or 385 (24 hour answering and recording service).

Entry charges may be adjusted on certain days for special events.

BARFORD PARK

ENMORE, NR BRIDGWATER

Set in a large garden and looking out across a ha-ha to a park dotted with fine trees, it presents a scene of peaceful domesticity, a miniature country seat, on a scale appropriate today. The well proportioned rooms, with contemporary furniture, are all in daily family use. The walled flower garden is in full view from the house and the woodland and water gardens and archery glade with their handsome trees form a perfect setting for the stone and red-brick Queen Anne building.

OPENING TIMES OPPOSITE

BRYMPTON d'EVERCY

YEOVIL

"I know no other house of which the whole impression is more lovely and none that summarises so exquisitely English Country Life"—Christopher Hussey.

PROPERTY (*showing map reference*)	LOCATION (*with nearest Rly. Stn.*)	OPENING TIMES AND ADMISSION CHARGES CATERING FACILITIES	COACH AND RAIL TOURS BUS SERVICES (*showing alighting points*)
SOMERSET—*continued*			
CLAPTON COURT, Crewkerne *map 2 S* *Capt. S. J. Loder* One of Somerset's great gardens with an amazing collection of unusual trees, shrubs and plants in beautiful park-like setting. Interesting at all seasons.	3 m S of Crewkerne on B3165 *Stn: Crewkerne* (3 m)	GARDENS ONLY: All the year—Mons. to Fris. 10–5; Suns. 2–5. *Closed Sats.* (*except Easter Sat. & all Sats. in May only*). Adm. £1, Chd. 30p. Special rates for pre-booked coach & private parties (*not Suns. prior to August*). Plant Centre open all year—times as for Gardens above. *No dogs in garden. Free car parking.* ☕ home-made cream teas Suns. & Bank Hols., also some weekdays April to Aug. Meals by arrangement for parties. ☎ *Crewkerne* (0460) 73220 ✕ lunches available at Blue Boy Inn, Clapton	No reasonable public transport
COLERIDGE COTTAGE, Nether Stowey *The National Trust* *map 2 R* Home of S. T. Coleridge from 1797–1800, where he wrote 'The Ancient Mariner'	At W end of village on S side of A39; 8 m W of Bridgwater *Stn: Bridgwater* (8m)	PARLOUR ONLY: April to end of Sept.—Daily (except Fris. & Sats.), 2–5. *Closed Good Friday.* Adm. 50p. *No reduction for parties or children.* Parties are asked to notify the tenant beforehand where possible. *Adm. in winter by written application to the tenant.* No dogs. Unsuitable for wheelchairs & coaches ☕✕ in village ☎ *Nether Stowey* 732 662	Southenr National 215, Bridgwater–Nether–Stowey (*not Suns.*) (*passes cottage*)
COMBE SYDENHAM HALL, Monksilver *Mr. & Mrs. W. Theed* *map 2 R* The Hidden Valley of Sir Francis Drake's "Romance". Hall under restoration; valley walks to fisheries. British Birds of Prey Care Centre	5 m N of Wiveliscombe & 3 m S of Watchet, on B3188 Map Ref 102 R *Stn: Strogumber* (*W S'set Rly.* 2½ *m*)	Spring Bank Hol. May 28, 29 & 30. June to Sept.—Tues., Weds. & Fris. (also Mons. & Thurs. in July & Aug.). Fisheries & Birds of Prey 11–5; House & Gardens 1–5. Las adm. 4.30. Adm. (1983 rates) £1.20, Chd. 50p. ☕ Tea rooms; lunches available	No reasonable public transport
DUNSTER CASTLE, Dunster *map 2 R* *The National Trust* Castle dating from 13th cent., remodelled by Anthony Salvin in 19th cent. Fine 17th cent. staircase and plaster ceilings	In Dunster, 3 m SE of Minehead on A396 *Stn: Dunster* (*West Somerset Rly.*) (¾ *m*)	April to end of Sept.—Sats. to Weds. 11–5. Oct. to Nov. 4—Sats. to Weds. 12–4. Last adm. half-hour before closing. Adm. £2. Chd. £1. Parties of 15 or more by written appointment with the Administrator, £1.50. Dogs in park only. Shop. Wheelchair access. ✕ Luttrell Arms, Dunster ☎ *Dunster* 314	North Devon/Southern National tours from Minehead & Bridgwater, Lynton & Lynmouth Southern National 218 from Minehead (*alight Dunster steep*)
EAST LAMBROOK MANOR, Sth. Petherton Δ *F. H. Boyd-Carpenter, Esq.* *map 2 S* 15th cent. house with 16th cent. additions and panelling. Interesting cottage style garden with rare plants. A memorial to the late Margery Fish	2 m N of Sth. Petherton; turn left off Martock rd (B3165), 4 m from A303, 8 m W Yeovil	House: March to October—Thurs. 2–5. Other times by arrangement. Garden & Nursery: Daily 9–5. Adm. House 50p, Chd. 25; Garden 30p, Chd. 20p	Southern National 261, 263, Taunton–South Petherton (*alight West Lambrook* 1¼ *m*) Safeway Yeovil–South Petherton (2 *m*)
GAULDEN MANOR, Tolland, nr Taunton Δ *Mr. & Mrs. James LeGendre Starkie* *map 2 R* Small historic red sandstone Manor House of great charm. A real lived-in home. Past Somerset seat of the Turberville family, immortalised by Thomas Hardy. Great Hall has magnificent plaster ceiling and oak screen to room known as the Chapel. Fine antique furniture. Interesting grounds include bog garden with primulas and other moisture loving plants. Herb garden	9 m NW of Taunton 1 m E of Tolland Church. Tolland signpostedfromA358 Taunton–Williton rd just N of Bishops Lydeard. Nearest village Lydeard St. Lawrence (1½ m). *Stn: Taunton* (8½ *m*)	May 6 to September 9—Thurs. & Suns. 2–6. Also Easter Sun. & Mon. & all Bank Hol. Mons. 2–6 and during July & Aug. only, also open Weds. 2–6. Adm. House & Garden £1.40, Chd. (under 13) 60p. Garden only 60p (adult). *Parties other days by prior arrangement, morning, afternoon or evening & out of season.* Shop—books & plants. ☕ teas in garden Tearoom ☎ *Lydeard St. Lawrence* 213	No reasonable public transport
HADSPEN HOUSE, Castle Cary *map 2 S* *Trustees of the late Sir Arthur Hobhouse* 8 acre garden on a south-facing slope, containing many unusual plants in an 18th century setting	2 m SE of Castle Cary on A371 to Wincanton *Stn: Castle Cary,* (3 *m*)	GARDEN ONLY. All the year (except Jan.) Tues. to Sats. 10–5. Also open Suns. 2–5, April to Oct. Adm. 50p. No dogs. Plants for sale. ☕ teas—Suns. when garden open.	*Bus:* Wake's service, Yeovil–Castle Cary–Shepton Mallet (*not Suns.*) (*alight Castle Cary,* 2 *m*).
HATCH COURT, Hatch Beauchamp *map 2 R* Δ *Commander & Mrs. Barry Nation* A Palladian style Georgian house in Bath stone with superb views of Somerset. A house of great elegance and charm. Small Canadian Military Museum. China room. Deer park.	6 m SE of Taunton midway between Taunton & Ilminster on A358 *Stn: Taunton* (6½ *m*)	July 1 to Sept. 16—Thurs. 2.30–5.30 (*no coaches*). Adm. £1. Coaches & organised parties by prior appointment only—May to Sept. (*except Thurs.*) 2.30–5.30. Special rates for organised parties. Members of H.H.A. free. ☕ by arrangement. Cup of tea & biscuits available Thurs. ☎ *Hatch Beauchamp* (0823) 480208 ✕ Hatch Inn & Farthings Restaurant.	Southern National 494, 495, 496, Taunton–Ilminster–Chard–Weymouth (*Hatch Inn*)
KING JOHN'S HUNTING LODGE, Axbridge *The National Trust* *map 2 S* Early Tudor merchant's house extensively restored in 1971. Museum of local history and archaeology	On corner of the Square *Stn: Weston Milton* (8 *m*)	April to September—Daily 2–5. Adm. free. No dogs. including Guide dogs. Unsuitable for wheelchairs.	*Bus:* Bristol 126 from Weston-super-Mare, Cheddar, Wells (*not Suns. April, May & Sept.*)
LYTES CARY MANOR, Ilchester *map 2 S* *The National Trust* 14th and 15th century manor house with chapel; formal garden	On W side of Fosse Way (A37); 2½ m NE of Ilchester signposted on bypass (A303)	March to end of October—Weds. & Sats. 2–6 (last admission 5.30). Adm. £1.30, Chd. 65p, Parties £1. *Dogs in garden only, on leads.* No lavatories. Wheelchairs provided. N.B. Large coaches cannot pass gate piers	Southern National 264, Taunton–Yeovil (*alight Kingston,* 1¼ *m*)
MIDELNEY MANOR, Drayton, nr. Langport *Major R. E. F. Cely Trevilian, T.D., D.L.* Δ 16th to 18th cent. Manor House. Originally island manor of Abbots of Muchelney and property of Trevilian family since the dissolution. 17th cent. Falcons Mews. Gardens; heronry.	Signposted from A378 at Bell Hotel, Curry Rivel & from B3168 Hambridge—Curry Rivel rd & in Drayton	All Bank Holiday Mondays 2–5.30. June 1 to Sept. 4—Weds. 2–5.30. Adm. £1, Chd. 50p. *Members of H.H.A. free.* Coach parties by appointment. No dogs.	Safeway, Taunton–South Petherton (*connections from Yeovil*) (*alight White Cross,* ¾ *m*)
MONTACUTE HOUSE, Yeovil *map 2 S* *The National Trust* Magnificent Elizabethan house of Ham Hill stone begun in the 1590s by Sir Edward Phelips. Fine heraldic glass, tapestries, panelling and furniture. National Portrait Gallery Exhibitions of Elizabethan and Jacobean portraits. Fine formal garden	In Montacute village 4 m W of Yeovil on N side of A3088 3 m S of A303 nr Ilchester *Stns: Yeovil Pen Mill* (5½ *m*); *Yeovil Jct.* (7 *m*); *Crewkerne* (7 *m*)	House: April to Nov. 4—Daily (except Tues.) 12.30–6 Last admission 5.30 (or sunset if earlier). *Parties by written appointment with the Administrator.* Garden & Park: All the year—Daily (except Tues.) 12.30–6 (or sunset if earlier). Adm.: House, Garden & Park £2, Chd. £1; Parties of 15 or more £1.50. Garden & Park only: Oct. to May 40p; June to Sept. 80p. Chd. half-price. Dogs in car park only. Wheelchairs in garden only. ☕ Light lunches & teas (April to Oct. 1–5.30). *Parties catered for by arrangement with the Administrator.* ☎ *Martock* 823289	Tours from all parts of the West Country National Coach, London–Ilfracombe & Bournemouth–Ilfracombe Safeway, Yeovil–South Petherton

DUNSTER CASTLE

SOMERSET

THE NATIONAL TRUST

Aerofilm photograph

The fortified home of the Luttrell family for over six hundred years, the Castle dominates the village of Dunster nestling beneath its Tor. A deer park and terraced gardens, filled with sub-tropical shrubs, surround the Castle. Within—the collection of family portraits, the magnificent late 17th century staircase, the fine plaster ceilings of hall and dining room and the flourishing conservatory capture the eye.

GAULDEN MANOR

TOLLAND, near Taunton, Somerset

Small historic red sandstone Manor house of great charm and history originating from the 12th century. A real lived-in home. Past seat of the Turberville family immortalised by Thomas Hardy. The Great Hall has a magnificent plaster ceiling and oak screen to the room known as the Chapel. Fine antique furniture. Interesting grounds include Bog garden with primulas and other moisture loving plants. Herb garden. Plants for sale and teas in Garden tea room.

OPENING TIMES OPPOSITE

CLAPTON COURT GARDENS

near CREWKERNE, SOMERSET

3 miles south of Crewkerne on B3165

One of the most beautiful and interesting gardens in the West Country with many rare and unusual trees and shrubs of botanical interest in immaculate formal gardens and fascinating Woodland Garden. The 10 acres includes Terraces, Rose Garden, Rockery and Water Garden. A garden for all seasons from Springtime bulbs to Autumn colours. Plant Centre offering high quality and unusual container shrubs, plants, alpines, ferns etc. also specialising in fuchsias and over 100 varieties of pelargoniums.

OPENING TIMES OPPOSITE

HATCH COURT

HATCH BEAUCHAMP, Nr. Taunton

A fine Bath stone mansion in the Palladian style, designed in 1755 by Thomas Prowse of Axbridge. Curved wings, magnificent stone staircase and much of the internal decoration carried out around 1800. The house has a good collection of pictures, 17th and 18th century furniture and unusual semicircular china room. The medieval parish church of St. John the Baptist is situated nearby.

OPENING TIMES OPPOSITE

MONTACUTE HOUSE

SOMERSET

THE NATIONAL TRUST

A. F. Kersting photograph

Magnificent Elizabethan house of Ham stone begun in the 1590s by Sir Edward Phelips. Fine heraldic glass, tapestries, panelling and furniture. National Portrait Gallery exhibition of Elizabethan and Jacobean portraits in Long Gallery and adjoining rooms. Fine formal gardens.

OPENING TIMES OPPOSITE

PROPERTY (showing map reference)	LOCATION (with nearest Rly. Stn.)	OPENING TIMES AND ADMISSION CHARGES CATERING FACILITIES	COACH AND RAIL TOURS BUS SERVICES (showing alighting points)
SOMERSET—*continued*			
POUNDISFORD PARK, Poundisford, nr Taunton *map 2 R* *Mr. & Mrs. Ralph Vivian-Neal* 16th and 18th cent. house. Fine plaster ceilings, armorial glass. Family china and costume collections. Garden. Views to Quantock and Blackdown Hills.	3½ m S of Taunton on Trull-Pitminster rd; ½ m W of B3170 Taunton–Honiton rd *Stn: Taunton (4½ m)*	Easter to mid Sept.—Suns., Thurs. & Bank Hol. Mons. 2–6. Adm. £1.25, Chd. 60p. Pre-booked parties of 20 or more £1 per person (organiser free). N.B. Large coaches may not be able to get up the drive; 200 yards walk. *Blagdon Hill* (082 342) 244 light refreshments, cream & plain teas in Tearoom luncheons & dinners in Well House Restaurant (the Tudor Kitchen) by prior booking only. *Blagdon Hill* (082 342) 566	Southern National 208 Taunton–Pitminster *(alight Green Lane) (weekdays only—infrequent)*
PRIEST'S HOUSE, Muchelney *map 2 S* *The National Trust* Late medieval house, originally the residence of the secular priests who served the parish church	1½ m S of Langport	Hall & Parlour only shown, by written appointment with the tenant. Priest's House, Muchelney, nr. Langport. Adm. 50p. *No reduction for parties or children.* No dogs. Unsuitable for wheelchairs. No parking facilities.	Southern National 264, Taunton–Yeovil *(alight Huish Episcopi, 1 m)*
STOKE-SUB-HAMDON PRIORY *map 2 S* *The National Trust* Complex of buildings begun in 14th century for the priests of the chantry chapel of St. Nicholas (destroyed).	Between A303 & A3088, 2 m W of Montacute between Yeovil & Ilminster	All the year—Daily 10–6 (or sunset if earlier). Adm. free *Great Hall only open to the public.* No dogs.	Safeway Yeovil–South Petherton *(alight Stoke-sub-Hamdon crossroads)*
STOWELL HILL, Templecombe *map 2 S* *Mr. & Mrs. Robert McCreery* Spring bulbs; collection of flowering shrubs, including rhododendrons, azaleas, magnolias, etc. Japanese Cherries	5 m S of Wincanton, turn at Stowell ½m from Templecombe on A357 *Stn: Sherborne (5 m)*	GARDEN ONLY: Suns. in May also Bank Hol. Mons. May 7 & 28: 2–6. Adm. 40p, Chd. 15p. *In aid of National Gardens' Scheme or Gardeners' Charities.* No dogs.	Southern National 468, Yeovil–Wincanton *(not Suns.)*
TINTINHULL HOUSE, Yeovil *map 2 S* *The National Trust* Modern formal garden surrounding 17th century house	5 m NW of Yeovil, ½ m S of A303 on outskirts Tintinhull *Stns: Yeovil Pen Mill (5½ m); Yeovil Jct. (7 m)*	April to end of Sept.—Weds., Thurs. & Sats., also Bank Hol. Mons., 2–6 (last adm. 5.30). Adm. £1.30. *No reductions for parties or children.* Coach parties by written arrangement with the tenant. No dogs. Wheelchairs provided—garden only accessible.	Southern National 472, Yeovil–Bower Hinton *(not Bank Hols.) (alight Tintinhull, ½ m)*
SOUTH YORKSHIRE *(see also North & West Yorkshire)*			
CANNON HALL, Cawthorne *map 5 C* *Barnsley Metropolitan Borough Council* 18th cent. house by Carr of York. Collections of fine furniture, paintings, glassware and pottery. The William Harvey Bequest of Dutch and Flemish paintings (loaned by the National Loan Collection Trust) now on permanent display. Also the Regimental Museum of the 13th/18th Royal Hussars. 70 acres of parkland	5 m W of Barnsley on A635 1 m NW of Cawthorne	All the year—Weekdays 10.30–5; Sundays 2.30–5. Adm. free *Closed Christmas Day, Boxing Day, December 27 & Good Friday* *Barnsley* 790270	Yorks. Traction 236, Barnsley–Cawthorne–Huddersfield *(alight Park Gates or Raw Green)*
THE SUE RYDER HOME, HICKLETON HALL, nr Doncaster *map 5 D* *The Sue Ryder Foundation* This Home cares for 50 physically handicapped and others who are homeless and unable to cope on their own.	6 m NW of Doncaster; on A635 Doncaster–Barnsley rd (behind Hickleton Church). *Stn: Doncaster (6 m)*	Individuals wishing to visit the Home may do so Mons. to Fris. 2–4 without prior appointment. Please report your arrival to the Office in the main entrance. Hotels & Restaurants in Doncaster	Local bus service
STAFFORDSHIRE			
CHILLINGTON HALL, nr Wolverhampton *Mr. & Mrs. Peter Giffard* *map 2 H* Georgian house. Part 1724 (Francis Smith); part 1785 (Sir John Soane). Fine saloon. Grounds and lake by "Capability" Brown. Extensive woodland walks.	4 m SW of A5 at Gailey, 2m Brewood 8 m NW Wolverhampton 14 m S of Stafford	May to September 13—Thurs. (also Suns. in Aug.) 2.30–5.30. Open Easter Sun. & Suns. May 6 & 27: 2.30–5.30. Adm. £1.10; Grounds only 50p. Chd. half-price. *Parties other days by arrangement* *Brewood* 850236	Bus from Wolverhampton Railway Stn. *(alight Brewood)* *No entrance at Codsall Wood. Visitors should take Brewood–Codsall Rd. (Port Lane) and follow signposts*
DOROTHY CLIVE GARDEN, Elds Wood, Willoughbridge *map 2 D* *Willoughbridge Garden Trust* 7 acre woodland and rhododendron garden; shrub roses, water garden and a large scree	9 m SW Newcastle-under-Lyme. On A51 between junctions with A525 & A53	Garden only: March to November. Admission 50p, Chd. 20p. Large car park.	No reasonable public transport
HANCH HALL, Lichfield *map 3 E* *Mr. & Mrs. Douglas Milton-Haynes* Original mansion built in reign of Edward I. Home of the Aston family until end of the 16th cent. then the Ormes, staunch supporters of Charles I. Present house exhibits Tudor, Jacobean, Queen Anne and Georgian architecture. Wealth of oak panelling; Observation Tower; interesting collections. Landscaped gardens, trout pool, waterfowl. N.B. *The owners reserve the right to change days and hours of opening and to close all or parts of the Hall without prior notice*	4 m NW of Lichfield on Uttoxeter rd (B5014) *Stns: Lichfield City (4 m); Lichfield Trent Valley (5 m); Rugeley (5½ m) (no Sun. services)*	April 1 to Sept. 30—Suns. & Bank Hol. Mons. & Tues. following 2.30–6. July & Aug.—Weds., Thurs., Sats. & Suns. 2.30–6 (last tour of House 5 p.m.). Parties of 20 or more, daily, mornings, afternoons or evenings by arrangement. Adm. House & Gardens £1.50, Chd. 80p. Reduction for parties of 20 or more. Free car park. Gift & Bric-a-brac shop. *Regret no dogs. No stiletto heels in the house.* Dining Room & Ballroom available for private functions; Dinners, Wedding Receptions, Conferences etc. throughout the year. Candlelight tours by arrangement. For further information contact Mrs. Milton-Haynes. *Armitage* (0543) 490308 tea & home baking in 17th century Stable Block hot or cold meals by arrangement	Midland Red 825, Lichfield–Armitage–Handsacre–Stafford *(alight Hanch Hall crossroads)*
HOAR CROSS HALL, Hoar Cross, Burton-on-Trent *map 3 A* Elizabethan-style mansion set in 20 acres of woodland. Designed by Henry Clutton and built by the Meynell-Ingram family between 1862 and 1871. Ornamental plasterwork, oak panelling. William Morris wallpaper. Gardens, undergoing restoration.	7 m W of Burton-on-Trent; 10 m N of Lichfield; 15 m E of Stafford; 10 m S of Uttoxeter. Off A38, A515 & B5234	For details of opening times & charges telephone Hoar Cross (028 375) 224 (Mrs. Gwynyth J. Jones or Mr. D. Gareth Evans (Welsh Tenor). Medieval Banquets are held during the year, generally on Fris. & Sats. *Hoar Cross* (028 375) 224 cream teas, refreshments; party catering & weddings	No reasonable public transport
PILLATON OLD HALL, Penkridge *map 2 D* *Mr. R. W. & The Hon. Mrs. Perceval* 15th century gatehouse wing and chapel	1 m E of Penkridge on Cannock Rd (B5012); turn r. at Pillaton Hall Farm	Open by appointment. Admission 50p. *Penkridge* (078 571) 2200	Bus Penkridge—Cannock *(alight Pillaton)*
SHUGBOROUGH, Stafford *map 2 D* *The National Trust (administered by Staffordshire County Council)* Seat of the Earls of Lichfield. Architecture by James Stuart and Samuel Wyatt. Chinese garden house, classical temple, extensive grounds in area of river, beautiful trees and shrubs	5½ m SE of Stafford; turn off A513 at Milford; 10 mins. drive from M6 *Stn: Stafford (6 m)*	Mid March to October. House, Farm, Museum & Gardens—Tues. to Fris. & Bank Hol. Mons. 10.30–5.30; Sats. & Suns. 2–5.30. Adm.: Gardens & Museum only 70p, Chd. 30p; House (additional) 70p, Chd. 30p; Farm (weekends only) 40p, Chd. 20p. Reduced rates for O.A.Ps. Gardens & Museum 50p per person; House (additional) 50p per person. *No reduced rates for parties but guided tours available weekdays at no extra cost if booked in advance. Parties can be booked in at the farm on weekdays at 40p per head (adults) & 25p (Chd.) inclusive of guided tours (minimum number 10).* Charges subject to alteration. Special adm. charges for special events. Museum & Farm open mid-Oct. to mid-March—Tues. to Fris. 10.30–4.30 also first & third Sun. each month 2–4.30; also House for parties by appointment only.	Midland Red, 823, 824, Stafford–Rugeley–Lichfield *(alight at Shugborough Park, 1 m)* National tour from the Midlands

HANCH HALL, LICHFIELD, STAFFORDSHIRE

"Homes & Garden" photograph

The house is an unusual combination of architecture from Tudor to early Victorian which gives each room a fresh interest. Fine strapwork staircase, armorial window mentioned in Samuel Pepys Diary, 15th century timbers. Observation Tower giving extensive views of the estate. Elizabethan Cellars with escape tunnel. Period furniture including a four-poster bed associated with Percy Bysshe Shelley. Doll Museum, Needlework Museum, collections of teapots, early parchments, seashells. Exhibitions of costumery, 19th century Christening gowns, waxworks and "Postmen through the Ages".

Visitors receive a one hour guided tour through 18 rooms of this privately owned family home and are welcomed by Mr. and Mrs. Douglas Milton-Haynes and their family who have, without inheritance, taken up the challenge of restoring this historic mansion on a do it yourself basis. Featured by ITV, Staffordshire Magazine, Derbyshire Life, Home & Gardens 1981, etc. Landscaped gardens, lawns and partly wild grounds and pools. Free roaming peacocks, pheasants, old fashioned turkeys and bantams, guinea-fowl, geese, ducks. Swans and Wildfowl Sanctuary on Trout Pool.

OPENING TIMES OPPOSITE

POUNDISFORD PARK

POUNDISFORD, NR. TAUNTON

Small "lived in" Tudor house set in the former Deer Park of Taunton Castle. Family china and costume collections. Unusual plaster ceilings, enclosed gallery to Great Hall, rare surviving detached kitchen (converted to famous Well House Restaurant). Fine brick Gazebo in the garden. Garden being restored.

OPENING TIMES OPPOSITE

SHUGBOROUGH STAFFORDSHIRE

A National Trust property maintained and administered by Staffordshire County Council.

A gracious National Trust House lived in by Lord Lichfield. 18 acres of formal gardens; 900 acres of parkland, woodland and farmland. Historic monuments in the park; two museums and a farm. Café and Shop. Picnic areas and garden walks.

OPENING TIMES OPPOSITE

THE SUE RYDER HOME HICKLETON HALL

Nr DONCASTER

This Home cares for 50 physically handicapped and others who are homeless and unable to cope on their own.

Individuals wishing to visit the Sue Ryder Home may do so on any afternoon between the hours of 2 p.m. and 4 p.m. Monday to Friday without prior appointment.

Please report your arrival to the Office in the main entrance.

HOAR CROSS HALL

BURTON-ON-TRENT, STAFFORDSHIRE

The Hall, of an interesting Elizabethan-style set in 20 acres of woodland and gardens, was designed by Henry Clutton. It was built by the Meynell-Ingram family between 1862 and 1871, being modelled in part on the family's Elizabethan mansion, Temple Newsam, near Leeds. The ornamental plasterwork of the ceilings in the Great Banqueting Hall and oak-panelled Long Gallery is an example of the work of G.F. Bodley. He was also the creator of the imposing carved screen in the Entrance Hall. The wallpaper in the Banqueting Hall is the original paper, hung in 1869 and designed by William Morris. Leading off the Long Gallery is the fine panelled oak staircase leading to the private apartments. A later addition was the Chapel in the East Wing; this was completed in 1897 and has several notable features. The gardens were planned according to Bacon's "Essay on Gardens"; they contain fine trees and shrubs, yew-tree walks and ponds and are at present undergoing restoration. Adjacent to the gardens stands the Church of the Holy Angels, generally regarded as one of the finest Victorian churches in the country.
Medieval Banquets are held during the year on Fridays, Saturdays and other days to meet individual requirements. The Hall is a particularly appropriate setting for publicity, sales-promotional, film location, musical, auto-club and rallying activities. Please tel. Hoar Cross (028 375) 224 for information and opening times.

PROPERTY (*showing map reference*)	LOCATION (*with nearest Rly. Stn.*)	OPENING TIMES AND ADMISSION CHARGES CATERING FACILITIES	COACH AND RAIL TOURS BUS SERVICES (*showing alighting points*)
STAFFORDSHIRE—*continued*			
TAMWORTH CASTLE, Tamworth *map* 3 *E* *Corporation of Tamworth* Medieval Keep and tower with Tudor and Jacobean additions. Houses a museum	**In Tamworth, 15 m NE of Birmingham** *Stn: Tamworth (¼ m) (not Suns.)*	All the year—Weekdays except Fris.) 10–5.30; Suns. 2–5.30. Open Bank Hols. *Closed Fridays and Christmas Eve, Christmas Day & Boxing Day.* Adm. charge. ☎ *Tamworth* 422 (*Ext.* 389)	**Mid. Red X99, Birmingham–Nottingham, (*hourly*); 110, 116, 198 Birmingham–Tamworth 765, Coventry–Lichfield (*alight gates*)**
WESTON PARK—SEE UNDER SHROPSHIRE			
SUFFOLK			
BELCHAMP HALL—SEE UNDER ESSEX			
CHRISTCHURCH MANSION, Ipswich *The Borough of Ipswich* *map* 3 *G* Extensive Tudor town house in park. Furnished period rooms, 16th to 19th century; outstanding decorative art collections of china, glass etc. Attached art gallery includes work by Gainsborough, Constable and other Suffolk artists up to the present day. Temporary art exhibition programme.	In Christchurch Park, near centre of Ipswich *Stn: Ipswich (2 m)*	All the year—Mons. to Sats. 10–5 (*dusk in winter*); Suns. 2.30–4.30 (*dusk in winter*). Open Bank Hols. *Closed Dec. 24 & 25 and Good Friday.* Adm. free. All written enquiries to: Director of Recreation & Amenities, Civic Centre, Civic Drive, Ipswich ☎ *Ipswich* (0473) 53246	Eastern Counties & Borough Transport (*alight near Christchurch Park gates*)
EUSTON HALL, Thetford *map* 3 *G* *The Duke of Grafton* 18th century house. Fine collection of paintings, including Stubbs, Van Dyck, Kneller and Lely. Pleasure grounds by John Evelyn and William Kent Gardens and 17th century parish church in Wren style	A1088; 3 m SE Thetford *Stn: Thetford (4 m)*	June 7 to September 27—Thurs. only, 2.30–5.30. Adm. £1.20, O.A.Ps. & Schoolchildren 60p. picnic area	Eastern Counties 906 & 907 Thetford–Bury St. Edmunds (*infrequent*) (*alight Euston Post Office*)
GAINSBOROUGH'S HOUSE, Sudbury *Gainsborough's House Society* *map* 3 *G* Gainsborough's birthplace. Pictures etc.	46 Gainsborough St., Sudbury (Suffolk) *Stn: Sudbury (¼ m)*	Open all the year—Tues. to Sats. 10–12.30, 2–5; Suns & Bank Hol. Mons. 2–5. *Closed Mons., Good Friday & between Christmas & New Year.* Adm. 50p; Students, Chd. & O.A.Ps. 25p. ☎ *Sudbury* (0787) 72958	Eastern Counties, Eastern National, Chamber's etc. Theobald's serving Sudbury (Suffolk)
GLEMHAM HALL, nr Woodbridge *map* 3 *H* *Lady Blanche Cobbold* Red brick Elizabethan house. Altered early 1700. Panelled rooms, fine staircase, Queen Anne furniture. Red-brick walled garden	3 m NE of Wickham Market; 5 m SW of Saxmundham; 17 m NE of Ipswich	Easter Monday to September 30—Suns., Weds. & Bank Holidays 2–5.30 Adm. House & Garden £1, Garden only 50p; Chd. & O.A.Ps. half-price. No dogs. Free car park. at House ☎ 746 219	Eastern Counties 262, 263, 264, Aldeburgh–Saxmundham–Ipswich (*alight Parham Lane, 5 mins. walk*)
THE GUILDHALL, Hadleigh *map* 3 *G* *Hadleigh Market Feoffment Charity* Dating from 15th century	In Hadleigh 10 m W of Ipswich on A1071	All the year—Thurs. 10–6 (October to March closes at 4). Adm. free (collecting box) White Lion, Hadleigh	Eastern Counties 205/6, Ipswich–Hadleigh–Sudbury
HAUGHLEY PARK, nr Stowmarket *map* 3 *G* *Mr. A. J. Williams* Jacobean manor house. Gardens and Woods	4 m W of Stowmarket off A45 nr. Wetherden	May to September—Tues. 3–6. Adm. £1, Chd. 50p	Eastern Counties 924/5/6/7 from Stowmarket or Bury St. Edmunds (*alight Wetherden, ½ m*)
HELMINGHAM HALL, Ipswich *map* 3 *G* *The Lord & Lady Tollemache* The House was completed in 1510 by the Tollemache family and is surrounded by a wide moat with drawbridges which are raised every night. The large park contains herds of Red and Fallow deer and Highland Cattle and the gardens, which date with the house, are renowned for the herbacious borders.	9 m N of Ipswich on B1077 *Stn: Westerfield (7½ m)*	GARDENS ONLY: Easter Sun. to Sept 30—Suns. only 2–6. Adm. £1.10, Chd. 60p, O.A.Ps. 85p. Safari rides 50p, Chd. 30p. Craft shop. *House not open to the public* cream teas	No reasonable public transport.
ICKWORTH, nr Bury St. Edmunds *map* 3 *G* *The National Trust* The house, begun c. 1794, was not completed until 1830. Contents of this architectural curiosity include late Regency and 18th cent. French furniture, magnificent silver, pictures. Formal gardens, herbaceous borders, orangery. 18th cent. walks in woodland and around the lake	3 m SW of Bury St. Edmunds on W side of A143 *Stn: Bury St. Edmunds (3 m)*	Rotunda, Corridors & Garden: April 21 to May 31 & Sept. 15 to Oct. 14—Daily (except Mons. & Fris.) 2–6. June 1 to Sept. 14—Daily (except Mons.) 2–6. Open Bank Hol. Mons. also Sats. & Suns. April 7/8 & 14/15: 2–6. Adm. £1.60, Chd. (with adult) 80p. Reduced fee of £1.10 for pre booked parties Tues. to Fris. only during April, May, Sept. & Oct. Park open daily—adm. 50p. (refunded to house visitors). Dogs in park only, on leads. Wheelchair access, one provided; special car park for disabled. Shop. lunch & tea in old Servants' Hall ☎ *Horringer* 270	Norfolk Motors tours from Yarmouth and Lowestoft every Sun. Eastern Counties 931, 932, 933, 934, 936 Bury St. Edmunds–Stradishall (*not Suns.*) (*alight Horringer village, 1 m*)

There's more than meets the eye . . .

to

Ipswich Museums and Galleries

Discover the rest at:

IPSWICH MUSEUM and the HIGH ST. EXHIBITION GALLERY

High Street, Ipswich, Suffolk

Geology, Archaeology, Natural History and the Mankind Galleries

CHRISTCHURCH MANSION and the WOLSEY ART GALLERY

Christchurch Park, Ipswich, Suffolk

Period rooms, decorative and fine arts

For further information telephone:

Ipswich (0473) 213761

GAINSBOROUGH'S HOUSE,

SUDBURY

Richard Burn ***photograph***

Gainsborough's birthplace, elegantly furnished house with works by the greatest of English painters, also exhibitions of contemporary and historic art. Open all year. Tuesday to Saturday 10–12.30, 2–5; Sunday and Bank Holiday Mondays 2–5.

Closed Mondays (except Bank Holidays), Good Friday & between Christmas & New Year.

Admission 50p; Children, Students & O.A.Ps. 25p.

KENTWELL HALL LONG MELFORD

Have *you* seen the *progress* at Kentwell?

Kentwell Hall is a magnificent mellow redbrick Tudor House surrounded by a broad moat. Externally little altered with original E-plan and inner courtyard intact. Nearly lost through long neglect it was acquired in 1971 and is now the subject of a unique attempt to refurbish the House, collect contents appropriate to it and recreate its once fine gardens. Its special attraction is that these efforts may be seen in progress and nearly the whole Hall and its gardens are open to view. The efforts being made to save this delightful House and the fact that it is once again a family home gives Kentwell its unique flavour.

The Principal Rooms remodelled by Hopper in a variety of styles have been embellished and enhanced in recent works.

OTHER ATTRACTIONS:

Little altered XVth century Moat House, major part of earlier dwelling, open in 1984 as XVth century home.

XVIIth century Walled Garden with numerous old espaliered fruit trees.

Developing collection of rare breeds and old farm implements and craft tools.

"Aerofilms Ltd." photograph

Homemade Teas and other catering for parties.

June 24th–July 15th. UNIQUE RE-CREATION OF TUDOR DOMESTIC LIFE.

Open to booked school parties only on Weekdays and to the public on Sats. and Suns. 11–5.

August 2nd–18th OPEN AIR THEATRE SEASON including 'LOVE'S LABOURS LOST'.

OPENING TIMES (apart from special events) 2–6 p.m.

Easter	Good Friday to Tues.
April 25th to June 23rd	Weds., Thurs., Suns.
June 24th to July 15th	See above.
July 25th to Sept. 30th	Weds. to Suns.
Bank Holidays	Sats. and Mons.

For other information of times, admission charges etc. see entry details.

HELMINGHAM HALL

Between IPSWICH and DEBENHAM

Country Life photograph

Home of the Tollemache family since 1480, when it was built, to the present day – probably the last and finest house of the Tudor period, surrounded by a wide moat with drawbridges raised every night. A superb garden and immaculate kitchen garden with lovely herbaceous borders and walks extending for several acres, set in 400 acres of ancient deer park with large herds of Red and Fallow deer.

OPENING TIMES OPPOSITE

ICKWORTH

Suffolk

THE NATIONAL TRUST

"Aerofilms Ltd." photograph

This great house was begun in 1794, to his own design, with Francis Sandys as architect, by the 4th Earl of Bristol, Bishop of Derry; it was completed by his son in 1830. It consists of an elliptical rotunda connected by two curved corridors to flanking wings. The overall length is some 600 feet. The contents include a good collection of pictures (principally family portraits), fine 18th century English and French furniture and magnificent silver.

OPENING TIMES OPPOSITE

PROPERTY (*showing map reference*)	LOCATION (*with neatest Rly. Stn.*)	OPENING TIMES AND ADMISSION CHARGES CATERING FACILITIES	COACH AND RAIL TOURS BUS SERVICES (*showing alighting points*)
SUFFOLK—*continued*			
IPSWICH MUSEUM, **Ipswich** *map 3 G* *Ipswich Borough Council* Suffolk geology, archaeology (Sutton Hoo and Mildenhall treasure replicas and Ipswich torcs), natural history, new ethnology galleries (Africa, Asia, Pacific, Australia and the Americas) opened in 1980	High St., in town centre *Stn: Ipswich*	Mons. to Sats. 10–5. Temporary exhibition programme. Adm. free. All written enquiries to: Director of Recreation and Amenities, Civic Centre, Civic Drive, Ipswich. ☎ *Ipswich* (0473) 213761/2	
Δ **IXWORTH ABBEY**, **nr Bury St Edmunds** *Mrs. Alan Rowe* *map 3 G* House contains 12th century monastic buildings with 15th to 19th century additions. 13th Ⓔ century Undercroft and 15th century Priors Lodging recently restored.	6 m NE of Bury St. Edmunds, 8 m SE of Thetford; at jct. of A143 & A1088	May 1 to Aug. 31—Tues. & Suns. 2.30–5; also May 7, Spring & Summer Bank Hol. Mons. 2.30–5. Adm. £1, Chd. & O.A.Ps. 80p. Open at other times throughout the year also morning & evening visits by prior arrangement. Guided visits only. Unsuitable for wheelchairs. ☕ meals by prior arrangement only.	Eastern Counties 911, 912, 913, 914, 917, 918 from Bury St. Edmunds (*approach through churchyard*)
KENTWELL HALL, **Long Melford** *map 3 G* *J. Patrick Phillips, Q.C.* Red brick Elizabethan E-plan mansion surrounded by a broad moat. Exterior little Ⓔ altered. Interior being refurbished. Interconnecting gardens with specimen trees and magnificent avenue of ancient limes	Entrance on W of A134, N of Green in Long Melford. 3 m N of Sudbury	Good Friday to Tues. following (April 20–24); then April 3 to June 25—Weds., Thurs. & Suns.; July 25 to Sept. 30—Weds. to Suns.; Bank Hol. Sats., Suns, & Mons.: 2–6. Adm. £1.75, Chd. (accompanied) 90p, O.A.Ps. £1.20 (Thurs. only). June 24 to July 15—Historical Recreation: Weekdays—booked school parties only; general public at weekends: 11–5 (special adm. charges). Reduction of 20% for pre-booked parties over 20 on open days, also groups at other times by arrangement. No dogs. ☕ teas in the Hall	National Coach 082, 095 London–Long Melford–Norwich **Chamber's** Colchester–Sudbury–Bury St. Edmunds **Theobald's** Sudbury–Clare–Haverhill (*alight Long Melford*)
LITTLE HALL, **Lavenham** *map 3 G* *Suffolk Preservation Society* 15th century "hall" house, rooms furnished with Gayer Anderson collection of furniture, pictures, china, books etc.	E side Lavenham Market Place	Easter to mid-October Sats., Suns. and Bank Hols. 2.30–6. *Groups by appointment.* Adm. 50p, Chd. 25p	H. C. Chambers service Colchester-Sudbury—Bury St. Edmunds (*except Suns.*) (*alight Lavenham*)
MELFORD HALL, **nr Sudbury** *map 3 G* *The National Trust* Built between 1554 and 1578 by Sir William Cordell, contains fine pictures, furniture and Chinese porcelain. Interesting garden and gazebo. Beatrix Potter display	In Long Melford on E side of **A134**; 3 m N of **Sudbury**; *Stn: Sudbury (4 m)*	Principal Rooms & Gardens: April 4 to end of Sept.—Weds., Thurs., Suns. & Bank Hol. Mons. 2–6. Adm. £1.30, Chd. (with adult) 65p. Pre booked parties of 15 or more £1, Weds. & Thurs. only. No dogs. Wheelchair access, one provided ✕ In Long Melford	Eastern Counties tour from London—(*Suns. only*) **Chambers**, Colchester–Sudbury–Bury St. Edmunds **Theobalds**, Sudbury–Clare–Haverhill **National** Coach 082, 095 London–Long Melford–Norwich
NETHER HALL, **Cavendish, nr Sudbury** *B. T. Ambrose, Esq.* *map 3 G* Listed 15th century Manor House situated in the centre of scenic Stour Valley village, beside its churchyard and famous village green. Surrounded by its own vineyards producing prize-winning Estate white wines	12 m S of Bury St. Edmunds; beside A1092	Open daily for tours & wine tasting 11–4. Adm. £1.50, Chd. (accompanied) free, O.A.Ps. £1. Parties by appointment. ✕☕ Grapevine Restaurant, Cavendish	Theobald's, Sudbury–Clare–Haverhill (*alight Cavendish*)
Δ **OTLEY HALL**, **nr Ipswich** *map 3 H* *Mr. J. G. Mosesson* 15th century Moated Hall (Grade I) and Gardens. Home for 250 years of the Gosnold family. Fine timbers, herring-bone brick, pargetting. Historical associations	10 m N of Ipswich, via B1077 / B1078; ¼ m NE of Otley village *Stn: Ipswich (10 m)*	Easter Sun. & Mon. (April 22 & 23); Spring Bank Hol. Sun. & Mon. (May 27 & 28); Summer Bank Hol. Sun. & Mon. (Aug. 26 & 27): 2–6. Open by appointment to parties, special interest groups etc. Guided tours. Lectures available on associated history, architectural background, etc. Adm. £1.80, Chd. (with adult) 90p. ✕☕ tea & light refreshments, buffet meals available by arrangement.	Bickers' Coaches Ipswich–Otley (*not Suns*)
THE PRIORY, **Lavenham** *map 3 G* Δ *Mr. & Mrs Alan Casey* Complex timber-frame building dating from 13th to 16th century. Entire structure visible; Jacobean staircase, inglenook fireplaces and wall paintings. One of very few privately-owned Grade I buildings in Suffolk. Collection of Paintings, Drawings and Stained Glass by Ervin Bossanyi (1891–1975)	In Water St., Lavenham; 10 m S of Bury St. Edmunds	April 20 to Sept. 30—Daily 2–5.30. Adm. £1, Chd. 50p. Guided tours for groups, by appointment only, at all times of the year. Catering for groups can be arranged nearby. ☎ *Lavenham* (0787) 247417	Buses to Lavenham from Colchester, Sudbury & Bury St. Edmunds
PYKENHAM GATEHOUSE, **Ipswich** *map 3G* *Ipswich Building Preservation Trust Limited* 15th century Gatehouse formerly forming part of the Archdeacon's house.	Northgate St., in town centre. *Stn: Ipswich*	Open by appointment in writing to the Secretary of the Trust, Ipswich Building Preservation Trust Limited, 7 Northgate St., Ipswich IP1 3BU.	Local & national bus services

WINGFIELD CASTLE

& 14th C. WINGFIELD COLLEGE SUFFOLK

Wingfield Castle is probably the prettiest romantic moated and inhabited castle in England. It is the historic seat of the de La Poles who were to become Earls and Dukes of Suffolk and one of the most powerful families in 15th Century England. Today, visitors can see not only the 14th Century Castle but also the Tudor Manor House and Gardens within the moat. Telephone Stradbroke (037984) 393.

Wingfield College, 700 year old home of the Wingfield family, has a magnificent Mediaeval Great Hall, Cloister, Gallery and Lodgings Range, with Elizabethan and Georgian interiors, disguised by a neo-classical facade—and all in a picturesque setting of small walled gardens. Collection of ceramics, prints and textiles.

There is an annual programme of arts and music with exhibitions and special events. Home-made teas. Telephone: Stradbroke (037984) 505.

Both Wingfield Castle and College are open from Easter Saturday to September 30th on Saturdays, Sundays and Bank Holidays 2.00–6.00 p.m. and parties at other times by appointment throughout the year.

Wingfield is on the Norfolk/Suffolk border, 7 miles south-east of Diss, 20 miles south of Norwich, 26 miles north of Ipswich, 22 miles west of Southwold.

For details of opening times see **Page 134**

PROPERTY (*showing map reference*)	LOCATION (*with nearest Rly. Stn.*)	OPENING TIMES AND ADMISSION CHARGES CATERING FACILITIES	COACH AND RAIL TOURS BUS SERVICES (*showing alighting points*)
SUFFOLK—*continued*			
SOMERLEYTON HALL, nr Lowestoft *The Lord & Lady Somerleyton* map 3 H Early 19th century mansion on which no expense was spared. Beautiful gardens, famous maze; miniature railway.	5 m NW Lowestoft off B1074, 7 m Yarmouth (A143) *Stn: Somerleyton (1¼ m)*	Easter Sun. to Sept. 30. House & Gardens—Thurs., Suns. & Bank Hols.; also Tues. & Weds. in July & Aug.: 2–5.30. Garden only open all other days (except Sats.) 2–5.30. Adm. (1983 rates) £1.30, Chd. 75p.	National tour from Norwich (*Belle Ave.*) on certain Thurs. & Suns. Coaches from Yarmouth & Lowestoft on most open days
WINGFIELD CASTLE, Eye map 3H *Gerard Fairhurst, Esq.* A 14th century moated castle with a Tudor Manor House and gardens. Richard II granted a licence of crenellation to Michael de La Pole (1st Earl) to build the stone and flint castle with splendid south gatehouse and curtain walls.	Signposted off B1118; 7 m SE of Diss. *Stn: Diss (7 m)*	Easter Sat. (April 21) to Sept. 30—Sats., Suns. & Bank Hols. 2–6. Open for parties at other times throughout the year by appointment. home-made teas *Stradbroke* (037 984) 393	No reasonable public transport
WINGFIELD COLLEGE, Eye map 3H Δ *Ian Chance, Esq.* Founded in 1362 on the 13th century site of the Manor House by Sir John de Wingfield, a close friend of the Black Prince. Magnificent Mediaeval Great Hall. Surrendered to Henry VIII in 1542 and siezed by Cromwell's Parliament in 1549. Mixed period interiors with 18th century neo-classical facade. Collegiate Church with tombs of founder and benefactors, the Dukes of Suffolk. Walled Gardens. Celebrated Arts and Music season.	Signposted off B1118; 7 m SE of Diss. *Stn: Diss (7 m)*	Easter Sat. (April 21) to Sept. 30—Sats., Suns. & Bank Hols. 2–6. Guided tours for groups at other times throughout the year by appointment. No dogs. Concerts, recitals and special events. For programme telephone *Stradbroke* (037 984) 505 home-made teas	No reasonable public service
SURREY			
ALBURY PARK, Albury, Guildford map 6 C *Mutual Households Association* Country mansion by Pugin	1½m E of Albury *Stns: Chilworth (2m); Gomshall (2 m)*	May to September—Weds. & Thurs. 2–5. Adm. 50p, Chd. 25p. Free car park. No dogs admitted.	London Country 425, 439, Guildford–Dorking–Redhill Brown and Tillingbourne Valley services from Guildford (*alight Albury Park gates*)
CHILWORTH MANOR, nr Guildford *Lady Heald* map 6 C Garden laid out in 17th century on site of 11th century monastery; 18th century walled garden; spring flowers, flowering shrubs, herbaceous border, 11th century stewponds	3¾ m SE of Guildford off A248 in Chilworth Village turn at Blacksmith Lane *Stn: Chilworth (¾ m)*	GARDEN: Sat. & Sun. April 14/15; Sat., Sun. & Bank Hol. Mon. May 26/27/28; Sats. & Suns. June 23/24, July 7/8 & 14/15, Aug. 4/5: 2–7. *Other times by appointment.* Car park open 12.30 for picnics. Adm. 30p, Chd. free. House 30p extra. Cars free. *In aid of National Gardens' Schemes or Gardeners' Sunday* at the house	London Country 425, 439, Guildford–Dorking–Redhill (*alight Blacksmith Lane*) Brown and Tillingbourne Valley Services from Guildford
CLANDON PARK, nr Guildford map 6 C *The National Trust* A Palladian house built 1731–35 by Giacomo Leoni. Fine plasterwork. Collection of furniture, pictures and porcelain. Museum of the Queen's Royal Surrey Regiment. Maori house.	At West Clandon 3 m E Guildford on A247, S of A3 & N of A246 *Stn: Clandon (1 m)*	April 1 to October 14—Daily (except Mons. & Fris.) 2–6 (last admission 5.30). Open Bank Hol. Mons. *closed Tues. following*). Parties & guided tours by arrangement with the Administrator (*no reduced rate at weekends & Bank Hols*). Adm. House and Garden £1.50, Chd. 75p. Shop. Picnic area. Dogs in car park & picnic area only, on leads. Wheelchairs provided. *Guildford* 222482 Restaurant in house 12.30–2, 3.30–5.30.	Green Line 710, 715, 740, 741 to Guildford then: London Country 408, Guildford–Croydon; 416, Guildford–Great Bookham (*not Suns.*); (*alight Clandon crossroads—300 yds from House*) 437, Guildford–Working–Weybridge (*passes gates*)
CLAREMONT, Esher map 6 C *The Claremont Fan Court Foundation Ltd.* Excellent example of Palladian style; built 1772 by "Capability" Brown for Clive of India; Henry Holland and John Soane responsible for the interior decoration. It is now a co-educational school run by Christian Scientists	½ m SE from Esher on Esher–Oxshott rd A244. Turn right thro Lodge gates opp. Milbourne Lane *Stns: Claygate (1½ m); Esher (2 m) (not Suns.); Hersham (3 m)*	Feb. to Nov.—first complete weekend (Sat. & Sun.) in each month 2–5. Adm. 75p, Chd. & O.A.Ps. 35p. Reduced rates for parties. Souvenirs. refreshments *Esher* 67841	Green Line, 715 to Guildford Mole Valley, Esher–Cobham–Leatherhead (*alight entrance gate*)
CLAREMONT LANDSCAPE GARDEN, Esher map 6 C *The National Trust* The earliest surviving English landscape garden, recently restored. Begun by Vanbrugh and Bridgeman before 1720, extended and naturalized by Kent. Lake, island with pavilion, grotto and turf amphitheatre, viewpoints and avenues. House not National Trust property	½ m SE of Esher on E side of A307. *NB:* no access from A3 by-pass *Stns: Esher (2 m) (not Suns.); Hersham (2 m); Hinchley Wood (2½ m); Cobham & Stoke d' Abernon (3 m)*	All the year—April to end of Oct.—Daily 9–7 (or sunset if earlier). Nov. to end of March—Daily 9–4 (last admission half hour before closing). *Closed Christmas Day & New Year's Day.* Adm. 60p, Chd. half price. Guided tours (minimum 15 persons) 80p by prior booking. Wheelchair access. No reduction for parties. Dogs admitted on leads. *Refreshment Kiosk open Easter to end of Oct. Sats & Suns. 11–5, Tues., Weds. & Thurs. 2–5, March, Sats. & Suns. only 2–4.*	Green Line 715 (*alight entrance gate*)

Somerleyton Hall GARDENS AND MAZE Nr. Lowestoft

The home of Lord and Lady Somerleyton

Somerleyton Hall is an extravagantly splendid early Victorian mansion built around a Tudor and Jacobean shell, epitomising an era of self confident expansion. No expense was spared in the building or the fittings. Stone was brought from Caen and Aubigny and the magnificent carved stonework created by John Thomas (who worked on the Houses of Parliament) has recently been fully restored.

In the State rooms there are paintings by Landseer, Wright of Derby and Stanfield, together with fine wood carving by Willcox of Warwick and from the earlier house, Grinling Gibbons.

Twelve acres of gardens surround the Hall with magnificent specimen trees, azaleas, rhododendrons and splendid statuary. There are handsome glass houses designed by Paxton. The most notable feature is the MAZE, planted in 1846, which ranks among the finest in this country.

The stable tower clock by Vulliamy made in 1847 is the original mode for a great clock to serve as the Tower Clock in the new Houses of Parliament, now world famous as Big Ben.

A quarter mile long MINIATURE RAILWAY carries passengers at the edge of the park.

Tea in the Winter Garden Tea Room. Free car parking. No dogs allowed.

OPENING TIMES OPPOSITE

CLANDON PARK

WEST CLANDON, GUILDFORD, SURREY

THE NATIONAL TRUST

The Palladian house was built by Giacomo Leoni in the early 1730s for the Onslow family. Restoration has revealed much of the original decoration. The important contents include Mrs. Gubbay's famous collection of furniture and porcelain and the Museum of the Queen's Royal Surrey Regiment. The old kitchen in the basement, with its 19th-century cooking apparatus, is on show. A restaurant (lunches and teas) has been made in the brick-vaulted basement. The restaurant opens at 12.30 on visiting days, but is available out of normal hours for private parties by arrangement. Maori house in the garden.

Open April 1st to October 14th. Daily except Mondays and Fridays 2 p.m. to 6 p.m. (last admission 5.30 p.m.). Open Bank Holiday Mondays, *closed Tuesday following.*

Parties by arrangement with the Administrator (no reduced rate at weekend or B. Hols.)

Admission: House and Gardens £1.50, Children 75p.

CLAREMONT
LANDSCAPE GARDEN

ESHER, SURREY

THE NATIONAL TRUST

An eighteenth century landscape garden, fifty acres in extent. Originally laid out by Sir John Vanbrugh and Charles Bridgeman before 1720, naturalised by William Kent and further improved by 'Capability' Brown. Lake and viewpoints. Only surviving Turf Amphitheatre in Europe. The National Trust was awarded the Europa Nostra Diploma of Merit in 1980 for restoring the garden.

Queen Victoria spent her happiest childhood days here. Also associated with Clive of India, Prince Leopold (later King of the Belgians) and Princess Charlotte.

Open daily throughout year, except 25th December and 1st January from 9 a.m. (see opposite for details).

PROPERTY (*showing map reference*)	LOCATION (*with nearest Rly. Stn.*)	OPENING TIMES AND ADMISSION CHARGES CATERING FACILITIES	COACH AND RAIL TOURS BUS SERVICES (*showing alighting points*)
SURREY—*continued*			
DETILLENS, Limpsfield *map 6 C* *Mr. & Mrs. D. G. Neville* Mid 15th cent. Wealden House. Fine inglenooks, firebacks and panelling. 2½ acres of walled garden	Centre Limpsfield village opposite Bull Inn off A25 *Stn: Oxted (1 m)*	May to June—Sats.; July to Sept.—Weds. & Sats.: 2–5. *Bank Hols. during above periods.* Guided tours at other times by prior arrangement. Adm. £1.25, Chd. 60p. ☎ *Oxted* (088 33) 3342	London Country 410 Bromley–Reigate; **464** Oxted–Limpsfield (*alight Detillens Lane*)
DUNSBOROUGH PARK, Ripley *map 6 C* *C. F. Hughesdon, Esq.* Spring flowers, rose garden, greenhouses with tropical plants and peach houses.	E of Woking; turn off A3 *Stn: Woking (4 m)*	GARDEN ONLY—Suns. April 29, June 24, July 22 & Aug. 12: 2–6. Adm. 50p, Chd. 25p. *In aid of National Gardens' Scheme.*	*Bus:* GL715 (*alight Ripley village*)
FARNHAM CASTLE, Farnham *map 6 C* *Church Commissioners* Bishop's Palace built in Norman times with Tudor and Jacobean additions. Fine Great Hall re-modelled at the Restoration	½ m N of town centre on A287 *Stn: Farnham*	All the year—Weds. 2–4. Parties at other times by arrangement. *Closed Christmas week.* Adm. 30p, Chd. & Students 15p. Parties of 25: 20p, Chd. & Students 10p. All visitors are given guided tours. Centrally heated in winter.	Alder Valley 207
FEATHERCOMBE GARDENS, Hambledon *Mrs. Wieler & Miss Parker* *map 6 C* Wide views, flowering shrubs, heathers	S of Godalming on Hambledon Rd. *Stn: Milford (2 m)*	GARDENS ONLY: Bank Hol. Suns. & Mons., May 6 & 7, 27 & 28: 2–6. Adm. 30p, Chd. free. Picnic area. Plants for sale.	No reasonable public transport
GORSE HILL MANOR, Virginia Water *Mrs. E. Barbour Paton* *map 6 C* 3-acre garden; over 450 different varieties of trees and shrubs, all identified, which are a speciality. Two donkeys, pit pony, croquet and putting	Turn off A30 at Wheatsheaf; cont. ½ m then 1st l. at roundabout then 1st r. along lane to car park.	GARDEN ONLY: Bank Hol. Mons. April 23, May 28 & Aug. 27; also Sun. Oct. 14; 2.30–5.30. *Collecting box in aid of National Gardens' Scheme.* No very young children and no dogs. Other times by previous appointment for individuals & parties (of up to 40) who are very welcome. ☎ *Wentworth* (099-04) 2101	Rail services from London, Staines, Reading, Guildford, Weybridge to Virginia Water
GREATHED MANOR, Lingfield *map 6 C* *Mutual Households Association* Victorian Manor house	On the outskirts of the village of Dormansland, 5 m SE of Lingfield *Stn: Dormans (1½ m)*	May to September—Weds. & Thurs. 2–5. Adm. 50p, Chd. 25p. Free car park. No dogs admitted	London Country 419 East Grinstead–Croydon (*alight Dormansland, "Plough" P.H.*)
GUILDFORD HOUSE, Guildford *map 6 C* *Guildford Borough Council* 17th century town house now an art gallery. Fine carved staircase, plaster ceilings and iron-work. Temporary Exhibition Programme	155 High St., town centre; off A3 (1½ m) *Stn: Guildford*	Monday to Saturday 10.30–4.50. *Closed when staging exhibition.* Adm. free. Suitable for disabled (ground floor—also first floor if in light portable wheelchairs). ✕☕ Hotels & Restaurants in the town ☎ (0483) 505050, *Ext.* 3531 (*Mons.–Fris.*), 503406 (*Sats.*)	
HATCHLANDS, East Clandon *map 6 C* *The National Trust* Built by Admiral Boscawen in 18th century, interior by Robert Adam, with later modifications. Garden	E of East Clandon on N side of Leatherhead – Guildford rd (A246) *Stn: Clandon (2m)*	April to Oct. 14—Weds., Thurs. & Suns. only 2–6 (no admission after 5.30). Adm. £1, Chd. half price. Pre-booked parties 80p (not Suns.). No dogs. Wheelchair access to ground floor only. ☎ *Guildford* 222787	Green Line 714 to Leatherhead or 715,710, **740, 741** to Guildford then: London Country 408, Croydon–Guildford (*alight E Clandon—gates ¼ m*)
LITTLE HOLLAND HOUSE, CHEAM—SEE UNDER LONDON			
LOSELEY HOUSE, Guildford *map 6 C* *J. R. More-Molyneux, Esq.* Elizabethan mansion built 1562. Panelling, furniture, paintings, ceilings. Farm tours	2½ m SW of Guildford (take B3000 off A3 thro Compton); 1½ m N of Godalming (off A3100) *Stn: Guildford (3 m)*	May 28 to Sept. 29—Weds., Thurs., Fris. & Sats. 2–5; also Summer Bank Hol. Mon. 2–5. Adm. £1.20, Chd. 65p. Parties £1.10 per person. School parties 55p per person. Farm shop. ☕ home made teas ☎ *Guildford* 571881	**Green Line 715 to Guildford then: Alder Valley (Wayfarer) 245, 246, 268, 271, 274, 292, 294 from Guildford (*Bus Stn.*) & Godalming (*alight Lodge, 1½ m*)**
PINEWOOD HOUSE, Worplesdon Hill *Jack Van Zwanenberg, Esq.* *map 6 C* 7 acres of gardens and woodland. Attractive house (built 1967) copied from Roman villa, with atrium.	3½ m SW of Woking, off A322 *Stn: Worplesdon (1½ m)*	HOUSE & GARDEN: May only—Suns. 2–6. Adm. 50p, Chd. (accompanied by adult) 25p. *In aid of National Gardens' Scheme.* Plants for sale. Also open by appointment. ☕ tea & biscuits (30p) ☎ *Brookwood* 3241	
POLESDEN LACEY, nr Dorking *map 6 C* *The National Trust* Originally a Regency villa altered in Edwardian period. Greville collection of pictures, tapestries, furniture. 18th century garden extended 1906, with herbaceous borders, rose garden, clipped hedges, lawns, beeches. Views	3 m NW of Dorking, reached via Great Bookham (A246) & then rd leading S (1½ m) *Stns: Boxhill or Bookham (both 2½ m)*	March & Nov.—Sats. & Suns. 2–5; April to end of Oct.—Daily (except Mons. & Fris.) 2–6. Last adm. half hour before closing. Open Bank Hol. Mons. (*closed Tues. following*). Gafden open daily all year, 11–sunset. *Dogs allowed in grounds if on leads.* Adm. House & Garden £1.80, Chd. (with adult) 90p. Garden only 90p, Chd. (with adult) 45p. *Party reductions on Tues., Weds. & Thurs. only by prior arrangement with the Administrator.* Shop. Wheel chairs admitted & provided. ☎ *Bookham* 58203 ✕☕ Licensed Restaurant, in the grounds; open from 11 on days when House open. ☎ *Bookham* 56190	National tours from parts of Sussex Green Line 714 to Leatherhead, thence **London** Country 408, Croydon–Guildford (*alight Great Bookham, Rayleigh House 1½ m*).
RAMSTER, Chiddingfold *map 6 C* *Mr. & Mrs. Paul Gunn* Large Woodland garden, fine rhododendrons, azaleas, camellias, magnolias, trees and shrubs	On A283 1 m S of Chiddingfold *Stn: Haslemere (4 m)*	GARDEN ONLY: April 28 to June 3—Sats., Suns. & Weds. 2–7. Also Bank Hol. Mons. May 7 & 28. Adm. 50p, Chd. 10p. *In aid of National Gardens' Scheme.* ☕ teas Sats., Suns. & B.H. Mons. only	Alder Valley **271**, Guildford–Godalming–Chiddingfold **251**, Haslemere–Chiddingfold–Petworth
SUTTON PLACE, nr Guildford *map 6 C* *The Sutton Place Heritage Trust* Built between 1520 and 1530 by Sir Richard Weston, Sutton Place is one of the finest surviving examples of the English Renaissance period. Recently extensively restored and now containing a magnificent collection of works of art.	2 m N of Guildford; signposted from A3. *Stn: Guildford (2 m)*	House & Gardens open by previous appointment. Concerts, recitals & other performances take place throughout the year. Details of opening times etc. are available from the Booking Secretary. ☎ *Guildford* (0483) 504455 ☕ tea & coffee available at Reception Area	
VANN, Hambledon *map 6 C* *Mr. & Mrs. M. B. Caroe* 16th to 20th century house surrounded by 5 acre "paradise" garden. Water garden by Gertrude Jekyll.	6 m S of Godalming; A283 to Chiddingfold; turn off at green, signposted Vann Lane at P.O. *Stn: Witley (3 m)*	GARDENS ONLY: April 23 to 27 (Easter Mon. 2–7, Tues. to Fri. 10–6); May 7 to 11 (Bank Hol. Mon. 2–7, Tues. to Fri. 10–6); June 24 to 29 (Sun. 2–7, Mon. to Fri. 10–6). Adm. 60p, Chd. 10p. *In aid of National Gardens Scheme & Save the Children Fund.* Also open other days by appointment Easter to end of June. Plant & vegetable stall. ☕ home made teas (April 23, May 7, June 24 only) ☎ *Wormley* (042 879) 3413	
WHITEHALL, CHEAM— SEE UNDER LONDON			
WINKWORTH ARBORETUM, [**nr Godalming** *map 6 C* *The National Trust* 99 acres of trees and shrubs planted mainly for Spring and Autumn colour. Two lakes, fine views	2 m SE of Godalming on E side of B2130 *Stn: Godalming (2 m)*	Open all the year during daylight hours. Adm. 70p, Chd. 30p. No reduction for parties. *Coach parties please book to ensure parking space.* Dogs must be kept under control. Wheelchair access. ☕ refreshments May to end of Oct.—Tues., Weds., Thurs., Sats., Suns. & Bank Hol. Mons. 2–6. *Closed Tues. following Bank Hols.* Also open fine weekends in March & April.	Alder Balley 246 Cranleigh–Godalming–Elstead (*weekdays only*) (*alight Gardens*)
WISLEY GARDEN, Wisley, Ripley *map 6 C* *The Royal Horticultural Society* British gardening at its best in all aspects	In Wisley just off Portsmouth rd (A3) London (22 m) *Stn: West Byfleet (3 m)*	All the year—Mons. to Sats. 10–7 (or sunset if earlier); Suns. 2–7 (or sunset if earlier). *Closed Christmas Day.* Adm. £1.40, Chd. under 5 yrs. free, 6-14 yrs. 70p. *Special rates for parties by prior arrangement only* Dogs not admitted. Information centre, Shop & Plant sales centre. ✕☕ Licensed restaurant in garden (mid Feb.—mid Nov.) & cafeteria.	Green Line 715, 715A National tours from Kent, Sussex & Bournemouth

DETILLENS

LIMPSFIELD, SURREY

A medieval Manor House built circa 1450 with a vast King Post and Tie Beam. The Georgian front was added in 1725. Situated in the centre of this attractive village the contents include superb collections of furniture, china and militaria. The house also contains the largest collection of Orders of Chivalry of all nations in the U.K. A new attraction is the adjoining Slaughter House, which was in use until recently, laid out as a Museum of Country Crafts and Artifacts.

LOSELEY HOUSE

near GUILDFORD SURREY

The Elizabethan country house with the friendly atmosphere. Built in a glorious parkland setting by an ancestor of the present owner and occupier, of stone from Waverley Abbey, Queen Elizabeth I stayed here three times, James I twice. Queen Mary visited in 1932. Panelling from Henry VIII's Nonsuch Palace, fine ceilings, unique carved chalk chimney piece, inlaid cabinets, tapestries, needlework, but Loseley is a home, not a museum. Teas. Moat walk. Farm Tours. Farm Shop selling ice-cream, yoghourt, cream and cheese from the Loseley Jersey Herd and compost-grown vegetables. Open to visitors 2-5 p.m. on Monday, May 28th (Spring Bank Holiday) and thereafter every Wednesday, Thursday, Friday and Saturday until September 29th also Bank Holiday Monday, August 27th. Tel. Guildford 571881.

SUTTON PLACE

Nr. GUILDFORD, SURREY

Built between 1520 and 1530 by Sir Richard Weston, Sutton Place is one of the finest surviving examples of the English Renaissance period. Recently extensively restored and now containing a magnificent collection of works of art and pictures of all periods. The house and gardens are open to the public by previous appointment.

The new gardens and landscape have been acclaimed as the greatest garden scheme of the Twentieth Century and during 1984 the exhibition in the East Wing will be closely linked to the garden and its design as part of 'A Celebration of English Gardens'.

Concerts, recitals and other performances take place throughout the year, sometimes in the Garden Theatre.

Details of opening times etc. are available from:

The Booking Secretary between 10 a.m. and 4 p.m. Mondays to Fridays—Guildford (0483) 504455

POLESDEN LACEY

near Dorking, Surrey

THE NATIONAL TRUST

The house is situated in a beautiful setting, with a fine view from the south terrace to the Ranmore woods on the far side of the valley. It contains the Greville collection of important pictures, tapestries, furniture and other works of art. Large gardens with herbaceous borders, rose garden, clipped hedges, lawns and beech walks.

OPENING TIMES OPPOSITE

WISLEY GARDEN

WISLEY, near RIPLEY, Surrey

The Royal Horticultural Society

The quiet and peace of a glorious garden—Wisley offers that and more. The wooded slopes with massed rhododendrons and azaleas, the wild daffodils of the alpine meadow, the calm of the pinetum, the gaiety of the herbaceous border, the banked mounds of heathers, the panorama of the rock garden, the model fruit and vegetable gardens and the range of greenhouse displays are there waiting for you to enjoy them and to learn from them.

Open to the Public

The public are admitted on weekdays from 10 a.m. and **after 2 p.m. on Sundays, charge** £1.40; children 5 years and under, no charge; from 6 to 14 years 70p.

Closed on Christmas Day.

Licensed Restaurant and Cafeteria. Free Car Park.

Off main London-Portsmouth road (A3)

PROPERTY (*showing map reference*)	LOCATION (*with nearest Rly. Stn.*)	OPENING TIMES AND ADMISSION CHARGES CATERING FACILITIES	COACH AND RAIL TOURS BUS SERVICES (*showing alighting points*)
TYNE & WEAR			
GIBSIDE CHAPEL & AVENUE, Gibside *The National Trust* *map 1 R* Built to James Paine's design soon after 1760. Outstanding example of Georgian architecture approached along a terrace with an oak avenue.	6 m SW of Gateshead; 20 m NW of Durham between Rowlands Gill and Burnopfield	April to end of September—Daily (except Tues.) 2–6. Oct.—Weds., Sats. & Suns. 2–5. Other times by appointment with the Custodian. Adm. to car park, avenue & Chapel 50p, Chd. 25p. *Parties please notify Custodian in advance (no reductions)*. Dogs on terrace only, on leads. ☎ *Rowlands Gill* (0207) 542255	Northern General 611, 744, 745 Newcastle–Consett (*alight Rowlands Gill*) 718 Durham–Chopwell
WASHINGTON OLD HALL, Washington *The National Trust* *map 1 R* (*leased by Sunderland Borough Council*) ♿ Jacobean manor house incorporating portions of 12th cent. house of the Washington family	In Washington on E side of Ave (A182) 5 m W of Sunderland (2 m from A1) S. of Tyne Tunnel, follow signs for Washington New Town District 4 & then village	All year. March to end of Oct.—Daily (except Weds.) 12–5; Nov. to end of Feb.—Sats. & Suns., (or by appointment), 2–4. *Closed Christmas Day & New Year's Day*. Adm. 70p, Chd. 35p. *Parties of 15 or more 60p each, by prior arrangement only with the Custodian*. Information Centre & Shop. Dogs in garden only, on leads. Wheelchair access. ☕ teas next door at the church, daily (except Weds. & Suns. April to Sept. ☎ *Washington* 4166879	Metro from Newcastle to Heworth then Northern General 191/2/3 from Heworth or 185 from Sunderland (*alight The Avenue*); Other services to Washington, then local services from bus station to Washington village
WARWICKSHIRE			
ARBURY HALL, Nuneaton *map 3 E* △ *F. H. FitzRoy Newdegate, Esq.* ♧ George Eliot's "Cheverel Manor." 18th century Gothic mansion, pictures, period furniture etc. Park and landscape gardens.	2 m SW of Nuneaton off B4102 RAC direction signs *Stn: Nuneaton (3 m)*	Easter Sun. to October 7—Suns., Bank Hol. Mons. & Tues. following: 2.30–6. Adm. Hall & Gardens £1.30. Gardens & Park 85p; Chd. 60p. Subject to review. Other days for organised parties of 25 or more by previous arrangement. Free car park. ☕ Easter to Oct. 7 ✕ for booked parties ☎ *Fillongley* (0676) 40529	Midland Red frequent services from Nuneaton with connections from principal Midland centres (*alight Round Towers, Stockingford, 1 m*)
CHARLECOTE PARK, Warwick *map 3 E* △ *The National Trust* ♧ Originally built by the Lucy family, 1558. Shakespeare is alleged to have been caught ♿ poaching here. Deer park	5 m E of Stratford-upon-Avon on the N side of B4086 *Stns. Str'tf'd u Avon (5½ m); Warwick (6 m) (not Suns. April, May Sept., Oct.); Leamington Spa (8 m)*	April—Sats. & Suns. also Easter Mon. & Tues. following 11–5. May to end of Sept.—Daily (except Mons. & Thurs. but open Bank Hol. Mons.) 11–6 Oct.—Sats. & Suns. 11–5. Evening visits for pre arranged parties, 2nd Thurs. in each month 7.30–9.30. School parties by prior arrangement only. Adm. £1.80 Chd. 90p. Parties of 15 or more by prior written arrangement only £1.20. Full price for evening visits. No dogs. Wheelchairs provided. ☕ refreshments to end of Sept. ☎ *Stratford upon Avon* (0789) 840277	Midland Red 518, Stratford–Warwick–Leamington–Coventry (*alight entrance*)
COUGHTON COURT, Alcester *map 3 E* *The National Trust* Central gatehouse 1509. Two mid-Elizabethan half-timbered wings. Jacobite relics. The home of the Throckmorton family since 1409	2 m N of Alcester just E of A435 *Stns: Redditch (6 m) (not Suns.); Wooton Wawen (6½ m) (not Suns)*	April—Sats. & Suns. also Easter Mon. & Tues. to Thurs. following Easter 2–5. May to Sept.—Weds. to Suns & Bank Hol. Mons. 2–6. Oct.—Sats. & Suns. 2–5. Adm. £1.30, Chd. 65p. Parties of 15 or more by prior arrangement 90p. No dogs. Unsuitable for wheel chairs. ☕ at the House ☎ *Alcester* (0789) 762435	Midland Red X6, 146, Birmingham–Evesham; R5, Redditch–Alcaster; 208, 228 Redditch–Stratford upon Avon (*alight Coughton Post Office, ¼ m*)
FARNBOROUGH HALL, nr Banbury *map 3 E* *The National Trust* ♧ Dates from 17th and 18th century. Terrace walk with garden temples and splendid views	6 m N of Banbury, ½ m W of A423 *Stn: Banbury (6 m)*	April to end of Sept.—Weds., Sats. & Bank Hol. Mons. 2–6. Adm. House & Grounds £1.20; Grounds (inc. Terrace Walk) 80p; Terrace Walk only 50p. Chd. half price. *No reduction for parties*. Dogs in grounds only, on leads. Wheelchair access—grounds only. No indoor photography. N.B. The tenants are responsible for the showing arrangements.	Midland Red/Oxford X59 Coventry–Banbury–Oxford (*alight Farnborough*)
HARVARD HOUSE, Stratford-upon-Avon △ *Harvard House Memorial Trust* *map 3 E* Built 1596. Home of the mother of John Harvard, founder of the American University	High Street, Stratford-upon-Avon *Stn: Strfd-u-Avon (June–Aug. only)*	April to Oct.—Weekdays 9–1, 2–6; Suns. 2–6, Nov. to March—Thurs., Fris. & Sats. 10–1, 2–4. *Closed Suns. & Christmas Eve, Christmas Day, Boxing Day & New Year's Day*. Adm. 75p, Chd. 25p.	All local services
HONINGTON HALL, Shipston-on-Stour *Sir John Wiggin, Bart.* *map 3 E* Originally built by the Parker family in 1680. Contains fine 18th century plasterwork.	10 m S of Stratford-on-Avon; ¼ m E of A34 *Stn: Moreton-in-Marsh 8 m)*	May to Sept.—Weds. & Bank Hol. Mons. 2.30–5.30. Parties at other times by appointment. Adm. £1, Chd. 50p. ☎ *Shipston-on-Stour* (0608) 61434	Oxford/Midland Red, Birmingham–Stratford-upon-Avon–Oxford
KENILWORTH CASTLE *map 3 E* *Dept. of the Environment* Massive late 12th century Keep. Gatehouse	Kenilworth *Stns: Tile Hill (¾ m) (not Suns.); Coventry or Leamington Spa (5½ m)*	All the year: March 15 to Oct. 15—Weekdays 9.30–6.30; Suns. 2–6.30. Oct. 16 to March 14—Weekdays 9.30–4; Suns. 2–4. *Closed Dec. 24, 25, 26 & Jan. 1*. Adm. 50p, Chd. (under 16) & O.A.Ps. 25p.	Valliant-Cronshaw tours from London National tours from Stockport etc. Midland Red 517, 518, 537, 582, 590 & 592 *to Clock (same journeys pass Castle)*
LORD LEYCESTER HOSPITAL *map 3 E* △ *The Governors of Lord Leycester Hospital* Group of halls and residences 1383. Chapel 1100. Various historic exhibits	W gate of Warwick (A46) *Stn: Warwick (¾ m)*	All the year—Mons. to Sats. 10–5.30 (summer) 10–4 (winter). Gate closes 15 mins. earlier. *Closed Suns., Good Friday & Christmas Day*. Adm. 75p, Chd. (under 14) 25p. Reduced terms and guides for large pre-arranged parties. Free car park ☕ (*Easter to Sept.*) ☎ *Warwick* (0926) 492797 ✕ (for booked parties)	Venture from Marble Arch tour—weekly (*April to Nov.*) Midland Red services from Birmingham, Coventry, Stratford-upon-Avon, Leamington etc. (*alight Market Place, 300 yds*)
PACKWOOD HOUSE, Hockley Heath *The National Trust* *map 3 E* ♧ Timber framed Tudor house with mid-17th century additions. Tapestry, needlework, Carolean formal garden, and yew garden of c. 1650 representing the Sermon on the Mount	2 m E of Hockley Heath (which is on A34) 11 m SE of Birmingham *Stns: Lapworth (1½ m); Dorridge (2 m); Birmingham Int. (8 m)*	April to end of Sept.—Weds. to Suns. & Bank Hol. Mons. 2–6. *Closed Good Friday*. Oct.—Sats. & Suns. 2–5. Adm. £1.30, Chd. 65p. Parties of 15 or more by prior written arrangement only 90p. Garden only 80p. No dogs. No prams in House. Wheelchair access to part of garden & ground floor (difficult). ☎ *Lapworth* (056 43) 2024	Midland Red X20 Birmingham–Stratford-upon-Avon, (*hourly*). Mid. Red/Oxford X50 Oxford–Birmingham (*alight Hockley Heath Wharf, 2 m*)

ARBURY HALL

AND LANDSCAPE GARDENS

Nuneaton, Warwickshire

Arbury has been the home of the Newdegate family since the 16th century. For a country house the Gothic architecture is unique, the original Elizabethan house being Gothicized by Sir Roger Newdigate between 1750 and 1800 under the direction of Sanderson Miller, Henry Keene and Couchman of Warwick. Beautiful plaster ceilings, pictures and fine specimens of period furniture, china and glass. Fine stable block with designs by Wren. Arbury Hall is situated in very large grounds and is about one mile from any main road. Excellent carriage drives lined with trees.

Further details from: The Administrator, Estate Office, Windmill Hill, Astley, nr. Nuneaton Warwickshire. Telephone Fillongley (0676) 40529.

OPENING TIMES OPPOSITE

Eric de Mare photograph

CHARLECOTE PARK

STRATFORD-ON-AVON, Warwickshire

THE NATIONAL TRUST

Home of Lucy family since 1247. Present house built in the 1550s and later visited by Queen Elizabeth. Park, landscaped by 'Capability' Brown, supports herds of red and fallow deer, reputedly poached by Shakespeare, and a flock of Jacob sheep first introduced in 1759. Principal rooms altered 1830 in Elizabethan Gothic style.

COUGHTON COURT

WARWICKSHIRE

THE NATIONAL TRUST

In 1409 Coughton came to the Throckmorton family by inheritance and it remained in their possession until presented to the National Trust in 1946. Distinguished throughout the centuries by a tenacious allegiance to Roman Catholicism, the Throckmortons were not directly implicated in the Gunpowder Plot, although it was in one of the rooms of the Gatehouse that the wives of the instigators awaited the result. The house contains a number of Jacobite relics.

OPENING TIMES OPPOSITE

A. F. Kersting photograph

LORD LEYCESTER HOSPITAL

WARWICK

Walter Scott photograph

In 1100 the chapel of St. James was built over the West Gate of Warwick and became the centre for the Guilds established by Royal Charter in 1383. In 1571 Robert Dudley, Earl of Leycester, founded his Hospital for twelve "poor" persons in the buildings of the Guilds, which had been dispersed in 1546. The Hospital has been run ever since for retired or disabled ex-Servicemen and their wives. The buildings have been recently restored to their original condition including the Great Hall of King James, the Guildhall (museum), the Chaplain's Hall (Queen's Own Hussars Regimental Museum) and the Brethren's Kitchen.

PACKWOOD HOUSE

HOCKLEY HEATH, WARWICKSHIRE

THE NATIONAL TRUST

Eric de Mare photograph

Dating from Henry VIII's reign Packwood was enlarged between 1660 and 1670 by John Fetherston who added the office wing. The gardens include a Carolean formal garden and a notable Yew garden.

OPENING TIMES OPPOSITE

PROPERTY (*showing map reference*)	LOCATION (*with neatest Rly. Stn.*)	OPENING TIMES AND ADMISSION CHARGES CATERING FACILITIES	COACH AND RAIL TOURS BUS SERVICES (*showing alighting points*)
WARWICKSHIRE—*continued*			
RAGLEY HALL, Alcester *map 3 E* *The Marquess of Hertford* **Built in 1680. Fine paintings, china and furniture and works of art, and a valuable library.** Gardens, park and lake. Adventure wood, country trail and picnic areas	**2 m SW of Alcester on Birmingham–Alcester–Evesham rd** (A435), 8 m from Stratford upon Avon *Stns: Stratford upon Avon (8½ m) (not Suns. April, May, Sept., Oct.); Evesham (8½ m)*	HOUSE, GARDEN & PARK: April 1 to Sept. 30—Tues., Weds., Thurs., Sats., Suns. & Bank Hol. Mons. PARK open 11–6 (also open Mons. & Fris. in July & Aug.). HOUSE & GARDEN open 1.30–5.30. Adm.: Park with Adventure Wood & Country Trail £1, Chd. 50p. House, Garden & Park £2, Chd., O.A.Ps. & coach parties of 30 or more £1. Free car park. Dogs welcome on leads in park— *not in House, Garden or Adventure Wood.* Coach parties welcome at any time during the year by arrangement. Great Hall available for special functions throughout the year. Member of S.C.A.T.A. (Shakespeare Country Association of Tourist Attractions). For further information contact: The Marquess of Hertford, Ragley Hall, Alcester, Warwickshire. ☎ *Alcester* (0789) 762090 *or* 762455 ✕ ☕ Licensed coffee shop open 12.30 (advance booking essential except in July & Aug.). Lunches & teas—parties please write for menus.	Barton, Skills and National tours from **Nottingham** &c. National tours from Oxford, Gloucester, **Cheltenham**, Northampton, Stratford, Stoke, **Stockport etc.** York Bros. from Northampton **Mid. Red 148, 348, Birmingham–Evesham**
SHAKESPEARE'S BIRTHPLACE TRUST PROPERTIES—SEE PAGE 142			
STONELEIGH ABBEY, Kenilworth *map 3 E* *The Rt. Hon. The Lord Leigh* The Georgian mansion, originally a Cistercian Abbey, has now been restored following the disastrous fire in 1960. All four wings are reopening to visitors and include the family's private quarters and Chapel not previously shown. Children's Playground. Model Railway	3 m E of Kenilworth; 6 m S of Coventry; 5 m N of Leamington Spa; 6 m NE of Warwick; 1½ m S of Stoneleigh Village, via B4115 & A444. *Stns: Coventry (6 m); Leamington Spa (5m)*	April 22 to June 28 & Sept. 1 to 30—Suns., Mons. & Thurs. July 8 to Aug. 24—Suns., Mons., Weds. & Thurs. House 1–5.30. Gardens, Park, Woodlands 11.30–5.30. Adm. House, Gardens, Park & Woodlands £2.20, Chd. £1.10. Coach parties of 30 or more, booked in advance, £1.10. Gardens, Park & Woodlands only £1.10, Chd. 55p. Picnic areas.	Midland Red services via A444

STONELEIGH ABBEY

Kenilworth

RE-OPENING TO VISITORS IN 1984

Stoneleigh Abbey has been described as the grandest, most dramatic Georgian mansion of Warwickshire. But originally it was a Cistercian Abbey and one of the great attractions of the House is the interlocking of periods.

The colossal West Wing, so badly damaged by the disastrous fire and water—(a gravity fed tank in the roof burst due to the heat)—in the early hours of May 5th 1960, so dominates the building that it is difficult to realise that it is only one side, albeit the largest of the quadrangle of buildings surrounding what was the Cloister Garth of the Abbey.

Since the fire in 1960 Stoneleigh Abbey has been closed to visitors but having recently undergone a near £1,000,000 restoration Lord Leigh is now re-opening all four wings, including the family's private quarters in the East Wing and the family Chapel in the South Wing, not previously open for public viewing.

Other changes include a Children's Playground; Miniature Steam Railway; picnics in the Park and Grove Wood, overlooking the Abbey.

For further information and details contact The Administrator, Telephone Kenilworth (0926) 52116

PROPERTY (*showing map reference*)	LOCATION (*with nearest Rly. Stn.*)	OPENING TIMES AND ADMISSION CHARGES CATERING FACILITIES	COACH AND RAIL TOURS BUS SERVICES (*showing alighting points*)

WARWICKSHIRE—*continued*

SHAKESPEARE'S BIRTHPLACE TRUST PROPERTIES, Stratford-upon-Avon *map* 3 *E*

INCLUSIVE TICKET ADMITTING TO ALL FIVE PROPERTIES £3, CHD. £1.25

▲SHAKESPEARE'S BIRTHPLACE, Henley Street	The half-timbered house where Shakespeare was born, containing many rare Shakespearian exhibits, also B.B.C. Costume Exhibition	*April to October*—Weekdays 9–6 (9–5 Oct.); Sundays 10–6 (10–5 Oct.) *November to March*—Weekdays 9–4.30; Suns. 1.30–4.30. Adm. £1·10, Chd. 35p; Adm. inc. Exhibition £1.35, Chd. 50p
▲ANNE HATHAWAY'S COTTAGE, Shottery (1 mile)	The picturesque thatched home of Anne Hathaway before her marriage to Shakespeare	*April to October*—Weekdays 9–6 (9–5 Oct.); Sundays 10–6 (10–5 Oct.); *November to March*—Weekdays 9–4.30; Suns. 1.30–4.30. Adm. £1, Chd. 35p
▲HALL'S CROFT, in Old Town	A fine Tudor house complete with period furniture and walled garden where Shakespeare's daughter Susanna and Dr. John Hall lived	*April to October*—Weekdays 9–6 (9–5 Oct.); Sundays 2–6 (2–5 Oct.); *November to March*—Weekdays only 9–4. Adm. 75p, Chd. 25p
▲MARY ARDEN'S HOUSE, Wilmcote (3 miles)	The Tudor farmhouse where Shakespeare's mother lived, with a farming museum in the barns. Interesting dovecote	*April to October*—Weekdays 9–6 (9–5 Oct.); Sundays 2–6 (2–5 Oct.); *November to March*—Weekdays only 9–4. Adm. 75p, Chd. 25p
▲NEW PLACE, Chapel Street	Foundations of Shakespeare's last home, preserved in an Elizabethan garden setting with Nash's House adjoining	*April to October*—Weekdays 9–6 (9–5 Oct.); Sundays 2–6 (2–5 Oct.); *November to March*—Weekdays only 9–4. Adm. 75p, Chd. 25p

Inclusive adm. for School parties £1—College & University student parties £1.30

All properties closed Good Friday a.m., Christmas Eve, Christmas Day & Boxing Day

UPTON HOUSE, Edge Hill *map* 3 *E* ▲ *The National Trust* Fine collection paintings, porcelain. Tapestries. Beautiful terraced gardens	1 m S of Edge Hill, 7 m NW of Banbury on the Stratford rd (A422)	April to end of Sept.—Mons. (inc. Bank Hols.) to Thurs. 2–6. Also Sats. & Suns. May 5/6, 12/13; July 28/29; Aug. 4/5, 11/12, 18/19. Last adm. to House 5.30). *Closed Good Friday*. Adm. House & Grounds 1.60, Chd. 80p. Grounds only 75p. Parties of 15 or more (except weekends & Bank Hols.) by prior arrangement with the Estate Office, £1.10. No indoor photography. Dogs in garden only, on leads. Wheelchairs provided ☎ *Edge Hill* 266	National tours from Birmingham & Midlands Midland Red 210, 211, Kineton–Banbury, connections from Leamington Spa (*infrequent, alight House or bottom of Sunrising Hill,* 1*m —service* 210)
WARWICK CASTLE, Warwick *map* 3 *E* ▲ One of the finest inhabited medieval castles, standing on a steep rock cliff beside the River Avon, 8 miles from Stratford. The present castle is a fine example of 14th century fortification with towers and dungeons open to visitors all the year round. The State Rooms contain a magnificent collection of pictures by Rubens, Van Dyck and other Masters. Surrounded by acres of parkland landscaped by 'Capability' Brown, gardens where peacocks roam freely and a river island.	In the centre of Warwick *Stn: Warwick* (¼ *m*) *Leamington Spa* (1½ *m*)	Open daily (except Christmas Day) all year. March 1 to Oct. 31—Daily 10–5.30. Nov. 1 to Feb. 29—Daily 10–4.30. Admission charges not available at time of going to press. Car park. ✕ ☕ Licensed restaurant & cafeteria in the Castle. Medieval Banquets ☎ *Warwick* (0926) 45421	Frames tour from London Rickards tours from London—daily (*April to Oct.*); weekly (*Oct. to March*). National tour from London Valiant Cronshaw tour from London weekly Frequent Midland Red Services from Coventry, Leamington & Stratford-on-Avon Midland Red 587 from Birmingham; X91 Hereford–Worcester–Warwick–Leicester National tours from Cheltenham, Stockport etc. Britain Shrinkers from London Evan Evans from London Cooks tour from London

WEST MIDLANDS

ASBURY COTTAGE, Great Barr, *map* 3 *E* *Metro, Borough of Sandwell* The home of Francis Asbury, first Bishop of the American Methodist Church, who lived in the cottage from 1746 to 1771. Restored and furnished in period style.	In Newton Rd, 3 m NE from centre of W. Bromwich on A4041; exit M6 at jct. 7. *Stn: Hamstead* (2*m*)	All the year—Daily. Mons. to Fris. 2-4. Other times by appointment. *Closed Good Friday*. Adm. free ☎ 021-569 2325 *or* 021-556 0683	*Bus:* 452, 453 from West Bromwich Stn. (*alight Malt Shovel Inn*)
ASTON HALL, Birmingham *map* 3 *E* ▲ *Birmingham Metropolitan District Council* A fine Jacobean house built 1618–35 with Ⓔ Many rooms furnished as period settings. A branch of Birmingham Museums and Art Gallery	2½ m from centre of city. Entrance for coaches at Frederick Rd.; entrance for cars at Witton Lane. *Stns: Aston* (¾ *m*); *Birmingham New St.*	Easter to late Oct.—Mons. to Sats. 10–5; Suns. 2–5. Limited winter opening (details not available). *Closed Christmas Day, Boxing Day, New Year's Day & Good Friday*. Adm. (1982 rates subject to alteration) 50p, Chd. & O.A.Ps. 25p. School parties & Friends of the Museum adm. free. ☎ 021-327 0062	West Midland Transport 7 from City Centre; 11 Outer Circle Route
BADDESLEY CLINTON, Solihull *map* 3 *E* *The National Trust* A medieval moated manor house, with 120 acres, dating back to 1300 and little changed since 1634.	¾ m W of A41 Warwick to B'ham road, nr Chadwick End; 6 m N of Warwick; 11 m SE of Birmingham. *Stns: Lapworth* (2 *m*) (*not Suns.*); *Berkswell* (6 *m*) (*not Suns.*); *B'ham International* (9 *m*)	April to end of Sept.—Weds. to Suns. & Bank Hol. Mons. 2–6. *Closed Good Friday*. Oct.—Sats. & Suns. 2–5. Adm. £1.40, Chd. 70p. Parties by prior appointment only 95p. No coach parties. No prams or pushchairs in the house. No dogs. Wheelchair provided. Shop. N.B.—*Owing to large numbers visiting Baddesley Clinton entry to the house is by timed numbered ticket; the waiting period may be spent in the garden.* ☎ *Lapworth* (056 43) 3294	
BLAKESLEY HALL, Birmingham *map* 3 *E* *Birmingham Metropolitan District Council* A timber-framed yeoman's farmhouse c. 1575 with some rooms furnished as period settings and displays of local history material. A branch of Birmingham Museums and Art Gallery	3 m from city centre; ent. in Blakesley Rd. *Stns:Stechford* (¾*m*); *Birmingham New St.*	All the year—Mons. to Sats. 10–5; Suns. 2–5. *Closed Christmas Day(Boxing Day, New Year's Day & Good Friday*. Adm. (1983 rates) 30p, Chd. & O.A.Ps. 15p. School parties & Friends of the Museums & Art Gallery adm. free. ☎ 021-783 2193	West Midlands Transport 16, 17, 68 from City Centre; 11 Outer Circle route

ASTON HALL

Built between 1618 and 1635 by Sir Thomas Holte, Aston Hall is one of the most complete Jacobean houses in the country.
Information: 021-327 0062.

BLAKESLEY HALL

A timber-framed yeoman's farmhouse, c.1575, giving an insight into Birmingham's unexpected rural past.
Information: 021-783 2193.

BIRMINGHAM'S HISTORIC HOUSES

Near Stourbridge **HAGLEY HALL** West Midlands

The ruined castle, built in 1740 from stones from Halesowen Abbey.

Home of Viscount and Viscountess Cobham, Hagley Hall was designed by Sanderson Miller for George 1st Baron Lyttelton.

- Licensed Restaurant in the House serving lunches and teas.
- Receptions and private dinner parties by arrangement throughout the year.
- The attractive classical park frequently hosts exciting weekend events.
- Open for prebooked parties by arrangement throughout the year.

Opening dates: Bank Holiday Sundays and Mondays from Easter Sunday
Daily 1st July - 2nd September except Saturdays
12.30 - 5.00 pm

Enquiries: The Secretary, Hagley Hall, Near Stourbridge, West Midlands. Telephone Hagley (0562) 882408.

The House contains the finest examples of Italian Rococo plaster work by Francesco Vassali and a unique collection of 18th Century furniture and family portraits including works by Van Dyck, Reynolds and Lely.

MOSELEY OLD HALL

WOLVERHAMPTON

THE NATIONAL TRUST

This house in which King Charles II sheltered after the battle of Worcester has the bed in which he slept and the "hide" he used. There is a collection of furniture of that period and documents, portraits and other relics relating to the Whitgreave family, who sheltered the king, and to his flight. A formal garden, planted in the 17th century style, adds much charm to the property.
Parties should book in advance.

OPENING TIMES OPPOSITE

OAK HOUSE

WEST BROMWICH

A delightful example of a Tudor yeoman's house with a unique lantern tower. There is some fine Jacobean oak panelling and carving and an excellent collection of 16th to early 18th century furniture.

Open Weekdays 10–8 (April to September), 10–4 (October to March); Sundays (summer only) 2.30–8; closed Thursday afternoons. Admission free.

Only 10 mins. from M5.

WIGHTWICK MANOR **near WOLVERHAMPTON**

THE NATIONAL TRUST

Morris wallpapers, tapestrie, curtains, embroidery etc.

Pre-Raphaelite pictures by Rossetti, Burne - Jones, Madox - Brown, Millais.

Tiles by de Morgan.

Stained glass by Kempe.

Trees planted by famous personalities.

The home of Lady Mander.

Tel. Wolverhampton (0902) 761108.

A fine example of the William Morris revolution in interior decoration

All the year (except February) Thurs., Sats. & Bank Hol. Suns. & Mons. 2.30 p.m.–5.30 p.m.

Also open for pre-booked parties only Weds. 2.30–5.30 and Weds. & Thurs. evenings from May to September. Pre-booked school & student tours Weds. & Thurs. mornings & afternoons all year.

Closed Feb. & Dec. 25, 26, Jan. 1 & 2

Adm. £1.40 (Sat. afternoons £2.00 when extra rooms shown—no children under 10. *No extra rooms shown at Bank Hol. weekends.*); Students 60p; Gardens only 60p.

Parties must book in advance (no reductions).

No unaccompanied children.

Photography by permisison only.

WEST MIDLANDS—*continued*

PROPERTY (*showing map reference*)	LOCATION (*with nearest Rly. Stn.*)	OPENING TIMES AND ADMISSION CHARGES CATERING FACILITIES	COACH AND RAIL TOURS BUS SERVICES (*showing alighting points*)
HAGLEY HALL, nr Stourbridge *map 2 H* *The Viscount & Viscountess Cobham* ©The last of the great Palladian Houses, designed by Sanderson Miller and completed in 1760. Superb Italian plasterwork and the fine Lyttelton collection of 18th century paintings and furniture.	Just off A456 B'ham to Kidderminster; 12 m from B'ham within easy reach M5/M6 *Stns: Hagley (1 m) (not Suns.); Stourbridge Jct. (2 m)*	Bank Hol. Suns. & Mons. from April 22 (Easter) then July 1 to Sept. 2—Daily (except Sats.) 12.30–5. Adm. £1.50, Chd. 75p, O.A.Ps. £1.25. lunch & tea available in the House ☎ *Hagley* (0562) 882408	Midland Red buses from Birmingham, Kidderminster, Ludlow, Worcester, Stourbridge, Bromsgrove, Redditch to Hagley
Δ**MOSELEY OLD HALL, Wolverhampton** *The National Trust* *map 2 H* An Elizabethan house, formerly half-timbered, a refuge of Charles II after the battle of Worcester. Reproduction 17th century box ©parterre; period plants	4 m N of Wolverhampton, mid-way between A449 & A460 rds. Off M6 at Shareshill then via A460 *Stn: Wolverhampton (4 m)*	March & Nov.—Weds. & Suns. 2–6. April to end of Oct.—Weds., Thurs., Sats. & Suns. 2–6 (or dusk if earlier); Easter, Spring & Summer Bank Hol. Mons. & Tues. following 2–6. Adm. £1.20, Chd. 60p. Pre-booked school parties 40p. *Parties at other times except Mons. & Fris.) by prior arrangement.* No dogs. Wheelchair access. at the House ☎ *Wolverhampton* (0902) 782808	Midland Red 872, Wolverhampton–Cannock (*alight Bognop Road, 1 m*) Midland Red 876, Wolverhampton–Stafford; West Midlands 503, Wolverhampton–Fordhouses (*alight Fordhouse, 2 m*)
OAK HOUSE, West Bromwich *map 3 E* *Metro. Borough of Sandwell* The house is a delightful example of Tudor domestic architecture with Jacobean additions. The rooms contain some fine oak panelling and carving and an excellent collection of period furniture and furnishings. The house is set in a public park with Elizabethan style garden at the front	In Oak Rd ½ m from centre of West Bromwich & A41	April to September—Mons. to Sats. 10–8 (except Thurs. 10–1); Suns. 2.30–8. October to March—Mons. to Sats. 10–4. Adm. Free ☎ 021-553-0759 in Central West Bromwich	West Midlands Transport on A41 from Birmingham Dudley and Wolverhampton (*alight West Bromwich Town Hall ½ m*)
Δ**WIGHTWICK MANOR, Wolverhampton** *The National Trust* *map 2 H* William Morris period house. Garden of varied interest	3 m W of Wolverhampton, up Wightwick Bank (A454)	All the year (except Feb.)—Thurs. Sats. & Bank Hol. Suns. & Mons. 2.30–5.30. Also open for pre-booked parties only May to end of Sept.—Weds. 2.30–5.30 and Weds. & Thurs. evenings. Pre-booked school & student tours Weds. & Thurs. all year mornings & afternoons. *Closed Dec. 25, 26, Jan. 1, 2 & Feb.* Adm. £1.40 (Sat. afternoons extra rooms shown—£2; *no extra rooms shown at Bank Hol. weekends*). Chd. half-price. Students 60p. Gardens only 60p. *Parties must book in advance (no reductions).* No unaccompanied children. Photography by permission only. Dogs in garden only, on leads.	West Midlands 516, Wolverhampton–Pattingham; Midland Red 890, Wolverhampton-Bridgenorth (*alight Mermaid Inn*)

WEST SUSSEX (*see also East Sussex*)

PROPERTY (*showing map reference*)	LOCATION (*with nearest Rly. Stn.*)	OPENING TIMES AND ADMISSION CHARGES CATERING FACILITIES	COACH AND RAIL TOURS BUS SERVICES (*showing alighting points*)
ARUNDEL CASTLE, Arundel *map 3 P* *Arundel Castle Trustees Ltd.* Ancient castle rebuilt 18th century and altered 1890. Fine portraits and furniture dating from the 16th century. Also Fitzalan Chapel.	In Arundel, 9 m W of Worthing, 10 m E of Chichester Entrance for cars & pedestrians: Lower Lodge, Mill Rd *Stn: Arundel (½ m)*	April 1 to Oct. 26—Suns. to Fris. 1–5 (during June, July & Aug. and all Bank Hols. 12–5). Last admission any day 4 p.m. *The Castle is NOT open on Sats.* Adm. charges not available at time of going to press. No dogs. *Special rates for organised parties.* ☎ *Arundel* 883136	National tours from London and from South Coast resorts Southdown from Brighton, Worthing, Littlehampton, Chichester and Bognor. For times and fares enquire at any Southdown office Pilchers Coaches from the Medway Towns
BORDE HILL GARDEN, Haywards Heath *map 6 C* Large garden with woods and parkland of exceptional beauty. Rare trees and shrubs, herbaceous borders and fine views. Recent developments include a Woodland Walk, a water feature and the West Bank terrace.	1½ m N of Haywards Heath on Balcombe Rd. Brighton 17 m London 40 m, Gatwick 10 m *Stn: Haywards Heath (1½ m)*	March—Sats. & Suns.; April to Sept.—Weds., Thurs., Sats., Suns. & all Bank Hols.; Oct.—Sats. & Suns.: 10–6. Adm. £1, Chd. 50p; pre-booked parties of 20 or more 60p. Parking free. Delightful picnic area. Unusual plants for sale. Licensed—morning coffee, snacks, afternoon tea ☎ *Haywards Heath* (0444) 450326	Frequent fast train service from London (*Victoria*), Gatwick and Brighton (*alight Haywards Heath, 1½ m*)
CHRIST'S HOSPITAL, Horsham *map 6 C* *The Governors of Christ's Hospital* Painting by Antonio Verrio (c. 1639–1707) "The Foundation of the Royal Mathematical School of Christ's Hospital." The canvas (85 ft. by 14ft) hangs in the School dining hall	3 m SW of Horsham off A24 *Stn: Christ's Hospital*	April 28; May 2, 5, 12, 16, 19, 23; June 6, 9, 13, 16, 20, 27, 30; July 4; September 29; October 6, 10, 13, 17. *By appointment with the School Secretary.* Adm. £1.50. Free car park. No dogs. tea (50p) ☎ *Horsham* 52547	Southdown 294, Horsham–Storrington (*alight gates*)
COATES MANOR, nr Fittleworth *map 3 P* *Mrs. G. H. Thorp* One acre garden, mainly shrubs and foliage of special interest.	½ m S of Fittleworth, SE of Petworth; turn off B2138 sign-posted 'Coates' *Stn: Pulborough (3 m)*	GARDEN ONLY—Sun., Mon. & Tues. June 24, 25 & 26: 11–6. Adm. 40p, Chd. 20p. *In aid of National Gardens Scheme & Gardeners' Benevolent Fund* morning coffee, tea & cakes	Southdown 201, Worthing–Pulborough–Petworth–Midhurst (*alight Fittleworth, 1 m*)
COKE'S COTTAGE, West Burton *map 3 P* *Mrs. Nigel Azis* Cottage garden; bulbs, shrubs, mixed borders, roses; gravelled areas; orchard and vegetable garden.	5 m SW of Pulborough; W of A29 *Stn: Amberley (3 m)*	GARDEN ONLY: Suns. & Mons.—April 8/9 & 15/16: 2–5; May 6/7: 2–6; June 9 (Sat.)/10/11, 17/18 & 24/25: 2–7. Adm. 40p, Chd. 10p. *In aid of National Gardens' Scheme.* No dogs.	

ARUNDEL CASTLE WEST SUSSEX

Ancestral home of the Dukes of Norfolk

Home of the Dukes of Norfolk and their ancestors for over 700 years, Arundel Castle was built in or before the reign of Edward the Confessor. It occupies a commanding position overlooking the River Arun and surrounding countryside. Contains furniture from the 16th century and portraits by Van Dyck, Gainsborough, Reynolds, Mytens, Lawrence etc.

BORDE HILL GARDEN

HAYWARDS HEATH, Sussex

Home of Mr. & Mrs. Robert N. Stephenson Clarke

Over 40 acres of garden and woodland of great botanical interest, with a unique collection of rare trees and shrubs. Magnolias, rhododendrons, azaleas and camellias in spring and early summer and a wide range of other plants, make this a delightful garden to visit at all times of the year.

OPENING TIMES ABOVE

PROPERTY (*showing map reference*)	LOCATION (*with nearest Rly. Stn.*)	OPENING TIMES AND ADMISSION CHARGES CATERING FACILITIES	COACH AND RAIL TOURS BUS SERVICES (*showing alighting points*)
WEST SUSSEX—*continued*			
DANNY, Hurstpierpoint *map 3 P* *Mutual Households Association* Elizabethan E-shaped house, dating from 1593	Between Hassocks and Hurstpierpoint *Stn: Hassocks (1 m)*	May to September—Weds. & Thurs. 2–5 Adm. 50p, Chd. 25p Free car park. No dogs admitted	National Coach 064 London–Brighton; Southdown 173, Brighton–Haywards Heath also) Hassocks–Hurstpierpoint (connections from Brighton) (*alight College Lane, Hurstpierpoint, ¼ m*)
DENMANS, Fontwell *map 3 P* *Mrs. J. H. Robinson* Walled gardens extravagantly planted for overall, all year interest in form, colour and texture. School of Garden Design in adjacent Clock House	Between Arundel & Chichester; turn off A27 into Denmans Lane (W of Fontwell racecourse) *Stn: Barnham (2 m)*	GARDENS ONLY: March 31 to Oct. 28—Sats. & Suns. 2–6. Other days by appointment only. Adm. 75p. Plants for sale. *No dogs please.*	Southdown 266, Chichester–Walberton (*alight Fontwell*)
GOODWOOD HOUSE, Chichester *map 3 P* *Goodwood Estate Company Ltd.* Home of the Dukes of Richmond since 1697 and of their Collections of artistic and historical treasures, some dating from before the birth of the first Duke to King Charles II's French Mistress, some brought back from her Chateau of Aubigny. Chambers, then Wyatt, enlarged the House to hold these Collections. Country Park near Racecourse on crest of South Downs. (See display advertisement).	3½ m NE of Chichester, approach rds A285 & A286 A27 Airfield 1 m from house *Stn: Chichester (3½ m)*	Easter Sun. & Mon., then May 6 to October 8—Suns. & Mons. (except Sept. 17 & Oct. 1 and event days); also Tues., Weds. & Thurs. in August (*except Aug. 1 & 2*): 2–5 *For all information & group rates contact the House Secretary, Goodwood House, Chichester, West Sussex.* ☕ teas in State Supper Room for pre-booked parties only (min. 20); unbooked teas are served at the Richmond Arms Hotel which has recently returned to Goodwood ownership. Located at the Park gate (East) the hotel has ample parking space ☎ *Chichester* (0243) 774107	*Bus:* 268, 269 dep. Chichester Bus Stn. arr./dep Richmond Arms Hotel (at Goodwood Pk. gates.—*Weekdays only* (*not Suns.*) Check with Bus Stn. for timetable. ☎ *Chichester* (0243) 783251
HEASELANDS, Haywards Heath *map 3 P* *Mrs. Ernest Kleinwort* Over 30 acres of garden with flowering shrubs and trees; water gardens; woodland; aviary and small collection of waterfowl	1 m SW of Haywards Heath Hospital on A273 to Burgess Hill *Stn: Haywards Heath (1½ m)*	GARDEN ONLY: Weds.—May 9, 16 & 23; Suns.—May 13, 20 & 27 also July 22: 2–6.30. Parties by arrangement for Autumn colour. Adm. £1, Chd. 25p. Cars free. *In aid of National Gardens' Scheme and World Wildlife.* Coaches by appointment. *No dogs.* ☕ at the House.	Southdown, 161, 162, Haywards Heath–Cuckfield (*not Suns.*) (*alight Butler's Green, Heaselands 1 m*)
THE HIGH BEECHES, Handcross *map 6 C* *Hon. Edward Boscawen* 16 acres woodland gardens. Spring and autumn colour. Water gardens. Landscaped picnic area.	1 m E of Handcross on B2110 *Stn: Balcombe (2 m)*	GARDENS ONLY—Bank Hol. Mons., April 4 May 2 & 30; Sun., Oct. 23: 10–5. All the year for parties of 20 or more, by appointment, £1.20.	No reasonable public transport
LEONARDSLEE, Horsham *map 6 C* *The Loder Family* Extensive spring-flowering shrub garden, valley filled with camellias, rhododendrons, lakes. Two new lakes on view for the first time. Also magnificent autumn tints	In Lower Beeding, 4½ m SE of Horsham on Horsham–Brighton rd (A281) *Stn: Horsham (4½ m)*	April 20 to June 10—Daily 10–6. *Closed during summer months.* Autumn Tints—open all Sats. & Suns. in October. Adm. £1.80, Chd. 80p. Pre-booked coach parties £1.50 (except Suns. in May when £1.80). *No dogs, please.* Plants & souvenirs. ☕ refreshments & cafeteria.	Coach tours from London & South Coast resorts Southdown 117, Horsham–Brighton
MALT HOUSE, Chithurst, nr. Midhurst *Mr. & Mrs. Graham Ferguson* *map 3 P* Approximately 4 acres; flowering shrubs, including exceptional rhododendrons and azaleas, leading to 50 acres of lovely woodland walks.	3½ m W of Midhurst via A272, turn N to Chithurst cont. 1½ m; or via A3, 2 m S of Liphook turn SE to Milland & Chithurst	GARDEN ONLY: April 22 to June 3—Suns. also Bank Hol. Mons. April 23, May 7 & 28: 2–7. Also Suns. Oct. 21 & 28: 12–4. Adm. 50p, Chd. 25p. *In aid of National Gardens' Scheme.* Also open by appointment for parties. Plants for sale ☎ *Rogate* (073 080) 433	
NEWTIMBER PLACE, Newtimber *map 3 P* *His Honour Judge & Mrs. John Clay* Moated house—Etruscan style wall paintings	1 m N of Pyecombe 7 m N of Brighton off London rd (A23)	May to August—Thurs. 2–5. Adm. 85p. ☎ *Hurstpierpoint* (0273) 833104	Southdown 107, 117, 137 Brighton–Horsham
NYMANS GARDEN, Handcross *map 6 C* *The National Trust* Extensive garden, partly enclosed by walls, with exceptional collection of rare trees, shrubs and plants, herbaceous borders, bulbs. Exhibition on the history of the garden	At Handcross just off London–Brighton M23/A23 *Stns: Balcombe (4½ m); Crawley (5½ m); Haywards Heath (6½ m); Horsham (7 m)*	Garden only April to end of Oct.—Daily (except Mons. & Fris.) 11–6 or sunset if earlier. Open Bank Hol. Mons. Last adm. 1 hour before closing. Adm. £1.20, Chd. 60p. Parties of 15 or more (90p) any day by prior arrangement with Head Gardener. No dogs. Wheelchair provided. Shop. ☕	National tour from London National Coach 064 London–Brighton; Southdown 173, Brighton–Haywards Heath–Crawley (*not Suns.*); 773, Brighton–Crawley direct (*Mons. to Fris.*). London Country 475, Crawley–Handcross (*Mons. to Fris*).
PARHAM, Pulborough *map 3 P* Fine gardens of Elizabethan Mansion include a beautiful 4-acre walled garden with herbaceous borders, herb garden and orchard. Also an 18th century garden with fine trees, statuary and lake.	4 m SE of Pulborough on the Storrington rd (A283), *Stn: Pulborough (4 m)*	GARDENS ONLY: April 1 to Oct. 1—Sats., Suns., Weds., Thurs. & Bank Hol. Mons. 1–6. Adm. £1, Chd. 60p, O.A.Ps. 75p. Booked parties of 25 or more 60p per person. Suitable for wheelchairs. Coach park. Picnic area (available from 12 noon). HOUSE OPEN BY APPOINTMENT ONLY. ☎ *Storrington* (090 66) 2866	No reasonable public transport
PETWORTH HOUSE, Petworth *map 6 C* ***The National Trust*** Rebuilt 1688–96 by the 6th Duke of Somerset. Later reconstruction by Salvin, in large and beautiful deer park, landscaped by 'Capability' Brown and painted by Turner. 14th century chapel. Important collection of paintings, sculpture and furniture	In centre of Petworth 5½ m E of Midhurst *Stn: Pulborough (5½ m)*	April to end of Oct.—Weds., Thurs., Sats., Suns. & Bank Hol. Mons. 2–6 (last adm. 5.30). Adm. £1.80, Chd. 90p. Pre-booked parties of 15 or more welcome all open days—reduction (£1.50) Weds., Thurs. & Sats. only. Connoisseurs' Day (open to all, extra rooms shown): Tues. (*except Tues. following Bank Hol. Mons.*) 2–6 Adm. £2.20, Chd. £1.10. No dogs in House or Pleasure Grounds. Car park for visitors to House during open hours, through Grand Entrance Gate. Shop. Wheelchairs provided. No prams or pushchairs in showrooms. Deer Park open daily all year 9-sunset, adm. free. Car park for Park only on A283, 1½ m N of Petworth. Dogs must be kept under control ☎ *Petworth* 42207 ☕ tea room in House on open days, 2.30–5.30.	National tours from Coastal towns Southdown 201, Worthing–Petworth–Midhurst; 295 Petworth–Horsham (*not Suns.*)

NYMANS GARDEN

HANDCROSS, WEST SUSSEX

THE NATIONAL TRUST

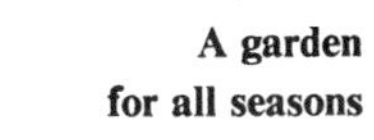
A garden for all seasons

30 acres of rare and beautiful plants from all over the world. Illustrated leaflets on sale for Spring, Summer and Autumn Garden walks.

Open:
April to end of October: Daily (except Mons. and Fris.) 11–6 or sunset if earlier. Open Bank Hol. Mons. Adults £1.20, Children half-price. Shop and Teas.

S. of Crawley, just off London-Brighton road (M23/A23)

PETWORTH HOUSE

WEST SUSSEX

THE NATIONAL TRUST

Petworth House, dating mainly from the late 17th century and with some alterations 200 years later to the designs of Anthony Salvin, has been the home of the Percy, Seymour and Wyndham families. It contains one of the largest and finest collections of pictures in the country, and remarkable examples of the work of Grinling Gibbons. Overlooking one of the most beautiful parks in England, a park that 'Capability' Brown landscaped, and Turner painted. An archive room has recently been opened in the house.

GOODWOOD HOUSE

Near Chichester, West Sussex

Ducal Treasure House

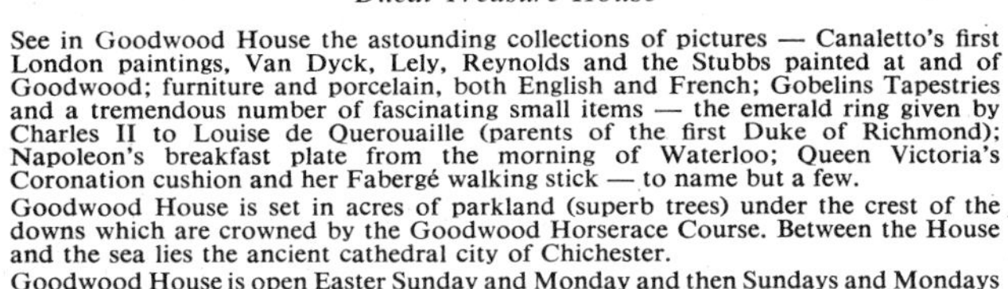
See in Goodwood House the astounding collections of pictures — Canaletto's first London paintings, Van Dyck, Lely, Reynolds and the Stubbs painted at and of Goodwood; furniture and porcelain, both English and French; Gobelins Tapestries and a tremendous number of fascinating small items — the emerald ring given by Charles II to Louise de Querouaille (parents of the first Duke of Richmond); Napoleon's breakfast plate from the morning of Waterloo; Queen Victoria's Coronation cushion and her Fabergé walking stick — to name but a few.
Goodwood House is set in acres of parkland (superb trees) under the crest of the downs which are crowned by the Goodwood Horserace Course. Between the House and the sea lies the ancient cathedral city of Chichester.
Goodwood House is open Easter Sunday and Monday and then Sundays and Mondays 6 May to 8 October 2-5 p.m. plus Tuesdays, Wednesdays and Thursdays in August (*except* event days).

Contact: The House Secretary, tel. Chichester (0243) 774107

PARHAM

PULBOROUGH,

WEST SUSSEX

FOR OPENING DETAILS OF GARDENS SEE OPPOSITE

SACKVILLE COLLEGE

EAST GRINSTEAD

C. Crosthwaite photograph

Lovely old Jacobean almshouses—East Grinstead's showpiece—founded by Robert Sackville, 2nd Earl of Dorset, in 1609. Common Room, Chapel, Dining Hall, the study of the Rev. John Mason Neale, Warden 1846-1866; original furniture, arms. Open from May 1st to September 30th every day from 2 p.m.–5 p.m. Admission: Adults 50p, Children 25p.

WEST SUSSEX—*continued*

PROPERTY (*showing map reference*)	LOCATION (*with nearest Rly. Stn.*)	OPENING TIMES AND ADMISSION CHARGES CATERING FACILITIES	COACH AND RAIL TOURS BUS SERVICES (*showing alighting points*)
SACKVILLE COLLEGE, East Grinstead *Earl de la Warr* *map* **6** *C* Jacobean almshouses, founded in 1609. Common room, Chapel, Dining Hall and Study. Original furniture.	High St., on main rd thro E. Grinstead *Stn: East Grinstead*	May 1 to Sept. 30—Daily, 2–5. Adm. 50p, Chd. 25p. Suitable in part for disabled.	Local bus service (*alight at College*)
ST. ROCHE'S ARBORETUM, nr Chichester *E. F. W. James, Esq.* *map* 3 *P* Rare trees and shrubs.	5 m N of Chichester at Singleton Hill, West Dean *Stn: Chichester (6 m)*	ARBORETUM ONLY: April 30 to May 6—Daily; June 4 to 10—Daily; also Sun. Oct. 28: 12–5. Adm. 50p, Chd. 30p. *In aid of National Gardens' Scheme.* No dogs.	
STANDEN, East Grinstead *map* 6 *C* *The National Trust* Built 1894 by Philip Webb. William Morris wallpapers and textiles. Period furniture, paintings. Hillside garden with fine views across Medway Valley	1½ m S of East Grinstead signposted from the Turners Hill rd (B2110) *Stn: E. Grinstead (2 m)*	April to end of Oct.—Weds., Thurs., Sats. & Suns. 2–5.30 (last adm. 5). Adm. £1.50; Garden only 75p. Chd. half-price. Pre-booked parties £1.20 Weds. & Thurs. only; telephone Custodian-in-Charge. *Dogs admitted to garden only, must be on leads.* Wheelchairs provided; disabled drivers may park near house. shop. ☎ *East Grinstead* (0342) 23029	London Country 474 from East Grinstead or Crawley (*not Suns.*) (*alight Saint Hill*)
UPPARK, South Harting, nr Petersfield *The National Trust* *map* 3 *P* Romantic house (1690), high on the Downs. Interior decoration and furnishings virtually unaltered since 1750. Victorian kitchen with original fittings. Queen Anne dolls' house. Small garden landscaped by Humphrey Repton	5 m SE of Petersfield entrance on E side of South Harting-Emsworth rd(B2146) *Stns: Petersfld. (5½ m); Rowland's Castle (6½ m)*	April to end of Sept.—Weds., Thurs., Suns. & Bank Hol. Mons. 2–6. Last admission 5.30 (Weds. 5). Adm. £1.50, Chd. 75p. *Reductions (£1.20) for pre-booked parties of 15 or more by arrangement with Administrator.* All visitors guided on Weds. (exc. Aug. to Sept. 12); last tour leaves at 5. Shop. No dogs. Wheelchairs provided. teas ☎ *Harting* 317 or 458	Southdown 261, 262, Midhurst–Petersfield (*alight South Harting 1¼ m, hilly approach*)
WAKEHURST PLACE GARDEN, nr Ardingly *map* 6 *C* *The National Trust (administered by Royal Botanic Gdns., Kew)* A wealth of exotic plant species including many fine specimens of trees and shrubs. Picturesque watercourse linking several ponds and lakes. Heath garden and rock walk	1½ m NW of Ardingly on B2028 *Stns: Balcombe (5 m); Haywards Heath (5½ m); East Grinstead (6½ m); Horsted Keynes (Bluebell Rly. 3¾ m)*	All the year—Daily: Jan., Nov. & Dec., 10–4; Feb. & Oct., 10–5; March, 10–6; April to end of Sept. 10–7. Last admission, ½ hr. before closing. *Closed Christmas Day & New Year's Day.* Adm. £1.25, Chd. (under 16 yrs.) 60p. Parties 80p, Chd. (under 16) 40p. N.B. Adm. charges may be subject to revision. *No dogs.* Wheelchairs provided. Exhibition in Mansion. Bookstall. Gift shop (not N.T.) open April–Oct. April to mid-Oct. ☎ *Ardingly* (0444) 892701	Southdown 171. Haywards Heath—Crawley (*Mons. to Fris. & summer Suns. only*)
THE WEALD AND DOWNLAND OPEN AIR MUSEUM, Singleton, nr Chichester *map* 3 *P* A collection of historic buildings saved from destruction, including medieval houses, farm buildings, working watermill. 40 acres of park and woodland.	6 m N of Chichester on A286 just S of Singleton *Stn: Chichester (6 m)*	April to Oct.—Daily 11–5. Nov. to March—Weds. & Suns. only 11–4. Adm. charges not available at time of going to press. Parties by arrangement ☎ *Singleton* (024 363) 348	Southdown 260, Bognor Regis–Chichester–Midhurst (connections at Midhurst to and from Petworth or Petersfield (*not Suns.*) (*alight Singleton village*)
WEST DEAN GARDENS, nr Chichester *The Edward James Foundation* *map* 3 *P* 35 acres of informal gardens, fine specimen trees; 300ft. pergola; gazebo; borders; wild garden; picnic and play area. Walled garden with Victorian glasshouses containing a collection of lawnmowers and a garden history exhibition.	6 m N of Chichester on A286, nr Weald & Downland Open Air Museum *Stn: Chichester (6m)*	April to Sept.—Daily 11–6 (last adm. 5). Adm. 85p, Chd. 50p, O.A.Ps. 75p. Parties by arrangement at reduced rates. Garden shop with a wide range of container grown plants for sale. Coach & car parking. *No dogs.* teas, refreshments & home made cakes etc. available in Orangery (afternoons)	Southdown 260, Bognor Regis–Chichester–Singleton (*not Suns.*)

WEST YORKSHIRE

(*see also North & South Yorkshire*)

PROPERTY (*showing map reference*)	LOCATION (*with nearest Rly. Stn.*)	OPENING TIMES AND ADMISSION CHARGES CATERING FACILITIES	COACH AND RAIL TOURS BUS SERVICES (*showing alighting points*)
ACKWORTH SCHOOL, Pontefract *map* 5 *D* *Co-educational Boarding School* *Society of Friends* Georgian building (1750)—only remaining building of London Foundling Hospital	3½ m S of Pontefract on A628	During School vacations—Monday to Friday 10–4 (by appointment) Adm. charges not available at time of going to press ☎ *Hemsworth* 611401	Yorks. Traction/S. Yorks Road Trans. 245 Pontefract–Hemsworth–Barnsley (*passes School*) West Riding 248 Pontefract–Upton (*passes school*) 485 Doncaster–Wakefield
BANKFIELD MUSEUM, Halifax *map* 5 *C* *Calderdale Borough Council* Early 19th century stone mansion. Collections of costumes and fabrics. Military display, Natural History and temporary exhibitions	½ m NE of Halifax on Halifax–Queensbury rd. (A647)	Mons. to Sats. 10–5: Suns. 2.30–5.	Metro Calderdale 576, Halifax–Bradford
BOLLING HALL, Bradford *map* 5 *C* *Bradford Metro. Council* Furnished Manor House built between the 15th and 18th centuries	Bowling Hall Road, Bradford BD4 7LP	All the year—Daily (except Mons. but open Bank Hol Mons.) 10–5. *Closed Christmas Day, Boxing Day & Good Friday.* Adm. free (Public Museum). ☎ *Bradford* 723057	Metro Bradford 621 from Bus Interchange
BRAMHAM PARK, Wetherby *map* 5 *C* *Mr & Mrs George Lane-Fox* The house was created during the first half of the 18th century and affords a rare opportunity to enjoy a beautiful Queen Anne mansion containing fine furniture, pictures and porcelain—set in magnificent grounds with ornamental ponds, cascades, tall beech hedges and loggias of various shapes—unique in the British Isles for its grand vistas design stretching out into woodlands of cedar, copper beech, lime and Spanish chestnut interspersed with wild rhododendron thickets	5 m S of Wetherby on the Great North Road (A1)	GROUNDS ONLY: Easter weekend (April 21/22 23); Spring Bank Hol. weekend (May 26/27/28). HOUSE & GROUNDS: June 10 to Aug. 30—Suns., Tues., Weds. & Thurs. also Bank Hol. Mon. (Aug. 27) 1.15–5.30. Last adm. 5. For adm. charges, concessionary rates contact The Estate Office, Bramham Park, Wetherby, W. Yorks LS23 6ND. ☎ *Boston Spa* (0937) 844265 BRAMHAM HORSE TRIALS—May 31 to June 3, 1984.	West Yorks. 741, Leeds–Wetherby; 742 Leeds–Tadcaster (*alight at Terry Lug, before Bramham village*)
BRONTË PARSONAGE, Haworth *The Brontë Society* *map* 5 *C* Georgian Parsonage, containing many relics of the Brontë family, including furniture, clothes, manuscripts and drawings. Small formal garden	4 m SW of Keighley on A6033 at Haworth	All the year—Daily: April to Sept. 11–5.30; Oct. to March 11–4.30. Adm. 50p, Chd. & O.A.Ps. 25p. Slide talks by arrangement. *Closed mid Dec., re-open immediately after Christmas hol.* ☎ *Haworth* 42323	Keighley & Worth Valley Rly. Sats. & Suns. (daily in July & Aug.) (*alight Haworth*) West Yorks 665, Bradford—Haworth (via Keighley)) National coaches from adjoining Counties and the Midlands
EAST RIDDLESDEN HALL, Keighley *The National Trust* *map* 5 *C* 17th cent. manor house. Magnificent tithe barn Small formal garden. Exhibition in the stable	1 m NE of Keighley on S side of A650, on N bank of Aire *Stn: Keighley (1½ m)*	July & Aug.—Weds. to Suns. & Bank Hol. Mons. 11–6. Sept. & Oct.—Weds. to Suns. 2–6. Last adm. 5.30. Adm. £1, Chd. 50p. Parties 80p. Shop. Dogs in grounds only, on leads.	West Yorks. 665, 666, 667, 668, 669 Bradford–Keighley–Haworth (*alight gates*)
HAREWOOD HOUSE & BIRD GARDEN, Leeds *map* 5 *C* *The Earl of Harewood* 18th century house designed by John Carr and Robert Adam and still the home of the Lascelles family. As well as superb ceilings, plasterwork and Chippendale furniture it contains fine English and Italian paintings and Sevres and Chinese porcelain. In the grounds, landscaped by 'Capability' Brown, are lakeside and woodland walks, displays of roses and rhododendrons and a herbaceous border running the length of the Terrace.	7 m S of Harrogate; 8 m N of Leeds on the Leeds–Harrogate rd; junction A61/659 at Harewood village; 5 m from A1 at Wetherby 22 m from York	HOUSE, GROUNDS, BIRD GARDEN & ALL FACILITIES: April 1 to Oct. 31—Daily. Gates open 10 a.m. House open 11 a.m. Limited opening Nov., Feb. & March—Suns., Tues., Weds. & Thurs. *Harewood closed Dec. & Jan.* except for holiday opening. Opening of Bird Garden & Adventure Playground only—daily, Dec. 26 to first Sun. in Jan. *Concession rates for Coach parties. School parties welcome at all times.* Adm. charges & details of SUMMER WEEKEND EVENTS—including Car Rallies & Leeds Championship Dog Show available from D. P. S. Wrench, Visitors' Information, Estate Office, Harewood, Leeds LS17 9LQ. State Dining Room (max. 48), available. Cafeteria Restaurant, also Courtyard Functions Suite for Conferences/product launches throughout the year. ☎ *Harewood* (0532) 886225	Road & Rail, Travellers International, Venture Tours—London; J. Abbott, Blackpool; Epsom Coaches, Surrey; Yelloway Motors, Rochdale; Woodcock International, York; National Bus Co. tours from Brighton, Chesterfield, Exeter, Liverpool, Liversedge, Manchester, Newcastle, Sheffield, etc. Wrays & West Yorks tours from Harrogate; Pullman & West Yorks tours from York; Wallace Arnold tours from Bradford & Leeds; United & West Yorks regular service 36 Leeds—Harrogate—Ripon (*alight village, 1m from House*)

WEALD & DOWNLAND OPEN AIR MUSEUM

SINGLETON, CHICHESTER, WEST SUSSEX

The Museum is rescuing and re-erecting historic Buildings from South-East England. The Collection illustrates the history of vernacular architecture in the Weald and Downland area. Exhibits include Medieval Farmhouses, a Tudor Market Hall, a 16th century Treadwheal, Farm Buildings including two 18th century Barns and a Granary, a Blacksmiths' Forge, Plumbers' and Carpenters' Workshops and a Charcoal Burner's Camp. The Lurgashall Watermill is in regular operation producing Stoneground flour. The Museum's beautiful Downland site contains picnic areas and woodland walks.

UPPARK

nr. PETERSFIELD WEST SUSSEX

THE NATIONAL TRUST

"Country Life" photograph

The house was built in 1690 to Talman's designs. The rooms, furnished mainly between 1750 and 1770, retain much of their original decoration and are a remarkable survival of an 18th century interior. Associated with H. G. Wells and Emma Hamilton.

BANKFIELD MUSEUM

HALIFAX

Bankfield Museum has one of the most comprehensive collections of costume and fabric in the United Kingdom. The collection is particularly rich in peasant work from the Balkans and Burma. There is also a fine military display of The Duke of Wellington's Regiment and the 4th/7th Royal Dragoon Guards. There is a Natural History section on the flora, fauna and geology of the area, as well as continuing programmes of temporary exhibitions. Opening hours: Monday to Saturday 10–5; Sunday 2.30–5. Museum Headquarters.

Home of the Earl and Countess of Harewood

HAREWOOD HOUSE & BIRD GARDEN

LEEDS YORKSHIRE

Gates Open 10 a.m. (House 11 a.m.) DAILY 1 APRIL to 31 OCTOBER

& Sunday, Tuesday, Wednesday & Thursday in February, March & November

- ★ Adventure Playground
- ★ Terrace & Lakeside Gardens
- ★ Picnic Area ★ Shops
- ★ Exhibition
- ★ Restaurant & Cafeteria

see page 148 *for details*

BRAMHAM PARK

WETHERBY, WEST YORKSHIRE

Magnificent Queen Anne Mansion.

66 acres of gardens unique in the British Isles. Inspired by Andre Le Notre who created Versailles.

Pleasure Grounds — bounded by two massive beech avenues with rides radiating from temples and an obelisk.

Location — 5 miles South of Wetherby just off the A1.

OPENING TIMES OPPOSITE

HEPTONSTALL OLD GRAMMAR SCHOOL

WEST YORKSHIRE

This is a 17th century Grammar School which has been opened as a school and local museum. It contains school furniture of the 17th century, local agricultural and domestic articles and will eventually extend into adjoining cottages where will be displayed craft workshops of the Calder Valley. The school is in the centre of one of the finest hill villages in the West Riding, facing the ruins of the 14th century Church of St. Thomas à Becket. A History Trail has been devised for the district.

OPENING TIMES SEE PAGE 150

BRONTË PARSONAGE

HAWORTH

"Yorkshire Post" photograph

Haworth Parsonage, where the Brontë sisters wrote their novels and poems, is preserved as nearly as possible as it was in the days when "Jane Eyre" and "Wuthering Heights" were written. It contains many relics of the famous family, including furniture, pictures and dresses. Manuscripts include the notable Bonnell collection.

OPENING TIMES OPPOSITE

PROPERTY (*showing map reference*)	LOCATION (*with nearest Rly. Stn.*)	OPENING TIMES AND ADMISSION CHARGES CATERING FACILITIES	COACH AND RAIL TOURS BUS SERVICES (*showing alighting points*)
WEST YORKSHIRE—*continued*			
HARLOW CAR GARDENS, Harrogate *The Northern Horticultural Society map 5 A* 60 acres of ornamental gardens and woodlands	1½ m from centre of Harrogate, Otley rd *Stn: Harrogate (1½m)*	All the year—Daily 9–7.30 (or sunset if earlier). Small admission charge	West Yorks. 12, 12A (*alight Plantation Road*); 5, 6 (*weekdays*) (*alight Crag Lane End*)
HEPTONSTALL OLD GRAMMAR SCHOOL MUSEUM, Hebden Bridge *map 5 C* *Corporation of Calderdale* 17th century stone.	¾ m from the Halifax/Todmorden road A646	April to Sept.—Sats. & Suns. 2–6. Easter week 11–12.30, 1.15–4. May to Aug.—Mons., Weds., Thurs. & Fris. 11–12.30, 1.15–4; Sats. & Suns. 12–5. Oct. to March—Sats. & Suns. 1–5. Adm. 15p, Chd. 5p.	Metro Calderdale 516 Halifax–Blackshaw Head
LEDSTON HALL, nr Castleford *map 5 D* *G. H. H. Wheler, Esq.* 17th century mansion with some earlier work	2 m N of Castleford off A656	Exterior only. May & June—Mon. to Fri. 9–4. Other days by appointment. Selby Fork Motor Hotel (2 m)	West Riding 175, 176 from Castleford (*alight Ledston Village, short walk to Hall*)
LOTHERTON HALL, Aberford *map 5 D* *Leeds Metro. District Council* Edwardian house with attractive gardens. Gascoigne collection of pictures and furniture	1 m E of A1 at Aberford on the Towton rd (B1217)	All the year—Tues. to Sun. 10.30–6.15 (or dusk if earlier); Thurs. from May to September 10.30–8.30. *Closed Mons. except Bank Hol. Mons.* Adm. 50p, Chd. & O.A.Ps. 20p, Students free. Season ticket £2.25 (includes Temple Newsam).	West Yorks. 748, Leeds–Barwick–Aberford; West Riding 176 Castleford–Aberford (*Sats. only*)
MANOR HOUSE, Ilkley *map 5 C* *Bradford Metro. Council* Small Tudor Manor built on part of the site of a Roman fort. Lively exhibitions programme	Castle Yard, Ilkley, LS29 9DT *Stn: Ilkley*	All year—Daily (except Mons. but open Bank Hol. Mons.) 10–5. *Closed Christmas Day, Boxing Day & Good Friday*. Adm. free (Public Museum). ☎ *Ilkley* 600066	Trains from Leeds, Bradford. Buses from Skipton, Leeds, Bradford, Harrogate, etc.
NOSTELL PRIORY, Wakefield *map 5 D* *The National Trust* Built for Sir Rowland Winn by Paine; a wing added in 1766 by Robert Adam. State rooms contain pictures and Chippendale furniture belonging to Lord St. Oswald, who gave the house and whose home it remains	6 m SE of Wakefield, on N side of A638 *Stns: Wakefield Kirkgate (4½ m); Wakefield Westgate (5½ m); Pontefract Baghill (5 m); Pontefract Monkhill (5½ m) (not Suns.)*	April, May, June, Sept. & Oct.—Thurs. & Sats. 12–5; Suns. 11–5. July & Aug.—Daily (except: Fris.) 12–5. Bank Hol. Suns., Mons. & Tues. 11–5. Adm. £1.70, Chd. 90p (if accompanied). Garden & Grounds £1, Chd. 50p. *Pre-booked parties of 15 or more* £1.40 *per adult, Chd.* 70p. *Party rates do not apply Suns. & Bank Hol. Mons.* Car park charge (inc. N.T. members. No dogs. Wheelchair access (lift available). in the Riding Tea Rooms (not N.T.). ☎ *Wakefield* 863892	West Riding 485, Wakefield–Doncaster (*not Suns.*); 245, Pontefract–Barnsley; 482, Leeds–Hemsworth; 121, 122, 123, Wakefield–Brierley–Grimethorpe; 183 Leeds–Castleford–South Elmsall; 190 Pontefract–South Elmsall. United Services. Wakefield–Doncaster W. R. & P. Bingley, Wakefield–Doncaster
OAKWELL HALL, Birstall *map 5 C* *Kirklees Metro. Council* Elizabethan moated manor house (1583) with Civil War and Brontë connections. It was "Fieldhead" of Charlotte Brontë's novel "Shirley"	Birstall, Batley	All the year—Mons. to Sats. 10–5; Suns. 1–5. Adm. free. ☎ *Batley* 474926	Yorks 281, 282, Dewsbury–Birstall (*alight Nova Lane*) 603, 604 from Bradford (*alight Cambridge Road*)
RED HOUSE, Gomersal *map 5 C* *Kirklees Metro. Council* Built in 1660 of red brick. Associations with Charlotte Brontë who often spent weekends there—"Briarmains" of her novel "Shirley"	3½ m SSE of Bradford	All the year—Mons. to Sats. 10–5; Suns. 1–5. Adm. free. ☎ *Cleckheaton* 872165	Yorkshire 224, Leeds–Halifax (*alight Birkenshaw*); 229, Batley–Scholes; 267, Batley–Birkenshaw Yorkshire & Yorkshire Traction, 259 Heckmondwike–Bradford, 260, Huddersfield–Bradford
SHIBDEN HALL & FOLK MUSEUM, Halifax *Corporation of Calderdale* *map 5 C* 15th cent. timber-framed house	½ m SE of Halifax on the Halifax–Hipperholme rd (A 58)	April to September—Mons. to Sats. 10–6, Suns. 2–5. Oct., Nov. & March—Mons. to Sats. 10–5, Suns 2–5. February—Suns. only 2–5. *Closed December to January*. Adm. Summer: 70p, Chd. 30p; Low season: 50p, Chd. 25p. *Conducted tours after normal hours* (Fee payable) *January*. Adm. Summer: 70p, Chd. 30p; Low season: at the Hall ☎ *Halifax* (0422) 52246	Metro Calderdale 48, 49, 508, 681, 682 (*alight Hall gates*)
TEMPLE NEWSAM, Leeds *map 5 D* *Leeds Metro. District Council* Tudor-Jacobean house, birthplace of Lord Darnley, with collection of pictures and furniture	5 m E of Leeds; 1 m S of A63 (nr junction with A642) *Stn: Leeds (5 m)*	All the year—Tues. to Sun. 10.30–6.15 (or dusk if earlier); Weds. from May to September, 10.30–8.30. *Closed Mons. except Bank Hol. Mons.* Adm. 50p, Chd. & O.A.Ps. 20p. Students free. Season ticket £2.25 (includes Lotherton Hall).	Metro Leeds 22 from Corn Exchange direct to the house
THORNTON HALL, Thornton, nr Bradford *P. B. F. Whitaker, Esq.* *map 5 C* 17th century manor house typical of the area.	4 m W of Bradford on B6145	Open by telephone appointment only. June to Sept.—Sunday afternoons. ☎ (0274) 833151	Metro Bradford 607 from bus interchange
WILTSHIRE			
THE ABBEY HOUSE, Malmesbury *Tavistock Trust* *map 2 M* The vaulted undercroft of the abbot's dwelling described by Brakespear, '*Archaeologia 1913*', now the basement of the house built on the site of the abbey buildings.	In centre of town, via A29 or A434 *Stns: Kemble (7½ m); Chippenham (9 m)*	By appointment only with the Sister in Charge. ☎ (066 62) 2212 Castle Hotel or Abbot's Restaurant in the town	Athelstan Coaches 19 Swindon–Malmesbury
AVEBURY MANOR, nr Marlborough *map 3 J* *D. & S. Nevill-Gliddon* Romantic Elizabethan Manor House with beautiful plasterwork, panelling and furniture. Extensive gardens with herb border and topiary.	1 m N of London/Bath rd at jct of A361 & B4003; 7 m W of Marlborough; 1½ m from Silbury Hill; 9 m from Swindon exit on M4 *Stn: Pewsey (10 m) (not Suns.)*	April to Oct.—Mons. to Sats. 11.30–6–30; Suns. 1.30–6.30. Nov. to March—Sats. & Suns. 1.30–5. Adm. charges not available at time of going to press. Car parking. Picnic area. N.B. The above times are often considerably extended during fine weather. Out of hours visiting & parties by arrangement. teas in the Manor ☎ *Avebury* (06723) 203 Red Lion Hotel, Avebury	Tours from Nottingham, S. Wales, London and the West Country Swindon & District 71 Swindon–Devizes (*not Suns.*) (*alight Avebury village, Manor North Drive*)

Oakwell Hall

Birstall

Elizabethan moated manor house (1583) with Civil War and Brontë connections. It was 'Fieldhead' of Charlotte Brontë's novel 'Shirley'

OPENING TIMES OPPOSITE

NOSTELL PRIORY

WAKEFIELD, YORKSHIRE

THE NATIONAL TRUST

Begun in 1733 for Sir Rowland Winn by James Paine and added to in 1766 by Robert Adam. The state rooms, designed mainly by Robert Adam with plasterwork by Rose and panels by Zucchi, contain furniture specially made for the house by Thomas Chippendale.

Refreshments are available.

OPENING TIMES OPPOSITE

Red House

Gomersal

Built 1660 of red brick which gave rise to its name. Additions by succeeding owners. Associations with Charlotte Brontë who immortalised it in her novel "Shirley" where it is given the name "Briarmains".

OPENING TIMES OPPOSITE

LOTHERTON HALL

ABERFORD, near LEEDS, West Yorkshire

Lotherton Hall was built round an earlier house dating from the mid-eighteenth century. The extensions to the east were completed in 1896 and those to the west in 1903. The Hall, with its art collection, park and gardens, was given to the City of Leeds by Sir Alvary and Lady Gascoigne in 1968 and opened as a country house museum in 1969. The Gascoigne collection, which contains pictures, furniture, silver and porcelain of the 17th and 18th centuries, as well as works of a later period, includes a magnificent portrait by Pompeo Batoni and an impressive group of silver race cups ranging in date from 1776 to 1842. The first floor and costume galleries were opened in 1970 and the oriental gallery in 1975. There is also a Museum shop and audio visual room.

TEMPLE NEWSAM HOUSE

LEEDS, West Yorkshire

The Temple Newsam estate belonged to the Knights Templar and later passed to the D'Arcy family who retained it until 1537. The house, which was the birthplace of Lord Darnley and a centre of English and Scottish intrigue during the reign of Elizabeth I, was later acquired by Sir Arthur Ingram, whose descendants became Viscounts Irwin. It was eventually inherited by the late Lord Halifax who sold it to Leeds Corporation in 1922. The house has many fine features of 16th and 17th century date, as well as a magnificent suite of Georgian rooms, and contains some superb furniture, silver, ceramics and a fine collection of pictures. There is also a Museum shop in the house and an exhibition galley (for temporary exhibitions) in the Stable Block.

OPENING TIMES OPPOSITE

SHIBDEN HALL

HALIFAX

WEST YORKSHIRE FOLK MUSEUM

An early 15th century half-timbered house with later additions, furnished with 17th and 18th century material. The 17th century barn and outbuildings are equipped with early agricultural implements and craft workshops, the museum is set in a large park and surrounded by terrace gardens. Snack bar facilities. Admission: Summer—Adults 70p, Chd. 30p. Low Season—Adults 50p, Chd. 25p.

OPENING TIMES OPPOSITE

AVEBURY MANOR **near MARLBOROUGH**

Dating from before the Conquest (Avebury Manor was built on the site of a Benedictine Cell) and standing beside the Great Stone Circle of Avebury, this early Elizabethan Manor house, having been carefully restored, is now a family home. Oak panelled rooms and coved plasterwork ceilings—State rooms visited by Queen Anne and Charles II. Much early oak and fine furniture in period setting. Portraits dated from 1532 (many by courtesy of the Marquess and Marchioness of Ailesbury). The Queen Anne bedroom with imposing state bed and Mary Tudor travelling chest is of particular note, also the Cavalier bedroom (linked with tales of the supernatural and recounted by more than one visitor staying at the Manor).

Surrounding garden and parkland are equally intriguing. Topiary—old yew and box—pleasantly emphasise the historic atmosphere. Walled gardens, herb border and wishing well, 16th century dovecote. Jacobs sheep and Fallow deer roam the parkland.

Car parking within the Manor Gounds. South Library Tea Room and picnic area. Souvenir shop. The Alexander Keiller Archaeological Museum (formerly the Manor Coach House) and model railway stand within the grounds.

Parties and out of hours visiting by arrangement. To enquire telephone Avebury (06723) 203.

Bowood

CALNE, WILTSHIRE
Home of the Earl of Shelburne

Bowood House, which has an intriguing architectural history, nestles in the centre of a magnificent park which has been said to combine 'the sublime, the picturesque and the beautiful'. This classical example of English landscaping was created by Capability Brown between 1763 and 1766.

The house, as it exists today, was once part of a much larger house originally purchased by the first Earl of Shelburne in 1754. He and his successors employed such famous architects as Keene, Adam, Dance, Cockerell, Smirk and Barry to make alterations and improvements.

In 1955 the 8th Marquess of Lansdowne, father of the present Earl of Shelburne, had to take the decision to demolish the 'Big House', leaving the present house as a perfectly balanced 18th century classical structure set in one of the most beautiful parks in the country. It is the residence of the Earl of Shelburne and his family. Over half of the house is open to the public.

The southern elevation, built by Robert Adam in 1770, houses Adam's own famous library, the room which was Dr. Joseph Priestley's laboratory where he discovered oxygen gas and the Orangery where hangs the Lansdowne Collection of paintings. Leading off the Orangery is Charles Cockerell's Chapel, an addition to the house in 1821.

Between 1978 and 1980 Lord Shelburne converted the old stables and grooms' quarters to form an extensive range of new exhibition rooms. Here the visitor will find the Sculpture Gallery with ancient Roman statuary, silver and Indiana collected by the fifth Marquess when Viceroy of India from 1888 to 1894, costumes and court dresses worn by the 1st Marquess (Prime Minister in 1783) and his wife and the Albanian costume worn by Lord Byron in his famous portrait and given to a member of the Lansdowne family in 1814.

A great attraction for visitors to Bowood is the important collection of water-colours and drawings by David Roberts, William Callow, Edward Lear and other celebrated 19th century artists including a large group of drawings by R. P. Bonington.

The Gardens are a delight to visit at any time with carpets of bluebells, daffodils and narcissi in Springtime and spectacular roses on The Terraces in summer. These terraces link the front of the house to the gently sloping parklands and 90 acres of pleasure gardens are then available to visitors. The gardens include the largest area of mown lawn in the country.

Dominating the scenery is the magnificent lake, typical of Capability Brown's work, and walks around the lake enable the visitor to view the Doric Temple, the Hermit's Cave and a delightful Cascade designed by Charles Hamilton in the rococo style in 1785.

The Grounds also include an Arboretum, which early records state was started in 1770, and Pinetum which was started in 1848/9. Over 200 different kinds of trees and shrubs are now included in the collection.

In the rhododendron season there is an immense variety of beautiful blooms in a separate 50 acre woodland plantation dominated by Robert Adam's famous Mausoleum, designed in the Palladian style in 1761, beneath which lie the Lansdowne family vaults.

There is an Information Centre showing the history of the house, the family and the Estate right up to the present time. Other visitor facilities include a Gift Shop, a Garden Centre with a catalogue representative of the 900 varieties of plants growing in the Grounds, a licensed restaurant specialising in home produced, home cooked luncheons and teas, a Garden Tea Room set in a sheltered walled garden and, from mid-June, 14 acres of 'Pick Your Own' strawberries, gooseberries, raspberries, tayberries and blackberries followed by green beans and sweetcorn.

Parking in the large grass car park is free. There are ramps and special toilet facilities for the disabled. Coaches are welcome but dogs are not permitted in the Grounds or in the Rhododendron Walks.

BOWOOD HOUSE AND GARDENS: OPEN APRIL 1st–JUNE 30th and SEPTEMBER: Tuesdays to Sundays inclusive. JULY and AUGUST: open every day. Also open Bank Holiday Mondays. 11 a.m.–6 p.m.

Admission (including V.A.T.): Adults £1.70, Children 90p, Senior Citizens £1.20. Reduced rates for parties of 20 and over if booked and paid for 10 days in advance.

Entrance: Off the A4 in Derry Hill Village, midway between Calne and Chippenham.

RHODODENDRON WALKS: OPEN MID-MAY TO MID-JUNE, 11 a.m.–6 p.m.

CLOSED MONDAYS EXCEPT FOR BANK HOLIDAYS.

Admission (including V.A.T.): Adults 80p, Children 50p (no reduced rates for Senior Citizens or party bookings).

Entrance: Off the A342 Chippenham to Devizes road midway between Derry Hill and Sandy Lane Villages.

The Management reserves the right to alter catering facilities depending on adverse weather conditions or visitor demand.

CORSHAM COURT

WILTSHIRE

An Elizabethan Manor with magnificent Georgian State Rooms added in 1760

Home of The Lord METHUEN, A.R.I.C.S. and the Bath Academy of Art

Contains one of the oldest and most distinguished collections of Old Masters and Furniture

Between Chippenham and Bath M4 exit 17

FITZ HOUSE

TEFFONT MAGNA, Nr. SALISBURY

"A most romantic house which I used to long to have for my own" wrote Edith Olivier the authoress, of Fitz House, Teffont, one of the prettiest of all the Wiltshire villages. This wish was fulfilled when she rented the property in the Twenties, as did Siegfried Sassoon the author. Their dreamhouse remains to this day surrounded by its beautiful terraced gardens. Yew and beech hedges enclose a haven of tranquillity.

PROPERTY (*showing map reference*)	LOCATION (*with nearest Rly. Stn.*)	OPENING TIMES AND ADMISSION CHARGES CATERING FACILITIES	COACH AND RAIL TOURS BUS SERVICES (*showing alighting points*)
WILTSHIRE—*continued*			
BOWOOD HOUSE & GARDENS Calne *The Earl of Shelburne* *map* 2 *M* 100 acre garden containing many exotic trees, 40 acre lake, waterfall, cave, and Doric Temple. Arboretum, Pinetum, rose garden and Italian garden. 60 acres of rhododendrons. Chapel and a series of Exhibition Rooms featuring classical sculpture, costumes, furniture, ceramics and other interesting objects collected by the Lansdowne family over the last 200 years. Picture Gallery and an important collection of water colours and drawings by English masters	2½ m W of Calne 5 m SE of Chippenham. Immediately off A4, 8 m S of M4. *Stn: Chippenham (5 m)*	Daily (except Mons. in April, May, June & Sept. but open Bank Hol. Mons.). HOUSE, GARDEN & GROUNDS (*ent. off A4 at Derry Hill*)—April 1 to Sept. 30: 11–6. RHODODENDRON WALKS (*ent. off A342 at Kennels Lodge*)—mid-May to mid-June (depending on season), 11–6. Adm.: House, Gardens & Grounds: £1.70, Chd. 90p, O.A.Ps. £1.20. *Reduced rates for parties booked & paid for in advance.* Rhododendron Walks (in season) 80p, Chd. 50p. Information apply Estate Office, Bowood Estate, Calne, Wilts. Free Car Park. *No dogs allowed.* ☎ *Calne* (0249) 812102 Licensed Restaurant & Children's adventure playground in Pleasure Grounds.	Bristol 232 Bath–Chippenham–Calne–Devizes (*Suns. & B. Hols. only*); 233 Chippenham–Calne–Devizes (*not Suns.*)
BROADLEAS, Devizes *map* 2 *M* *Lady Anne Cowdray* A garden with rare and unusual plants and trees. Rhododendrons, magnolias and interesting perennials and ground cover.	1½ m SW of Devizes on A360	March 31 to Oct. 31—Suns., Weds. & Thurs. 2–6. Adm. Suns. 80p, Weds. & Thurs. 50p; Chd. (under 12) 20p on each day. Parties by arrangement. Own plants propagated for sale. ☎ *Devizes* 2035 home-made teas Suns. only or by arrangement	Bristol 270, 271, 272, 273, Salisbury–Devizes Bath (*alight Lodge*) (*not Suns.*)
CHALCOT HOUSE, Westbury *map* 2 *S* *Mr. & Mrs Anthony Rudd* Small 17th century Palladian Manor	2 m W of Westbury on A3098 to Frome *Stn: Dilton Marsh*	July & August—Daily 2–5. Adm. £1 including brochure (subject to alteration). *Parties at other times by arrangement.*	**British Rail to Westbury station (1½ *hrs from Paddington* and then by taxi)**
CORSHAM COURT, Chippenham *map* 2 *M* *The Lord Methuen, A.R.I.C.S.* Elizabethan (1582) and Georgian (1760–70) house, fine 18th century furniture. British, Spanish, Italian and Flemish Old Masters. Park and gardens laid out by "Capability" Brown and Humphrey Repton.	In Corsham 4 m W of Chippenham off the Bath rd (A4) *Stn: Chippenham (4 m)*	Staterooms open Jan. 15 to Dec. 15—Tues., Weds., Thurs., Sats., Suns. & Bank Hols. 2–4 (June to Sept. & all Bank Hols. 2–6; last adm. 5.30). Other times by appointment. Parties welcome. Adm. (inc. gardens) £1.50. Chd. 80p, parties of 15 or more £1.20. Gardens only 80p, Chd. 40p. *N.B. Picture Gallery not available until late 1984. Adm. charges reduced.* ☎ *Corsham* (0249) 712214 Methuen Arms, Corsham (*parties by prior arrangement*)	Bristol 231, 232 from Bath, Chippenham; 271 from Devizes also X55 from Bristol (*not Suns.*) (*alight Newlands rd., Corsham*) **National tour from Cheltenham**
THE COURTS GARDEN, Holt *map* 2 *M* *The National Trust* 7 acre garden of mystery—of interest to amateur and botanist.	2½ m E of Bradford-on-Avon on S side of A3053, 3 m N of Trowbridge *Stns: Bradford-on-Avon (2½ m); Trowbridge (3¼ m)*	GARDEN ONLY: April to end of Oct.—Mons. to Fris. 2–6. Adm. 70p, Chd. free (if accompanied). Other times by appointment; please telephone the Head Gardener. House not open. No dogs. Wheelchair access. ☎ *North Trowbridge* (0225) 782340	Bristol 237 Chippenham–Melksham–Trowbridge (*not Suns.*)
FITZ HOUSE, Teffont Magna *map* 2 *S* *Major & Mrs. Mordaunt-Hare* Romantic 16th/17th century greenstone farmhouse admired by Nikolaus Pevsner in his 'Wiltshire Guide'; 14th century tythe barn etc. by stream in the pretty village. 4 acre garden with terraces, yew and beech hedges and orchard with old-fashioned roses. Entirely maintained by owners.	On B3089 Barford St. Martin (A30) to Mere rd (A303) in the village; 10 m W of Salisbury on direct route Wilton House-Stourhead *Stns: Tisbury (5 m); Salisbury (10 m)*	GARDEN ONLY: April 1 to Oct. 31—Weds., Suns. & Bank Hol. Mons. 2–6. Adm. 75p. No dogs. No coaches. home-made teas & gifts	British Rail to Salisbury (*infrequent bus service to Teffont passes gate*) & to Tisbury (*no bus service*)
GREAT CHALFIELD MANOR, Melksham *The National Trust* *map* 2 *M* 15th century moated manor house restored in the 20th century	2½ m NE Bradford-on-Avon via B3109 *Stns: Bradford-on-Avon (3 m); Trowbridge (4½ m)*	April 4 to end of Oct.—Weds. 12–1, 2–5 (tours start 12.15 & 2.15). *Closed Bank Hols.* Adm. £1.30. *Historical & other Societies by written arrangement. No reductions for parties or chd.* No dogs. Unsuitable for wheelchairs. Swan Hotel, Bradford-on-Avon Kings Arms, Melksham	**Bristol 237, Trowbridge–Broughton Gifford–Melksham** (*not Suns.*) (*alight Broughton Gifford 1½ m*)
HEALE HOUSE, Woodford, Salisbury *map* 3 *N* *Major & Mrs. David Rasch* Early Carolean manor house where King Charles II hid during his escape. Beautiful river garden; hybrid, musk and other roses; authentic Japanese tea house	4 m N of Salisbury, nr Wilton & Stonehenge (turn W off A345 at High Post Hotel, signposted Woodford). *Stn: Salisbury (5 m)*	GARDENS ONLY—Good Friday to end of September—Mons. to Sats. & first Sun. of the month 10–5. Adm. 70p; accompanied children under 14 yrs. free. Tours of the house, lunches, teas & suppers in the house for parties up to 40 at any time by arrangement with Mrs. Rasch. Participating in the 'Welcome to the Gardens of the West Country 1984'. ☎ *Middle Woodford* (072273) 207 Suitable for disabled if able to negotiate low steps	Wilts & Dorset 201, Salisbury–Amesbury (*alight at gates*) (*not Suns. or Bank Hols.*)

HEALE HOUSE

WOODFORD, SALISBURY

Early Carolean manor house, where King Charles II hid for several days after the battle of Worcester in 1651.

The River Avon runs through the beautiful established garden: herbaceous and mixed borders, with hybrid, musk and other roses. Charming authentic Japanese tea house and water garden.

OPENING TIMES ABOVE

SALISBURY MUSEUM THE KING'S HOUSE

Delightfully situated opposite the West Front of Salisbury Cathedral. Nationally important Collections include Stonehenge finds, Pitt-Rivers Collection, the Salisbury Giant, Ceramics, Costume and much more besides.

OPENING TIMES SEE PAGE 154

PROPERTY (*showing map reference*)	LOCATION (*with nearest Rly. Stn.*)	OPENING TIMES AND ADMISSION CHARGES CATERING FACILITIES	COACH AND RAIL TOURS BUS SERVICES (*showing alighting points*)

WILTSHIRE—*continued*

PROPERTY	LOCATION	OPENING TIMES	TOURS / BUS SERVICES
KING'S HOUSE, Salisbury *map 3 N* *Salisbury & South Wiltshire Museum* Medieval and later Grade 1 house recently converted to rehouse Salisbury Museum	65 The Close, Salisbury. *Stn: Salisbury*	Easter to Sept.—Mons. to Sats. 10–5; Suns. (July & Aug. only) 2–5. Oct. to Easter—Mons. to Sats. 10–4. *Closed Christmas to New Year.* Adm. £1, Chd. 20p, O.A.Ps. 70p. Reduced rates for parties by prior arrangement. Souvenir shop. light refreshments planned, detail not finalised at time of going to press *Salisbury* (0722) 332151	B.R. from London, Exeter, Southampton & Bristol Hants & Dorset, Wilts & Dorset } services to Salisbury
LACOCK ABBEY, nr Chippenham *map 2 M* Δ *The National Trust* 13th century abbey converted into a house in 1540, with 18th century "Gothick" alterations. The Medieval Cloisters, the Brewery and the house are open to the public. Fine trees	In the village of Lacock, 3 m N of Melksham, 3 m S of Chippenham just E of A350 *Stn: Chippenham (3½ m)*	HOUSE & GROUNDS: April to Nov. 4—Daily (except Tues.) 2–6. Last adm. 5.30. *Closed Good Friday.* Nov. to March—Historical and other societies by previous written arrangement. Adm. House & Grounds £1.60, Chd. 80p. Parties of 15 or more £1.20. Grounds only 50p, Chd. 25p. *No dogs.* Wheelchairs in grounds, village & museum only.	Bristol 234, 237 Trowbridge–Chippenham (*no Sun. services*) (*alight Lacock, "George Inn"*)
LITTLECOTE, nr Hungerford *map 3 J* Δ *Sir Seton Wills, Bt.* Historic Tudor manor *circa* 1490–1520. Moulded plaster ceilings, panelled rooms. Magnificent Great Hall with unique Cromwellian armoury	3 m W of Hungerford, just off A4 at Froxfield, M4 access No. 14 *Stn: Hungerford (3 m) (not Suns. but B. Hols.)*	April to June—Sats., Suns. & Bank Hol. Mons. 2–6; July to Sept.—Mons. to Fris. 2–5, Sats., Suns. & Bank Hol. Mon. 2–6. Pre-booked parties of 20 or more any day. Special facilities for school parties. Adm. charges not available at time of going to press. Tour approx. 1 hour. *Hungerford* (0488) 82170 (*office hours*), 82528 (*weekends*) home-made teas Bear Hotel, Hungerford	Hellyers tours from Southsea Conway, Hunt, Safeguard & Venture tours from London
LONGLEAT HOUSE, Warminster *map 2 S* Δ *The Marquess of Bath* This great and friendly Elizabethan Treasure House is very much a home, alive with the daily presence of the indomitable Thynnes who have maintained it for 404 years. Ancestors have commissioned alterations by Wyatville, ceilings by Italian craftsmen, and have added constantly to vast Libraries. Contemporary acquisitions include a Makepeace Table, a Graham Sutherland portrait and the magnificent embroidered Wall Hanging "The Longleat Tree". JULY 12th–OCTOBER 28th A major INTERNATIONAL DOLLS HOUSE EXHIBITION in the Great Hall will be staged by The Save the Children Fund. The Longleat Gardens were restored by Russell Page. They complement Capability Brown's rolling parkland and Wyatville's evocative Orangery. The modern Garden Centre specialises in fuchsias and pelargoniums.	4 m SW of Warminster; 4½ m SE of Frome on A362 (between Bath & Salisbury) *Stns: Frome (4 m) (not Suns. except May – Sept.), Warminster (5 m)*	All the year—Daily (except Christmas Day), inc. Suns. Easter to September 30: 10–6; remainder of year: 10–4. Reduced rates for parties booking in advance. *Maiden Bradley* (098 53) 551 Whilst at Longleat—visit the Safari Park. Open March to Oct.—Daily 10–6 (or sunset if earlier). Adm. charges not available at time of going to press. *Maiden Bradley* (098 53) 328 SCHOOL PARTIES MOST WELCOME AT ALL TIMES OF THE YEAR—(Educational material available on request). at the House & in the Restaurant complex. Helicopter landing facilities available, given advance notice. *Maiden Bradley* (098 53) 663 Caravan Club site.	Fast trains from Paddington & Exeter to Westbury (taxi) Bus 253 & 254. Bath–Warminster, (*alight gates 2½m*). Britain Shrinker Tours from London weekdays (*summer only*). British Rail "Awayday" Rail & Road Tours from Waterloo in height of season. Coach tours:—Wallace Arnold, Devon. Thos. Cook & London Transport, London. W. Robinson, Lancs. Cosy Coaches, South Coast. Baker's & Wems, Weston-super-Mare. Pilchers, Chatham. National from Birmingham, Cheltenham, Bristol, South Wales, Bath, Reading, London, Oxford, Kent, Bournemouth, Southampton, Salisbury, Weymouth & Devon. National Travel from major towns & cities.

At the turn of MAY/JUNE the 2 mile Azalea drive is amazing.
MAY 27th/28th WORLD'S FIRST IDEAL GNOME EXHIBITION
JUNE 8th/9th/10th BONSAI at LONGLEAT
JULY 1st SCARECROW SUNDAY (Provisional)
JULY 13th/14th/15th THE FUCHSIA EXPERIENCE '84
In summer the SAFARI PARK and every Exhibition and attraction is open including the Victorian Kitchens, Pets Corner, Railway, Boats, Maze and Donkey Rides—masses for children to do.
New for 1984: LORD BATH'S BYGONES and THE ENID BLYTON BOOK SHOP

PROPERTY	LOCATION	OPENING TIMES	TOURS / BUS SERVICES
LUCKINGTON COURT, Luckington *The Hon. Mrs. Trevor Horn* *map 2 M* Mainly Queen Anne with magnificent group of ancient buildings. Beautiful mainly formal garden with fine collection of ornamental trees and shrubs	6 m W of Malmesbury on B4040 Bristol Road	All the year—Weds. 2–6. Outside only, 20p. Inside view by appointment 3 weeks in advance, 50p. Open Sun. May 13, 2.30–6. *Collection box for National Gardens' Scheme* *Sherston* 205 teas in garden or house (in aid of Luckington Parish Church)	No reasonable public transport
Δ**LYDIARD MANSION, Lydiard Park, Purton** *Borough of Thamesdown* *map 3 J* Dating from mediaeval times, reconstructed 1743–49. Outstanding mid-Georgian decoration	5 m W of Swindon just N of A420; *sign-post Lydiard Park* *Stn: Swindon (5 m)*	Weekdays 10–1, 2–5.30; Suns. 2–5.30. Adm. (to April 1) 40p, Chd. & O.A.Ps. 20p; (from April 2) 50p, Chd. & O.A.Ps. 25p. *Special terms for parties*	Swindon & District/Thamesdown Joint 3A/B Swindon–Purton (*not Suns.*) (*alight Lydiard Tregoze Turn, ¾ m*)
MOMPESSON HOUSE, Salisbury *map 3 N* *The National Trust* Fine Queen Anne town house in Salisbury Cathedral Close. Georgian plasterwork	In the Close on N side of Choristers' Square *Stn: Salisbury (½ m)*	April to end of October—Mons., Tues., Weds., Sats. & Suns. 12.30–6 (or dusk if earlier). Adm. £1, Chd. 50p. *No reduction for parties.* No dogs.	Bus service from station. Wilts & Dorset services from all parts of Wiltshire, Hampshire and Dorset (*5 mins. walk from Bus Station*) **National Coach 705, 706 London–W. of England**
NEWHOUSE, Redlynch *map 3 N* *Mr. & Mrs. George Jeffreys* Brick Jacobean "Trinity" house, c. 1619, with two Georgian wings. Contents include costume collection, Nelson relics and "Hare" picture.	9 m S of Salisbury; 3 m from Downton, off B3080	Bank Hol. Mons. April 23 (Easter) & May 28 (Spring) then Sats. & Suns. in June, July & Aug. and Bank Hol. Mon. Aug. 27 (Summer): 2–6. *Closed May 7. Other days by appointment.* Adm. £1, Chd. 50p. ***Downton*** **20055** at the house	Wilts & Dorset 243, 244 (*1 mile walk*) (*not Suns.*)
PHILIPPS HOUSE, Dinton *map 2 S* *The National Trust* Classical house completed in 1816, by Sir Jeffry Wyattville for the Wyndham family	9 m W of Salisbury; on N side of B3089 *Stns: Tisbury (5 m); Salisbury 8½ (m)*	By prior appointment only with the Warden. Adm. 80p. *No reduction for parties or children.* House used for conferences. No dogs.	Wilts & Dorset 225, 226, 227, Salisbury–Hindon (*alight Dinton crossrds ¾ m*)
PYTHOUSE, Tisbury *map 2 S* *Mutual Households Association* Palladian style Georgian mansion	2½ m W of Tisbury 4½ m N of Shaftesbury *Stn: Tisbury (2½m)*	May to September—Weds. & Thurs. 2–5 Adm. 50p, Chd. 25p. Free car park. No dogs admitted.	Wilts & Dorset 226, Salisbury–Tisbury–Hindon; 228, Salisbury–Tisbury–Shaftesbury (*alight Tisbury*)

NEWHOUSE

REDLYNCH,

Nr. SALISBURY

John Brealey photograph

The central part of Newhouse dates from before 1619. Two Georgian wings were added in 1742 and 1760. It is one of very few houses built in the shape of the letter 'Y', probably to the design of the architect John Thorpe. It has been in the Eyre family since 1633 and houses a Costume Collection, Nelson Relics, family portraits and the "Hare" picture. Open Bank Holiday Mondays April 23rd, May 28th and August 27th also Saturdays and Sundays in June, July and August: 2 p.m.–6 p.m. Other days by appointment. Admission £1. Children (under 15 years) 50p. Tel. Downton (0725) 20055.

LONGLEAT

HOUSE AND GARDENS

Home of the Sixth Marquess of Bath

Victorian Kitchens

The great and friendly House with superb parkland and gardens is a magical experience throughout the year: quiet and majestic in winter—bustling and busy in summer. Many Events and Exhibitions—particularly this year for children.

Details from Comptroller, LORD CHRISTOPHER THYNNE

The Saloon

LACOCK ABBEY

WILTSHIRE

THE NATIONAL TRUST

The Augustinian Convent was consecrated in 1232. After its dissolution in 1539 Sir William Sharington made a dwelling house above the cloisters and conventual rooms. Much of this rare Tudor Renaissance work can be seen, including the octagonal tower and stables. Notable too is the 18th century "Gothick" entrance hall by Sanderson Miller. Fox-Talbot made the first photographic negative in 1835 at the Abbey. The Fox-Talbot Photographic Museum is now open in the village.
The village, with houses dating from the 15th to 18th centuries, is considered one of the most beautiful in England and also belongs to the Trust.

OPENING TIMES OPPOSITE

LITTLECOTE HOUSE

near Hungerford

Historic Tudor Manor—circa 1490-1520; Great Hall with unique Cromwellian Armoury. Cromwellian Chapel, Long Gallery, famous Haunted Bedroom. Antique Oak Furniture, china, carpets etc. Six acres lovely walled gardens with trout stream, sundial etc. all set in the peaceful Kennet Valley.

Opening Times:

April, May & June: Sats., Suns. & Bank Hols. 2–6 p.m.

July, August & September: Sats., Suns. & Bank Hols. 2–6 p.m. Weekdays 2–5 p.m.

Pre-booked parties of 20 or more any day. Special facilities for school parties.

Excavations in the Park of Roman Villa with famous Orpheus Mosaic floor. Open daily April to September 30th.

Tour approximately 1 hour. Home-made teas.

Tel. Hungerford (0488) 82170 (office hours) or 82528 (weekends).

MOMPESSON HOUSE

SALISBURY

THE NATIONAL TRUST

The entrance front of the Close, Salisbury *Jonathan Gibson photograph*

Built for Charles Mompesson in 1701, Mompesson House is one of the most distinguished in Salisbury Cathedral Close. The splendid plasterwork and graceful staircase date from about 1740 when the main rooms were redecorated. Later it became the home of the Townsend family for nearly one hundred years.

It is now shown as a fine example of a Georgian provincial town house with handsome furniture, especially assembled for it, and an important collection of 18th century drinking glasses, the largest at any Trust property. The peaceful garden with herbaceous borders surrounding a lawn is enclosed to the north by the imposing wall of the Cathedral Close.

OPENING TIMES OPPOSITE

Hall and Staircase *Jonathan Gibson photograph*

PROPERTY (*showing map reference*)	LOCATION (*with nearest Rly. Stn.*)	OPENING TIMES AND ADMISSION CHARGES CATERING FACILITIES	COACH AND RAIL TOURS BUS SERVICES (*showing alighting points*)
WILTSHIRE—*continued*			
SHELDON MANOR, Chippenham *map 2 M* *Major Martin Gibbs, D.L., J.P.* Plantagenet Manor House, lived in as a family home for 700 years. 13th century porch, 15th century detached chapel. Terraced garden with ancient yew trees, water, interesting trees and shrubs, connoisseur collection of old-fashioned roses.	1¼ m W of Chippenham, signposted from A420; eastbound traffic also signposted from A4, E of Corsham (2¼ m) *Stn.: Chippenham (2¼ m)*	April 1 to Oct. 7— Thurs., Suns. & B. Hols. 12.30–6. Gardens open 12.30 for lunches. House open at 2. Other times by arrangement for parties (for whom home-cooked meals can be provided). Majority of property suitable for wheelchairs. Visitors to Sheldon will find the food 'a major consideration'. home-made lunches & cream teas. Coaches welcome by appointment *Chippenham* (0249) 653120	Bristol 231, 232 Bath–Chippenham (*alight Sheldon Rd./ Hungerdown Lane jct., 1 m*)
STOURHEAD, Stourton, nr Mere *map 2 S* Δ *The National Trust* Celebrated mid 18th century, landscape gardens; fine trees. Palladian House designed in 1722 by Colen Campbell. Thomas Chippendale the Younger furniture.	3 m NW of Mere (A303) in the village of Stourton off the Frome – Mere road (B3092) *Stns: Gillingham (6½ m); Bruton (7 m) (Suns. May–Sept only)*	HOUSE: April & Oct. to Nov. 4—Mons., Weds., Sats. & Suns. 2–6 (or sunset if earlier). May to Sept. —Daily (except Fris.) 2–6 (or sunset if earlier). *Other times by written arrangement with the Administrator.* Adm. £1.60, Chd. 80p. Parties of 15 or more £1.20. GARDENS: All the year—Daily 8–7 (or dusk if earlier)—last adm. 6.30. Adm. £1.20, Chd. 60p. Parties of 15 or more £1 (half-price Dec. to Feb.). Dogs in gardens Oct. to end of Feb. only. Wheelchairs provided—access to gardens only. Spread Eagle, Stourton	National tour from Bournemouth Leathers, Mere–Frome (*Weds. & Sats.*) Brutonian Shaftesbury–Wincanton (*alight Frome Turn, 1¼ m*) Wilts & Dorset X24 from Poole, Bournemouth, Wimborne & Shaftesbury (*end July–beginning Sept., Mons., Thurs., Suns. only*)
WARDOUR CASTLE, Tisbury *map 2 S* Δ *The Governors of Cranborne Chase School* Magnificent house designed in the Palladian manner by James Paine in 1768. Fine rooms	2 m SW of Tisbury just N of A30; 15 m W of Salisbury *Stn: Tisbury (2 m)*	July 20 to September 5—Mons., Weds., Fris. & Sats., 2.30–6. *Dates provisional.* Adm 80p, Chd. (under 14) 40p. *Parties of 12 or more 20% reduction if notified in advance.*	Wilts & Dorset 226 Salisbury–Shaftesbury (*alight Wardour*)
WESTWOOD MANOR, Bradford-on-Avon Δ *The National Trust* *map 2 S* 15th century stone manor house altered in the late 16th century. Modern topiary garden	1¼ m SW of Bradford-on-Avon off Frome Rd (B3109) *Stns: Avoncliff (1 m); B-on-Avon (1½ m)*	April to end of Sept.—Mons., Weds. & Suns. 2–6 (last adm. 5.30). Adm. £1.30. *Other times parties of 15 or more by written application to the tenant. No reduction for parties or children. No photography.* No dogs. Unsuitable for wheelchairs.	Bristol 264, X41, Bath–Trowbridge (*alight Bradford on-Avon Station 1½m*)
WILTON HOUSE, Salisbury *map 3 N* Δ *The Earl of Pembroke* In present form work of Inigo Jones (c. 1650) and later James Wyatt (1810). Notable fine cedar trees, Palladian bridge. Exhibition of 7,000 model soldiers, set in Diorama scenes, also "The Pembroke Palace" Dolls House. Adventure Playground for children. Model railway and model shop.	In town of Wilton, 2½ m W of Salisbury on Exeter rd (A30) *Stn: Salisbury (2½ m)*	April 10 to Oct. 14—Tues. to Sats. & Bank Hol. Mons. 11–6; Suns. 1–6. Last adm. 5.15. Adm. House & Grounds £2; Chd. (under 16), O.A.Ps., Students & Party rates (over 20 persons) £1.20. Free car park. No dogs, except guide dogs for the blind. Facilities for the disabled. Licensed Restaurant—self-service; waitress service for booked parties.	British Rail "Awayday" from Waterloo to Salisbury-Wilts & Dorset 260, 261 to & from Salisbury (*every ½ hr.*) (*alight main gates*); X22 from Poole & Bournemouth (*end July–beginning Sept., Tues. only*); Wilts & Dorset/Bristol X41 Bristol–Bath–Trowbridge–Warminster–Salisbury National Coach 705 London–W. for England (*stops by request*) Coach tours from London, Midlands and the West Country
WALES			
CLWYD			
BODRHYDDAN HALL, nr Rhyl *map 2 C* Δ *Col. the Lord Langford* 17th century manor house of historic interest Famous portraits, armour, furniture; garden; arboretum	4 m SE of Rhyl, midway between Rhuddlan & Dyserth *Stns: Rhyl (4 m); Prestatyn (4 m)*	June to September—Tues. & Thurs. 2–5.30. Adm. 75p, Chd. 25p. *Special terms for parties.* at the hall. Picnic areas.	Crosville M35/36, P35/36, Rhyl–Dyserth–Rhuddlan–Rhyl (*circular*); *frequent service* (*alight Home Farm, 200 yds*)
CHIRK CASTLE, nr Wrexham *map 2 D* Built 1310. Exterior is a unique, unaltered example of a border castle of Edward I's time. Inhabited continuously for 660 years. Interesting portraits, tapestries etc. Gardens.	½ m from Chirk (on A5 trunk rd) then 1½ m private driveway: 20 m NW of Shrewsbury 7 m SE of Llangollen *Stn: Chirk (2 m)*	April 22 to May 30 & Oct. 1 to Nov. 4—Weds., & Suns. 2–5. May 31 to Sept. 30—Tues., Weds., Thurs. & Suns. 12–5. All Bank Hol. Mons. 12–5. Adm. £1.50, Chd. 50p; Parties of 20 or more (pre-booked) £1.15. Shop. No dogs. Very limited access for wheelchairs. tearooms (light lunches & teas) *Chirk* 777701	Barton Transport tour from Nottingham; Valliant Cronshaw tours from London; National tours from Chester, Wirral, Llandudno, Birmingham, the Potteries, Liverpool, Lancs. & Sheffield; Wallace Arnold tour from London; Galleon World Travel Assn., Ltd., from London S.W.1 Crosville D2, Chester—Oswestry–Wrexham (*alight Chirk village*)
ERDDIG, nr Wrexham *map 2 D* *The National Trust* Late 17th century house with 18th century additions and containing much of the original furniture, set in a garden restored to 18th century formal design and containing varieties of fruit known to have been grown there during that period. Range of domestic outbuildings include laundry, bakehouse, sawmill and smithy, all in working order; the extensive restoration work on house and garden is now complete. Agricultural museum containing early farm implements	2 m S of Wrexham off A525. *Stns: Wrexham Central (1¾ m); Wrexham General (2½ m), includes 1 m driveway to House*	April to end of Sept.—Daily (except Fris.) 12–5.30. Oct. 3 to Nov. 4—Weds., Sats. & Suns. 12–3.30. Open Good Friday & Bank Hol. Mons. 12–5.30. Last admission 1 hour before closing. Adm.: House, Grounds & Museum £1.80; Grounds & Museum 85p. Chd. 60p (except to Grounds & Museum when Chd. 30p). Pre-booked parties of 20 or more £1.40. Coaches by appointment. Shop. No dogs. Wheelchairs provided, ground floor only accessible. Braille guide. Guide dogs in grounds only. *N.B. Certain rooms have no electric light; visitors wishing to make a close study of pictures & textiles should avoid dull days early & late in season. Due to extreme fragility the Tapestry & Chinese Rooms will be open only on Weds. & Sats.* light lunches & teas *Wrexham* (0978) 355314	Crosville D1, Chester–Wrexham–Llangollen. D2, Wrexham–Oswestry. D93, D94, Wrexham–Corwen–Bala–Barmouth. D3, D4, Wrexham–Rhos (*alight Felin Puleston, ¾ m, then 1 m to house*)
EWLOE CASTLE, nr Hawarden *map 2 C* *Welsh Office* Native Welsh castle with typical round and aspidal towers	1 m NW of Hawarden *Stns: Hawarden (1¾ m); Shotton (2 m)*	Access at all reasonable hours. *Closed Dec. 24, 25, 26 & Jan. 1.* Adm. free.	Crosville A6 Chester–Holywell; A1 Chester–Rhyl; B4 Chester–Denbigh
GYRN CASTLE, Llanasa, Holywell *Sir Geoffrey Bates, BT., M.C.* *map 2 C* Dating, in part, from 1700; castellated 1820. Large picture gallery, panelled entrance hall. Pleasant woodland walks	26 m NW of Chester (off A55); 4 m SE of Prestatyn *Stn: Prestatyn (4½ m)*	All the year—by appointment. Adm. £1.50. Parties welcome. refreshments by arrangement	Crosville M34 Rhyl circular (*not Suns.*)

WILTON HOUSE Nr. SALISBURY

2½ miles west of Salisbury on A30.

Open 10th April to 14th October, Tues.–Sats. and Bank Holidays 11–6; Suns. 1–6. Guided tours daily except Sunday afternoons.

Excellent fully licensed self-service Restaurant – open House hours. Home-made cooking (in Egon Romay's 'Just a Bite' Food guide). Last admission to Restaurant 5.30 p.m. and House 5.15 p.m.

Rates available for parties of 20 or more. Free car and coach parking.

Facilities for the disabled.
No dogs allowed except for the blind.

Home of the Earls of Pembroke for over 400 years

Superb 17th c. State rooms by Inigo Jones. World famous collection of paintings and other treasures. Exhibition of 'The Pembroke Palace' dolls' house and 7,000 model soldiers. 'England's Heritage' in miniature – model railway in 14th c. Almonry. Twenty acres of lawn with giant Cedars of Lebanon. Adventure Playground. 14th c. Washern Grange, the Holbein Porch and Hunting Room may be seen by appointment. Garden Centre.

Frequent day trains from WATERLOO and many other Southern and Western region stations to SALISBURY. Buses 260 and 261 every ½ hour from SALISBURY to WILTON.

QUALITY ANTIQUES FAIR—30th & 31st MARCH and 1st APRIL.

SOUTH OF ENGLAND FLOWER SHOW—28th & 29th JULY.

Details from the Administrator – Telephone (0722) 743115.

SHELDON MANOR

CHIPPENHAM

There has been a house here since early Plantagenet times. The present Great Porch and Parvise above, dating from 1282, were built by Sir Geoffrey Gascelyn, Lord of the Manor and Hundred of Chippenham and were 700 years old in 1982.

Succeeding generations and other families, notably the Hungerfords, have added to the beautiful house, its forecourt and surrounding buildings. All the house is lived-in and it is shown by the family. There are good collections of early oak furniture, Nailsea glass, porcelain and Persian saddle bags.

OPENING TIMES OPPOSITE

STOURHEAD WILTSHIRE

Situated at Stourton, 3 miles N.W. of Mere

THE NATIONAL TRUST

The Gardens at Stourhead are among the finest in Europe. They were laid out by the London banker Henry Hoare, in the middle of the 18th century and were inspired by classical literature and the landscape paintings of Claude Lorraine. Henry Flitcroft designed the temples surrounding the lake and these contain sculpture by Michael Rysbrack and John Cheere.

C. W. Bampfylde 1758 *John Bethell photograph*

The house was designed by Colen Campbell in 1722 and was enlarged by Richard Colt Hoare at the end of the 18th century. It contains a fine picture collection and furniture made by Thomas Chippendale the Younger.

OPENING TIMES OPPOSITE

CHIRK CASTLE • NORTH WALES

The Castle is a unique example of a marcher fortress and was completed in 1310. Chirk Castle has been continuously inhabited ever since. For the first 280 years of its history it remained in the gift of the Crown, and was granted among others to Sir Thomas Seymour, Lord High Admiral, who married Catherine Parr, widow of Henry VIII, and later by Queen Elizabeth I to Robert Dudley, Earl of Leicester. This latter deed of grant is still extant in the Castle. Sir Thomas Myddelton, bought Chirk Castle and lands in 1595. King Charles I stayed in the Castle on two occasions in 1645. The Castle contains much interesting furniture and decorations of the 16th, 17th, 18th and early 19th centuries.

The entrance gates are by the Davies Brothers 1721.

WALES—*continued*

CLWYD—*continued*

PROPERTY (*showing map reference*)	LOCATION (*with nearest Rly. Stn.*)	OPENING TIMES AND ADMISSION CHARGES CATERING FACILITIES	COACH AND RAIL TOURS BUS SERVICES (*showing alighting points*)
RHUDDLAN CASTLE, Rhuddlan *map 2 C* *Welsh Office* Begun by Edward I in 1277: concentric castle of simple design	In Rhuddlan *Stn: Rhyl* (3 *m*)	March 15 to Oct. 15—Daily 9.30–6.30. Oct. 16 to March 14—Weekdays 9.30–4; Suns. 2–4. *Closed Dec.* 24, 25, 26 *& Jan.* 1. Adm. 50p, Chd. & O.A.Ps. 25p	Crosville M34, M35, P35, M36, P36, M39, M51 from Rhyl, Colwyn Bay, Denbigh, Ruthin

DYFED

PROPERTY	LOCATION	OPENING TIMES	BUS SERVICES
COLBY LODGE GARDEN, Amroth *map 2 K* *The National Trust* Small garden in wooded valley with rhododendrons, azaleas, shrubs and trees	NE of Tenby off A477; E of jct. A477/A478 *Stn: Kilgetty* (2½ *m*)	May to end of Sept.—Tues. & Thurs. 2–4. Also Weds. 2–4, by appointment only. ☎ *Llandeilo* 823476	Bristol/Nat. Welsh Joint X12 Bristol–Kilgetty–Haverfordwest
KIDWELLY CASTLE, Kidwelly *map 2 K* *Welsh Office* Originally founded during Henry I's reign	In Kidwelly *Stn: Kidwelly* (½ *m*)	March 15 to Oct. 15—Daily 9.30–6.30. Oct. 16 to March 14—Weekdays 9.30–4; Suns. 2–4. *Closed Dec.* 24, 25, 26 *& Jan.* 1. Adm. 60p, Chd. & O.A.Ps. 30p	South Wales Transport from Llanelli (*hourly Mons.–Sats.*)
MANORBIER CASTLE, nr Pembroke *map 2 K* Birthplace of Giraldus Cambrensis. Castle built between the 12th and 14th centuries	5 m SSE of Pembroke off A4139 on B4585 in Manorbier *Stn: Manorbier* (1 *m*)	Easter for 1 week then May 25 to Sept. 30—Daily 11–6 Adm. 60p, Chd. 20p, O.A.Ps. 30p.	Silcox Motor Coach Ltd., Service 10, Tenby–Manorbier–Jameston; 4 Pembroke Dock–Manorbier–Tenby (*mid July–Aug.*)
PENTRE MANSION, Newchapel *map 2 F* *W. Parkes-Gibbon, Esq.* Landscaped grounds with fine trees. Rockery containing alpines and interesting plants. Thousands of naturalised spring bulbs; cyclamen and autumn crocus. Rhododendrons; herbaceous borders with unusual and beautiful plants	2 m N of Newchapel; 5 m SE of Cardigan; 3 m S of Llechryd	GARDEN ONLY: April 14 to end of Sept.—Daily (except Tues.) 11–6. Adm. £1. Chd. 50p. Plants for sale. ✕☕ refreshments in Mansion; home-made lunches & fresh cream teas ☎ *Boncath* (023 974) 474	No reasonable public transport
PICTON CASTLE, Haverfordwest *map 2 K* *The Hon. Hanning & Lady Marion Philipps* A scheduled ancient monument, home of the Philipps family since the 12th century	4 m SE of Haverfordwest. S off A40 via the Rhos *Stn: Haverfordwest* (4½ *m*)	Grounds & garden only (*not Castle*): Easter Sat. to Sept. 30—Daily (except Mons. but open Bank Hol. Mons.) 10.30–5.30. Graham Sutherland Gallery (at rear of Castle) open daily (except Mons. but open Bank Hol. Mons.) 10.30–5.30. Adm. Gardens £1, Gallery 50p. Chd. & O.A.Ps. half price. Car park free.	No reasonable public transport
TUDOR MERCHANT'S HOUSE, Tenby *The National Trust* *map 2 K* An example of a merchant's house of the 15th century.	Quay Hill, Tenby *Stn: Tenby* (8 *mins. walk*) (*not Suns. except June–Aug.*)	Easter to Sept.—Mons. to Fris. 10–1, 2.30–6; Suns., 2–6. *Closed Good Friday.* Adm. 50p, Chd. 25p. Shop. No dogs. Unsuitable for wheelchairs.	Buses from Pembroke, Haverfordwest Bristol/Nat. Welsh Joint X12 Bristol–Tenby–Haverfordwest

GWENT

PROPERTY	LOCATION	OPENING TIMES	BUS SERVICES
CHEPSTOW CASTLE, Chepstow *map 2 M* *Welsh Office* Great Tower dates from late 11th century	On W bank of the Wye, near Chepstow Bridge *Stn: Chepstow* (½ *m*)	March 15 to Oct. 15—Daily 9.30–6.30. Oct. 16 to March 14—Weekdays 9.30–4, Suns. 2–4. *Closed Dec.* 24, 25, 26 *& Jan.* 1. Adm. 70p, Chd. & O.A.Ps. 35p.	National Welsh local buses Bristol 300 from Bristol National tours from Stockport, Weymouth & Somerset etc.
LLANFIHANGEL COURT, Abergavenny Δ *Col. & Mrs. Somerset Hopkinson* *map 2 M* 15th century manor house. Fine 16th century ceilings and yew staircase. Family pictures and period furniture.	4½ m N of Abergavenny on A465 to Hereford; in Llanfihangel Crucorney village *Stn: Abergavenny* (5½ *m*)	August—all Suns.; also Easter & Summer Bank Hol. Suns. & Mons.; 2.30–6. Adm. charges not available at time of going to press. *Parties at all times by appointment with the Custodian.* ✕☕ at the House.	Abergavenny–Pandy; National Welsh 84 Abergavenny–Hereford (*alight Skirrid Inn,* ¼ *m*) North Western tours from Stockport etc.
PENHOW CASTLE, nr Newport *map 2 M* *Stephen Weeks, Esq.* Ⓔ Norman Border Castle—the oldest inhabited castle in Wales, the first home in Britain of the famous Seymour family and now being fully restored	Midway between Newport & Chepstow on the A48. 7 m from Severn bridge *Stns: Severn Tunnel Jct.* (5½ *m*); *Newport* (8 *m*)	Guided tours Good Friday (April 20) to end of Sept. —Weds. to Suns. & Bank Hols. 10–5.15. *Schools & parties welcome, by appointment, all year round.* Audio Tours (in four languages) included in admission charge. Gift shop. ☕ refreshments ☎ *Penhow* 400800	National Welsh 73, Gloucester–Cardiff
TREDEGAR HOUSE, Newport *map 2 L* *Newport Borough Council* For over 500 years the ancestral home of the Morgans and one of the finest country houses in Wales. The Country Park includes an Aquarium, Bird Garden, Rare Breeds Farm and a 10 acre lake for boating and coarse fishing.	SW of Newport nr M4 jct. 28 *Stn: Newport* (3 *m*)	COUNTRY PARK: Daily 6.15 a.m. to 1 hour after sunset. HOUSE & ATTRACTIONS: Good Friday to Sept. 30—Weds. to Suns. & Bank Hols. Tour of House every ½ hour from 1.30–5. House open at other times by appointment. Adm. (1983 rates) £1, Chd. 50p, O.A.Ps. 80p. Children's Farm 11–6. Adm. (1983 rates) 40p, Chd. 20p. Boats 60p per ½ hour. Fishing £1 (Chd. 50p) during season. Touring Caravans £2 per unit/night. Camping £1. Coach & school parties to be booked in advance. All enquiries to the Visitor Centre. ✕☕ lunch & teas at the Old Brewhouse Bar & Tea Room ☎ *Newport* (0633) 62275	Local buses 15, 15C from Newport
TREWYN, Abergavenny *map 2 M* *Miss K. Telford* Grade II William and Mary mansion in process of restoration; with evidence of medieval work. The house includes fine oak panelling and staircases, minstrel gallery. 6 acres of ornamental grounds in the Brecon Beacons National Park, terraces, arboretum, rhododendrons, walled and rose gardens. Views of the Black Mountains, National Park with Offa's Dyke lying to rear of property.	5 m N of Abergavenny at Pandy off A465 to Hereford *Stn: Abergavenny* (6½ *m*)	GARDENS: March 3 to Oct. 28—Tues. to Fris. 11–5.30; Sats., Suns. & Bank Hols. 10–6.30. *Closed Mons. except Bank Hols.* Oct. 30 to March 2 open by appointment. Adm. 50p, Chd. 25p. Special rates for pre-booked parties & organisations. *House open throughout year by appointment only.* Adm. 50p, Chd. 25p. Plants, vegetables & preserves for sale. Accommodation available—please enquire. ✕☕ light lunches, afternoon teas 12–5. Party bookings for tea rooms ☎ *Crucorney* (087 382) 541	National Welsh 84 from Abergavenny Bus Stn. (*alight Pandy Hotel*)

GWYNEDD

PROPERTY	LOCATION	OPENING TIMES	BUS SERVICES
ABERCONWY HOUSE, Conwy *map 2 C* *The National Trust* Medieval house that dates from 14th cent., now houses the Conwy Exhibition, depicting the life of the borough from Roman times to the present day	In the town at jct. of Castle St. & High St *Stn: Llandudno Junc.* (¼ *m*)	April 20 to end of Sept.—Daily (except Tues.) 11–5. Oct. 6 to Nov. 4—Sats. & Suns. only 11–5. Adm. 50p, Chd. 20p *Parties all year by special arrangement with the Curator; no reductions.* Shop. ☎ *Conwy* (0492 63) 2246	Crosville L1, M5, M13, M16, M18, M19, M20, M22 from Caernarfon, Bangor, Llandudno, Colwyn Bay, Rhyl, Chester & Llanrwst
BEAUMARIS CASTLE, Beaumaris *map 2 C* *Welsh Office* Last of great castles of the Edwardian conquest	In Beaumaris *Stn: Bangor* (6½ *m*)	March 15 to Oct. 15—Daily 9.30–6.30. Oct. 16 to March 14—Weekday 9.30–4; Suns. 2–4. *Closed Dec.* 24, 25, 26 *& Jan.* 1. Adm. 70p, Chd. & O.A.Ps. 35p	Crossville N56/57/58/59 from Bangor, Menai Bridge
BODNANT GARDEN, Tal-y-Cafn *map 2 C* *The National Trust* Begun in 1875 by Henry Pochin. The garden is amongst the finest in the country. Magnificent collections of rhododendrons, camellias, magnolias and conifers	8 m S of Llandudno & Colwyn Bay on A470. Ent. by Eglwysbach Rd *Stn: Tal-y-Cafn* (1¼ *m*) (*not Suns. except peak*)	March 17 to end of Oct.—Daily 10–5. Adm. £1.40. Chd. 70p. Pre-booked parties of 20 or more £1.20 per person. Free car park. *No dogs (except guide dogs for the blind).* Wheelchairs provided but garden is steep & difficult. Braille guide ☕ at car park Kiosk ☎ *Tyn-y-Groes* 460	Crosville M11 to Eglwysbach (*alight entrance*); M10, M22 (connections from Llandudno & Colwyn Bay) Crosville buses from Llandudno and Colwyn Bay National tours from Llandudno, Colwyn Bay, Southport, Stockport, the Potteries, etc. Royal Red tours from Colwyn Bay

Penhow Castle

Gwent Wales

Cross our drawbridge and discover the most enchanting Knight's Castle on the Welsh Border. Our Award-Winning Tours explore the Castle from battlements to kitchens. Discover Penhow and lose yourself in the past!

WALES' OLDEST LIVED-IN CASTLE
SEVEN MILES FROM THE SEVERN BRIDGE

Spend the last 850 years in an unhurried Audio-Tour of the Castle. Tours in 4 languages — and a special young person's tour which will captivate your children. On the tour discover the 15th century Great Hall with its minstrels' gallery, or the homely warmth of the Victorian Housekeeper's Room. Discover the 12th century Norman Bedchamber, or the unfolding countryside view from atop the battlements. The Castle is being lovingly restored by its young owner, and every year there is more to see. This year the tour goes through several new rooms and you can watch the progress on the splendid panelled Charles II rooms which are currently under restoration. Penhow — cradle of the famous Seymour Family — is an ideal visit to combine with Tintern Abbey or Chepstow, and our Gift Shop has an interesting selection of our own publications. Our new Tea Room is open for refreshments all through the season.

Opening Times Opposite.

MANORBIER CASTLE

DYFED

Situated on the outskirts of Manorbier village about 5 miles from Pembroke and Tenby, Manorbier Castle was built between the 12th and 14th centuries. Here was born Giraldus Cambrensis—famous for his descriptions of life in 12th century Wales. There is a regular bus service to Manorbier from Tenby during the summer and a souvenir Shop for the convenience of visitors. Life-sized wax figures on display.
The Castle is open at Easter for 1 week and from Whitsun to September 30—Daily.
Visiting Hours: 11 a.m.–6 p.m.
Admission: Adults 60p, Children 20p, O.A.Ps. 30p.

LLANFIHANGEL COURT

ABERGAVENNY

"B.T.A." photograph

A medieval house which, as it now stands, is the result of Tudor and Stuart modernising. The original house was clearly an open hall with a dais still in position. Fine plaster ceilings of 1559 are in excellent condition as is the oak panelling in the Morning room and bedrooms. An exceptional feature is the beautiful yew staircase dating from mid 1600. The house has been little touched in modern times and is a typical family home.

TREWYN

ABERGAVENNY, GWENT

William and Mary mansion in process of restoration, with evidence of medieval work. The house includes fine oak panelling and staircases and a minstrel gallery. Six acres of ornamental grounds in the Brecon Beacons National Park; terraces, arboretum, rhododendrons, walled and rose gardens. Views of the Black Mountains. Offa's Dyke lies to the rear of the property.

OPENING TIMES OPPOSITE

TREDEGAR HOUSE

NEWPORT, GWENT

Tredegar House is one of the architectural wonders of Wales. This magnificent 17th century house, set in glorious parkland, was for over 500 years the ancestral home of the Morgan family, later Lords of Tredegar.

OPENING TIMES OPPOSITE

BRYN BRAS CASTLE

LLANRUG, Nr. CAERNARFON, N. WALES

The gardens are one of the largest private gardens in Wales open to public. Peaceful lawns, woodland walks, stream, waterfalls, pools, ½ mile mountain walk with magnificent views of Snowdonia and Anglesey, statues, walled knot garden, over a mile of tranquil pathways, rhododendrons, roses, hydrangeas. The Castle was built in c. 1830 in the Romanesque Style on an earlier structure built before 1750. This romantic Castle is a delightful lived-in home, part of which is open to view: reception hall, galleried staircase, drawing room, morning room, dining room, library.

Refreshments in Garden Tearoom and on lawns. Picnic area.

OPENING TIMES SEE PAGE 160

GWYNEDD—*continued*

PROPERTY (*showing map reference*)	LOCATION (*with nearest Rly. Stn.*)	OPENING TIMES AND ADMISSION CHARGES CATERING FACILITIES	COACH AND RAIL TOURS BUS SERVICES (*showing alighting points*)
BRYN BRAS CASTLE, Llanrug *map 2 C* *Mrs. M. Gray-Parry & R. D. Gray-Williams Esq.* ✿ Castle built in 1830's around an earlier structure built before 1750. Extensive gardens include peaceful lawns, woodland walks and a mountain walk with panoramic views of Anglesey and Snowdonia.	4½ m E of Caernarfon; 3½ m NW of Llanberis; ¼ m off A4086 *Stn: Bangor (7½ m)*	Spring Bank Hol. to mid-July & September—Daily (except Sats.) 1–5. Mid-July to end August—Daily (except Sats.) 10.30–5. Adm. £1, Chd. 50p. 25% *reduction for parties.* Free car park. Picnic area. ☕ in garden tearoom & on lawns ☎ *Llanberis* 870 210	Crosville N77, Bangor–Llanberis (*weekdays only*) N99, Caernarfon–Llanberis–Nant Peris N98, Caernarfon–Pen-y-gwryd (*summer only*)
CAERNARFON CASTLE (1283-1322) Caernarfon *Welsh Office* *map 2 B* The most important of Edward I's castles	In Caernarfon *Stn: Bangor (8½ m)*	March 15 to Oct. 15—Daily 9.30–6.30. Oct. 16 to March 14—Weekdays 9.30–4, Suns. 2–4. *Closed Dec.* 24, 25, 26 & *Jan.* 1. Adm.: Summer period £1.50, Chd. & O.A.Ps. 75p. Winter period £1, Chd. & O.A.Ps. 50p Adm. includes Royal Welsh Fusiliers Museum & 'Caernarfon our Heritage' A.V. Theatre.	National Coach 864 from Liverpool National tours from Lancs., Merseyside & the Potteries Crosville Cymru coastliner L1 from Chester, Rhyl, Colwyn Bay, Llandudno, Bangor Crosville from Porthmadog, Pwllheli, Beddgelert, Llanberis, etc.
CONWY CASTLE (1283–9), Conwy *Welsh Office* *map 2 C* Built by Edward I to command Conwy ferry	In Conwy *Stn: Llandudno Jt. (¼ m)*	March 15 to Oct. 15—Daily 9.30–6.30. Oct. 16 to March 14—Weekdays 9.30–4, Suns. 2–4. *Closed Dec.* 24, 25, 26 & *Jan.* 1, Adm. 70p, Chd. & O.A.Ps. 35p.	Crosville buses from Chester, Rhyl, Llandudno, Colwyn Bay, Llanwrst, Bangor, Caernarfon etc. National coach 863, 864, 866 from Liverpool National tours from Merseyside & Lancs. Yelloway tours from Oldham & Rochdale districts
CRICCIETH CASTLE, Criccieth *map 2 B* *Welsh Office* Native Welsh castle dating mainly first half 13th century	In Criccieth *Stn: Criccieth (½ m) (not Suns.)*	March 15 to Oct. 15—Daily 9.30–6.30. Oct. 16 to March 14—Weekdays 9.30–4, Suns. 2–4. *Closed Dec.* 24, 25, 26 & *Jan.* 1. Adm. 50p, Chd. & O.A.Ps. 25p	Crosville L1 (connection from Caernarfon); R2/R3 from Porthmadog (*peak Suns. only*); R3 from Pwllheli (*peak Suns. only*); X9 from Liverpool, Chester
HARLECH CASTLE, Harlech *map 2 C* *Welsh Office* Built 1283–9 by Edward I. Concentric plan	In Harlech *Stn: Harlech (¼ m)*	March 15 to Oct. 15—Daily 9.30–6.30. Oct. 16 to March 14—Weekdays 9.30–4, Suns. 2–4. *Closed Dec.* 24, 25, 26 & *Jan.* 1. Adm. 70p, Chd. & O.A.Ps. 35p.	National tours from Merseyside, Stockport, the Potteries, etc. Crosville R38 Dolgellau–Barmouth–Maentwrog (with connections from Porthmadog & Blaenau Ffestiniog)
PENRHYN CASTLE, Bangor *map 2 C* *The National Trust* ✿ The 19th cent. Castle is a unique and outstanding example of neo-Norman architecture. ♿ The garden and grounds have exotic and rare trees and shrubs. There is an Industrial Railway Museum and exhibition of dolls. Victorian formal garden. Superb views of mountains and Menai Strait	3 m E of Bangor, on A5122. *Stn: Bangor (3 m)*	April 20 to end of May & Oct. to Nov. 4—Daily (except Tues.) 2–5. June to end of Sept. & all Bank Hol. weekends—Daily (except Tues.) 11–5. Adm. £1.80. Chd. 60p. Pre-booked parties of 20 or more £1.40. Shop. No dogs. Wheelchair access—2 provided. Braille guidebook. ☎ *Bangor* 353084 ✕☕ light lunches & teas at Castle	Crosville buses, Bangor, Conwy, Llandudno, connecting buses from Bethesda & Betws-y-Coed (*alight Grand Lodge*) National tours from Stockport, etc. Creams weekly tours from Llandudno Royal Red tours from Llandudno
PLAS MAWR, Conwy *map 2 C* *Royal Cambrian Academy of Art* Built by Robert Wynne, 1577–80	High St., Conwy *Stn: Llandudno Junction (¼ m)*	All the year—Daily 10–5.30 (winter 10–4). Adm. 50p, Chd. 20p, O.A.Ps. & Students 35p. *Closed December to mid-January* ☕ summer only	Crosville buses from Caernarfon, Bangor, Llanrwst, Llandudno & Colwyn Bay
PLAS NEWYDD, Isle of Anglesey *map 2 C* *The National Trust* ✿ 18th cent. house by James Wyatt in unspoilt position adjacent to Menai Strait. Magnificent ♿ views to Snowdonia. Fine spring garden. Rex Whistler's largest wall painting. Military museum	1 m SW of Llanfairpwll on A4080 to Brynsiencyn; turn off A5 to Llanfairpwll at W end of Britannia Bridge *Stn: Llanfairpwll (1¾ m)*	April 20 to Sept. 30—Daily (except Sats.) 12–5. Oct. 1 to Nov. 4—Daily (except Sats.) 2–5. Last adm. 4.30. Adm. £1.50, Chd. 50p. Pre-booked parties of 20 or more £1.15. Shop. No dogs. Wheelchairs admitted (& provided) but limited access. ☕ tearooms (light lunches & teas) ☎ *Llanfairpwll* (0248) 714795	Crosville N42 & 43, Bangor–Llangefni (*not Suns.*) N44–49, Bangor–Holyhead (*alight Llanfairpwll 1½ m*)
TY MAWR, Wybrnant *map 2 C* *The National Trust* The birthplace of Bishop William Morgan. (c. 1541–1604), the first translator of the Bible into Welsh	At the head of the little valley of Wybrnant, 3½ m SW of Betws-y-Coed; 2 m W of Penmachno *Stn: Pont-y-Pant (3 m) (not Suns. except peak)*	April 20 to end of Sept.—Daily (except Mons. & Sats.) 12–5. Oct. by appointment only. Adm. 30p, Chd. 15p. *Parties by appointment* (The Custodian, Ty Mawr, Wybrnant, Dolwyddelan, Gwynedd). No dogs. Wheelchair access to one room only. *N.B. Approach roads unsuitable for large vehicles & coaches.* ☎ *Penmachno* (069 03) 213 ☕ light refreshment available.	No reasonable public transport

POWYS

PROPERTY	LOCATION	OPENING TIMES	TRANSPORT
POWIS CASTLE, Welshpool *map 2 G* *The National Trust* ✿ General aspect of 13th–14th century castle, although reconstructed in early 17th century. ♿ Fine plaster work, murals, furniture, paintings and tapestry. Historic terraced garden; herbaceous borders, rare trees and shrubs	1 m S of Welshpool on A483. Pedestrian access from High St. (A490) Cars enter rd to Newtown (A483), 1 m *Stns: Welshpool (1½ m) Welshpool Raven Square (1½ m); B.R. service Aug. only*	CASTLE & GARDEN: April 21 to June 30 & Sept. —Weds. to Suns. 1–6. July 1 to Aug. 31.—GARDEN open daily 12–6; CASTLE open daily (except Mons.) 1–6. All Bank Hol. Mons. 11.30–6. Last adm. 5.30 Adm.: Castle & Garden £1.80, Chd. 60p; Parties of 20 or more (pre-booked) £1.40. Garden *or* Castle only £1.20, Chd. 40p. Shop. Free car park. No dogs. Wheelchairs (provided) in tearoom, shop & parts of garden only. ☎ *Welshpool* (0938) 4336 ☕ tearooms (light lunches & teas)	National tours from Cardiff, Liverpool, the Potteries Stockport, Bolton, Barnsley etc. Crosville D71 Oswestry–Welshpool Crosville D75, Shrewsbury–Welshpool–Newtown–Llanidloes
TREBINSHWN HOUSE, nr Brecon *Robin Watson, Esq.* ✿ A medium sized 16th century manor house which underwent extensive restoration in 1800. Fine courtyard and walled garden.	7 m SE of Brecon; 1½ m from Bwlch & A40; 4 m from Llangorse (B4560)	May 1 to Aug. 31—Mons. & Tues. 10–5. Adm. charge ✕☕ Red Lion Hotel, Llangorse (4 m).	No reasonable public transport
TRELYDAN HALL, Welshpool *map 2 G* *Mr. & Mrs. J. Trevor-Jones* Tudor house with original timbers and attic priest hole. Once the home of Capt. John Gwyn, armourer to Charles I. The late Georgian drawing room houses a rare collection of Victorian wedding dresses and antique lace	1 m from Welshpool, off A490 Welshpool-Llanfyllin rd. 18 m from Shrewsbury. *Stns: Welshpool (2½ m) (not Suns. except Aug.) Welshpool Raven Sq. (2½ m)*	Pre-booked Groups only. Candlelight dinners & entertainment at 8 p.m. on Fridays & Saturdays. Limited accommodation. ✕☕ light refreshments & pre-booked meals	Local services from Welshpool–Llanfyllin & Welshpool–Guilsfield (*approx. 1 m walk from bus stop*)
TRETOWER COURT & CASTLE, Crickhowell *map 2 L* *Welsh Office* One of the finest medieval houses in Wales	3½ m NW Crickhowell between A40 & A479 rds *Stn: Abergavenny (10 m)*	March 15 to Oct. 15—Weekdays 9.30–6.30, Suns. 2–6.30. Oct. 16 to March 14—Weekdays 9.30–4, Suns. 2–4. *Closed Dec.* 24, 25, 26 & *Jan.* 1. Adm. 50p, Chd. & O.A.Ps. 25p.	Western Welsh 142, Brecon–Crickhowell–Abergavenny (via Bwlch)

MID GLAMORGAN

PROPERTY	LOCATION	OPENING TIMES	TRANSPORT
LLANHARAN HOUSE, Llanharan *Owain Williams, Esq.* *map 2 L* ✿ Mainly Georgian country house with some fine plasterwork, family pictures, furniture. The ♿ 2-storey spiral stone staircase is perhaps the main architectural feature. Hill walks.	2½ m W of Llantrisant via A473 *Stn: Bridgend (8 m)*	Bank Hol. Suns. & Mons. May 6/7, 27/28 & Aug. 26/27. July 1 to Sept. 19—Suns. & Weds. 2.30–5.30. Adm. House & Garden £1, Chd. 50p, O.A.Ps. 70p. Parties at reduced rates by arrangement throughout the year. Shop, unique range of Welsh products. ☕ teas in old dining room or garden ✕ Bear Hotel, Cowbridge	Local buses will stop at gates

POWIS CASTLE

POWYS

THE NATIONAL TRUST

A. F. Kersting photograph

Powis Castle is a medieval castle of red limestone spectacularly sited on a lofty ridge near Welshpool. The home of the Powis family, it has been inhabited without interruption over 500 years. It contains fine plasterwork, woodwork, murals by Lanscroon and tapestry. The terraced gardens, laid out by the Earl of Rochford before 1722, contain some superb topiary work and lead statuary.

PLAS NEWYDD

Isle of Anglesey, Gwynedd

THE NATIONAL TRUST

The house, the home of the Marquess of Anglesey, stands on the edge of an unspoilt stretch of the Menai Strait with magnificent views to Snowdonia. It was designed in the late eighteenth century Gothic style by James Wyatt and his assistant, Joseph Potter of Lichfield. The dining room is decorated with Rex Whistler's largest wall painting of an Italianate coastal scene. There is a military museum with important relics of Waterloo. The grounds consist of a spring garden with massed shrubs, fine trees and lawns sloping down to the Strait.

OPENING TIMES OPPOSITE

TRELYDAN HALL

Welshpool Powys

18 miles from Shrewsbury and the setting for several films, this predominantly private Tudor home of great character is magnificently sited on the foundations of a secluded medieval Catholic hospice and reputed Roman Villa named LATEO on Offa's Dyke. It contains a wealth of remarkably well preserved, original timbers and an interesting attic priest hole.

It was once the home of Capt. John Gwyn (directly descended from the Princes of Powys) whose "curious pedigree" is recorded as far back as the legendary "Brochwell Ysgythrog". John Gwyn was armourer to Charles I and author of "The Military Memoirs of the Civil War" (published under the editorship of Sir Walter Scot).

The late Georgian drawing room houses a rare collection of Victorian wedding dresses and antique lace.

Small intimate candlelight dinners, great log fires, harp music and song, traditional Welsh clog-dancing at 8 p.m. on Fridays and Saturdays.

Overnight suites in Tudor rooms and a self-contained Georgian Dower House.

Unique lecture/demonstrations on floral designs combined with a personal record of the impressive restoration of her home and garden are given by top International T.V. flower arranger Iona Trevor-Jones. Pre-booked groups only.

LLANHARAN HOUSE

LLANHARAN, MID GLAMORGAN

2½ m W of Llantrisant on A473, exit 34 or 35 from M4

Mainly Georgian Country House with some fine plasterwork, family pictures and furniture. Two-storey spiral staircase is, perhaps, the main architectural feature.
Teas in old dining room or garden. Hill Walks. Shop—has an unique range of Welsh products.
Open Bank Holiday Sundays and Mondays May 6th/7th & 27th/28th and August 26th/27th; also Sundays and Wednesdays from July 1st to September 19th—2.30 p.m. to 5.30 p.m. Admission: House and Garden £1. Children 50p, O.A.Ps. 70p. Parties at reduced rates by arrangement throughout the year at times to suit. Tel. (0443) 226253.

CARDIFF CASTLE

In the heart of modern Cardiff stands Cardiff Castle—a building representing 1900 years of history. Stretches of the ten feet thick walls built by the Romans are still to be seen and the grounds are still dominated by the Norman keep. In the last century the 3rd Marquess of Bute employed William Burges, A.R.A., to restore the castle. Visitors can tour the colourful interior created by Burges with exquisite wood carving, sculpture and murals that tell of the castle's long history. A new attraction is the Welch Regiment Museum.

TOURS
March, April and October (Standard tour approx. 1 hour).
Weekdays (at 30 min. intervals) 10 a.m.–12.30 p.m.; 2 p.m.–4 p.m.
Sundays—Tours at 10 a.m., 11 a.m., 12 noon, 2 p.m., 3 p.m. and 4 p.m.

May to September (Tour includes Roof Garden and part Clock Tower, approx. 1 hour).
Daily (at 20 min. intervals) 10 a.m.–12.40 p.m.; 2 p.m.–5 p.m.
Sundays (at 30 min. intervals) 10 a.m.–12.30 p.m.; 2 p.m.–5 p.m.

November to February (Standard Tour)
Weekdays—Tours at 11 a.m., 12 noon, 2 p.m. and 3 p.m.
Sundays—Tours at 11 a.m., 12 noon and 3 p.m.

From 1 May to 30 September, the Castle Green/Roman Wall, Norman Keep and Welch Regiment Museum are open to the public daily from 10 a.m. to 6 p.m.; March, April and October from 10 a.m. to 5 p.m. and from November to February 10 a.m. to 4 p.m. The castle is closed to the public on Christmas and New Year Bank Holidays.

Further information from the Technical Services Department, Hodge House, St. Mary Street, Cardiff. Tel. 0222-31033, ext. 716.

WALES—*continued*

SOUTH GLAMORGAN

PROPERTY (*showing map reference*)	LOCATION (*with nearest Rly. Stn.*)	OPENING TIMES AND ADMISSION CHARGES CATERING FACILITIES	COACH AND RAIL TOURS BUS SERVICES (*showing alighting points*)
CARDIFF CASTLE map 2 L *Cardiff City Council* Begun 1090 on site of Roman Castrum. Rich interior decorations. Location for Cardiff Searchlight Tattoo.	In centre of Cardiff city *Stn: Cardiff Cen. (¼ m)*	March, April & Oct.—Daily 10–5 (cond. tours 10–4; Suns. 10, 11, 12, 2, 3, 4); May to Sept.—Daily 10–6 (cond. tours 10–5; Suns. 10–5); Nov. to Feb.—Daily 10–4 (cond. tours 11, 12, 2 & 3; Suns. 11, 12 & 3). The Castle is closed occasionally for special events. Adm. charges not available at time of going to press.	British Rail 125 from London (1 hr 50 mins) Good rail & coach services from all parts
CASTELL COCH, Tongwynlais map 2 L *Welsh Office* 13th century castle, restored on original lines for the Marquess of Bute in 19th cent. and made habitable	6 m N of Cardiff off Pontypridd rd by village of Tongwynlais *Stn: Taffs Well (1½ m)*	March 15 to Oct. 15—Daily 9.30–6.30. Oct. 16 to March 14—Weekdays 9.30–4, Suns. 2–4. *Closed Dec.* 24, 25, 26 *& Jan.* 1. Adm. 85p, Chd. & O.A.Ps. 40p.	City of Cardiff 36, Cardiff–Tredegar (*hourly*) Rhondda/Western Welsh 330, 332, Cardiff–Pontypridd
CAERPHILLY CASTLE, Caerphilly map 2 L *Welsh Office* Second largest castle area in Britain	In Caerphilly; 6 m N of Cardiff *Stn: Caerphilly (½ m)*	March 15 to Oct. 15—Daily 9.30–6.30. Oct. 16 to March 14—Weekdays 9.30–4; Suns. 2–4. *Closed Dec.* 24, 25, 26 *& Jan.* 1. Adm. 70p, Chd. & O.A.Ps. 35p	City of Cardiff 36, Cardiff—Tredegar
ST. FAGANS CASTLE, Cardiff map 2 L *Welsh Folk Museum* 16th century house built within curtain wall of 13th century castle. Extensive Folk museum	4½ m W of City centre *Stn: Cardiff Central (4½ m)*	All the year—Weekdays 10–5, Suns. 2.30–5. Adm. 30p, Chd. & O.A.Ps. 15p. Car park 20p. Coaches 50p. *Closed Christmas Eve, Christmas Day, Boxing Day, New Year's Day, Good Friday and May* 7 in the grounds	City of Cardiff Transport 32, from Central Bus St. (*hourly*) (*alight gates*)

WEST GLAMORGAN

PROPERTY	LOCATION	OPENING TIMES AND ADMISSION CHARGES CATERING FACILITIES	COACH AND RAIL TOURS BUS SERVICES
MARGAM COUNTRY PARK, nr Port Talbot *West Glamorgan County Council* map 2 L This 850 acre country park has historic buildings including the famous Orangery, attractive gardens, a deer herd, boating on the lake, putting, horse and donkey rides, an adventure playground, a sculpture park, an indoor exhibition and the Coach House Theatre	On A48 between Pyle & Margam, exits 37 or 38 off M4 *Stn: Port Talbot (4 m)*	April to Oct.—Daily (except Mons. but open Bank Hol. Mons.) 10.30–8. Nov. to March—Weds. to Suns. 10.30–1 hour before dusk. Adm. (1983 rates) 40p, Chd. & O.A.Ps. 20p; Chd. under 5 yrs. & Registered Disabled free. Party rates by prior arrangement. Toilets. Enquiries: *Port Talbot* (0639) 881635 refreshments	South Wales Transport XI & 136 from Swansea (*alight at entrance to park*)

IRELAND

PROPERTY	LOCATION	OPENING TIMES AND ADMISSION CHARGES CATERING FACILITIES	COACH AND RAIL TOURS BUS SERVICES
BANTRY HOUSE, Bantry, Co. Cork *Egerton Shelswell-White, Esq.* map 4 T Partly-Georgian mansion standing at edge of Bantry Bay, with beautiful views. Seat of family of White, formerly Earls of Bantry. Unique collection of tapestries, furniture etc. Terraces and Statuary in the Italian style in grounds	In outskirts of Bantry (¼ m) 56 m SW of Cork	Open all year—Daily 9–6 (*open until* 8 *on most summer evenings*). Adm. House & Grounds £2, Chd. 7–14 yrs. incl. 50p (6 yrs. & under, free), O.A.Ps. & Students £1. Parties of 20 or more £1.50. Craft shop. Tearoom *Bantry* 50047	C.I.E. Bus Service, Cork–Bandon–Dunmanway–Bantry (*alight Lodge gates*)
CASTLETOWN HOUSE, Celbridge, map 4 L *Irish Georgian Society* [Co. Kildare Built in 1722, the finest Georgian country house in Ireland	12 m W of Dublin	Jan. to March—Suns. only 2–5. April to Sept.—Weds., Sats. & Suns. 2–6. *Closed Oct., Nov. & Dec.* Adm. £1.20, Chd. 60p; Parties of 20 or more £1. *Adm. for parties (any number) by appointment.* at the House at weekends in summer	C.I.E. 67, Dublin (Abbey St.—Celbridge (*alight gates*)
FOTA, Fota Island, Carrigtwohill, Co. Cork *Miss Christina Neylon* map 4 U Regency mansion formerly the home of the Earls of Barrymore. Collection of Irish paintings by Barry, Maclise, O'Connor, Roberts, etc. Rooms furnished with Irish 18th and 19th century pieces. Arboretum and Wildlife Park.	10m E of Cork City, on Cobh rd., off main Waterford rd. *Stn: Fota*	March to Oct.—Mons. to Sats. 11–6; Suns. 1–6. Remainder of the year Sats. & Suns. 2–6. Parties any time by appointment with the Administrator. Adm. £1 (working); Chd., Students & O.A.Ps. 50p. Ground floor only suitable for the disabled (toilet provided). Coffee shop in Wildlife Park Restaurants & hotels in Cobh (4 m) *Cork* (021) 812555	Fota has its own station (*frequent service*). Boat transport from Cobh, Passage West & Cork (*summer only*)
JOHNSTOWN CASTLE, Wexford map 4 R *An Foras Taluntais (The Agricultural Institute)* Grounds and gardens only. Many acres of well laid out grounds, with artificial lakes and fine collection of ornamental trees and shrubs. Nature Trails. Agricultural museum	5 m SW of Wexford	All the year—Daily 9.30–5 Guidebook available at Castle	No reasonable public transport
LISMORE CASTLE, Lismore, Co. Waterford *Trustees of the Lismore Estates* map 4 P Beautifully situated walled and woodland gardens. Yew walk.	In town of Lismore; 45 m W of Waterford; 35 m NE of Cork	GARDENS ONLY: May 7 to Sept. 14—Daily (except Sats.) 1.45–4.45. Adm. 60p, Chd. (under 16) 25p. Reduced rates for parties. *Dungarvon* (058) 54424	No reasonable public transport
LISSADELL, Sligo map 4 F *Josslyn Gore-Booth, Esq.* The finest Greek-revival country house in Ireland. Splendid views of the surrounding countryside.	8 m NW of Sligo overlooking Sligo Bay	Easter week then May 1 to Sept. 30—Weekdays 2.30–5.15. *Closed Suns.* Adm. £1.	No reasonable public transport
MOUNT USHER GARDENS, map 4 S **Ashford, Co. Wicklow** *Mrs. Madelaine Jay* The Gardens expand along the Vartry River in beautiful County Wicklow, known as "The Garden of Ireland". Mount Usher's creation as a garden, started over 100 years ago, has been expanded and improved ever since. The Gardens are laid out in the informal, Robinsonian style; comprising rare plants, shrubs and trees collected from many parts of the world.	In Ashford; 3 m from Wicklow on main rd Dublin–Wexford	March 17 to Sept. 30—Mons. to Sats. 10.30–6; Suns. 2–6. Adm. £1.20. Chd. under 15 yrs. 60p. (under 5 yrs. free); O.A.Ps. & Students 60p. Parties of 20 or more adults £1 per person; 20 or more Chd., O.A.Ps. or Students 50p per person. Antiques shop. Free car park. Tea room serving snacks (at entrance to Gardens)	Bus service Dublin–Wicklow passes through Ashford
NATIONAL BOTANIC GARDENS, map 4 L **Glasnevin, Dublin 9** *Department of Agriculture* Founded 1795. 47 acres in extent containing 25,000 different living plant species and varieties. Flowering shrubs. Dwarf conifers. Orchids. Herbarium	2 m from city centre	All the year—Daily (except Christmas Day): Weekdays 9–6 (*summer*), 10–4.30 (*winter*). Sundays 11–6 (*summer*), 11–4.30 (*winter*). CONSERVATORIES: Mons. to Fris. 9–12.45, 2.15–5 (*summer*), 10–12.45, 2.15–4.15 (*winter*); Sats. 9–12.15, 2.15–5.45 (*summer*), 10–12.15 2.15–4.15 (*winter*); Suns. 2–5.45 (*summer*), 2–4.15 (*winter*) Adm. free	City Services 13 and 19, Cross City Service from O'Connell Street; 34, 34A from Middle Abbey St. (*alight entrance gates*)
RIVERSTOWN HOUSE, **Glanmire, Co. Cork** map 4 P Remarkable Francini plasterwork.	4 m NE of Cork off Dublin rd.	May to September—Thurs., Fris., Sats. & Suns. 2–6. *Tours all year round by arrangement only.* Adm. £1 Chd. 40p.	C.I.E. bus services Dublin–Naas–Thurles–Cahir–Mitchelstown–Cork
RUSSBOROUGH, Blessington, Co. Wicklow *Alfred Beit Foundation* map 4 L Palladian house in romantic setting in the Wicklow mountains, built 1740-50 and housing the Beit Art Collection. Irish silver collection (1680-1820)	2½ m S of Blessington. SW of Dublin, NW of Wicklow	Easter to October—Suns. & Bank Hols. also Weds., June to Aug. & Sats., July to Aug.; 2.30–6.30 (last admission 5.30). Adm. £1.50, Chd. (5–15) 90p. Silver & bedrooms 75p. Rhododendron garden (when in bloom) 50p. *Reduced rates for parties.* Tea room *Naas* 65239	Modest service Dublin–Blessington (*alight Blessington, 3 m walk*) Occasional services run nearer to the house (*alight Russborough, ½ m walk to house*)

For information on

EDUCATIONAL SERVICES

SEE PAGE 8

NATIONAL MUSEUM OF WALES

WELSH FOLK MUSEUM ST. FAGANS

St. Fagans Castle

Recently this Elizabethan house within the curtain wall of a Norman Castle has been refurbished and largely restored to its 17th century appearance. The ground floor is divided in half between the work rooms, including the kitchen with its two open fire-places, and the more ornate rooms frequented by the family. The Great Chamber at the top of the staircase has a large coloured overmantel while the Long Gallery is the earliest known in Glamorgan and possibly in South Wales. Bed Chambers, Withdrawing Rooms and a Nursery make up the rest of the first floor.

BANTRY HOUSE

CO. CORK

Partly-Georgian mansion standing at the edge of Bantry Bay, with beautiful views. Seat of the White family, formerly Earls of Bantry. A unique collection of tapestries, furniture, etc. Terraces and Statuary in the Italian style in the grounds.

OPENING TIMES OPPOSITE

MOUNT USHER GARDENS CO. WICKLOW

Mount Usher Gardens expand along the Vartry River in beautiful County Wicklow, known as "The Garden of Ireland". Mount Usher's creation as a garden started over 100 years ago and has been expanded and improved ever since. The Gardens are laid out in the informal 'Robinsonian' style comprising rare plants, shrubs and trees collected from many parts of the world.

Spacious Tea Room overlooking river and garden. Selective shops. Open every day from 10.30 a.m. to 6.00 p.m. (Sunday 2.00 p.m. to 6.00 p.m.)—March 17th (St. Patrick's Day) to September 30th.

RUSSBOROUGH

BLESSINGTON, CO. WICKLOW

Russborough was built between 1740-50 and is the finest house in Ireland open to the public. It is set amidst beautiful mountain scenery and houses the world-famous Beit Art Collection (paintings by Vermeer, Goya, Metsu, Gainsborough, Rubens, Reynolds and others) which is seen as part of the tour of the main rooms. A second tour shows the bedrooms and an outstanding collection of Irish Silver (1680-1820) which has been lent to the house.

OPENING TIMES OPPOSITE

FOTA, FOTA ISLAND

CARRIGTWOHILL, CO. CORK

This Regency mansion, 10 miles east of Cork City, formerly the home of the Earls of Barrymore, is the centrepiece of Fota Island, with its world-famous arboretum and newly-opened Wildlife Park. Recently renovated with authenticity, it houses an important collection of Irish paintings displayed in their natural setting. Artists represented include Barry, Maclise, O'Connor, Roberts. The rooms are furnished with fine examples of Irish eighteenth and nineteenth century pieces.

OPENING TIMES OPPOSITE

The National Trust Northern Ireland Properties

For further information about properties in the care of the National Trust in Northern Ireland apply to The National Trust, Rowallane, Saintfield, Co. Down. Telephone: Saintfield 510721.

SPRINGHILL

MONEYMORE, CO. LONDONDERRY

"Belfast Museum & Art Gallery" photograph

Springhill is a 17th century Manor House of great character. With slate roof and roughcast walls it impresses chiefly by its balanced proportions and the simplicity of its design. The courtyard in front of the house is flanked by attractive and unusual barns with curving gables and carved stone urns. The house contains a magnificent oak staircase, also much interesting furniture and paintings. There is a costume museum and a cottar's kitchen.

CASTLE WARD

STRANG FORD, CO. DOWN

The house was built by the first Lord Bangor in 1765. The S.W. front is Palladian, the N.E. Strawberry Hill Gothick. Set in 600 acres of woodland, park and gardens, running down to Strangford Lough.

"Country Life" photograph

MOUNT STEWART HOUSE & GARDEN

GREYABBEY, CO. DOWN

"A. & C. Photography" photograph

Interesting house with close associations with Lord Castlereagh. Eighty acres of magnificent formal and informal garden designed by Edith, Seventh Marchioness of Londonderry and containing rare plants, trees and shrubs from all over the world.

CASTLE COOLE

ENNISKILLEN, CO. FERMANAGH

"A. & C. Photography" photograph

Built in 1789 for the 1st Earl of Belmore, Castle Coole is among the most beautiful and architecturally satisfying of late Georgian houses. It is probable that James Wyatt was called in to modify plans by Richard Johnston, of Dublin, in accordance with a more restrained Grecian taste. Wyatt was wholly responsible for the interior and the plasterwork was carried out by Joseph Rose.
N.B. In 1984 only the parkland will be open.

ARDRESS

CO. ARMAGH

"A. & C. Photography" photograph

A 17th-century house with main front and garden facade added in the second half of the 18th century by George Ensor, owner-architect. Fine plasterwork in the drawing-room by Michael Stapleton of Dublin after Robert Adam.

ROWALLANE GARDEN

SAINTFIELD, CO. DOWN

Fifty acres divided into a series of fine gardens. Outstanding collection of rhododendrons, azaleas, magnolias and cherries. Created by the late Mr Armytage Moore.

Patrick Rossmore photograph

PROPERTY (*showing map reference*)	LOCATION (*with nearest Rly. Stn.*)	OPENING TIMES AND ADMISSION CHARGES CATERING FACILITIES	COACH AND RAIL TOURS BUS SERVICES (*showing alighting points*)

NORTHERN IRELAND

PROPERTY	LOCATION	OPENING TIMES	BUS SERVICES
ARDRESS HOUSE, Co. Armagh *map 4 G* Δ *The National Trust* 17th cent. country house with fine plasterwork. Small garden, agricultural display in farmyard. Woodland play area	**7 m W of Portadown on Portadown –Moy rd (B28) 2 m from Loughgall intersection on M1** *Stn: Portadown (7 m)*	April to end of Sept.—Daily (except Fris.) 2–6. Open Good Friday 2–6. Adm. 60p, Chd. 30p; Parties 40p. Car park (weekends) 30p. Wheelchairs admitted. Picnic area. ☎ *Annaghmore* 851236	Ulsterbus 51, 251, Belfast (*Gt. Victoria St.*)–Portadown, thence 67 to Kesquin (*not Suns.*) (*alight Ardress Corner, ¼ m*)
Δ **THE ARGORY, Co. Armagh** *map 4 G* *The National Trust* 295 acre estate with neo-classical house, built c. 1820	4 m from Moy on Derrycaw Rd.; 3 m from Coalisland intersection	April to end of Sept.—Daily (except Fris.) 2–6. Open Good Friday 2–6. Last adm. to House 5.30. Adm. 75p, Chd. 35p. Parties 50p. Cars 30p. Coaches free—please book with Custodian. Dogs in grounds only, on leads. Wheelchairs provided—access to ground floor only. ☎ *Moy* 753	Ulsterbus 67, 75 Portadown–Dungannon (*alight Charlemont (67) or Verner's Inn (75), 2½ m from either*)
CASTLE COOLE, Co. Fermanagh *map 4 G* Δ *The National Trust* Magnificent 18th century mansion by James Wyatt with plasterwork by Joseph Rose	1¼ m SE of Enniskillen on Belfast–Clogher–Enniskillen rd (A4)	*Because of a major stonework restoration programme to preserve the fabric of the house, Castle Coole will be closed until further notice. Visitors are invited to make use of the parkland and to view the work in progress, including an information display.*	Ulsterbus to Lisbellaw local buses from Enniskillen (*alight Weir's Bridge Lodge entrance*); other buses at Enniskillen (*1¼ m*)
CASTLE WARD, Co. Down *map 4 H* Δ *The National Trust* Built by the first Lord Bangor in 1765 in a beautiful setting. Laundry museum. Wildfowl collection on lake	7 m NE of Downpatrick; 1¼ m W of Strangford village (A25)	HOUSE: April to end of Sept.—Daily (except Fris.) 2–6. Open Good Friday 2–6. *Grounds and Wildfowl collection open all the year, daily.* Adm.: House 90p, Chd. 45p. Parties 70p. (Evening parties £1.20); Grounds only £1.10 per car. Dogs in grounds only, on leads in specified areas. Wheelchairs access (3 provided). ☎ *Strangford* 204 ☕ at the house (lunches by request)	**Ulsterbus 15, Belfast (*Oxford St.*)–Downpatrick then** 16 to Strangford (*not Suns.*) (*alight Ballyculter crossrds., 1 m*)
DERRYMORE HOUSE, Co. Armagh Δ *The National Trust* *map 4 G* A thatched 18th century manor house	**1¼ m NW of Newry on Newry–Newtonhamilton rd (A25)**	Open by appointment with The National Trust, Rowallane, Saintfield, Co. Down.	Ulsterbus 238 Belfast (*Gt. Victoria St.*)–Newry thence 41, 42 & 44 (*not Suns.*) (*alight Yellow House ¼ m*) C.I.E. Dublin–Drogheda–Dundalk–Newry
DOWNHILL CASTLE, Londonderry *map 4 C* *The National Trust* Built by the Earl of Bristol, Bishop of Derry, in 1783 with Downhill Castle (now in ruins)—Mussenden Temple, the Bishop's Gate, the Black Glen and the Bishop's Fish Pond	5 m W of Coleraine on Coleraine–Downhill rd (A2) *Stn: Castlerock*	TEMPLE: April to end of Sept.—Daily (except Fris.) 2–6. Open Good Friday 2–6. Castle open at all times. Glen open free at all times. Dogs admitted. Limited wheelchair access.	Ulsterbus 134, Coleraine – Downhill – Limavady – (connections from Londonderry) (*not Suns.*) (*alight Downhill*)
FLORENCE COURT, Co. Fermanagh Δ *The National Trust* *map 4 F* Important 18th cent. house built by John Cole. Excellent rococo plasterwork. Pleasure Gardens	**7 m SW of Enniskillen via A4 and A32; 1 m W of Florencecourt village**	April to end of Sept.—Daily (except Fris.) 2–6. Open Good Friday 2–6. Last adm. 5–30. Adm. 70p, Chd. 35p. Parties 50p. Parking 80p. Dogs in pleasure gardens only, on leads. Wheelchair access—ground floor only. ☎ *Florence Court* 249	Ulsterbus 192 *Enniskillen–Swanlinbar* (*not Suns.*) (*¼ m*)
GRAY'S PRINTING PRESS, Strabane, Co. Tyrone *map 4 G* *The National Trust* The shop was in existence in 18th-cent. It has close links with Scots-Irish tradition in America	In Main Street, Strabane	April to end of Sept.—Daily (except Thurs., Suns. & Bank Hols.) 2–6. Adm. 35p, Chd. half-price. Parties 25p.	Ulsterbus 273, Belfast–Strabane–Londonderry ; 98 Londonderry–Strabane; 97 Omagh–Strabane
HEZLETT HOUSE, Co. Londonderry Δ *The National Trust* *map 4 C* Thatched cottage of particular importance because of the unusual cruck/truss construction of the roof.	4 m W of Coleraine on Col./Downhil coast rd. (A2)	April to end of Sept.—Daily (except Fris.) 2–6. Open Good Friday 2–6. Adm. 45p, Chd. half-price. Parties 30p. No dogs. Unsuitable for wheelchairs. ☎ *Castlerock* 477	Ulsterbus, 134 Coleraine–Downhill–Limavady (*alight Liffock crossroads*)
MOUNT STEWART, Co. Down Δ *The National Trust* *map 4 H* Interesting house with important associations with Lord Castlereagh. Gardens designed by the late Dowager Marchioness of Londonderry. Fine topiary work, flowering shrubs and rhododendrons. Temple of the Winds, modelled on that at Athens, built 1783.	**On E shore of Strangford Lough, 5 m SE of Newtownards, 15 m E of Belfast (A20)**	House & Temple of the Winds: April to end of Sept.—Daily (except Fris.) 2–6. Open Good Friday 2–6. Gardens only—Daily (except Fris.): April, May & Sept. 2–6. June to end of Aug. 12–6. Adm. House, Garden & Temple of the Winds, £1.30; Garden & Temple of the Winds, 90p. Temple of the Winds only, 35p. *Special rates for parties & children.* Dogs in gardens only, on leads. Wheelchairs provided. ☎ *Greyabbey* 387 ☕ **at the house**	Ulsterbus from Belfast (*Oxford Street*)–Portaferry (*¼ m*)

PROPERTY (*showing map reference*)	LOCATION (*with nearest Rly. Stn.*)	OPENING TIMES AND ADMISSION CHARGES CATERING FACILITIES	COACH AND RAIL TOURS BUS SERVICES (*showing alighting points*)

NORTHERN IRELAND—*continued*

PROPERTY	LOCATION	OPENING TIMES	TRANSPORT
ROWALLANE GARDEN, Saintfield, Co. Down *map 4 H* *The National Trust* Beautiful gardens containing large collection of plants, chiefly trees and shrubs. Of particular interest in spring and autumn	**11 m SE of Belfast 1 m S of Saintfield on the W of the Downpatrick rd (A7)**	April & July to end of Oct.—Mons. to Fris. 9–6; Sats. & Suns. 2–6. May & June—Mons. to Fris. 9–9; Sats & Suns. 2–6. Nov. to end of March—Mons. to Fris. 9–4.30 (*closed Sats. & Suns.*). Adm. £1, Chd. 50p. Parties 70p. Dogs admitted, on leads, to indicated areas. Wheelchair access (1 provided). ☎ *Saintfield* 510131	Ulsterbus 15, Belfast (*Oxford Street*)–Saintfield–Downpatrick (*alight entrance*)
SPRINGHILL, Moneymore, Co. Londonderry *The National Trust* *map 4 G* House dating from 17th cent. Magnificent oak staircase and interesting furniture & paintings. Costume museum. Cottar's kitchen	On Moneymore–Coagh rd (1 m from Moneymore)	April to end of Sept.—Daily (except Fris.) 2–6. Open Good Friday 2–6. Last adm. 5–30. Adm. 70p, Chd. 35p. Parties 50p. Dogs in grounds only, on leads. Wheelchair access to ground floor & museum. ☎ *Moneymore* 210 lunches, high teas & dinners at Manor House, Main St., Moneymore ☎ *Moneymore* 200	Ulsterbus 110 Antrim–Moneymore–Cookstown (connections from Belfast (*alight Moneymore village, ½ m*)
TEMPLETOWN MAUSOLEUM, Co. Antrim *The National Trust* *map 4 H* Built 1783 by Robert Adam	Castle Upton Graveyard, Templepatrick (A6)	All the year—Daily at any time during daylight hours. Adm. free. Dogs admitted. Access difficult for wheelchairs.	Ulsterbus 120, Belfast–Antrim–Ballymena 110, Belfast–Cookstown (*alight Templepatrick*)
ULSTER-AMERICAN FOLK PARK, Camphill, Omagh, Co. Tyrone *map 4 G* The great migrations of Ulster people to the New World and the contribution they made to the U.S.A. during its birth and growth are told through the medium of restored or recreated buildings and log dwellings	4 m from Omagh	May 1 to Aug. 31—Mons. to Sats. 11–6.30; Suns. 11.30–7. Sept. 1 to April 30—Daily 10.30–4.30. Last admission 1 hour before closing. Adm. 50p, Chd. 30p. Children on educational visits 50p. *Closed weekends & public holidays from mid October to mid March.* Café on site	No reasonable public transport
WELLBROOK BEETLING MILL, Cookstown, Co. Tyrone *map 4 G* *The National Trust* **A water-powered mill built in 18th century with 19th century modifications**	3 m from Cookstown on Cookstown-Omagh rd	April to end of Sept.—Sats. & Suns. only 2–6 or by special arrangement. Open Good Friday 2–6. Adm. 35p. *Special rates for parties & children.* No dogs. Unsuitable for wheelchairs.	Ulsterbus 90 Omagh–Greencastle (*not Suns.*) (*½ m*) (connections from Belfast)

SCOTLAND

BORDERS REGION

PROPERTY	LOCATION	OPENING TIMES	TRANSPORT
ABBOTSFORD HOUSE, Melrose *map 1 L* *Mrs. P. Maxwell-Scott* The home of Sir Walter Scott, containing many historical relics collected by him	3 m W of Melrose just S of A72 5 m N of Selkirk	March 19 to October 31—Weekdays 10–5; Suns 2–5. Adm. £1.20, Chd. 60p. Party rate 90p. Chd. 45p. *Cars with wheelchairs or disabled visitors enter by private entrance.* Gift shop. Teashop	Eastern Scottish from Edinburgh daily (*March 26 to Sept. 26*); half-day, Tues & Fris. (*June 5 to Sept. 7*) Eastern Scottish 95, X95 Edinburgh–Galashiels–Selkirk–Hawick–Carlisle
AYTON CASTLE, Eyemouth *map 1 L* Victorian castle in red sandstone.	7 m N of Berwick-upon-Tweed on A1	May to September—Weds. & Suns. 2–5 or by appointment with the Curator ☎ (03902) 212	Eastern Scottish 436 from Berwick-u-T; 504 Edinburgh–Berwick-u-T
BOWHILL, nr Selkirk *map 1 L* *His Grace the Duke of Buccleuch & Queensberry K.T.* Border home of the Scotts of Buccleuch. Famous paintings include a Leonardo, 8 Guardis, a large Canaletto, Claudes, Gainsboroughs, Reynolds and a selection from one of the world's finest collection of Miniatures. Superb French furniture and porcelain. Monmouth, Sir Walter Scott and Queen Victoria relics. Restored Victorian kitchen. Exciting Adventure Woodland Play Area.	3 m W of Selkirk on A708 Moffat St. Mary's Loch Rd., Edinburgh, Carlisle, Newcastle approx. 1½ hrs by rd	April 20 to 23 (Easter); May, June & Sept.—Daily (except Tues. & Fris.); July & Aug.—Daily (except Fris.) Weekdays 12.30–5; Suns. 2–6. Last adm. 45 mins. before closing time. Last open day Sun. Sept. 16. Adm. House & Grounds £1.50; Parties of 20 or more £1; Grounds only 75p; Chd. (under 16) 75p. Wheelchairs & Chd. under 5, free. Adventure Woodland Play Area; Nature Trail; Gift & Garden Shop. Free Car & Coach parking. **Tea room** ☎ ***Selkirk* (0750) 20732**	**Buses to Selkirk from Carlisle, Edinburgh, Galashiels Hawick** **Eastern Scottish tours from Edinburgh**
DAWYCK ARBORETUM, nr Peebles *Dept. of Agriculture & Fisheries of Scotland* *map 1 K* **Impressive woodland garden**	8 m SW of Peebles; 28 m S of Edinburgh	**April to Sept.—Daily 10–5. Adm. (car & passengers) 50p. No animals**	**No reasonable public transport**

PROPERTY (*showing map reference*)	LOCATION (*with nearest Rly. Stn.*)	OPENING TIMES AND ADMISSION CHARGES CATERING FACILITIES	COACH AND RAIL TOURS BUS SERVICES (*showing alighting points*)

SCOTLAND—*continued*

BORDERS REGION—*continued*

Property	Location	Opening times	Coach and rail tours / Bus services
FLOORS CASTLE, Kelso map 1 L *The Duke of Roxburghe* Built in 1721 by William Adam and later added to by Playfair. Magnificent tapestries, fine French and English furniture, paintings, porcelain	**N of Kelso**	Easter weekend (April 20 to 23) then May 6 to Sept. 30—Suns. to Thurs. (inc. Bank Hol. Mons.). Grounds, Gardens & Castle: 11–5.30 (last adm. to Castle 4.45). The Castle will be open on Fris. to coach parties by appointment only. *Closed Sats.* Adm. £1.40, Chd. 70, O.A.Ps. £1.10. *Party rates on request from the Factor, Roxburghe Estate Office.* Garden Centre; Gift Shop. ✕ Licensed Restaurant ☎ *Kelso* (0573) 23333 ☕ in Courtyard	**Eastern Scottish buses from Berwick, Edinburgh, Galashiels, Hawick, Jedburgh, Melrose, Newcastle, Wooler etc., to Kelso (1 *m*); Services 510, 511 pass gates.**
HERMITAGE CASTLE, Liddlesdale *Secretary of State for Scotland* map 1 R Here in 1566, Queen Mary visited her wounded lover Bothwell.	In Liddlesdale, 5½ m NE of Newcastleton	April to Sept—Weekdays 9.30–7; Suns. 2–7. Oct. to March—Weekdays 9.30–4; Suns. 2–4. *Closed Tues. & alternate Weds. in winter.* Adm. 30p, Chd. under 16 & O.A.Ps. 15p.	
KAILZIE GARDENS, by Peebles map 1 K *Mrs. A. M. Richard* Beautifully situated private gardens re-created in the last 20 years. Magnificent spring show of snowdrops and daffodils; mature timber. Herbaceous borders, shrub and floral beds in old walled garden. New formal rose garden. Large greenhouse. Wild Garden and Burnside walk. Over 300 varieties of fuschia.	**2½ m SE from Peebles on B7062**	March to Oct.—Daily 11–5.30. Adm. 70p, Chd 35p Car park. Picnic area. Shop. Pottery. Art Gallery. Owls. Waterfowl Pond & Pheasantry. Plant sales specialising in fuschias and alpines. ✕☕ Licensed tearoom; home-made cream teas, lunches	**No reasonable public transport**
MANDERSTON, Duns map 1 L *Mr. and Mrs. Adrian Palmer* The finest Edwardian house in the classical style in Britain. Remarkable picturesque group of farm and dairy buildings; gardens.	2 m E of Duns on A6105; 14 m W of Berwick upon Tweed	May 20 to Sept. 30—Thurs. & Suns.; also Tues. during August and Bank Hol. Mons. May 28 & Aug. 27: 2–5.30. Adm. charges not available at time of going to press. Chd. (under 14) in family parties, free. *Parties at any time by appointment.* Gift shop. ☕cream teas ☎ *Duns* (0361) 83450	**Buses from Galashiels & Berwick-u-Tweed (*alight at entrance*). Edinburgh passengers change at Earlston**
MELLERSTAIN, Gordon map 1 L *The Lord Binning* Scotland's famous Adam mansion. Beautifully decorated and furnished interiors. Terraced gardens and lake. Tweeds and gifts on sale	**9 m NE of Melrose, 7 m NW of Kelso, 37 m SE of Edinburgh**	Easter weekend (April 20–23) then May 1 to Sept 30—Daily (except Sats.) 12.30–5. Last adm. to House 4.30. Admission charges not available at time of going to press. Free parking. *Special terms for organised parties by appointment, apply Curator.* ☕ in Tearooms ☎ *Gordon* (057 381) 225	**National tours from Tyneside & Durham** **Eastern Scottish tour from Edinburgh (St. Andrew Sq.) *Suns. & Thurs. June 3 to August 23, Weds. July 4 to August 29*** **Eastern Scottish Edinburgh–Kelso–Newcastle to Earlston then: Eastern Scottish 360, Galashiels–Earlston–Berwick (*infrequent*)**
MELROSE ABBEY, Melrose map 1 L *Secretary of State for Scotland* Beautiful Cistercian Abbey founded by David I.	In Melrose	April to Sept.—Weekdays 9.30–7; Suns. 2–7 Oct. to March—Weekdays 9.30–4; Suns. 2–4. *Closed Tues. & alternate Weds. in Winter.* Adm. 70p, Chd. under 16 & O.A.Ps. 35p.	
NEIDPATH CASTLE, Peebles map 1 K *Lord Wemyss Trust* Medieval castle, altered in the 17th century, situated on a bluff above the River Tweed. Pit prison, a well hewn out of solid rock and fine views	1 m W of Peebles on A72	April 19 to mid Oct.—Mons. to Sats. 10–1, 2–6; Suns. 1–6. Last adm. 12.30 & 5.30. Adm. 50p, Chd. 15p, O.A.Ps. 25p. Parties at reduced rates—enquiries to The Factor, Estates Office, Longniddry, East Lothian. ☎ *Aberlady* (087 57) 201 ✕☕ Hotels in Peebles	**Eastern Scottish, Edinburgh–Peebles**
PRIORWOOD GARDEN, Melrose map 1 L *The National Trust for Scotland* Garden featuring flowers suitable for drying. Shop and Trust visitor centre	In Melrose	April 1 to 30 & Nov. 1 to Dec. 24—Mons. to Sats. 10–1, 2–5.30; Suns. 2–5.30. May 1 to Oct. 31—Mons. to Sats. 10–5.30 (July, Aug. & Sept. 10–6); Suns. 1.30–5.30. Adm. by donation ☎ *Melrose* (089 682) 2555	**Eastern Scottish, Edinburgh–Galashiels & Galashiels–Melrose; Edinburgh–Earlston & Earlston–Melrose**
THIRLESTANE CASTLE—SEE PAGE 170			
TRAQUAIR Innerleithen map 1 L *P. Maxwell Stuart, Esq.* Historic mansion, originally a Royal Hunting Lodge. Rich in associations with Mary Queen of Scots, the Jacobite risings and the Catholic persecution	1 m from Innerleithen; 6 m from Peebles; 29 m from Edinburgh at junct. of B709 & B7062	April 15 to Sept. 30—Daily 1.30–5.30 (July, Aug. & Sept. 1 to 16 10.30–5.30). Last adm. 5 p.m. Limited opening Oct. 1 to 21—Daily 1.30–5.30 (guided tours). Adm. charges not available at time of going to press. *Parties (reduced rates) at other times by arrangement.* Gift shop. Antique shop. ✕☕ home cooking at the Cottage restaurant & Bear Cottage from 12 noon (licensed) ☎ *Innerleithen* (0896) 830323	**Eastern Scottish Edinburgh–Galashiels, via Peebles (*hourly to Innerleithen Post Office*)** **Eastern Scottish, tours from Edinburgh via Peebles, (*departures Suns. May 13 to September 16; also mid-week tours Mons. & Weds. from June 18–Sept. 19 & Edinburgh Hol. Mons. May & Sept.*)**

TRAQUAIR

INNERLEITHEN PEEBLESSHIRE

THE OLDEST INHABITED AND MOST ROMANTIC HOUSE IN SCOTLAND

B.T.A. photograph

27 Kings have visited Traquair. Now the 20th Laird and his family welcome you. Discover its secrets and treasures—books, manuscripts, embroideries and pictures reflecting nearly ten centuries of Scottish political and domestic life. Stroll in the romantic grounds. Visit our traditional Brew House and Craft Workshops. Sample our cakes and strong ale.

SUNDAY 15th APRIL to
SUNDAY 30th SEPTEMBER
DAILY from 1.30 p.m.–5.30 p.m.
JULY, AUGUST & SEPTEMBER 1st to 16th
10.30 a.m. — 5.30 p.m.
LAST ADMISSION 5 p.m.
LIMITED OPENING AFTERNOONS
OCTOBER 1st to 21st
Craft Workshops close September 30th
Special rates for parties.
Other times by arrangement.
Free parking.
Telephone: Innerleithen (0896) 830323

The Bear Gates closed since 1745

HOME COOKING at the
COTTAGE RESTAURANT
from 12 p.m. (licensed)
HOME BAKING at BEAR COTTAGE
Gift Shop; Antique Shop; Craft Workshops (pottery, silk-screen printing, candlemaking, painting)
Woodland and River Tweed walks; Brewhouse; newly planted Maze
EVENTS and EXHIBITIONS throughout the season include:
TRAQUAIR FAIR 4th & 5th AUGUST
(special rates of admission)
TWO ANTIQUE FAIRS 21st & 22nd JULY and 25th & 26th AUGUST

Manderston

Duns Berwickshire

"Manderston, its buildings, park and gardens form a superb ensemble unique in Britain".

The swan-song of the great classical house. Georgian in its taste but with all the elaborate domestic arrangements designed for Edwardian convenience and comfort.
Superb classical yet luxurious rooms and the only silver staircase in the world, in a house on which the architect was ordered to spare no expense. The extensive 'downstairs' domestic quarters are equally some of the grandest of their type.
Outside the grandeur is continued. See the most splendid stables and picturesque marble dairy. Acres of formal and woodland garden and lakeside walks

SCOTLAND—*continued*

BORDERS REGION—*continued*

PROPERTY (*showing map reference*)	LOCATION (*with neatest Rly. Stn.*)	OPENING TIMES AND ADMISSION CHARGES CATERING FACILITIES	COACH AND RAIL TOURS BUS SERVICES (*showing alighting points*)
THIRLESTANE CASTLE, Lauder *Captain Maitland Carew* *map 1 L* Described as the finest country house in Scotland, surrounded by wooded parkland. Original keep c. 1590 and the extensive additions c. 1840. The building forms a T-shape and features stair turrets, panelled rooms with ornamental plaster ceilings and State rooms recently completely restored. Woodland and Riverside walks. Formal Garden. The Border Country Life Museum is based on the Estate.	29 m S of Edinburgh on A68; ½ m from A697; approx. 13 m N of St. Boswells	Mid May to June 30 & Sept.—Weds. & Suns.; July & Aug.—Daily (except Fris.): 2–5. Grounds open 12–6. Adm. charge. Special rate for parties. Free car park. Shop. For further information Tea room ☎ *Lauder* (05782) 254 *or* 560	No reasonable public transport

CENTRAL REGION

PROPERTY	LOCATION	OPENING TIMES AND ADMISSION CHARGES	BUS SERVICES
CASTLE CAMPBELL, Dollar *map 1 K* *Secretary of State for Scotland* 15th century oblong tower with later additions.	1 m N of Dollar; on N stop of Ochil Hills at head of Dollar Glen	April to Sept.—Weekdays 9.30–7; Suns. 2–7. Oct. to March—Weekdays 9.30–4; Suns. 2–4. *Closed Thurs. p.m. & Fris.* Adm. 40p, Chd. undei 16 & O.A.Ps. 20p.	No reasonable public transport
LINLITHGOW PALACE, Linlithgow *Secretary of State for Scotland* *map 1 K* Birthplace of Mary Queen of Scots	In Linlithgow *Stn: Linlithgow* (½ *m*)	All the year—April to Sept.—Daily 9.30–7 (Suns. 2–7). Oct. to March—Daily 9.30–4 (Suns. 2–4). *Closed Dec.* 25 & 26; *Jan.* 1 & 2. Adm. 60p, Chd. 30p	Eastern Scottish & Alexander (Mid.) Service. Edinburgh–Linlithgow–Falkirk–Stirling (*every* 30 *mins*)
MENSTRIE CASTLE *map 1 K (Central)* *Clackmannan District Council & the National Trust for Scotland* Birthplace of Sir William Alexander who became James VI's lieutenant for the Plantation of Nova Scotia. Commemoration rooms only open to the public	In Menstrie 5 m NE of Stirling	Commemoration Rooms: May to September 30—Weds., Sats. & Suns. 2.30–5. Adm. free	Alexander's (Mid.) & (Fife) 23 Glasgow–Stirling St. Andrews *daily, reduced service Suns.* 63 Leven-Stirling (*Mons. to Fris. only*)
STIRLING CASTLE, Stirling *map 1 K* *Secretary of State for Scotland* Royal Castle on a great basalt rock	In Stirling *Stn: Stirling* (¼ *m*)	May, Sept. & Oct.—Weekdays 9.30–6; Suns. 11–6. June to Aug.—Weekdays 9.30–7; Suns. 11–6. Nov. to April—Weekdays 9.30–5.05; Suns. 12.30–4.20. Adm.: Summer (from April) £1.20, Chd. 60p (charges include adm. to Visitors Centre); Winter (from Jan to March) 30p, Chd. & O.A.Ps. 15p.	Eastern Scottish, Edinburgh–Linlithgow–Falkirk–Stirling (*every* 30 *mins.*) Alexander's (Mid.) Services from Glasgow, Edinburgh. Falkirk, Dundee, Perth (*alight Stirling Bus Stn.*)

DUMFRIES & GALLOWAY REGION

PROPERTY	LOCATION	OPENING TIMES AND ADMISSION CHARGES	BUS SERVICES
ARBIGLAND GARDENS, Kirkbean *map 1 P* *Captain J. B. Blackett* Woodland, formal and water gardens arranged round a secluded bay. The garden where Admiral Paul Jones worked as a boy.	15 m SW of Dumfries on A710	May to September—Tues., Thurs. & Suns., 2–6 Adm. 60p, Chd. 30p, Toddlers free. Car park free. Picnic area by sandy beach. Dogs on leads please. Produce Shop. Tearoom Hotels in Dumfries or Southerness (2 *m*)	Infrequent bus, Dumfries–Kirkbean
CAERLAVEROCK CASTLE, nr Dumfries *Secretary of State for Scotland* *map 1 P* One of the finest examples of early classical Renaissance in Scotland and chief seat of the Maxwell family.	7 m SE of Dumfries on the Glencaple rd (B725)	April to Sept.—Weekdays 9.30–7; Suns. 2–7. Oct. to March—Weekdays 9.30–4; Suns. 2–4. *Closed Fri.* p.m. Adm. (under review) 40p, Chd. under 16 & O.A.Ps. 20p.	
CARLYLE'S BIRTHPLACE, Ecclefechan *The National Trust for Scotland* *map 1 P* Thomas Carlyle was born here in 1795. Mementoes and MSS.	5 m SE of Lockerbie on the Lockerbie–Carlisle rd (A74)	April 20 to Oct. 31—Mons. to Sats. 10–6. *Closed Suns.* Adm. 45p, Chd. 20p (under 5, free). O.A.Ps. & Students (on production of their cards) adm. at half the standard rate. ☎ *Ecclefechan* (057 63) 666 Ecclefechan Hotel	Western S.M.T. 90, 90A Carlisle–Lockerbie 85, Annan–Lockerbie
CASTLE KENNEDY GARDENS, Stranraer *The Earl & Countess of Stair* *map 1 N* Beautiful gardens laid out on a peninsula between two lochs, Rhododendrons, azaleas, magnolias, embothriums and many other plants from overseas	3 m E of Stranraer on A75; Stranraer/Dumfries rd (ent by Castle Kennedy Lodge only) *Stn: Stranraer Harbour* (4 *m*) (*not Suns. until late June*)	April to September—Daily 10–5. Adm. £1, Chd. (under 16) 25p, O.A.Ps. 80p. Party rates on application. Free parking. Plant Centre. ☎ *Stranraer* (0776) 2024 light refreshments only Hotels Eynhallow, Castle Kennedy & Stranraer	Western SMT 76 Stranraer–Dumfries (*alight Lodge gates*)
DRUMLANRIG CASTLE, nr Thornhill *His Grace the Duke of Buccleuch & Queensberry K.T.* *map 1 P* Exquisite pink castle, 1679–91, filled with world famous art treasures in lovely rooms. A Rembrandt, outstanding silver, superb furniture gifted by Charles II and Bonnie Prince Charlie's relics. Exciting adventure woodland play area and nature trails	18 m N of Dumfries; 3 m N of Thornhill off A76; 16 m from A74 at Elvanfoot; approx 1½ hrs by road from Edinburgh, Glasgow & Carlisle	April 20 to 23 (Easter), 28 & 29: 12.30–5, (Suns. 2–6). May & June—Daily (except Fris.) 12.30–5, (Suns. 2–6). July & Aug.—Daily (except Fris.) 11–5, (Suns. 2–6). Last adm. to Castle 45 mins. before closing time. Last open day Mon. Aug. 27. Adm. Castle & Grounds £1.50; Parties of 20 or more £1; Grounds only 75p; Chd. (under 16) 75p. Wheelchairs & Chd. under 5, free. Adventure Woodland Play Area, Nature Trials, Gift Shop. Free car & coach park. afternoon teas ☎ *Thornhill* (0848) 30248	Western S.M.T. 05, Glasgow — Kilmarnock — Thornhill—Dumfries—Carlisle; Scotia Tours, Glasgow 47 Ayr—Thornhill–Dumfries (*alight end of drive*)
LOGAN BOTANIC GARDEN, Port Logan *Dept. of Agriculture & Fisheries for Scotland* *map 1 N* A wide collection of plants from the warm temperate regions of the world	10 m S of Stranraer	April to September—Daily 10–5. Adm. 50p (car and passengers). No animals	No reasonable public transport
MAXWELTON HOUSE, nr. Moniaive *Maxwelton House Trust* *map 1 P* A stronghold of the Earls of Glencairn, in the 14/15th century, later the birthplace of Annie Laurie of the famous Scottish ballad. House, chapel, gardens and museum of agricultural and early domestic life.	3 m S of Moniaive 13 m N of Dumfries on B729	House, Museum & Gardens open Weds. & Thurs. 2–5. Adm. (1983 rates) £1.20, Chd. (under 12) 20p. Private Chapel open daily May to Sept., 10 to sunset.	Western S.M.T. 75, Dumfries–Moniaive (*alight gates*)
RAMMERSCALES, Lockerbie *map 1 P* *A. M. Bell Macdonald, Esq.* Georgian manor house dated 1760 set on high ground with fine views over Annandale. Pleasant policies and a typical walled garden of the period	5 m W of Lockerbie (M6/A74); 2½ m S of Lochmaben on B7020 *Stn: Lockerbie* (5½ *m*) (*not Suns.*)	June 26 to September 6—Tues., Weds. & Thurs.; also Suns. July 1, 15, 29 & Aug. 12, 26: 2–5. Adm. £1, Chd. 50p. Other times *during the season* by written or tel. appointment with the Estate Office. ☎ *Lochmaben* (038-781) 361 Free car park, Picnic areas & wood walks	No reasonable public transport.

DRUMLANRIG CASTLE

NR. THORNHILL, DUMFRIESSHIRE

Home of The Duke of Buccleuch & Queensberry K.T.

OPEN: April 20th–23rd (Easter) & 28th/29th 12.30–5 p.m. May & June—Daily (except Fridays) 12.30–5 p.m. July & August—Daily (except Fridays) 11 a.m.–5 p.m. Sundays 2–6 p.m. throughout. Last admission to Castle 45 mins. before closing.

LAST OPEN DAY MONDAY 27th AUGUST.

Admission charges see entry.

"Surely the rarest and richest experience among Scotland's Stately homes."

Magnificent pale pink Castle built 1679–91 on an old Douglas stronghold, filled with history, romance and exquisite art treasures, including one of Rembrandt's finest works: a sumptuous cabinet made for Versailles: a solid silver chandelier of 1680 weighing 9 stone; Bonnie Prince Charlie's relics. Two floors of beautiful rooms and courtyard open to view. Extensive Grounds and Garden, Woodland Walks, Tea Room, Gift Shop and

EXCITING ADVENTURE WOODLAND PLAY AREA.

Tel. Thornhill (0848) 30248.

ARBIGLAND GARDENS

Kirkbean, Dumfries

Built in the 18th century, on land that long ago belonged to the Murrays, the house is set amongst woodland, formal and water gardens arranged round a secluded bay in the Solway Firth.

The garden in which John Paul Jones, regarded by history as the father of the United States Navy, worked as a boy.

THIRLESTANE CASTLE

LAUDER, BERWICKSHIRE

Thirlestane Castle, described as the finest country house in Scotland, stands in an imposing position above the Leader Water and is surrounded by wooded parkland, approximately half a mile from Lauder. The castle and estate are owned by Captain Maitland Carew, grandson of the 15th Earl of Lauderdale, in whose family the estate has remained since 1218. The castle consists of two major elements: the original keep dating from around 1590 and the extensive additions by David and John Bryce constructed around 1840. The building forms a T-shape.

The scale and complexity of the building is breathtaking and the plan form of the 1590 keep with its corner towers and stair turrets is unique amongst Scottish mansion houses. The internal features of the castle include numerous panelled rooms with ornamental plaster ceilings considered to be the finest ceilings in existence of the Restoration period. Recently all the main State rooms have been completely restored.

Free Car Park — Woodland and Riverside Walks

Restored Formal Garden — Caravan Park, Tea-Room, Shop

The Border Country Life Museum is based on the Thirlestane Estate with displays, both static and active, of agricultural implements and farming methods. Small fields are cultivated using vintage machinery and horse drawn implements.

Opening times:

Mid-May to June 30 and September
Wednesdays and Sundays 2–5 p.m.
July and August
Every day (except Friday) 2–5 p.m.
Grounds open 12 noon–6 p.m.
Admission charge

Special rates for parties:

For further information tel. Lauder (05782) 254 or 560.

CASTLE KENNEDY GARDENS

STRANRAER, WIGTOWNSHIRE

The Gardens, which are set in an area of natural beauty, are nationally famous for their rhododendrons, azaleas, magnolias and embothriums.

Situated on a peninsula between two beautiful lochs the Gardens offer a choice of quiet peaceful walks to visitors. The ruined Castle Kennedy which was burned down in 1716 was replaced in 1867 by Lochinch Castle which is the home of the present Earl and Countess of Stair.

The Gardens are situated 3 miles East of Stranraer on the A75 Stranraer-Dumfries road.

OPENING TIMES OPPOSITE

RAMMERSCALES

Lockerbie, Dumfries

Rammerscales was begun in 1760 for Dr. James Mounsey, Physician to the Empress Elizabeth of Russia. After his death in 1773 it was purchased by a local family, James Bell of Between-the-Waters. His sister Mary married Donald Macdonald in 1798 and later they inherited the Estate where their descendants still live. The House in the 200 years since it was completed has remained substantially unaltered. It contains a fine circular staircase, elegant public rooms and a long library at the top of the House. There are Jacobite relics and links with Flora Macdonald retained in the family. Also there is a small collection of works by modern artists.

PROPERTY (showing map reference)	LOCATION (with nearest Rly. Stn.)	OPENING TIMES AND ADMISSION CHARGES CATERING FACILITIES	COACH AND RAIL TOURS BUS SERVICES (showing alighting points)

SCOTLAND—*continued*

DUMFRIES & GALLOWAY REGION—*continued*

PROPERTY	LOCATION	OPENING TIMES	BUS SERVICES
SWEETHEART ABBEY, New Abbey *map* 1 *P* *Secretary of State for Scotland* Cistercian monastery famous for the touching and romantic circumstances of its foundation.	6 m S of Dumfries on coast rd (A710)	April to Sept.—Weekdays 9.30–7; Suns. 2–7. Oct. to March—Weekdays 9.30–4; Suns. 2–4. Adm. 50p Chd. under 16 & O.A.Ps. 25p.	
THREAVE GARDEN, nr Castle Douglas *The National Trust for Scotland* *map* 1 *P* The Trust's School of Gardening. Gardens now among the major tourist attractions of S.W. Scotland. Visitor centre.	1 m W of Castle Douglas off A75	GARDENS: All the year—Daily 9–sunset WALLED GARDEN & GLASSHOUSES—Daily, 9–5. Visitor Centre: April 1 to October 31. Adm. £1.05, Chd. 50p. Adult parties 75p, Schools £5 per coach. Chd. under 5 yrs. free, O.A.Ps. & Students (on production of their cards) adm. at half the standard adult rate ☎ *Castle Douglas* (0556) 2575	Western S.M.T., Dumfries–Castle Douglas–Kirkcudbright–Stranraer (*alight Lochbank*)

FIFE REGION

PROPERTY	LOCATION	OPENING TIMES	BUS SERVICES
CULROSS PALACE, Fife *map* 1 *K* *Secretary of State for Scotland* Built between 1597 and 1611. Contains very fine series of paintings on wooden walls and ceilings	In the village of Culross on the Firth of Forth between Kincardine and Dunfermline (A985)	All the year: April to September—Daily 9.30–7 (Suns. 2–7). October to March—Daily 9.30–4 (Suns. 2–4). *Closed Dec. 25 & 26; Jan. 1 & 2.* Adm. 60p, Chd. 30p ✕ Dundonald Arms, Culross	Alexander's (Mid.)/Alexander (Fife) 90, Dunfermline–Culross–Falkirk, 27 Glasgow–Culross–Kirkcaldy–Leven
EARLSHALL CASTLE, Leuchars *map* 1 *L* *Major & Mrs. D. R. Baxter* Magnificent 16th century castle with fine painted ceilings and world famous topiary yew garden. Fine collection of Scottish broadswords, arms and armour and Jacobite relics.	6 m NW of St. Andrews; 1 m E of Leuchars off A919; 9 m S of Dundee; 49 m NE of Edinburgh. *Stn: Leuchars* (1½ *m*)	April 20 to Sept. 30—Weds., Thurs., Fris. & Sats. 11.30–12.30, 1.30–5.30; Suns. 1.30–5.30. Last adm. 4.45. Adm. Castle & Gardens £1.50, Chd. £1, O.A.Ps. £1 (on production of card). Special rates for pre-booked parties. Free car park. Castle unfortunately not suitable for disabled. tea room ☎ *Leuchars* (033 483) 205	Local buses from St. Andrews stop approximately 1m from Castle Taxi service from Leuchars
FALKLAND PALACE & GARDEN, Fife *map* 1 *K* *Her Majesty the Queen. Hereditary Constable, Capt. & Keeper: Ninian Crichton Stuart. Deputy Keeper: The National Trust for Scotland* Attractive 16th century royal palace, favourite retreat of Stewart kings and queens. Gardens now laid out to the original Royal plans	In Falkland, 11 m N of Kirkcaldy on A912	April 1 to Sept. 30—Mons. to Sats. 10–6; Suns. 2–6. Oct. 1 to 31—Sats. 10–6; Suns. 2–6. Last adm. to Palace 5.15. Adm. Palace & Gardens £1.25, Chd. 60p. Adult parties 95p. Schools 45p. Gardens only 75p, Chd. 35p (under 5, free). O.A.Ps. & Students (on production of their cards) adm. at half the standard adult rate. ✕ Bruce Arms, Falkland ☎ *Falkland* (033 75) 397	Alexander's tour from Dundee or Aberdeen Alexander's (Fife) tour from Fife towns Alexander's (Fife) 336, Perth–Newburgh–Kirkcaldy 337 Perth–Strathmiglo–Kirkcaldy; 367 Cupar–Falkland

PROPERTY (showing map reference)	LOCATION (with nearest Rly. Stn.)	OPENING TIMES AND ADMISSION CHARGES CATERING FACILITIES	COACH AND RAIL TOURS BUS SERVICES (showing alighting points)

SCOTLAND—*continued*

FIFE REGION—*continued*

PROPERTY	LOCATION	OPENING TIMES	TOURS / BUSES
HILL OF TARVIT, nr Cupar *map 1 L* *The National Trust for Scotland* Mansion house remodelled 1906. Collection of furniture, tapestries, porcelain and paintings. Gardens	**2½ m SW of Cupar A916**	House: April 21 to Sept. 30—Daily (except Fris.) 2–6. Oct. 1 to 31—Sats. & Suns. 2–6. Last admission 5.30. Gardens & grounds all year. 10–dusk. Adm. House & Gardens £1.05, Chd. 50p. Adult parties (20 or more) 75p. Gardens only 50p, Chd. 25p. Chd. under 5 yrs., free. O.A.Ps. & Students (on production of their cards) adm. at half the standard adult rate. ☎ *Cupar* (0334) 53127	No reasonable public transport
KELLIE CASTLE, Fife *map 1 L* *The National Trust for Scotland* Fine example of 16th–17th century domestic architecture of lowland counties of Scotland	**3 m NNW of Pittenweem; on B9171**	CASTLE: April 21 to Sept. 30—Daily (except Fris. 2–6. Oct. 1 to 31—Sats. & Suns. 2–6. Last adm. 5.30. GARDENS: All the year—Daily 10–dusk. Adm. Castle & Gardens £1.05, Chd. 50p. Adult parties (20 or more) 75p. Gardens only 50p, Chd. (accompanied by adult) 25p (under 5, free). O.A.Ps. & Students (on production of their cards) adm. at half the standard adult rate. *Gardens only, suitable for disabled.* ☎ *Arncroach* (033 38) 271	Alexander's (Fife) Anstruther–Arncroach (*infrequent*)
THE TOWN HOUSE & THE STUDY, Culross *map 1 K* *The National Trust for Scotland* Outstanding survival of Scottish 17th century burgh architecture, carefully restored to 20th century living standards	**12 m W of Forth road Bridge, off A985**	The Town House—April 1 to Oct. 13—Mons. to Sats. 9.30—12.30, 2–5.30; Suns. 2–5.30. The Study—Oct. 14 to March 31—Sats. 9.30–12.30, 2–4; Suns. 2–4. *Visits at other times—four days notice required.* Adm.: Town House & audio-visual 35p, Chd. 15p; the Study 25p, Chd. 10p. (under 5, free). O.A.Ps. & Students (on production of their cards) adm. at half the standard adult rate. ☎ *Newmills* (0383) 880359	Alexander's Fife/Alexander's Midland 27, Glasgow–Culross–Kirkcaldy–Leven, 90, Falkirk–Culross–Dunfermline

GRAMPIAN REGION

PROPERTY	LOCATION	OPENING TIMES	TOURS / BUSES
BALMORAL CASTLE, nr Ballater *map 1 F* *Her Majesty the Queen* Grounds and Exhibition open	**8 m SW of Ballater on A93**	Gardens and Exhibition open during May, June and July—Daily (except Sundays) 10–5. Adm. (1983 rates) £1, Chd. 45p. Donation to charities ✕ Invercauld Arms, Braemar	Alexander's (Nth.) 1, Aberdeen–Ballater–Braemar (*alight Crathie*) Alexander's (Mid) 142 Pitlochry–Balmoral (*Tues. during summer*) Excursions and tours from all parts of Scotland
BRAEMAR CASTLE, Braemar *map 1 F* *Captain A. A. C. Farquharson of Invercauld* Romantic 17th century castle, originally of the Earls of Mar, of architectural and historical interest. A private residence of surprising charm	**½ m NE of Braemar on A93**	May to October 1—Daily 10–6. Adm. £1, Chd. (13 years & under) 50p. Car park free. ☎ *Braemar* (033 83) 219	Alexander's (Nth.) 1, Aberdeen–Braemar; Alexander's (Mid.) 142, Pitlochry–Braemar. (*Tues. during summer*)
BRODIE CASTLE, nr. Nairn, Moray *map 1 B* *The National Trust for Scotland* Ancient seat of the Brodies, burned in 1645 and largely rebuilt, with 17th/19th century additions. Fine furniture, porcelain and paintings	**Off A96 between Nairn & Forres.** *Stn: Forres (3½ m)*	April 20–23 then May 1 to Sept. 30—Mons. to Sats. 11–6; Suns. 2–6 (last adm. 5.15). Grounds open all year 9.30–sunset. Adm. £1.25, Chd. 60p (under 5, free). Adult parties £1, Schools 50p. O.A.Ps. & Students (on production of their cards) adm. at half the standard adult rate. Grounds by donation. ☎ *Brodie* (030 94) 371	Inverness–Aberdeen bus route, regular service (*alight Castle gates*)
CASTLE FRASER, Sauchen *map 1 G* *The National Trust for Scotland* One of the most spectacular of the Castles of Mar. Z-plan castle begun in 1575 and completed in 1636. "Castles of Mar" exhibition	**3 m S of Kemnay off B993; 16 m W of Aberdeen**	May 1 to September 30—Daily 2–6 (last admission 5.15). Adm. £1.05, Chd. 50p (inc. Exhibition). Adult parties 85p, Schools 45p. Chd. under 5 yrs. free. O.A.P.s. & Students (on production of their cards) adm. at half the standard adult rate. Garden & grounds open all year. 9.30–sunset, admission by donation. Picnic area. ☎ *Sauchen* (033 03) 463	*Bus:* Alexander's (Nth.) 18, Aberdeen–Alford (*alight Craigearn Turn, 2 m*)
CRAIGIEVAR CASTLE, Lumphanan *map 1 G* *The National Trust for Scotland* Exceptional tower house. Structurally unchanged since its completion in 1626	**6 m S of Alford on A980; 26 m W of Aberdeen**	May 1 to Sept. 30—Daily (except Fris.) 2–6 (last admission 5.15). Parties of 12 or more at other times by arrangement. Adm. £1.25, Chd. 60p. Adult parties £1.05, Schools 55p. Chd. under 5 yrs. free, O.A.Ps. & Students (on production of their cards) adm. at half the standard adult rate. Grounds open all year 9.30–sunset. Adm. by donation. *It is recommended that all coach parties should book in advance. Pre-booked coach parties received any day, including Fridays.* ☎ *Lumphanan* (033 983) 635	Alexander's (Nth.) 3, Aberdeen–Tarland (*alight Camphill crossroads, 1½ m walk*)

SCOTLAND—*continued*

GRAMPIAN REGION—*continued*

PROPERTY (*showing map reference*)	LOCATION (*with nearest Rly. Stn.*)	OPENING TIMES AND ADMISSION CHARGES CATERING FACILITIES	COACH AND RAIL TOURS BUS SERVICES (*showing alighting points*)
CRATHES CASTLE & GARDEN, Banchory *map* 1 *G* Δ *The National Trust for Scotland* (1951) **Fine 16th century baronial castle. Remarkable early painted ceilings. Beautiful gardens**	**3 m E of Banchory on A93; 15 m W of Aberdeen**	CASTLE: April 20–23 then May 1 to Sept. 30—Mons. to Sats. 11–6; Suns. 2–6. Last admission 5.15. GARDENS & GROUNDS. All the year—Daily 9.30–sunset. Adm. Castle only £1.05, Chd. 50p. Gardens only 55p, Chd. 25p. Grounds 30p, Chd. 15p. (May to Sept. only, other times by donation). Combined ticket £1.65, Chd. 80p. Adult parties £1.35, Schools 60p. Chd. under 5 yrs. free, O.A.Ps. & Students (on production of their cards) adm. at half the standard adult rate. Visitor Centre Restaurant (April 20–23; May to Sept., daily 11–6) ☎ *Crathes* (033 044) 525	**Alexander's (Nth.) tour from Aberdeen & Dundee** **Alexander's (Nth.) 1, Aberdeen–Banchory–Braemar; 1C, Aberdeen–Banchory** (*alight East Lodge, Crathes, ¼ m*)
DRUM CASTLE, nr Aberdeen *map* 1 *G* *The National Trust for Scotland* **The oldest part of the historic Castle, the great square tower—one of the three oldest tower houses in Scotland—dates from the late 13th cent. Charming mansion added in 1619**	**10 W of Aberdeen, off A93**	May 1 to September 30—Daily 2–6 (last admission 5.15). Adm. Castle £1.05, Chd. 50p. Adult parties 85p, Schools 45p. Chd. under 5 yrs. free, O.A.Ps. & Students (on production of their cards) adm. at half the standard adult rate. Grounds open all year 9.30–sunset. Admission by donation. ☎ *Drumoak* (033 08) 204	*Bus:* Alexander's (Nth.) 1, 1c, Aberdeen–Banchory–Aboyne–Braemar (*alight* A.A. *box, Drum ¼m*)
DRUMINNOR CASTLE, Rhynie *map* 1 *G* *Andrew Forbes, Esq.* **15th century castle and museum. Stonghold of the Clan Forbes. Built 1440, restored in 1966**	**1 m off Rhynie-Huntly rd. Junct. of A97 & A941**	By appointment Adm. £1, Chd. (under 15) half-price ☎ *Rhynie* (046 46) 248,	
DUFF HOUSE, Banff *map* 1 *C* *Secretary of State for Scotland* 18th century mansion designed by William Adam.	½ m S of Banff	April to Sept.—Weekdays 9.30—7; Suns. 2–7. *Closed in winter.* Adm. (under review) 30p, Chd. under 16 & O.A.Ps. 15p	
DUNNOTTAR CASTLE, nr Stonehaven *The Dunnottar Trust* *map* 1 *G* **An impressive ruined fortress 160 ft. above sea. Stronghold of Earls Marischal of Scotland**	**2 m S of Stonehaven ¼ m off Stonehaven–Montrose rd (A92)** ***Stn: S'haven* (2 m)**	All the year—**Weekdays 9–6; Suns. 2–5.** *Closed Sats. November–March.* Adm. 75p, Chd. 35p *"Whig's Vault" is shown to visitors*	Alexander's (Nth.) 11 Aberdeen–Stonehaven–Montrose–Arbroath–Dundee (*alight Castle approach*)
HADDO HOUSE, nr Methlick *map* 1 *G* Δ *The National Trust for Scotland* **Georgian house designed in 1731 by William Adam. Home of the Gordons of Haddo for over 500 years. Terraced gardens**	**4 m N of Pitmedden; 19 m N of Aberdeen (A981 & B999)**	May 1 to Sept. 30—Daily 2–6 (last admission 5.15). *Closed May* 12 & 13. Adm. £1.25, Chd. 60p (under 5, free). Adult parties £1, Schools 50p. O.A.Ps. & Students (on production of their cards) adm. at half the standard adult rate. Gardens & grounds open all year, 9.30–sunset, admission by donation. Wheelchair access. ☎ *Tarves* (065 15) 440	**Alexander's (Nth.) tours from Aberdeen–Dundee** **Alexander's (Nth.) 69A, Aberdeen–Udny–Tarves–Methlick–Cairnorrie (book to Keithfield Lodge)**
KILDRUMMY CASTLE GARDEN, Donside *Kildrummy Castle Garden Trust* *map* 1 *G* 10 acre garden with shrubs, heaths, gentians, rhododendrons, lilies etc. Alpine and water garden dominated by ruins of 13th century castle	**On A97 off A944 10 m W of Alford 15 m S of Huntly 35 m W of Aberdeen**	GARDENS ONLY. April to October—Daily 9–5. Adm. 50p, Car park 10p. Coach park 50p, Plants for sale. ☎ *Kildrummy* (03365) 264 *or* 277 ✕ **at Kildrummy Castle Hotel in the grounds** (*please make reservations*) ☎ *Kildrummy* (033 65) 288) The Kildrummy Inn ☎ *Kildrummy* (033 65) 227	**Alexander's (Nth.) 4, Aberdeen–Strathdon** (*alight Kildrummy Castle Hotel*)
LEITH HALL, Kennethmont *map* 1 *G* *The National Trust for Scotland* **Home of the Leith family from 1650. Jacobite relics. Charming garden**	**1 m W of Kennethmont on B9002; 34 m NW of Aberdeen**	May 1 to September 30—Daily 2–6 (last admission) 5.15). Gardens and Grounds all the year—Daily 9.30–sunset. Adm. House £1.05, Chd. 50p (under 5 free). Adult parties 75p, Schools 35p. O.A.Ps. & Students (on production of their cards) adm. at half the standard adult rate. Admission to gardens & grounds by donation. Picnic area. ☎ *Kennethmont* (046 43) 216	**Alexander's (Nth.) Afternoon tour from Aberdeen–Daily** **Alexander's (Nth.) Highland 7, Aberdeen–Elgin–Inverness** (*alight West Lodge*)
MUCHALLS CASTLE, Stonehaven *map* 1 *G* Δ *Mr. & Mrs. Maurice A. Simpson* Early 17th cent. Elaborate plaster work ceilings and fireplaces. Built by Burnetts of Leys, 1619	5 m N Stonehaven 9 m S Aberdeen, ¾ m off Aberdeen–Stonehaven rd (A92)	May to September—Tues. & Suns. 3–5. **Adm. 30p, Chd. 10p** ☎ *Newtonhill* (0569) 30217	Alexander's (Nth.) 10, 10A, 11 & 11A, Aberdeen–Stonehaven–Dundee (*alight Walker Drive*)
PITMEDDEN, Udny *map* 1 *G* *The National Trust for Scotland* **Reconstructed 17th century garden with floral designs, fountains and sundials. Display on the evolution of the formal garden. Museum of Farming Life**	**14 m N of Aberdeen on A920**	Garden & grounds open all year—Daily 9.30–sunset. Museum & other facilities: May 1 to Sept. 30—Daily 11–6 (last admission 5.15). Adm.: Garden & Museum (May to Sept.) £1, Chd. 50p. (under 5, free). Adult parties 65p, Schools 30p, O.A.Ps. & Students (on production of their cards) adm. at half the standard adult rate. Garden by donation at other times of year. *House not open.* ☎ *Udny* (065 13) 2445	**Alexander's (Nth.) 69A, Aberdeen–Pitmedden–Udny–Methlick–Cairnorrie** **Alexander's (Nth.) tour from Aberdeen, etc.**
PROVOST ROSS'S HOUSE, Aberdeen *City of Aberdeen District Council* *map* 1 *G* Aberdeen Maritime Museum in one of the oldest surviving houses in Aberdeen, built 1593	In Shiprow, off Castle St. *Stn: Aberdeen* (¼ *m*)	Opening April 1984 then open all the year—Mons. to Sats. 10–5. *Closed Suns.* Adm. free. ☎ *Aberdeen* (0224) 646333	Served by Grampian Region services
PROVOST SKENE'S HOUSE, Aberdeen *City of Aberdeen District Council* *map* 1 *G* Example of Scottish 17th century domestic architecture	In Guestrow, Aberdeen *Stn: Aberdeen* (¼ *m*)	All the year—Mons. to Sats. 10–5. Adm. free. Provost Skene's Kitchen ☎ *Aberdeen* (0224) 641086	Served by Grampian Region services

SCOTLAND—*continued*

HIGHLAND REGION

PROPERTY (*showing map reference*)	LOCATION (*with nearest Rly. Stn.*)	OPENING TIMES AND ADMISSION CHARGES CATERING FACILITIES	COACH AND RAIL TOURS BUS SERVICES (*showing alighting points*)
ARDTORNISH, Lochaline, Morvern *Mrs. John Raven* *map* 1 *E* Garden of interesting mature conifers, rhododendrons and deciduous trees and shrubs set amidst magnificent scenery.	Off A82; 41 m SW of Fort William via A82, Corran Ferry & A861	April 1 to Oct 31—Daily 10–5. Adm. (by collecting box for garden upkeep) 50p, Chd. (under 16) free. Also Sun. May 27 *in aid of the Scottish Gardens Scheme & Morvern Parish Church* when teas are provided.	
CAWDOR CASTLE, nr. Inverness *map* 1 *B* *The Earl of Cawdor, F.R.I.C.S.* The 14th century Keep, fortified in the 15th century and impressive additions, mainly 17th century, form a massive fortress. Gardens, nature trails and splendid grounds. Shakespearian memories of Macbeth.	S of Nairn; on B9090 between Inverness & Nairn *Stn: Nairn* (5 *m*)	May 1 to Sept. 30—Daily 10–5.30 (last adm. 5). Adm (1983 rates) £1.60, Chd. (under 15) 80p, Students £1.30, O.A.Ps. £1.20. Parties of 20 or more adults £1.30; 20 or more children 60p. Gardens & grounds only 80p. Free coach & car park. Gift shop. Picnic area. Pitch & Putt course. Putting Green. Nature Trails. No dogs allowed in Castle or Grounds. Licensed restaurant (self-service); Snack bar. *Cawdor* (066-77) 615 Telex 75225	Highland 13, Inverness–Cawdor–Nairn (*alight in village*) Coaches from Aviemore
DUNROBIN CASTLE, Golspie *map* 1 *B* *The Countess of Sutherland* One of Scotland's oldest inhabited houses. Historic home of the Sutherland family. Furniture, paintings and plate. Exhibits of local and general interest.	½ m NE of Golspie on A9 *Stn: Golspie* (2 *m*)	June 15 to Sept. 15—Mons. to Sats. 10.30–5.30; Suns. 1–5.30. Last adm. half hour before closing. Coaches welcome all year by appointment Tearoom	No reasonable public transport
DUNVEGAN CASTLE, Isle of Skye *map* 1 *E* *John MacLeod of MacLeod* Dating from the 13th century and continuously inhabited by the Chiefs of MacLeod. Fairy flag	Dunvegan vill. (1 m) 23 m W of Portree on the Isle of Skye	Early April to mid May & Oct. 1 to Oct. 27—Daily 2–5; Mid May to end of Sept.—Daily 10.30–5. *Closed Suns.* Adm. charges not available at time of going to press. *Large parties by written appointment*	Coach tours from Kyleakin and Portree Local service from Portree (*Tues. & Sats.*)
EILEAN DONAN CASTLE, Wester Ross *J. D. H. MacRae, Esq.* *map* 1 *E* 13th century Castle. Jacobite relics—mostly with Clan connections	In Dornie, Kyle of Lochalsh; 8 m E of Kyle on A87	April to September 30—Daily (inc. Suns.) 10–12.30, 2–6. Adm. £1. at the Castle (*Easter to Sept.*) *Dornie* (059 985) 202	Highland Omnibuses service from Kyle to Inverness. (*alight crossroads, ½ m*)
HUGH MILLER'S COTTAGE, Cromarty *The National Trust for Scotland* *map* 1 *B* Birthplace (10 Oct. 1802) of Hugh Miller, stonemason, eminent geologist, editor and writer. Furnished thatched cottage built c.1711 for his grandfather contains an interesting exhibition on his life and work.	In Cromarty 22 m from Inverness A832	April 20 to September 30—Mons. to Sats. 10–12, 1–5; (also June to Sept. only, Suns. 2–5). Adm. 60p, Chd. 30p (under 5, free). O.A.Ps. & Students (on production of their cards) adm. at half the standard adult rate. *Cromarty* (038 17) 245	Highland, Inverness–Kessock Ferry then across ferry (*regular*) & to Cromarty; Dingwall–Cromarty
INVEREWE, Poolewe, Wester Ross *map* 1 *A* *The National Trust for Scotland* Remarkable garden created by the late Osgood Mackenzie. Rare and sub-tropical plants	7 m from Gairloch; 85 m W of Inverness, A832. *Stn: Achnasheen* (36 *m*)	Garden open all the year—Daily, 9–9 (or ½ hr. before dusk if earlier). Visitor Centre: March 31 to May 6 & Sept. 10 to Oct. 15—Mons. to Sats. 10–5; Suns. 12–5, May 7 to Sept. 9—Mons. to Sats. 10–6.30; Suns. 12–6.30. Adm. £1.30, Chd. 60p. Adult parties 90p. Cruise parties £1, Chd. 50p. Chd. under 5 yrs. free, O.A.Ps. & Students (on production of their cards) adm. at half the standard adult rate. Car park 10p. (*licensed*) restaurant in garden (*March* 31 *to October* 15) *Poolewe* 229 (Information Centre) *Poolewe* (044 586) 247 (Restaurant)	No reasonable public transport Highland Omnibus tours from Inverness, Dingwall, Strathpeffer, etc. Westerbus, one daily from Inverness Bus Stn. (*early evenings, returning early morning*)
URQUHART CASTLE, Loch Ness *map* 1 *F* *Secretary of State of Scotland* One of the largest Castles in Scotland	On W shore of Loch Ness 1½ m SE of Drumnadrochit	April to Sept.—Weekdays 9.30–7; Suns. 2–7. Oct. to March—Weekdays 9.30–4; Suns. 2–4. Adm. 70p, Chd. under 16 & O.A.Ps. 35p.	

LOTHIAN REGION

PROPERTY (*showing map reference*)	LOCATION (*with nearest Rly. Stn.*)	OPENING TIMES AND ADMISSION CHARGES CATERING FACILITIES	COACH AND RAIL TOURS BUS SERVICES (*showing alighting points*)
AMISFIELD MAINS, nr Haddington *Lord Wemyss Trust* *map* 1 *L* Georgian farmhouse with Gothic barn.	Between Haddington & East Linton on A1 Edinburgh – Dunbar rd.	Exterior only on view. Further details from Wemyss & March Estates, Estate Office, Longniddry, East Lothian. *Aberlady* (08757) 201	
BEANSTON, nr Haddington *map* 1 *L* *Lord Wemyss Trust* Georgian farmhouse with Georgian Orangery	Between Haddington & East Linton on A1 Edinburgh – Dunbar rd.	Exterior only on view. Further details from Wemyss & March Estates, Estate Office, Longniddry, East Lothian. *Aberlady* (08757) 201	
DALKEITH PARK, nr Edinburgh *map* 1 *K* *The Buccleuch Estates* Woodland and riverside walks in extensive grounds of Dalkeith Palace. Tunnel walk, and beautiful Adam Bridge. Nature trails and Exciting Adventure Woodland Play Area.	7 m S of Edinburgh City Centre from E end of Dalkeith High St, off A68	March 31 to Oct. 27—Daily 11–6, Nov.—Sats. & Suns. only. Adm (1983 rates) 60p, Chd. 60p (Chd. in parties 50p). Add 10p for project material. Educational facilities. Free car park & coach parking. Further information: *Edinburgh* (031-663) 5684	Eastern Scottish to Dalkeith from Edinburgh, Galashiels, Newcastle, Carlisle etc.
DALMENY HOUSE, South Queensferry *The Earl of Rosebery* *map* 1 *K* Rosebery Collection of paintings; Napoleonic and other historical items. Mentmore collection of superb French furniture, Geya tapestries and porcelain.	3 m E of S. Queensferry; 7 m W of Edinburgh; on B924 (off A90)	May 1 to Sept. 29—Suns. to Thurs. 2–5.30. Conducted tours. Adm. £1.40, Chd. & Students 90p, O.A.Ps. £1.20. Special parties £2.50. Pre-booked party rates available. Special parties on Fris. & at other times by arrangement with the Administrator. tea (031) 331 1888	Eastern Scottish from St. Andrew Sq. Bus Stn (*pasess gates, 1 m from house*)
DIRLETON CASTLE & GARDEN, Dirleton *Secretary of State for Scotland* *map* 1 *L* Well preserved 13th century castle, attractive gardens	In the village of Dirleton on Edinburgh–North Berwick rd (A198)	April to Sept. — Weekdays 9.30–7, Suns. 2–7. October to March—Weekdays 9.30–4, Suns. 2–4. *Closed Dec.* 25 & 26; *Jan.* 1 & 2. Adm. 60p, Chd. 30p	Eastern Scottish, Edinburgh–North Berwick, (*half-hourly*) (*alight Dirleton Toll*)
EDINBURGH CASTLE *map* 1 *K* *Crown Property* Ancient fortress of great importance. St. Margaret's Chapel has Norman features	Castlehill, Edinburgh	May to October — Weekdays 9.30–6, Suns. 11–6; November to April — Weekdays 9.30–5.05; Suns. 12.30–4.20. Last tickets sold 45 mins. before closing. *Castle closed Dec.* 25 & 26; *Jan.* 1, 2 & 3. Adm.: (Summer) £1.70, Chd. & O.A.Ps. 85p; (Winter) £1.30, Chd. & O.A.Ps. 65p (1983 charges—under review). Memorial & Precincts free. at the Castle (*summer months*).	Eastern Scottish & Edinburgh City Transport—regular sightseeing tours: Western S.M.T. tour from Ayrshire towns—*daily* (*May to Sept.*) Dodds tour from Ayrshire towns—*daily* (*May to Sept.*) Edinburgh City service—*frequent service*

Dalmeny House
South Queensferry·Edinburgh

Home of the Earl and Countess of Rosebery

Magnificently set in beautiful parkland on the shores of the Firth of Forth, 7 miles from Edinburgh. Designed in 1814 by William Wilkins, the first Gothic Revival house in Scotland.
The Rothschild Collection. Superb French 18th century furniture, tapestries, Sèvres porcelain and paintings from the Earls of Rosebery's English home, Mentmore.
The Rosebery Collections. Prime Minister the 5th Earl of Rosebery's important collection of political portraits by Reynolds, Gainsborough, Raeburn and Lawrence. Early Scottish portraits and 17th century furniture. Goya tapestries. Burns Collection. Rose and Primrose Racing Colours—mementos of the Mentmore stud that produced 7 Derby winners. The Napoleon Room. Paintings and furniture associated with the Emperor Napoleon and Wellington.

EILEAN DONAN CASTLE

ROSS & CROMARTY

Eilean Donan Castle stands at the junction of Loch Duich with Loch Alsh and Loch Long on a small rocky islet. It was built in 1220 by Alexander II to keep out the Danes and eventually passed into the hands of the great Mackenzie Clan who became Earls of Seaforth. In 1719 it was garrisioned by Spanish Jacobite troops and was blown up by an English Man o' War. For 200 years it remained a ruin until it was rebuilt by Colonel MacRae, a direct descendant of the last Constable of the Castle.
Open to visitors April to September: Weekdays and Sundays 10 a.m.–12.30 p.m., 2 p.m.–6 p.m. Adm. £1.

For information on

EDUCATIONAL SERVICES

SEE PAGE 8

CAWDOR CASTLE

The 14th Century home of the Thanes of Cawdor. Cawdor, Nairn Scotland.

Open seven days a week.
May 1st - September 30th
10am. - 5.30pm.
Last admission 5pm.
Ample Parking

Situated between Inverness and Nairn on the B9090 off the A96
For further information
Tel: CAWDOR 615 Telex: 75225

DALKEITH PARK

Nr. EDINBURGH

Dalkeith House from the Nature Trail

Nature Trails and Exciting Adventure Woodland Play Area, Picnic Area. Woodland and riverside walks in the beautiful grounds of Dalkeith Palace. Tunnel Walk, Adam Bridge. Educational packs and special facilities for School parties. Information Centre. Light Refreshments.

Open daily—March 31st to October 27th; Sats. & Suns. only in November: 11 a.m. to 6 p.m. Access from East end Dalkeith High Street. 3 miles from Edinburgh City Boundary off A68.

WEMYSS AND MARCH ESTATES

Invite you to visit in 1984

NEIDPATH CASTLE

(Medieval and XVIIth Century Castle)
Above the River Tweed 1 mile west of Peebles on A72
daily 19th April to 14th October
Admission details see entry

GOSFORD HOUSE

(Robert Adam and William Young)
between Aberlady and Longniddry on A198

Open May to September, Wednesdays and week-ends
Also Georgian Farmhouses (exterior only)

AMISFIELD MAINS
(with Gothic Barn)

BEANSTON
(with Georgian Orangery)

both between Haddington and East Linton on A1
Particulars Estate Office, Longniddry, East Lothian
Aberlady (08757) 201

PROPERTY (*showing map reference*)	LOCATION (*with nearest Rly. Stn.*)	OPENING TIMES AND ADMISSION CHARGES CATERING FACILITIES	COACH AND RAIL TOURS BUS SERVICES (*showing alighting points*)

SCOTLAND—*continued*

LOTHIAN REGION—*continued*

THE GEORGIAN HOUSE **No. 7 Charlotte Square, Edinburgh** *The National Trust for Scotland* *map* 1 K Ⓣ The north side of Charlotte Square is classed as Robert Adam's masterpiece of urban architecture. The main floors of No. 7 are open as a typical Georgian House. Audio-visual shows	In Edinburgh city centre	April 1 to Oct. 31—Mons. to Sats. 10–5; Suns. 2–5. Nov. 1 to Dec. 9—Sats. 10–4.30; Suns. 2–4.30. *Last admission ½ hour before closing time.* Adm. £1.05, Chd. 50p (under 5, free). O.A.Ps. & Students (on production of their cards) adm. at half the standard adult rate. ☎ 031-225 2160	Edinburgh City services
GLADSTONE'S LAND, Edinburgh *map* 1 K *The National Trust for Scotland* Built 1620 and shortly afterwards later occupied by Thomas Gledstanes. Remarkable painted wooden ceilings; furnished as typical 'Old Town' house of the period.	483 Lawnmarket, Edinburgh	April 1 to Oct. 31—Mons. to Sats. 10–5; Suns. 2–5. November 1 to Dec. 9—Sats. 10–4.30; Suns. 2–4.30. *Last admission ½ hour before closing time.* Adm. 85p, Chd. 40p (under 5, free). O.A.Ps. & Students (on production of their cards) adm. at half the standard adult rate. ☎ 031-226 5856	Edinburgh City services
GOSFORD HOUSE, nr Longniddry *Lord Wemyss Trust* *map* 1 L A Robert Adam and William Young house.	On A198 between Aberlady & Longniddry; NW of Haddington	May to September—Wednesdays & weekends. Further details from Wemyss & March Estates, Estate Office, Longniddry, East Lothian. ☎ *Aberlady* (08757) 201	
HAMILTON HOUSE, Prestonpans *map* 1 K *The National Trust for Scotland* Built in 1628 by John Hamilton, a prosperous Edinburgh burgess	8½ m E of Edinburgh on A198 *Stn: Prestonpans*	By prior arrangement with tenant. ☎ *Prestonpans* (0875) 811035	Eastern Scottish 124, 125
HOPETOUN HOUSE, South Queensferry *Hopetoun House Preservation Trust* *map* 1K Home of The Marquess of Linlithgow. Fine example of 18th century Adam architecture. Ⓔ Magnificent reception rooms, pictures, antiques	2 m from Forth Road Bridge nr South Queensferry, off A904	House & Grounds—Easter (April 20–23) then April 28 to Sept. 17—Daily 11–5.30. Adm. charges not available at time of going to press. Special rates for parties. Free parking. Gift shop. Deer parks. Picnic areas. Enquiries & bookings ☎ 031-331 2451/1546 Licensed restaurant	Special bus service & tours from St. Andrew Sq., Edinburgh & Waverley Bridge
THE HOUSE OF THE BINNS, by Linlithgow *map* 1 K Δ *The National Trust for Scotland* Ⓔ Historic home of the Dalyells. Fine plaster ceilings. Interesting pictures. Panoramic view-point	3½ m E of Linlithgow on Queensferry rd (A904) *Stn: Linlithgow* (3½ m)	April 21 & 22 then May 1 to Sept. 30—Daily (except Fris.) 2–5.30. Parkland open 10–7. Adm. £1.05, Chd. 50p (under 5, free). Adult parties 85p, Schools 40p. O.A.Ps. & Students (on production of their cards) adm. at half the standard adult rate. *Members of the Royal Scots Dragoon Guards (in uniform) admitted free.* ☎ *Philipstoun* 4255	Eastern Scottish 42, 43 44, Edinburgh–Bo'ness. (*alight Merrylees*)
INVERESK LODGE, Inveresk *map* 1 L *The National Trust for Scotland* New garden, with large selection of plants	In Inveresk village, 6 m E of Edinburgh off A1	GARDEN ONLY—all the year: Mons., Weds. & Fris. 10–4.30 (also Sats. & Suns. 2–5 when house is occupied). Adm. 40p, Chd. (with adult) 20p, under 5 yrs. free. O.A.Ps. & Students (on production of their cards) adm. at half the standard adult rate.	Eastern Scottish, regular services from St. Andrew Square, Edinburgh
LAMB'S HOUSE, Leith *map* 1 K *The National Trust for Scotland* Residence and warehouse of prosperous merchant of late 16th or early 17th century. Renovated 18th century. Now old people's day centre	In Leith	Adm. by appointment only on Mondays & Fridays ☎ 031-554 3131	Services to Leith
LAURISTON CASTLE, Edinburgh *map* 1 K Δ *City of Edinburgh District Council* Associated with John Law (1671-1729) founder of first bank in France	Cramond Rd South 4½ m from G.P.O., Edinburgh	CASTLE: All the year—April to October—Daily (except Fris.), 11–1, 2–5; Nov. to March—Sats. & Suns. only 2–4. Adm. (1983 rates) 80p. Chd. 40p. Guided tours only (last tour 40 mins. before closing time). GROUNDS—Daily (except Fris.) 9–dusk	Lothian Region 41 from The Mound & George Street
LENNOXLOVE, Haddington *map* 1 L *His Grace the Duke of Hamilton* Formerly Lethington Tower, ancient home of the Maitlands. The Lime Avenue, known as Politician's Walk, is named after William Maitland, Secretary to Mary Queen of Scots	1½ m S of Haddington on B6369; 18 m E of Edinburgh off A1	April to Sept.—Weds., Sats. & Suns. 2–5. At other times by appointment (minimum of 10 people); apply to Lennoxlove Estate Office, Haddington. Adm. (1983 rates) £1.25, Chd. 75p. Pre-booked parties of 10 or more £1, Chd. 50p. Price includes guided tour of House, entry to gardens and parking. ☎ *Haddington* (062 082) 3720	Eastern Scottish/United Jt. Edinburgh–Berwick–Newcastle (*approx. hourly*) Edinburgh–Haddington (*approx. every 20 mins.*)

PROPERTY (*showing map reference*)	LOCATION (*with nearest Rly. Stn.*)	OPENING TIMES AND ADMISSION CHARGES CATERING FACILITIES	COACH AND RAIL TOURS BUS SERVICES (*showing alighting points*)

SCOTLAND—*continued*

LOTHIAN REGION—*continued*

PROPERTY	LOCATION	OPENING TIMES AND ADMISSION CHARGES	COACH AND RAIL TOURS BUS SERVICES
LUFFNESS CASTLE, Aberlady *map* 1 *L* *Col. & Mrs. Hope of Luffness* 16th cent. castle with 13th cent. keep—dry moat and old fortifications Built on the site of a Norse raiders camp	18 m NE of Edinburgh	By request during summer months	Eastern Scottish 124, 125 Edinburgh–North Berwick (*half-hourly*)
MALLENY GARDEN, Balerno *map* 1 *K* *The National Trust for Scotland* A delightfully personal garden with a particularly good collection of shrub roses	In Balerno, off A70	GARDEN ONLY—May 1 to September 30—Daily 10 to dusk. Adm. 50p, Chd. 25p (under 5 free). O.A.Ps. & Students (on production of their cards) adm. at half the standard adult rate.	Eastern Scottish Edinburgh–Balerno
PALACE OF HOLYROODHOUSE, Edinburgh *Royal Palace* *map* 1 *K* Official residence of Her Majesty the Queen when in Scotland. Largely reconstructed by Charles II. Relics of Mary Queen of Scots N.B. *The Palace is, at times, subject to closure at short notice and opening times cannot be guaranteed.*		STATE & HISTORICAL APARTMENTS: Jan 5 to March 31 & Oct. 21 to Dec. 31 (except Dec. 25 & 26)—Mons. to Sats. 9.30–4.30; *Closed Suns.* April 1 to Oct. 20—Mons. to Sats. 9.30–6; Suns. 10.30–5.15. Adm. £1.20, Chd. & O.A.Ps. 60p. HISTORICAL APARTMENTS ONLY (*when remainder of Palace closed*): May 7 to 13, May 30 to June 20 & July 10 to 14—Mons. to Sats. 9.30–6; Suns. 10.30–5.15. Adm. 60p, Chd. & O.A.Ps. 30p. Last adm. 45 mins. before closing. *Closed Jan.* 1 *to* 4, *May* 14 *to* 29, *June* 21 *to July* 9 *& Dec.* 25 *&* 26. The dates may vary. Students, on production of a valid Student card, adm. at lower rate. Accompanied School Parties adm. free Nov. to April inclusive. Written application (at least a fortnight in advance) to the Superintendent, Palace of Holyroodhouse, Edinburgh EH8 8DX Enquiries: ☎ 031-556 7371	Eastern Scottish & Edinburgh City regular sightseeingtours Edinburgh City—frequent service
PRESTON MILL, East Linton *map* 1 *L* *The National Trust for Scotland* The oldest (16th century) of its kind still working and only survivor of many on the banks of the Tyne. Popular with artists. Renovated machinery.	5½ m W of Dunbar, off A1 *Stns: Drem (6½ m); Nth. Berwick (6½ m); Dunbar (7 m) (no Sun. services)*	April 1 to Oct. 31—Mons. to Sats. 10–12.30, 2–5.30 (closes 4.30 Oct. 1–31); Suns. 2–5.30 (closes 4.30 Oct 1–31). Nov. 1 to March 31—Sats. & Suns. only 10–12.30, 2–4.30. Adm. 75p, Chd. 35p (under 5, free). O.A.Ps. & Students (on production of their cards) adm. at half the standard adult rate. ☎ *East Linton* 860426	Starks 480 Dunbar–North Berwick (*alight entrance*)
ROYAL BOTANIC GARDEN, Edinburgh *Dept. of Agriculture & Fisheries for Scotland* *map* 1 *K* Founded 17th cent. Beautiful rock garden Exhibition Plant Houses	Inverleith Row, Edinburgh	All the year: March to Oct. (during B.S.T.)—Weekdays 9–one hour before sunset; Suns. 11–one hour before sunset. Remainder of year—Weekdays 9–sunset; Suns. 11–sunset. *Closed New Year's Day.* Planthouses—Weekdays 10–5; Suns. 11–5. Adm. free. ☕ in the garden (*April to Sept.*)	Edinburgh City 8, 9, 19, 23, 27, 39 from Princes Street, entrance East Gate in Inverleith Row; West Gate in Arboretum Road (*free parking*)
SUNTRAP, Gogarbank, nr Edinburgh *map* 1 *K* *The National Trust for Scotland & Lothian Regional Council* Garden advice centre offering courses of instruction for owners of small gardens	At Gogarbank. W of Edinburgh, between A8 & A71	Garden: all the year—Daily 9–dusk. Advice centre: all the year—Mons. to Fris. 9.30–5; also, April 1 to September 30—Sats. & Suns. 2.30–5. Adm. charge. ☎ 031-339 7283	Eastern Scottish, Edinburgh–Ratho
TANTALLON CASTLE, nr North Berwick *Secretary of State for Scotland* *map* 1 *L* Famous 14th century stronghold of the Douglases occupies a magnificent situation on the rocky coast of the Firth of Forth.	On the coast approx. 3 m E of North Berwick. *Stn: Nth. Berwick (3 m) (not Suns.)*	April to Sept.—Weekdays 9.30–7; Suns. 2–7. Oct. to March—Weekdays 9.30–4; Suns. 2–4. *Closed Tues. & alternate Weds. in winter.* Adm. 60p, Chd. under 16 & O.A.Ps. 30p.	
TYNINGHAME GARDENS, nr East Linton *The Earl of Haddington* *map* 1 *L* Beautiful gardens near the village of Tyninghame.	2 m E of East Linton on A198	June to Sept.—Mons. to Fris. 10.30–4.30. Adm. 70p, Chd. 25p, O.A.Ps. 40p. Free car park. No dogs.	Bus service to Tyninghame Village
WINTON HOUSE, Pencaitland *map* 1 *L* *Sir David & Lady Ogilvy* Built 1620. Famous twisted stone chimneys and beautiful plaster ceilings in honour of Charles I's visit. Enlarged 1800. Fine pictures and furniture. Terraced gardens.	Tranent (A1) 3 m, by B6355; Haddington (A1) by A6093 6m; Pathhead (A68) 6 m by A6093)	Open to parties only (and others very specially interested) at any time by prior arrangement with the owner. Adm. House (*personally conducted tour*) grounds and car park £1.20. ✂☕ Old Smiddy Inn, Pencaitland (1 m). ☎ *Pencaitland* (0875) 340 222	Eastern Scottish to Pencaitland (1 *m*)

LENNOXLOVE

HADDINGTON, EAST LOTHIAN

A. F. Kersting photograph

Lennoxlove, home of the Duke and Duchess of Hamilton, is a house with a three-fold interest; its historic architecture, the association of its proprietors with the Royal House of Stewart and the famous Hamilton Palace collection of works of art, including the Casket and Death Mask of Mary, Queen of Scots.

OPENING TIMES OPPOSITE

"Aerofilms Ltd." photograph

TYNINGHAME GARDENS

NR. EAST LINTON

These beautiful gardens, situated near the village of Tyninghame, will be open from June 1st to September 30th, 1984.

For details of times and admission charges see above.

WINTON HOUSE

EAST LOTHIAN

A brilliant example of Scottish architecture at its best with the inspiration of the Renaissance. Built by George Seton, 3rd Earl of Winton, in 1620, it is famous for its carved twisted stone chimneys and magnificent plaster ceilings decorated for the visit of King Charles I in 1633. Sir Walter Scott's model for Ravenswood Castle in *"The Bride of Lammermoor."* Terraced gardens, fine trees and lawns give the house a lovely setting. In Springtime masses of daffodils.

PROPERTY *(showing map reference)*	LOCATION *(with nearest Rly. Stn.)*	OPENING TIMES AND ADMISSION CHARGES CATERING FACILITIES	COACH AND RAIL TOURS BUS SERVICES *(showing alighting points)*

SCOTLAND—*continued*

STRATHCLYDE REGION

PROPERTY	LOCATION	OPENING TIMES AND ADMISSION CHARGES	COACH AND RAIL TOURS / BUS SERVICES
BACHELORS' CLUB, Tarbolton *map 1 K* *The National Trust for Scotland* 17th century thatched house where Burns and his friends formed their club in 1780. Period furnishings	In Tarbolton village 7½ m NE of Ayr (off A758)	April 1 to Oct. 31—Daily 10–6. Adm. 50p, Chd. 25p (under 5, free), O.A.Ps. & Students (on production of their cards) adm. at half the standard adult rate. *Other times by appointment.* Contact Representative, Mr. Sam Hay, 7 Croft St., Tarbolton ☎ *Tarbolton* (029 254) 424	Western S.M.T. Ayr–Tarbolton, Ayr-Burnfoot Mauchline–Ayr
BALLOCH CASTLE COUNTRY PARK *Dumbarton District Council* *map 1 K* 200 acres. Situated beside Loch Lomond contains many conifers, azaleas and other shrubs. Walled garden. Fairy Glen. Castle Visitor Centre, site of old castle and moat. Nature trail and countryside ranger service. Guided walks in summer.	Balloch, Dumbartonshire *Stn: Ballock (¼ m)*	All the year—Daily, 10 to dusk. Adm. free. Car parks For further details telephone: ☎ *Alexandria* (0389) 58216	Central S.M.T. bus service every ten mins., from Anderston Cross Bus Station taking 1¼ hours. Electric train service every ½ hour taking 45 mins.
BELLAHOUSTON PARK, Glasgow *map 1 K* *City of Glasgow District Council* 171 acres. Sunk, wall and rock gardens. Wild life. Dry ski-slope. Athletic and indoor sports centre.	Paisley Road West	All the year—Daily, 8 to dusk. Adm. free.	Greater Glasgow Paisley Road West, 15, 50, 52, 54 Mosspark Boulevard 34, 59, 69.
BENMORE (Younger Botanic Garden) *Dept. of Agriculture & Fisheries for Scotland* A woodland garden on a grand scale	7 m NW of Dunoon (off A815)	Daily—April to October—10–6. Adm. 20p, Chd. & O.A.Ps. 10p. Car park 10p ☕ at main entrance	No reasonable public transport
BOTANIC GARDENS, Glasgow *map 1 K* *City of Glasgow District Council* Covering 40 acres. Extensive botanical collections, tropical plants, herb and systematic gardens	Great Western Road	All the year—Daily (incl. Suns.) 7–dusk. Kibble Palace—10–4.45 (winter 10–4.15). Main range of glasshouses 1–4.45 (winter 1–4.15). Adm. free	Greater Glasgow 1, 11, 20, 32, 57, 58, 66, 89, 90
BRODICK CASTLE, GARDEN AND COUNTRY PARK, Isle of Arran *Map 1 J* *The National Trust for Scotland* Historic home of the Dukes of Hamilton. The castle dates in part from the 13th cent. Paintings, furniture, objets d'art. Formal and woodland gardens, noted for rhododendrons. Country park	1½ m N of Brodick pierhead on the Isle of Arran *Stn: Ardrossan Harbour (& thence by Caledonian Macbrayne ferry)*	CASTLE: April 20 to Sept. 30—Daily 1–5. Last adm. half hour before closing. COUNTRY PARK & GARDEN: all the year—Daily 10–5. Adm. Castle & Gardens £1.20, Chd. 60p; Adult parties £1, Chd. parties 50p. Gardens only 70p, Chd. 35p. Chd. under 5 yrs. free. O.A.Ps. & Students (on production of their cards) adm. at half the standard adult rate. Car park free. ☕ at the Castle ☎ *Brodick* (0770) 2202	Daily passenger & car ferry services from Ardrossan Harbour to Arran (*55 mins.*) *For information* ☎ *Gourock* 34568 *Service bus details* ☎ *Brodick* 2121
BURNS COTTAGE, Alloway *map 1 K* *Trustees of Burns Monument* Thatched cottage in which Robert Burns was born, 1759. Museum with Burns' relics	1½ m SW of Ayr *Stn: Ayr (1½ m.)*	April to October—Weekdays 9–7; Suns. 2–7 (June to Aug. 10–7). November to March—Weekdays 10–dusk. *Closed Suns.* Adm. Cottage & Monument 70p, Chd. & O.A.Ps. 35p. ☕ at cottage	Eastern Scottish tour from Edinburgh—*Suns., Mons., & Thurs. (June 13 to Sept. 13)* Alexander's (Mid.) tour from Glasgow Western S.M.T. 60, Ayr-Girvan, 59 Glasgow-Ayr-Newton Stewart (*alight Alloway, Monument Hotel*)
CRARAE WOODLAND GARDEN, *map 1 J* Crarae, Inverary *Sir Ilay Campbell, Bart.* 50 acres of trees, shrubs and plants in natural surroundings with waterfalls and magnificent panoramic views over Loch Fyne.	10 m SW of Inverary on A83 to Lochgilphead (14 m)	March 1 to Oct. 31—Daily 9–6. Adm. £1, Chd. free. Car parking free. Plants for sale: Retail 10–4.30; Wholesale by application to Mr. J. MacKirdy. ☎ (054 66) 633 *Office* (049 95) 218 *Home*	
CULZEAN CASTLE, GARDEN AND COUNTRY PARK, Maybole *map 1 P* *The National Trust for Scotland* One of the finest Adam houses in Scotland. Spacious policies and gardens. The house is not suitable for wheelchairs.	12 m SW of Ayr just off A719 *Stn: Maybole (3½ m) (not Suns April 1 & Sept.)*	CASTLE: April 1 to Sept. 30—Daily 10–6. Oct.—Daily 12–5. Last adm. ½ hour before closing. Adm. £1.50, Chd. 70p (under 5, free). Adult parties £1.05, Schools 60p. O.A.Ps. & Students (on production of their cards) adm. at half the standard adult rate. No party rates July & Aug. CULZEAN COUNTRY PARK (*NTS and Kyle & Carrick; Cunninghame; Cumnock & Doon Valley District Councils & Strathclyde Region*)—open all year. Adm. free. Cars £1.70, mini buses & caravans £3.20, Coaches £8.50, charges April to Oct. only, vehicles (except school coaches) free at other times. Exhibition centre, shop. Ranger-Naturalist service. ✕☕ at the Park centre (April to Oct.) ☎ *Kirkoswald* (065 56) 269	Western S.M.T. tours from Ayr, Paisley, Dumfries &c. Western S.M.T. 60, Ayr-Girvan, 59 Glasgow-Ayr-Newton Stewart (*alight gates*) Dodds tours from Ayrshire coast towns

PROPERTY (*showing map reference*)	LOCATION (*with nearest Rly. Stn.*)	OPENING TIMES AND ADMISSION CHARGES CATERING FACILITIES	COACH AND RAIL TOURS BUS SERVICES (*showing alighting points*)

SCOTLAND—*continued*

STRATHCLYDE—*continued*

FINLAYSTONE HOUSE AND GARDENS Langbank *map* 1 K *Mrs. G. MacMillan* Exhibition of international dolls. Flower books and other art forms. Woodlands with play area. Clan MacMillan centre	On A8 between Langbank & Port Glasgow; on S bank of River Clyde *Stn: Langbank* (20 *mins. walk*)	House open Suns. April to Aug. 2.30–4.30 & by appointment. Pre-booked groups welcome. Adm. 50p, Chd. 30p. Woods, Gardens & Garden Centre –open throughout year. afternoon tea Sats. & Suns. in summer ☎ *Langbank* 235	Bus from Glasgow Anderstone bus station (*hourly*) (*alight Mid Avenue*)
GREENBANK GARDEN, Glasgow *map* 1 K *The National Trust for Scotland* Garden advice centre for amateur gardeners, operated by the Trust. Attractive series of gardens, extending to 2½ acres, surrounding Georgian house.	Flenders road, near Clarkston Toll	Garden: all the year—Daily 10–dusk. Garden advice given Thurs. 2–5 at the garden or by telephone Adm. 55p, Chd. (accompanied by adult) 25p; Chd. party 20p. Chd. under 5 yrs. free, O.A.Ps. & Students (on production of their cards) adm. at half the standard adult rate. *House closed.* ☎ 041-639 3281	*Bus:* Western S.M.T. 02, from Anderston Bus Stn.
THE HILL HOUSE, Helensburgh *map* 1 K *The National Trust for Scotland* Overlooking the estuary of the River Clyde the house is considered to be the finest example of the domestic architecture of Charles Rennie Mackintosh. Commissioned in 1902 and completed in 1904 for the Glasgow publisher Walter W. Blackie	In Upper Colquhoun St., Helensburgh; NW of Glasgow via A814.	Open all year—Daily 1–5. Adm. 85p, Chd. 40p.	
INVERARAY CASTLE, Inveraray *map* 1 J *His Grace the Duke of Argyll* Since 15th century the headquarters of the Clan Campbell. Present castle built 18th century by Robert Morris and Robert Mylne	½ m NE of Inveraray on Loch Fyne 58 m NW of Glasgow	April 7 to October 14. April, May, June, Sept. & Oct. —Weekdays (except Fris.) 10–1, 2–6; Suns. 1–6. *Closed Fris:* July & Aug.—Weekdays 10–6; Suns. 1–6. Last adm. 12.30 (when applicable) & 5.30. Adm. £1.80, Chd. (under 16) £1, O.A.Ps. £1.30. Family tickets available. Gardens open on selected days. *Enquiries:* The Factor, Dept. H.H., Cherry Park, Inveraray, Argyll. ☎ *Inveraray* (0499) 2203 Telex no. 779914	Tours from Crieff, Glasgow, Oban, Perth and Stirling Western S.M.T. 26, Glasgow–Tarbert (*alight Castle, ½ m*)
LINN PARK, Glasgow *map* 1 K *City of Glasgow District Council* 212 acres pine and deciduous woodlands with enchanting riverside walks. Nature centre, Nature trail and Children's Zoo	Clarkston rd; Netherlee rd; Simshill Road—Linnview Av	All the year—Daily, 8 to dusk Adm. Free Car park at golf course & Nethererlee Road.	Western S.M.T. 2, Glasgow–Mearnskirk Greater Glasgow 13, 14, 22, 31, 37 to Castlemilk roundabout (*short walk*)
△**PENKILL CASTLE**, Girvan *map* 1 P *Elton A. Eckstrand, Esq.* 15th century Castle, impressive later additions. Fine furniture, tapestries and paintings. Favourite haunt of the Pre-Raphaelites, an inspiration to Dante Gabriel Rossetti and his sister Christina and other well known visitors.	2½ m E of Girvan on B734 Barr rd (off A77 Stranraer–Ayr rd)	Easter & Bank Hols. Open May to Sept. by appointment. Guided tour & Buffet lunch in Banqueting Hall £3.50 inclusive. For all details telephone Mrs. Wilson. ☎ *Old Dailly* (046587) 261	No reasonable public transport
POLLOCK HOUSE—SEE PAGE 182			
ROSS HALL PARK *map* 1 K *City of Glasgow District Council* 33 acres. Majestic trees by River Cart. Extensive heather and rock gardens, with water features, nature trails	Crookston Road SW *Stn: Crookston* (*closed Suns.*)	April 1 to September 30—Daily 1–8; October 1 to March 31—Daily 1–4. Adm. free	Greater Glasgow 23, 40, 52, 70
SOUTER JOHNNIE'S COTTAGE, Kirkoswald *map* 1 P *The National Trust for Scotland* Thatched home of the original Souter in Burns' "Tam o' Shanter". Burns' relics. Life-sized stone figures of the Souter, Tam, the Innkeeper and his wife, in garden	In Kirkoswald village 4 m W of Maybole on A77	April 1 to September 30—Daily (except Fris.) 12–5 (or by appointment) Adm. 55p, Chd. 25p (under 5, free). O.A.Ps. & Students (on production of their cards) adm. at half the standard adult rate. ☎ *Kirkoswald* (065 56) 603 *or* 243	Western S.M.T., 03, Glasgow–Ayr–Stranraer (*alight village*)
THE TENEMENT HOUSE, Glasgow *The National Trust of Scotland* *map* 1 K A restored first floor flat in a Victorian tenement building, built 1892, presents a picture of social significance.	No. 145 Buccleuch St., Garnethill (N of Charing Cross).	Because the flat is small adm. for all visitors, inc. N.T. members is only by pre-booking tickets available weekday's from the Trust's Glasgow office: 158 Ingram St., nr. George Square ☎ (041) 552 8391 April 1 to Oct. 31 daily 2–5; Nov. 1 to March 31 Sats. 10–4, Suns. 2–4. Weekday morning visits by educational & other groups (no more than 12) to be arranged by advance booking only. Adm. 80p, Chd. 40p; Chd. party 30p.	Local bus services

SCOTLAND—*continued*

PROPERTY (*showing map reference*)	LOCATION (*with nearest Rly. Stn.*)	OPENING TIMES AND ADMISSION CHARGES CATERING FACILITIES	COACH AND RAIL TOURS BUS SERVICES (*showing alighting points*)
STRATHCLYDE REGION—*continued*			
POLLOK HOUSE & PARK, Glasgow *City of Glasgow District Council* map 1 K Built 1747–52, additions by Sir Rowand Anderson 1890–1908. Contains Stirling Maxwell collection of Spanish and other European paintings; displays of furniture, ceramics, glass and silver. Nearby in Pollok Park is the Burrell Collection opened to the public by H.M. The Queen in October 1983	3½ m from City Centre *Stn: Pollokshaws West (closed Suns.)*	All the year—Weekdays 10–5, Sundays 2–5. Adm. free. *Closed Christmas Day & New Year's Day* ☎ 041-632 0274 Tearoom (Reservations: ☎ 041-649 7547)	Greater Glasgow 45, 57, 23, 39, 48, 48A from Union Street
TOROSAY CASTLE, Craignure, Isle of Mull *David Guthrie-James of Torosay, M.B.E., D.S.C. & The Hon. Mrs. James* map 1 J Early Victorian house by David Bryce with 11 acres of unexpected Italian terraced gardens laid out by Sir Robert Lorimer.	1½m SE of Craignure by A849, by Forest Walk or by Steam Railway	CASTLE: May 1 to Sept. 30—Daily 10–30–5.30 (last adm. 5). GARDENS: All the year during daylight hours. *Parties to Castle at other times by appointment only.* Adm. £1.20, O.A.Ps. £1, Chd. & Students 60p. Gardens only (when Castle not open) 80p; O.A.Ps., Chd. & Students 40p. Car park free. Dogs in garden only. Not suitable for wheelchairs owing to varying levels. Local Craft Shop. home-baked teas in Castle Estate Office: ☎ *Craignure* (068 02) 421	*Ferry*: Oban-Craignure return from Station Pier Oban (6 *times daily*) Miniature Steam Railway, Craignure Old Pier–Torosay
VICTORIA PARK Glasgow map 1 K *City of Glasgow District Council* Fossilised tree stumps, 300 million years old. 58 acres. Extensive carpet bedding depicting centennial events	Victoria Park Drive North	All the year—Daily, 7 to dusk. Fossil Grove open weekdays 8 to dusk; Suns. 10 to dusk Adm. free	Greater Glasgow 9, 10A, 15, 19, 56, 58, 64
WEAVER'S COTTAGE, Kilbarchan map 1 K *The National Trust for Scotland* Typical cottage of 18th century handloom weaver: looms, weaving equipment, domestic utensils	In Kilbarchan village 8 m SW of Glasgow off A737	April 21 to May 31 & Sept. 1 to Oct. 31—Tues., Thurs., Sats. & Suns. 2–5. June 1 to Aug. 31—Daily 2–5. Adm. 55p, Chd. 25p (under 5, free); Chd. party 20p. O.A.Ps. & Students (on production of their cards) adm. at half the standard adult rate.	Western S.M.T., 20, Anderston Bus Stn.–Kilbarchan
TAYSIDE REGION			
ANGUS FOLK MUSEUM, Glamis map 1 G *The National Trust for Scotland* Row of 19th cent. cottages with stone-slabbed roofs, restored by the Trust. Adapted to display the Angus Folk Collection, one of the finest in the country	In Glamis village 12 m N of Dundee A94	May 1 to September 30—Daily 12–5 (last admission 4.30). Adm. 80p, Chd. 40p (under 5, free). O.A.Ps. & Students (on production of their cards) adm. at half the standard adult rate.	Alexander's Northern 22 Dundee–Kirriemuir, 59 Perth–Coupar Angus–Forfar (*alight village*)
BARRIE'S BIRTHPLACE map 1 G Kirriemuir *The National Trust for Scotland* (1937) Contains mementoes of Sir James Barrie	No. 9 Brechin Rd. In Kirriemuir	May 1 to September 30—Mons. to Sats. 10–12.30, 2–6; Suns. 2–6. *Other times by appointment only.* Adm. 55p, Chd. 25p (under 5, free). O.A.Ps. & Students (on production of their cards) adm. at half the standard adult rate. ☎ *Kirriemuir* (0575) 72646 Airlie Arms Hotel	Alexander's (Nth.) 22A Dundee–Glamis–Kirriemuir 12, Dundee–Forfar–Kirriemuir
BLAIR CASTLE, Blair Atholl map 1 F *His Grace the Duke of Atholl* Comyn's Tower built c. 1269. Mansion in Scottish baronial style. Magnificent collection of furniture, paintings, arms and armour, lace and embroidery, china and Jacobite relics	8 m NW of Pitlochry off A9 *Stn: Blair Atholl* (¼ *m*)	Suns. & Mons. April 8/9 & 15/16 then April 19 to Oct. 14—Mons. to Sats. 10–5; Suns 2–5. Adm. £1.80, Chd. £1, O.A.Ps. £1.20. Reduced rates for parties. Free parking. ☎ *Blair Atholl* (079 681) 355 *or* 207 at the Castle	Alexander's (Mid), tour from Pitlochry & Crieff Alexander (Nth.) from Aberdeen Highland Omnibuses tour from Ft. William Eastern Scottish/Highland Jt., Edinburgh–Inverness Yule's Pitlochry–Blair Atholl (*alight Atholl Arms Hotel* ¼ *m*)
BRANKLYN GARDEN, Perth map 1 K *The National Trust for Scotland* One of the finest gardens of its size in Britain (2 acres)	1¼ m E of Perth on Dundee Rd (A85)	March 1 to October 31—Daily 10 to sunset. Adm. 75p, Chd. 35p (under 5, free). O.A.Ps. & Students (on production of their cards) adm. at half the standard adult rate. ☎ *Perth* (0738) 25535	Alexander's service; Glasgow–Perth–Dundee (*hourly*) (*alight Gardens*)
CASTLE MENZIES, Weem map 1 F *Menzies Clan Society* Fine example of 16th century fortified Z-plan tower house, ancient seat of Chiefs of Clan Menzies	1½ m from Aberfeldy on B846	April to Sept.—Weekdays 10.30–5; Suns. 2–5. Adm. 90p, Chd. 30p. Reductions for parties.	No regular public transport On bus tour routes
DRUMMOND CASTLE GARDENS, Muthill *The Grimsthorpe & Drummond Castle Trust Ltd.* map 1 K Gardens only are open	3 m S of Crieff, W off Crieff-Muthill rd (A822)–East Lodge	May 2 to 21 & Sept. 2 to 30—Weds. & Suns. only 2–6. May 31 to Aug. 31—Daily 2–6. Adm. £1, Chd. & O.A.Ps. 50p. Special Open Day for Charity—Sunday, Aug. 5. Free car park. *Gardens only are open to the public, according to the Rules in force*	Alexander's (Mid.) 46, Crieff–Perth; 40 Crieff–Edinburgh (*alight Muthill, East Lodge,* 1½ *m*)
EDZELL CASTLE & GARDENS, Edzell *Secretary of State for Scotland* map 1 G 16th cent. castle. Unique renaissance garden	1 m W of Edzell, 5 m N of Brechin off B996	April to Sept.—Weekdays (except Tues. & Thurs. a.m.) 9.30–7; Suns. 2–7. Oct. to March—Weekdays (except Tues. & Thurs. a.m.) 9.30–4; Suns. 2–4. *Closed Tues. (all day) & Thurs. morning also Dec. 25 & 26 and Jan.* 1 & 2. Adm. 40p, Chd. & O.A.Ps. 20p.	Alexander's (Nth.) 44, Montrose–Brechin–Edzell–Fettercairn–Laurencekirk (*alight Edzell village*)
GLAMIS CASTLE, Glamis map 1 G Δ *The Earl of Strathmore & Kinghorne* Owes present aspect to 3rd Earl of Strathmore and Kinghorne (1630–95), with portions much older. Celebrated for legend of secret chamber. Ground laid out by "Capability" Brown	12 m N of Dundee, 4 m S of Kirriemuir at junction at A94 & A928 *Stn: Dundee* (12 *m*)	Good Friday to Easter Bank Hol. Mon. (April 20–23) then May to Sept. 30.—Daily (except Sats.) 1–5. Adm. (1983 rates) £1.50; reduction for Chd. & O.A.Ps. Bus and car park free at the Castle	Eastern Scottish tour from Edinburgh Alexander's tours from Glasgow, Aberdeen Dundee, Perth, Pitlochry, Stirling etc. Forfar–Glamis (*alight South Lodge,* 1 *m*)
KELLIE CASTLE, Arbroath map 1 G *G. Coulson, Esq.* Built 1170 by William de Mowbray. Restored 1679. Built from pink sandstone quarried within the 30 acre estate.	12m from Dundee; 2 m W of Arbroath; 4m NE of Carnoustie	Tours arranged by special request. Bed and breakfast available.	Alexander's (Nth.) 11, 11B Dundee–Arbroath–Montrose–Aberdeen (*alight Balcathie Turn,* 1 *m*)
SCONE PALACE, Perth map 1 K *Rt. Hon. the Earl of Mansfield* This medieval palace was Gothicised for the third Earl of Mansfield in the early 19th century. Superb collections of French furniture, china, ivories, clocks, Vernis Martin vases and objets d'art.	2 m N of Perth on the Braemar rd (A93) *Stn: Perth* (2½ *m*)	Good Friday to mid-Oct.—Mons. to Sats. 10–5.30; Suns. 2–5.30 (July & Aug. 11–5.30). Last adm. 5. Adm. £1.80. Special rates for booked parties. Free car park. Shops. Picnic park. Playground. Winter tours by special arrangement. Coffee shop. Old Kitchen Restaurant (licensed). Home baking. Administrator: ☎ *Perth* (0738) 52300	Local bus service from Perth (*afternoons*) Regular tours from local bases. (please ask your local bus & travel agencies)

TOROSAY CASTLE ISLE OF MULL

A family home always full of flowers and laughter.
The only castle and garden in private occupation open daily to the public in the West Highlands. Early Scottish Baronial castle by the leading Victorian architect David Bryce with French Chateau south aspect and large windows overlooking Italian terraced gardens laid out by Sir Robert Lorimer. Statue walk with 19 life-sized figures by Antonio Bonazza, late 18th century Venetian. Sheltered water-garden with shrubs that flourish in Gulf-stream climate and a Japanese garden.
Castle refurbished to Edwardian taste with family portraits by Sargent, Poynter, de Laszio and, more recently, Carlos Sancha etc. Wildlife pictures by Landseer, Thorburn, Lodge and Sir Peter Scott. Photographic displays of the final epoch in sail, life in the Antarctic and evidence for the Loch Ness Monster. One hundred years of family scrap books to browse over.

Vistas over Firth of Lorne to Ben Cruachan and up Appin coast to Ben Nevis 36 miles distant.

"An atmosphere lost elsewhere" (visitors' book 1978)

Open daily 10.30 a.m.–5.30 p.m. (last admission 5 p.m.) from May 1st to September 30th. Gardens open hours of daylight throughout year. Tea-room with home baking in house.

Admission £1.20, O.A.Ps. £1, Children and Students 60p. Gardens only (when Castle not open) 80p; O.A.Ps., Children and Students 40p. Car park free. Dogs allowed in garden only.

POLLOK HOUSE GLASGOW

Original house built 1747-52, additions by Sir Rowand Anderson 1890-1908. Contains Stirling Maxwell collection of Spanish and other paintings and displays of European decorative arts.

Nearby in Pollok Park is the Burrell Collection opened to the public by H.M. The Queen in October 1983.

Open all the year: Weekdays 10 a.m. to 5 p.m., Sundays 2 p.m. to 5 p.m.

CLOSED CHRISTMAS DAY AND NEW YEAR'S DAY

KELLIE CASTLE

ARBROATH

Built in 1170 by William de Mowbray, Kellie Castle was forfeited to King Robert the Bruce during the Black Parliament then passed to Walter Stewart the Lord High Steward of Scotland. Restored in 1679. The Castle is built in pink sandstone quarried from within the 30 acre estate and with a unique courtyard and left-handed spiral stairway.
Artists and Craftsmen from throughout Europe exhibit their works in the Castle Gallery. Tours arranged by special request. Bed and breakfast available.

Further information may be obtained from Kellie Castle, Arbroath.

SCONE PALACE PERTH

Scone Palace has been a political and religious centre since the Dark Ages. It was home to the Stone of Scone or Destiny for nearly 500 years and was the crowning place of 40 kings of Scotland until Charles II in 1651. The Stone was removed from Scone to Westminster in 1296 by Edward I as a symbol of his victories in Scotland. Scone was first the capital of the Pictish kings then capital city of Kenneth MacAlpen, first king of Scots, and later of Macbeth and of Robert the Bruce, who held 16 parliaments during his 23 year reign. Scone has been home to the Murray family for 400 years and the present palace is the third to stand on this ancient site. On view in the state rooms are superb collections of French furniture, clocks, china, ivories, 16th century needlework (including bed hangings worked by Mary, Queen of Scots) and a unique collection of Vernis Martin vases and objets d'art. The extensive grounds include a woodland garden with magnificent species of rhododendrons and azaleas and a Pinetum which has one of the finest collections of rare conifers in the country including the original Douglas Fir.

UNIVERSITY OF CAMBRIDGE

NOTE. Admission to *Colleges* means to the Courts, not to the staircases and students' rooms. All opening times are subject to closing for College functions, etc., on occasional days. *Halls* normally close for lunch (12–2) and many are not open during the afternoon. *Chapels* are closed during services. *Libraries* are not usually open, special arrangements are noted. *Gardens* do not usually include the Fellows' garden. *Figures* denote the date of foundation, and existing buildings are often of later date. *Daylight hours*—some Colleges may not open until 9.30 a.m. or later and usually close before 6 p.m.—many as early as 4.30 p.m.

All parties exceeding 10 persons wishing to tour the colleges between Easter and October are required to register with the Tourist Information Centre, Wheeler Street, Cambridge, CB2 3QB to prevent over-congestion. Upon registration a Pass will be issued. This registration is usually carried out by Tour Operators or Guide Services.

Terms:—*Lent*, Mid-January to Mid-March; *Easter*, Mid-April to 2nd week June; *Michaelmas*, 2nd week October to 1st week December.

ADDRESS OF COLLEGE AND ENTRANCE GATE	OPENING ARRANGEMENTS
CHRIST'S COLLEGE (1505) St. Andrew's St. *Porter's lodge*	*College*—Daily, all day *Chapel*—Term—Daily, all day *Hall*—Weekdays, 10–1 *Library*—By appointment with Librarian *Fellows' Garden*—Weekdays 10.30–12.30, 2–4. *Closed Bank Hols. & Easter Week*
CLARE COLLEGE (1326) Trinity Lane *Porter's lodge*	*Hall*—2.15–5 (usually) inc. weekends *Chapel*—by prior arrangement with the Dean *Library*—by prior arrangement with the Librarian *Gardens*—Mons. to Fris. 2.30–4.45 (usually) *Closed Bank Hols*
CORPUS CHRISTI COLLEGE (1352) Trumpington St. *Porter's lodge*	Opening times shown at Porter's lodge
DOWNING COLLEGE (1800) Regent Street *Porter's lodge*	*College and Gardens*—Daily, daylight hours *Chapel*—Term—Daily, all day. Vacation—By appointment *Hall*—generally open when not in use *Library*—by arrangement only
EMMANUEL COLLEGE (1584) St. Andrew's St. *Porter's lodge*	*College*—Daily *Hall and Chapel*—Daily, except when in use *Library*—only by prior application to Librarian *Gardens and Paddock*—Daily until dusk *Fellows' Garden*—Not open to visitors *Closed for annual holidays, variable*
GONVILLE AND CAIUS COLLEGE (1348) Trinity Street *Porter's lodge*	*College and Chapel*—Daily, daylight hours *Library*—By appointment with Librarian *Closed to all guided parties.*
JESUS COLLEGE (1496) Jesus Lane *Porter's lodge*	*College*—Daily 9–5.30 *Chapel*—apply Porter's Lodge *Hall*—*Closed to the Public*
KING'S COLLEGE (1441) King's Parade *Porter's lodge*	*College*—Daily until 6. *Limited access mid-May to mid-June.* *Library*—Scholars, on application to Librarian *Chapel*—Term: Weekdays, 9–3.45: Suns. 2–3, 4.45–5.45 Summer Vacation: Weekdays 9–5.45 Suns. 10.30–5.45 *Closed Dec. 26 to Jan. 1 & July 2 & 3* *Dining Hall*—*Closed to the public*
MAGDALENE COLLEGE (1542) Magdalene Street *Porter's lodge*	*College and Chapel*—Daily 9–6.30 *Hall*—Daily during term 9.30–12.30 *Library*—*Pepys'* (groups not to exceed 10 persons) Jan. 17 to Mar. 17. & Oct. 9 to Dec. 7: Weekdays 2.30–3.30 Apr. 16 to Aug. 31: Weekdays 11.30–12.30, 2.30–3.30 *Gardens*—Daily 1–6.30
PEMBROKE COLLEGE (1347) Trumpington Street	Opening times shown at Porter's Lodge
PETERHOUSE (1284) Trumpington St. *Porter's lodge*	*Library*—By appt. with Librarian *Chapel*—*Daily* *Hall*—mornings only during term Guided parties of not more than 12, daily 1–5
QUEENS' COLLEGE (1448) Silver Street *Porter's lodge*	Visitor's entrance, Queens Lane. Open daily 2–4.30 & also 10.15–12.45 during July, Aug. & Sept. & for guided parties of not more than 12. Adm. charge.
ST. CATHARINE'S COLLEGE (1473) Trumpington St. *Porter's lodge*	*College and Chapel*—Daily, during daylight hours. *Closed May & June.* *Hall*—*Closed to the public*
ST. JOHN'S COLLEGE (1511) St. John's Street *Porter's lodge*	*College*—Daily until 5.30. *Closed May & June.* *Chapel*—Apply Porter's Lodge. *Hall*—*Closed to the public*
SIDNEY SUSSEX COLLEGE (1596) Sidney Street *Porter's lodge*	*College*—Daily, during daylight hours *Hall and Chapel*—apply Porter's lodge
TRINITY COLLEGE (1546) Trinity Street *Porter's lodge*	Opening times shown at Porter's lodge
TRINITY HALL (1350) Trinity Lane	*College, Hall, Chapel & Gardens*—Daily, daylight *Library*—Term only—Mons. to Fris. 10.30–12.30 (apply Porter's Lodge)

CONDUCTED TOURS IN CAMBRIDGE

Qualified, badged, local guides may be obtained from:—
Tourist Information Centre, Wheeler Street, Cambridge CB2 3QB.
Tel: 0223 358977, Ext. 441
or
Cambridge Guide Service, 2 Montague Road, Cambridge CB4 1BX.
Tel. 0223 356735 (Principal: John Mellanby M.A., Secretary: Mrs. E. Garner)—
We have been providing guides for English, Foreign language and special interest groups since 1950. We supply couriers for coach tours of East Anglia, visiting stately homes etc.

UNIVERSITY OF OXFORD

NOTE. Admission to *Colleges* means to the Quadrangles, not to the staircases and students' rooms. All opening times are subject to closing for College functions, etc. on occasional days. *Halls* normally close for lunch during term (12–2). *Chapel* usually closed during services. *Libraries* are not usually open, special arrangements are noted. *Gardens* do not usually include the Fellows' garden. *Figures* denote the date of foundation, and existing buildings are often of later date.

Terms :—*Hilary*, Mid-January to Mid-March ; *Trinity*, 3rd week April to late June ; *Michaelmas*, Mid-October to 1st week December.

ADDRESS OF COLLEGE AND ENTRANCE GATE	OPENING ARRANGEMENTS
ALL SOULS COLLEGE (1438) High Street *Porter's lodge*	*College*—Daily 2–5
BALLIOL COLLEGE (1263) Broad Street *Porter's lodge*	*Hall, Chapel and Gardens*—Daily 10–6 (summer), 10–dusk. (winter). Parties limited to 25
BRASENOSE COLLEGE (1509) Radcliffe Square *Porter on duty*	*College, Hall, Chapel and Gardens*—Daily 10–6 (summer), 10–dusk (winter) *Library*—*By special request only*
CHRIST CHURCH (1546) St. Aldate's *Meadow Gate*	*Cathedral*—Daily 9.30–12.30, 2–5 *Hall*—Daily 9.30–12, 2–4.30 Admission 60p *Picture Gallery*—Weekdays 10.30–1, 2–4.30 Admission 30p *Meadow*—Daily 7–dusk
CORPUS CHRISTI COLLEGE (1516) Merton Street *Porter's lodge*	*College, Hall, Chapel and Gardens*— Terms & Christmas vacation—Daily 2–4 Other vacations—Daily 10–6
EXETER COLLEGE (1314) Turl Street *Porter's lodge*	*College, Hall and Chapel*—Daily 10–5 *Fellows' Garden*—Daily 2–4
HERTFORD COLLEGE (1284, 1740 & 1874) Catte Street *Porter's lodge*	*College, Hall and Chapel*—Daily 10–6 * *Closed for a week at Christmas and Easter*
JESUS COLLEGE (1571) Turl Street *Gate in Turl Street*	*College, Hall and Chapel*—Daily 2.30–4.30 *Library*—Special permission of Librarian * *Closed Christmas and Easter holidays*
KEBLE COLLEGE (1868) Parks Road *Porter's lodge*	*College and Chapel*—Weekdays 10–dusk
LINCOLN COLLEGE (1427) Turl Street *Porter's lodge*	*College, Hall and Chapel*—Weekdays 2–5; Suns. 11–5 *Wesley Room*—on application to Porter's lodge *All Saints Library*—Tues. & Thurs. 2.30–4.30
MAGDALEN COLLEGE (1458) High Street *Front lodge*	*College, Chapel, Deer Park & Water Walks*—Daily 2–6.15
MERTON COLLEGE (1264) Merton Street *Porter's lodge* *Adm. 30p for Old Library and Max Beerbohm Room; apply Verger's Office*	*Chapel and Quadrangles*—Mons. to Fris. 2–4 (Mar 2 to Oct. 31, closes at 5); Sats. & Suns. 10–4 (Mar. 2 to Oct. 31, closes at 5). *Old Library and Max Beerbohm Room*—Mons. to Sats. 2–4
NEW COLLEGE (1379) *Admission at New College Lane*	*College, Hall, Chapel and Gardens*— Term—Mons. to Fris. 2–5, Sats. & Suns. 12–6 Vacation—Daily 11–6
NUFFIELD COLLEGE (1937) New Road *Porter's lodge*	*College only*—Daily 9–7
ORIEL COLLEGE (1326) Oriel Square *Main gate*	*College and Hall*—Daily 2–5 *Closed Easter & Christmas hols. & mid-Aug. to mid-Sept.*
PEMBROKE COLLEGE (1624) St. Aldate's *Porter's lodge*	*College, Hall, Chapel and Gardens*— Term—Daily 2–6.30. Vacation—Daily 9.30–6.30. *Closed Christmas and Easter holidays & occasionally in Aug.*
THE QUEEN'S COLLEGE (1340) High Street *Porter's lodge*	Due to extensive stone restoration work no members of the public are allowed access to the College until further notice.
ST. EDMUND HALL (1270) Queen's Lane *At the lodge*	*College, Old Hall, Chapel & Garden*—Daily, daylight hours *Crypt of St Peter in the East*—On application to Porter
ST. JOHN'S COLLEGE (1555) St. Giles' *Porter's lodge*	*College & Garden*— Term & Vacation—Daily 1–5 (or dusk if earlier). *Guided parties must obtain permission from the Lodge* *Hall and Chapel*—Summer: 2.30–4.30 (apply Porter) *Closed during conferences & College functions*
TRINITY COLLEGE (1554) Broad Street *Main gate*	*Hall, Chapel and Garden*—Daily 2–6 (summer), 2–dusk (winter)
UNIVERSITY COLLEGE (1249) High Street *Porter's lodge*	*College, Hall and Chapel*— Term 2–4, Vacation 10–12, 2–6
WADHAM COLLEGE (1610) Parks Road *Porter's lodge*	*College, Hall, Chapel and Gardens*— Daily 1.30–4.30 (subject to alteration).
WORCESTER COLLEGE (1714) Worcester Street *Porter's lodge*	*College and Gardens*—Term—Daily 2–6 Vacation—Daily 9–12, 2–6 *Hall and Chapel*—apply lodge

Supplementary list of Properties open by appointment

The list of Houses in England, Wales and Scotland printed here are those which are usually open "by appointment only" with the Owner, or open infrequently during the summer months. These are in addition to the Houses and Gardens which are open regularly and are fully classified on pages 29–158. * Indicates that these Houses are also classified and more details are shown under the respective "County" headings.

The majority of these properties have received a grant from the Minister of Housing and Local Government for urgent repairs, given on the advice of the Historic Buildings Councils. Public buildings, almshouses, tithe barns, business premises in receipt of grants are not usually included, neither are properties where the architectural features can be viewed from the street.

ENGLAND

HOUSE	OWNER (*with address if different from first column*)
AVON	
CONGRESBURY, THE VICARAGE, nr. Bristol	Rev. J. Simmonds *By appointment only Yatton* 833126
*LITTLE SODBURY MANOR, Chipping Sodbury	Mr. Gerald Harford *April to Sept. By appointment Chipping Sodbury* 312232
EASTWOOD MANOR FARM, East Harptree	Mr. A. J. Gay
PARTIS COLLEGE, Bath	The Secretary to Trustees of Partis College *Bath* 21532
WHITEHAVEN, Bathford, Bath	Whitehaven Trust, Ltd. *Written appointment only*
WOODSPRING PRIORY, Kewstoke	The Landmark Trust, Shottesbrooke, nr. Maidenhead, Berks. *Open daily*
BEDFORDSHIRE	
AVENUE HOUSE, Ampthill	Mr. S. Houfe *Written appointment only*
WARDEN ABBEY, nr. Biggleswade	The Landmark Trust, Shottesbrooke, nr. Maidenhead, Berks. *Written appointment only*
BERKSHIRE	
Nos. 1 & 25 THE CLOISTERS, Windsor Castle	Dean & Canons of Windsor *Written appointment only* Chapter Clerk, St. George's Chapel, Windsor Castle, SL4 1NJ
HIGH CHIMNEYS, Hurst, Reading	Mr. & Mrs. K. E. Ayers *Written appointment only* Mr. & Mrs. H. Farrar
ST. GABRIEL'S SCHOOL, Sandleford Priory, Newbury	The Headmistress *Newbury* 40663
BUCKINGHAMSHIRE	
BISHAM ABBEY, nr. Marlow	The Director, The Sports Council, Bisham Abbey *Marlow* 2818
BRUDENELL HOUSE, Quainton	Dr. H. Beric Wright *Written appointment only (1 week's notice)*
CHURCH OF THE ASSUMPTION, Hardmead, Newport Pagnell	Friends of Friendless Churches *For key apply to H. Tranter, Manor Cottage, Hardmead by letter or tel. (evenings only) North Crawley* 257
IVER GROVE, Shreding Green, Iver	Mr. & Mrs. T. Stoppard *Written appointment only*
CAMBRIDGE	
CHANTRY (THE), Ely	Mrs. T. A. N. Bristol *Written appointment only*
CHURCH OF ST. JOHN THE BAPTIST, Papworth St. Agnes	Friends of Friendless Churches *For key apply to D. Noble, Church House, Papworth St. Agnes, Cambs. by letter or tel. Huntingdon* 830728
LEVERINGTON HALL, Wisbech	Mr. & Mrs. S. G. Thompson *Written appointment only*
CHESHIRE	
BEWSEY OLD HALL, Warrington	The Administrator *Written appointment only*
CHARLES ROE HOUSE, Chestergate, Macclesfield	McMillan Martin Ltd. *Written appointment only*
CROWN HOTEL, Nantwich	Prop. P. J. Martin
SHOTWICK HALL, Shotwick	Mr. R. B. Gardner, "Wychen", St. Mary's Road., Leatherhead, Surrey *Written appointment only Chester* 880228
TUDOR HOUSE, Lower Bridge St., Chester	*By appointment only Chester* 20095
CLEVELAND	
ST. CUTHBERT'S CHURCH & TURNER MAUSOLEUM, Kirkleatham	Kirkleatham Parochial Church Counsil; Mr. R. S. Ramsdsale, Church Warden (0642) 475198; Mr. J. E. Sherlock, Church Warden (0642) 471423
CORNWALL	
COLLEGE (THE), Week St. Mary	The Landmark Trust, Shottesbrooke, nr. Maidenhead, Berks. *Written appointment only*
TOWN HALL, Camelford	Camelford Town Trust, 21 Clease Road *Camelford* 2370
TRECARREL MANOR, Trebullett, Launceston (*Hall & Chapel, restored*)	*Tel. application only to Mr. N. H. Burden. Coads Green* 286
*TRELOWARREN HOUSE & CHAPEL, Mawgan-in-Meneage, Helston	Sir John Vyvyan, Bart. (*parts of house*) *Written appointment only*; Trelowarren Fellowship (*parts of house*) *Mawgan* 366
CUMBRIA	
PRESTON PATRICK HALL, Milnthorpe	Mrs. J. D. Armitage *By appointment only Crooklands* 200
WHITEHALL, Mealsgate, Carlisle	Mrs. S. Parkin-Moore, 40 Woodsome Rd, London NW5 *Written appointment only*
DERBYSHIRE	
ELVASTON CASTLE, nr. Derby	Derbyshire County Council *Derby* 71342
NORBURY MEDIAEVAL HALL	Mr. M. B. B. Stapleton Martin, The Old Manor, Norbury, Ashbourne, Derbyshire *Written appointment only*
NORTH LEES HALL, Outseats, Hathersage, By Sheffield	Peak Park Joint Planning Board, Aldern House, Baslow Road, Bakewell, Derbyshire *Written appointment only*
4-11 NORTH STREET, Cromford	The Landmark Trust, Shottesbrooke, nr. Maidenhead, Berks. *Written appointment only*

HOUSE	OWNER (*with address if different from first column*)
DEVON	
BINDON MANOR, Axmouth	Mr. & Mrs. J. W. Loveridge *Written appointment only*
ENDSLEIGH HOUSE, Milton Abbot, nr. Tavistock	Endsleigh Fishing Club Ltd. *By appointment only Milton Abbot* 248
HARESTON HOUSE, Brixton	Mr. & Mrs. K. T. Bassett *By appt. (Mons., May–Sept.) Plymouth* 880 426
HAZELWOOD, Hennock, Newton Abbot	Mrs. Robert Kitson (*Gardens only*) *Written appointment only Bovey Tracey* 832441
LIBRARY (THE), Stevenstone, nr. Torrington	The Landmark Trust, Shottesbrooke, Maidenhead, Berks. *Written appointment only*
33/33a LOOE STREET, Plymouth	The Plymouth Barbican Association Ltd., 70 Mutley Plain, Plymouth
MANSION HOUSE (THE), Dartmouth	Battarbee's Ltd. *Dartmouth* 2272
SANDERS, Lettaford	The Landmark Trust, Shottesbrooke, nr. Maidenhead, Berks. *Written appointment only*
SHELL HOUSE (THE), Endsleigh Milton Abbot, nr. Tavistock	Endsleigh Fishing Club Ltd. (*April to Sept.*) *By appointment only Milton Abbot* 248
SHUTE BARTON, nr. Axminster	The National Trust *By appointment only with the tenants Axminster* 33682
SHUTE GATEHOUSE, Shute Barton, nr. Axminster	The Landmark Trust, Shottesbrooke, nr. Maidenhead, Berks. *Written appointment only*
WORTHAM MANOR, Lifton	The Landmark Trust, Shottesbrooke, nr. Maidenhead, Berks. *Written appointment only*
DORSET	
BETTISCOMBE MANOR, nr. Bridport	Mr. M. A. Pinney *Broadwindsor* 236
BLOXWORTH HOUSE, Bloxworth	*Mr. T. A. Dulake* *Written appointment only*
CLENSTON MANOR, Winterborne Clenston, Blandford Forum	Mr. & Mrs. M. Best *Written appointment only*
MOIGNES COURT, Owermoigne	Mr. A. M. Cree *Written appointment only*
PRIEST'S HOUSE, Wimborne	Miss H. M. Coles *Wimborne Minster* 2533
WOODSFORD CASTLE, Woodsford	The Landmark Trust, Shottesbrooke, nr. Maidenhead, Berks. *Written appointment only*
EAST SUSSEX	
ASHDOWN HOUSE, nr. Forest Row	The Headmaster, Ashdown House School *Forest Row* 2574
LAUGHTON TOWER, nr. Lewes	The Landmark Trust, Shottesbrooke, nr. Maidenhead, Berks. *Written appointment only*
ESSEX	
BELCHAMP HALL—SEE SUFFOLK	
BLAKE HALL LEISURE CENTRE, Chipping Ongar	Mr. R. Capel Cure (Parties catered for, except weekends). Tel. the Administrator: *Chipping Ongar* 362502
BRADWELL LODGE, Bradwell-juxta-Mare, nr. Southminster	Mr. James A. Mann *Written appointment only*
GUILDHALL (THE). Great Waltham	Mr. J. J. Tufnell
LITTLE CHESTERFORD MANOR, nr. Saffron Walden	Mr. W. H. Mason *Saffron Waldon* (0799) 30312
OLD ALL SAINTS, Langdon Hills	Mr. R. Mill *Basildon* 414146
RAINHAM HALL, Rainham	The National Trust (tenant Mr. Paul Silverthorne) *Written appt. (postcards) only*
ROUND HOUSE (THE), Havering-atte-Bower, Romford	Mr. M. E. W. Heap *By appointment only Romford* 28136
GLOUCESTERSHIRE	
ABBEY GATEWAY (THE), Tewkesbury	The Abbey Lawn Trust. *Key may be obtained from Abbey Sacristan*
ASHLEWORTH COURT, nr. Gloucester	Mr. H. J. Chamberlayne *Parties only Hartpury* 241
ASHLEWORTH MANOR, Ashleworth	Dr. Jeremy Barnes *Written appointment only*
BEARLAND HOUSE, Gloucester	The Administrator *Written appointment only*
CASTLE GODWYN, Painswick	Mr. & Mrs. John Milne *Written appointment only*
CHACELEY HALL, nr. Tewkesbury	Mr. W. H. Lane *Tirley* 205
CHELTENHAM COLLEGE (Thirlestaine House), Cheltenham	The Secretary to the Council, Bursar's Office, The College *Cheltenham* 22105
COTTAGE (THE), Stanley Pontlarge, Winchcombe	Mrs. S. M. Rolt *Written appointment only*
DANEWAY HOUSE, Sapperton	Sir Anthony Denny, Bt. *Written appointment only*
FRAMPTON COURT & GOTHIC ORANGERY, Frampton-on-Severn, Gloucester	Frampton Ct. Estate *Apply Mrs. Clifford, Gloucester* (0452) 740267
MATSON HOUSE, Gloucester	The Bursar, Selwyn School *Gloucester* 26572
MINCHINHAMPTON MARKET HOUSE, Stroud	*Apply to* Mr. B. E. Lucas *Brimscombe* 883241
OLD VICARAGE (THE), Church Stanway	'Lord Wemyss' Trust; Apply Estate Office, Stanway, Cheltenham *Stanton* 469 *or* 209
ST. MARGARET'S CHURCH, London Road, Gloucester	Gloucester Municipal Charities *Services Suns. 3 p.m. Other times by appt. with Warden Gloucester* 23316
STROUD SUBSCRIPTION ROOMS, Stroud	Stroud District Council, Tech. Services Dept. Old Town Hall, The Shambles, High Street, Stroud *Stroud* 4999

ENGLAND—*continued*

HOUSE	OWNER (*with address if different from first column*)
GREATER MANCHESTER	
CHETHAM'S HOSPITAL & LIBRARY, Manchester, M3 1SB.	The Feoffees of Chetham's Hospital & Library 061-834 9644
SLADE HALL, Slade Lane, Manchester, M13 0QP	Mr. R. A. Fieldhouse *Written appointment only*
HAMPSHIRE	
CHESIL THEATRE (formerly St. Peter Chesil Church)	Winchester Dramatic Society *Winchester* 67086
COURT HOUSE, East Meon	Mr. Piers Whitley *Written appointment only*
MANOR FARM HOUSE, Hambledon	Mr. S. B. Mason
MARSH COURT, Stockbridge	Headmaster, Marsh Court School *Andover* 810503
MOYLES COURT, Ringwood	Manor House School Trust Ltd. *Ringwood* 2856
HEREFORD & WORCESTER	
BRITANNIA HOUSE, The Tything, Worcester	The Alice Ottley School. *Apply* The Headmaster *Written appointment only*
CHURCH HOUSE, Evesham	The Trustees of the Walker Hall & Church House
GRAFTON MANOR, Bromsgrove	Mr. J. W. Morris *Bromsgrove* 31525
HEATH HOUSE, Leintwardine	Mr. Simon Dale, A.R.I.B.A. *Bedstone* 234
HUDDINGTON Court, nr. Droitwich	Professor Hugh D. Edmondson *Written appointment only*
•KENTCHURCH COURT, Hereford	J. E. S. Lucas-Scudamore *Written appointment only*
LEY (THE), Weobley	Lt. Col. Sir Richard Verdin, Stoke Hall, Nantwich *Wettenhall* 284
NEWHOUSE FARM, Goodrich, Ross-on-Wye	The Administrator *Written appointment only*
OLD PALACE (THE), Worcester	The Dean & Chapter of Worcester. *Apply to* Diocesan Secretary, Old Palace, Deansway, Worcester, WR1 2JE *Written appt. only*
HERTFORDSHIRE	
MANOR HOUSE, Little Gaddesden, Berkhamsted	Mr. A. Graham-Stewart *Written appointment only*
WOODHALL PARK, Watton-at-Stone, Hertford	The Abel Smith Trustees, *Apply to* The Headmaster Heath Mount School *Ware* 830230
KENT	
BARMING PLACE, Maidstone	Mr. J. Peter & Dr. Rosalind Bearcroft *Maidstone* 27844
FAIRFIELD HOUSE, Eastry Sandwich	Mr. & Mrs. Brian Kendall *Written appointment only*
6 MARKET PLACE, Faversham	Mr. J. B. Kerr *Written appointment only*
"MAY'S FOLLY", Hadlow Castle, Hadlow	Mr. S. Jensen *Written appointment only*
MERSHAM-LE-HATCH, nr. Ashford	Lord Brabourne (*apply* tenant—The Directors Caldecott Community) *Ashford (Kent)* 23954
NURSTEAD COURT, Meopham	Major R. W. Edmeades *Meopham* 812121
OLD COLLEGE OF ALL SAINTS, Maidstone	Mrs. M. A. Older (Warden) *By appt. only* *Maidstone* 50885
SALMESTONE GRANGE, Nash Road, Margate	The Warden, Flat 4 *Daily May to Sept. By appointment Oct. to April* *Thanet* 21136
STARKEY CASTLE, Wouldham, Rochester	Mr. & Mrs. Gerald Davies *Medway* 681600
YALDHAM MANOR, Wrotham	Mr. & Mrs. John Mourier Lade, Yaldham Manor, Kemsing, Sevenoaks, Kent TN15 6NN (*postal address*) *Written appointment only*
LANCASHIRE	
GISBURN PARK, Clitheroe	Mr. & Mrs. C. H. Hindley (*B. Hols. & Mons., Thurs. May to July* 9–1)
MUSIC ROOM (THE), Lancaster	The Landmark Trust, Shottesbrooke, nr. Maidenhead, Berks. *Open daily, times displayed*
SAMLESBURY HALL, nr. Preston	Samlesbury Hall Trust *Mellor* 2229
LEICESTERSHIRE	
MOAT HOUSE (THE), Appleby Magna	Mr. H. S. Hall *Measham* 70301
OLD GRAMMAR SCHOOL, Market Harborough	The Market Harborough Exhibition Foundation, 12 Hillcrest Avenue, Market Harborough
STAUNTON HAROLD HALL, Ashby de la Zouch	Cheshire Foundation *Melbourne* 2571
LINCOLNSHIRE	
FILLINGHAM CASTLE, nr. Gainsborough	Mr. W. Rose *Written appointment only*
FULBECK MANOR, Grantham	Mr. J. F. Fane *Written appointment only*
HARLAXTON MANOR, Grantham	University of Evansville *Written appointment only*
OLD MANOR HOUSE, Allington	Mr. J. H. Palin *Long Bennington* 358
PELHAM MAUSOLEUM, Limber, Grimsby	The Earl of Yarborough, Brocklesby Park, Habrough, Lincs.
SCRIVELSBY COURT, nr. Horncastle	Lt. Colonel J. L. M. Dymoke, M.B.E., D.L. *Written appoint. only*
LONDON	
ALL HALLOWS VICARAGE, Tottenham, N.17	Rev. R. Pearson 01-808 2470
24 THE BUTTS, Brentford	Mrs. Sally Mills *Written appointment only*
11-13 CAVENDISH SQUARE, W.1	Heythrop College *Written appointment only*
CHARLTON HOUSE, Charlton, S.E.7	Lon. Bor. of Greenwich. *Apply* Manager 01-856 3951
CHARTERHOUSE, Charterhouse Square, E.C.1	The Governors of Charterhouse *Written appointment only*
HEATHGATE HOUSE, 66 Crooms Hill, Greenwich, SE10 8HN	Rev. Mother Superior, Ursuline Convent 01-858-0779
HOUSE OF ST. BARNABAS, Soho	The Administrator *Written appointment only*
PERMANENT EXHIBITION OF JUDICIAL & LEGAL COSTUME, Law Courts, Strand	The Administrator *Adm. (free) whenever building open*
RED HOUSE, Red House Lane, Bexleyheath	Mr. & Mrs. Hollamby *Written appointment only* (*first Saturday and Sunday in month 2.30–4.30 p.m.*)
MERSEYSIDE	
• BLUECOAT CHAMBERS, School Lane, Liverpool	Bluecoat Society of Arts 051-709 5297)
NORFOLK	
BILLINGFORD MILL, nr. Scole; DENVER MILL, off A10; STRACEY ARMS MILL, nr. Acle, (A47)	Norfolk County Council *Norwich* 611122. *Ext.* 5224
6 THE CLOSE, Norwich	The Dean & Chapter of Norwich Cathedral. *Apply* tenant-subud Norwich *Written appointment only*
FISHERMAN'S HOSPITAL, Great Yarmouth	The Administrator *Written appointment only*
GOWTHORPE MANOR, Swardeston	Mrs. M. Steward *Mulbarton* 216
	Apply to Francis Hornor & Son, Queen Street, Norwich *Norwich* 29871
HOVETON HOUSE, Wroxham	Mr. T. R. C. Blofeld *Written appointments only*
LATTICE HOUSE, King's Lynn	The Administrator *Written appointment only*
LITTLE HAUTBOIS HALL, nr. Norwich	Steward to the Trustees, c/o Francis Hornor & Son, Queen Street, Norwich *Norwich* 29871
MANOR HOUSE (THE), Great Cressingham	Mrs. F. Chapman *Written appointment only*
MILL (THE), Little Cressingham, Thetford	The Administrator *Written appointment only*
MUSIC ROOM (THE), Wensum Lodge, King's Lynn	The Administrator *Written appointment only*
OLD VICARAGE (THE), Methwold, Thetford IP26 4NR	Mr. & Mrs. H. C. Dance, *Written appointment only*
SHERINGHAM HALL, Sheringham	Mr. Thomas Upcher *Written appointment only*
THORESBY COLLEGE, King's Lynn	King's Lynn Preservation Trust *Written appointment only*
TUDOR LODGINGS, Castle Acre, King's Lynn	The Lady Evershed *Written appointment only*
WILBY HALL, Quidenham	Mr. & Mrs. C. Warner *Written appointment only*
NORTHAMPTONSHIRE	
ASTWELL CASTLE, nr. Brackley	Mr. Graham Pidgeon *Written appointment only*
COURTEENHALL, Northampton	Sir Hereward Wake, Bt., M.C. *Written appointment only*
DRAYTON HOUSE, Lowick, Kettering	L. G. Stopford Sackville *Written appointment only*
MENAGERIE (THE), Horton, Northampton	Mr. Gervase Jackson-Stops *Written appointment only*
MONASTERY (THE), Shutlanger	Mr. & Mrs. R. G. Wigley *Written appointment only*
PAINES COTTAGES, Oundle	Mr. R. O. Barber *Written appointment only*
NORTHUMBERLAND	
CRASTER TOWER, Alnwick	Mr. J. H. Craster, Major J. M. Craster & Mrs. Reader *Written appointment only*
ELSDON TOWER, Elsdon	Mrs. G. N. Taylor *Otterburn* 20688
HARNHAM HALL, Belsay	Mr. J. Wake
NORTH YORKSHIRE	
BUSBY HALL, Carlton-in-Cleveland	Mr. G. A. Marwood *Written appointment only*
CULLODEN TOWER (THE), Richmond	The Landmark Trust, Shottesbrooke, Maidenhead, Berks. *Written appointment only*
HOME FARM HOUSE, Old Scriven, Knaresborough	Mr. G. T. Reece *Written appointment only*
MOULTON HALL, nr. Richmond	The National Trust (tenant the Hon. J. D. Eccles) *Written appointment only*
OLD RECTORY (THE), Foston, nr. York	Mrs. R. F. Wormald *Written appointment only*
WAKEMAN'S HOUSE, Ripon	Harrogate Museums & Art Gallery Services *May to Sept.* (0423) 503340
NOTTINGHAMSHIRE	
FLINTHAM HALL, nr. Newark	Mr. M. T. Hildyard *Written appointment only*
PRIORY GATEHOUSE, Worksop	The Manager (*open Mons., Tues., Weds.*) *Worksop* 476118
WORKSOP PRIORY CHURCH	The Parish Office *Worksop* 472180
OXFORDSHIRE	
39/43 THE CAUSEWAY, Steventon	Mr. & Mrs. H. C. Dance, The Old Vicarage, Methwold, Thetford, Norfolk IP26 4NR *Written appointment only*
COGGES PRIORY, Witney	The Oxford Diocesan Parsonages Board *Apply to* Rev. R. A. Leaver, Cogges Priory, Witney OX8 6LA *Written appointment only*
COTE HOUSE, Aston	Mrs. David Anderson *Written appointment only*
85 HIGH STREET, Banbury	Mrs. E. Zwirn, Mr. H. Cohen & Mr. S. Sherwood (Bennett's Estates (London) Ltd.) *Written appointment only*
HOPE HOUSE, Woodstock	Mrs. D. M. Money *Written appointment only*
MANOR (THE), Chalgrave	The Administrator *Written appointment only*
MONARCH'S COURT HOUSE, Benson	Mr. R. S. J. Hine *Written appointment only*
RIPON COLLEGE, Cuddesdon	The Principal *Written appointment only*
TWICKENHAM HOUSE, Abingdon-on-Thames	Mrs. Marie Alex *Written appointment only*

ENGLAND—*continued*

HOUSE	OWNER (*with address if different from first column*)	
SHROPSHIRE		
COUNCIL HOUSE (THE) Shrewsbury	Roman Catholic Bishop of Shrewsbury & Trustees of Diocese	
GUILDHALL (THE), Dogpole, Shrewsbury	Shrewsbury & Atcham Borough Council	*Written appointment only*
LONGNOR HALL, nr. Shrewsbury	Major & Mrs. N. S. Lawson	*Dorrington* 543
MORVILLE HALL, nr. Bridgnorth	The National Trust (tenant Miss Bythell)	*Written appt. only*
OLD GRAMMAR SCHOOL (THE), Oswestry	The Headmaster	*Written appointment only*
STANWARDINE HALL, Cockshutt, Ellesmere	Mr. D. J. Bridge	*Cockshutt* 212
SOMERSET		
COTHELSTONE MANOR AND GATEHOUSE, Cothelstone, Taunton	Mrs. E. Warmington, Cothelstone House Estate, Cothelstone Manor, Cothelstone	*Written appointment only*
DODINGTON HALL, Nether Stowey	Lady Gass, Fairfield, Stogursey (tenant Mrs. E. Webber)	*Tues. & Thurs. by appointment Holford* 422
MANOR FARM, Meare, Wells	Mrs. I. M. Bull (tenant Mr. C. J. Look)	
OLD DRUG STORE (THE) Axbridge	Mr. & Mrs. K. E. J. D. Schofield	*Written appointment only*
OLD HALL (THE), Croscombe	The Landmark Trust, Shottesbrooke, nr. Maidenhead, Berks.	*Written appointment only*
OLD MANOR (THE), Croscombe, nr. Wells	Mr. L. J. Lusby	*Written appointment only*
OLD MANOR HOUSE, Crowcombe	The Administrator	*Written appointment only*
WHITELACKINGTON MANOR Ilminster	Dillington Estate Office, Ilminster	*Written appointment only*
STAFFORDSHIRE		
BROUGHTON HALL, Eccleshall	The Administrator	*Written appointment only*
OLD HALL GATEHOUSE (THE), Mavesyn Ridware	Mr. J. R. Eades	*Armitage* 490312
PARK HALL, Leigh	Mr. E. J. Knobbs	*Written appointment only*
* PILLATON OLD HALL, Penkridge	Mr. R. W. & The Hon. Mrs. Perceval	*By appointment only Penkridge* 2200
TIXALL GATEHOUSE, Tixall	The Landmark Trust, Shottesbrooke, nr. Maidenhead, Berks.	*Written appointment only*
SUFFOLK		
* BELCHAMP HALL, by Sudbury (Suffolk)	Mr. M. M. J. Raymond	*Sudbury (Suffolk)* 72744
DEANERY (THE), Hadleigh	The Dean of Bocking	*Hadleigh* 822218
FLEMINGS HALL, Eye	Mr. Angus McBean	*Written appointment only*
HALL (THE), Great Bricett, nr. Ipswich	Mr. & Mrs. R. B. Cooper	*Written appointment only*
HENGRAVE HALL, Bury St. Edmunds	The Warden, Hengrave Hall Centre, Bury St. Edmunds	*Written appointment only*
LITTLE ST. MARY'S, Long Melford	The Administrator	*Written appointment only*
MOAT HALL, Parham, nr. Woodbridge	Mr. J. W. Gray	*Wickham Market* 746317
NEWBOURNE HALL, nr. Woodbridge	Mr. John Somerville	*Written appointment only*
NEW INN (THE), Peasenhall	The Landmark Trust, Shottesbrooke, nr. Maidenhead, Berks.	*Great Hall, open daily*
ROOS HALL, Barsham Road, Beccles	Mr. & Mrs. H. W. N. Suckling	*Beccles* 712115
THORPE HALL, Horham, nr. Diss	Mr. & Mrs. David Mlinaric	*Stradbroke* 375
WORLINGHAM HALL, Beccles	Viscount Colville of Culross	*Written appointment only*
WURLIE (THE), The Street, Badwell Ash	Mr. B. W. Belcher, Rickinghall, Diss, Norfolk	*Written appt. only*
SURREY		
CROSSWAYS FARM, Abinger Hammer	Mr. C. T. Hughes (tenant)	*Written appointment only*
RANGER'S HOUSE (THE), Farnham	Sir Brooks Richards K.C.M.G.	*Written appointment only*
SUNBURY COURT, Sunbury-on-Thames, Middx.	The Salvation Army	*Sunbury* 82196
TYNE & WEAR		
GIBSIDE BANQUETING HOUSE, nr. Whickham	The Landmark Trust, Shottesbrooke, nr. Maidenhead, Berks.	*Written appointment only*
WARWICKSHIRE		
FOXCOTE, Shipston-on-Stour	Mr. C. B. Holman	*Written appointment only*
NORTHGATE, Warwick	Mr. R. E. Phillips	*Written appointment only*
ST. LEONARD'S CHURCH, Wroxall	Mr. D. J. Brimfield, Bursar, Wroxall Abbey School, Warwick CV35 7NB	*Written appointment only*
WAR MEMORIAL TOWN HALL, Alcester	The Secretary, Mr. J. W. Roberts, 10 Haselor Close, Alcester B49 6QD	*By appointment Alcester* (0789) 762101 *or* Mr. J. Adams (762648) *or* Mrs. C. Newey (762579)
WEST SUSSEX		
CHANTRY GREEN HOUSE, Steyning	Mr. & Mrs. G. H. Recknell	*Steyning* 81-2239
CHAPEL (THE), BISHOP'S PALACE, Chichester	Church Commissioners, The Palace, Chichester	*Written appointment only to The Chaplain The Palace, Chichester*
GATEHOUSE COTTAGE, Canon Lane, Chichester	Church Commissioners	*Written appointment only to The Chaplain The Palace, Chichester*
WEST YORKSHIRE		
FULNECK BOY'S SCHOOL, Pudsey	I. D. Brimfield, BA., MPhil., Headmaster *Open during school hols. only.*	*Written appointment only*
GRAND THEATRE & OPERA HOUSE (THE), Leeds	Warren Smith, General Manager	0532-456014
HORBURY HALL, Wakefield	The Administrator	*Written appointment only*
OLD HALL (THE), Calverley, nr. Pudsey, Leeds	The Landmark Trust, Shottesbrooke, Maidenhead, Berks.	*Written appointment only*
TOWN HALL, Leeds	Leeds City Council	*By appointment only Leeds* 462352
WESTON HALL, nr. Otley	Lt. Col. H. V. Dawson	*Written appointment only*
WILTSHIRE		
* ABBEY HOUSE (THE), Malmesbury		*By appointment only to the Sister-in-Charge* 066-62 2212
68 THE CLOSE, Salisbury	Dean and Chapter, Salisbury Cathedral (tenant Sir Arthur Bryant, C.H., C.B.E.)	*Salisbury* 333869
FARLEY HOSPITAL, Farley	The Warden	*Farley* 231
GROVE (THE), Corsham	Trustees of Corsham Estate	*Written appointment only*
LITTLE CLARENDON, Dinton	The National Trust (Sq. Leader A. Southwold)	*Written appointment only*
MILTON MANOR, Pewsey	Mrs. Rupert Gentle	*Pewsey* 3344
OLD BISHOP'S PALACE, 1 The Close, Salisbury	The Bursar, The Cathedral School	*Salisbury* 22652
OLD MANOR HOUSE (THE), Whiteheads Lane, Bradford-on-Avon	Mr. John Teed	*Written appointment only*
ORPINS HOUSE, Church Street, Bradford-on-Avon	Mr. J. Vernon Burchell	*Written appointment only*
PORCH HOUSE (THE), Potterne, nr. Devizes		*Written appointment only*
ROCHE OLD COURT, Winterslow	Major H. B. Trevor Cox	*Written appointment only*
TOTTENHAM HOUSE, Savernake	The Administrator	*Written appointment only*

WALES

HOUSE	OWNER	
CLWYD		
FFERM, Pontblyddyn, Mold	Mrs. Elizabeth Jones-Mortimer (*apply to tenant*)	*Pontybodkin* 770371
GATEHOUSE AT GILAR FARM, Pentrefoclas	Mr. P. J. Warbourton-Lee	*Written appointment only*
HALGHTON HALL, Bangor-on-Dee, Wrexham	Mr. J. D. Lewis	*Written appointment only*
LINDISFARNE COLLEGE, Wynnstay Hall, Ruabon	The Headmaster	*Ruabon* 823407
NERQUIS HALL, Mold	Mr. A. W. Furse	*Written appointment only*
PEN ISA'R GLASCOED, Bodelwyddan	Mr. M. E. Harrop	*St. Asaph* 583501
PLAS UCHAF, Llangar	The Landmark Trust, Shottesbrooke, nr. Maidenhead, Berks.	*Written appointment only*
DYFED		
FRENCH MILL, Carew	Mr. Anthony Trollope-Bellew	*By appointment only (April to Sept.)*
OLD HALL (THE), Monkton, Pembroke	The Landmark Trust, Shottesbrooke, Maidenhead, Berks.	*Written appointment only*
ST. DAVID'S UNIVERSITY COLLEGE, Lampeter	Principal: Professor Brian Morris	*Lampeter* 422-351
TALIARIS PARK, Llandeilo	Messrs. J. H. S. & M. F. Williams	*Written appointment only*
GWENT		
BLACKBROOK HOUSE, Skenfrith	Mr. G. F. W. Buckland	*Skenfrith* 238
CASTLE HILL HOUSE, Monmouth	Mr. T. Baxter-Wright	*Written appointment only*
CLYTHA CASTLE, nr. Abergavenny	The Landmark Trust, Shottesbrooke, nr. Maidenhead, Berks.	*Written appointment only*
CWRT PORTH HIR, Llanover	Coldbrook & Llanover Est.	*Written appointment only*
GREAT CIL-LWCH, Llantilio Crossenny	Mr. J. F. Ingledew	*Written appointment only*
KEMYS HOUSE, Kemys Inferior, Caerleon	Mr. I. S. Burge	*Written appointment only*
OVERMONNOW HOUSE (formerly Vicarage), Monmouth	Mr. J. R. Pangbourne	*Written appointment only*
3/4 PRIORY STREET, Monmouth	Mr. H. R. Ludwig	*Written appointment only*
ST. JAMES HOUSE, Monmouth	The Governors of Monmouth School; The Haberdashers Co.	*Written appointment only*
TREOWEN, Wonastow, Monmouth	Mr. R. H. Wheelock	*By appointment only Dingeston* 224

Supplementary list of Properties open by appointment—*continued*

WALES—*continued*

HOUSE	OWNER (*with address if different from first column*)	
GWYNEDD		
BATH TOWER (THE), Caernarfon	The Landmark Trust, Shottesbrooke, nr. Maidenhead, Berks.	*Written appointment only*
CAPEL SILOAM, Rowen Conwy	Baptist Chapel (*Rented by the Women's Inst.*)	*Written appointment to Women's Inst.*
CYMRYD, Conwy	Miss D. E. Glynne, Llys Gwynedd, Bangor	*Bangor* 362315
DDUALLT, Tan y Bwlch, Blaenau, Ffestiniog	Col. A. H. K. Campbell	*Maentwrog* 272
DOLAUGWYN, Towyn	Mrs. S. Tudor	*Written appointment only*
NANNAU, Llanfachreth, nr. Dolgellau	Mr. E. Bowen	*Written appointment only*
PENMYNYDD, Alms Houses, Llanfairpwll	Rev. G. M. Hughes (*Hon. Secretary*)	*Written appointmen only*
PLAS COCH, Llanedwen, Llanfairpwll	Mr. D. Griffiths	*Llanfairpwl* (0248) 714272
ROYAL WELSH YACHT CLUB, Porth Yr Aur, Caernarfon	T. W. Williams, D.F.C., 64 High Street, Llanberis	*Llanberis* 331
MID GLAMORGAN		
LLANCAIACH FAWR, Nelson	Rhymney Valley District Council. *Apply* Public Relations Officer	*Hengoed* 815588
POWYS		
ABERCYNRIG, Llanfrynach	Mr. W. R. Lloyd, Abercynrig, Brecon, Powys LD3 7AQ	*Written appointment only*
1 BUCKINGHAM PLACE, Brecon	Mrs. Meeres	*Written appointment only*
2 BUCKINGHAM PLACE, Brecon	Mrs. C. Sims	*Written appointment only*
3 BUCKINGHAM PLACE, Brecon	Mr. & Mrs. A. Whiley	*Written appointment only*
MAESMAWR HALL HOTEL, Caersws	Mrs. V. H. M. Kendal	(068684) 255
NEWTON FARM, Brecon	Mrs. Ballance (*apply* in writing to Mr. D. L. Evans, tenant)	
PEN-Y-LAN, Meifod	Mr. S. R. J. Meade	*Meifod* 202
PIGEON HOUSE, Abercamlais	Capt. N. G. Garnons-Williams, M.B.E. (Ret'd)	*Written appointment only*
PLASAU DUON, Clatter	Mr. C. Breese	
PLAS LLANGATTOCK, Crickhowell	Mr. J. P. C. Sankey-Barker	*Crickhowell* 810484
RHYDYCARW, Trefeglwys, Caersws	Mr. M. Breese-Davies	*Trefeglwys* 363
TREFECCA FAWR, Talgarth	Major W. H. Lewis	*Written appointment only*
YDDERW, Llyswen	Mr. D. P. Eckley	*Written appointment only*
SOUTH GLAMORGAN		
FONMON CASTLE, Barry	Sir Hugo Boothby, Bt.	*Written appointment only*
GREAT HOUSE (THE), Llantwit Major	Mr. C. Baxter Jones	*Llantwit Major* 2483
WEST GLAMORGAN		
PENRICE CASTLE, Penrice, Gower	Mr. C. Methuen-Campbell	*Written appointment only*

SCOTLAND

HOUSE	OWNER	
BORDERS REGION		
DARNICK TOWER, Melrose	Mrs. T. H. Wilson	*Melrose* 2735
OLD GALA HOUSE, Galashiels	Ettrick & Lauderdale District Council	*Galashiels* 2611
SIR WALTER SCOTT'S COURTROOM, Selkirk	Ettrick & Lauderdale District Council (*mid June to Sept.*) *Mons. to Fris. Other times by appointment*	*Selkirk* 20096
WEDDERLIE HOUSE, Gordon TD3 6NW	Mrs. J. R. L. Campbell	*Westruther* 223
CENTRAL REGION		
BARDOWIE CASTLE, by Milngavie	Mr. R. T. Allen	*Balmore* 366
CASTLECARY CASTLE, by Bonnybridge, Stirlingshire	Mr. Hugo B. Millar	*Written appointment only*
GARGUNNOCK HOUSE, by Stirling	Miss V. H. C. Stirling, C.B.E.	*Written appointment only* *Gargunnock* 202
OLD TOLBOOTH BUILDING, Stirling	Stirling District Council, Municipal Buildings, Corn Exchange Road	*Stirling* 3131
PINEAPPLE (THE), Dunmore, Airth	The Landmark Trust, Shottesbrooke, nr. Maidenhead, Berks.	*Written appointment only*
TOUCH HOUSE, by Stirling	Mr. P. B. Buchanan	*Written appointment only*
DUMFRIES & GALLOWAY REGION		
BONSHAW TOWER, Kirtlebridge, nr. Annan	Mrs. Keys-Irving Straton-Ferrier	*Kirtlebridge* 256 *Written or telephone appointment only*
CARNSALLOCH HOUSE, Kirkton, nr. Dumfries	The Leonard Cheshire Foundation	*Dumfries* 54924
CRAIGDARROCH HOUSE, Moniaive	Major H. H. Sykes	*Moniaive* 202
KIRKCONNELL HOUSE, New Abbey, nr. Dumfries	Mr. F. Maxwell Witham	*New Abbey* 276
TOLBOOTH, Royal Burgh of Sanquhar	Mr. T. A. Johnston	*Sanquhar* 303
FIFE REGION		
CASTLE (THE), Elie	Miss Scott-Moncrieff	*Written appointment only*
GRAMPIAN REGION		
BALBITHAN HOUSE, Kintore	Mrs. M. McMurtrie	*Kintore* 32282
BALFLUIG CASTLE	Mr. Mark Tennant. *Written application only to* 8 New Square, Lincoln's Inn, London, WC2A 3QP	
BARRA CASTLE, Old Meldrum	Mrs. Andrew Boydon	*Written appointment only*
CASTLE OF FIDDES, Stonehaven	Dr. M. Weir	*Drumlithie* 213
CORSINDAE HOUSE, Sauchen	Mr. Laurence Fyffe	*Written appointment only*
CRAIG CASTLE, Lumsden	Mrs. C. G. M. Barlas of Craig	*Lumsden* 202
CRAIGSTON CASTLE, Turriff	Mr. Bruce Urquhart	*Written appointment only*
DRUMMINOR CASTLE, Rhynie	Mr. A. D. Forbes	*Written appointment only*
GORDONSTOUN SCHOOL, Elgin (*Round Square only*)	The Headmaster, Gordonstoun School	*Written appointment only*
GRANDHOME HOUSE, nr. Aberdeen	Mrs. J. D. Paton	*Aberdeen* 72 2202
KINTORE TOWN HOUSE, Kintore	Gordon District Council	*Inverurie* 20981
PHESDO HOUSE, Laurencekirk	Mr. J. M. Thomson	*Written appointment only*
PLUSCARDEN ABBEY, Elgin	The Abbot	*Dallas* 257
HIGHLAND REGION		
EMBO HOUSE, Dornoch	Mr. John G. Mackintosh	*Dornoch* 260
LOTHIAN REGION		
ARNISTON HOUSE, Gorebridge	Mr. & Mrs. A. R. Dundas-Bekker	*Written appointment only*
CAKEMUIR, Tynehead	Mr. M. M. Scott	*Written appointment only*
CASTLE GOGAR, Edinburgh	Lady Steel-Maitland	*Corstorphine* 1234
FORD HOUSE, Ford	F. P. Tindall, O.B.E.	*Written appointment only*
108–110 GRASSMARKET, Edinburgh	Mr. & Mrs. Paul Coutts	*Written appointment only*
LINNHOUSE, nr. Livingston	Mr. H. J. Spurway	*Written appointment only*
NEWBATTLE ABBEY COLLEGE, Dalkeith	The Principal	*Written appointment only*
NORTHFIELD HOUSE, Prestonpans	Mr. W. Schomberg Scott	*Written appointment only*
PEFFERMILL HOUSE, Peffermill Road, Edinburgh EH16 5UX	Nicholas Groves-Raines, Architects	031–661 7172/3
PENICUIK HOUSE, Penicuik	Sir John Clerk, Bt.	*Written appointment only*
PRESTON HALL, Pathhead	Major J. D. Callander, M.C.	*Written appointment only*
ROSEBURN HOUSE, Murrayfield	Miss M. E. Sturgeon	*Written appointment only*
TOLBOOTH, South Queensferry	The Town Clerk	031-331 1590
TOWN HOUSE, Haddington	East Lothian District Council	*Access at all reasonable times*
SHETLAND ISLANDS AREA		
LODBERRIE (THE), Lerwick	Mr. Thomas Moncrieff	
STRATHCLYDE REGION		
BARCALDINE CASTLE, Benderloch	Morton, Fraser & Milligan, W. S., 15 & 19 York Place, Edinburgh, EH1 3EL (Trustees of Sir A. W. D. Campbell)	*Written appointment only*
CRESSNOCK CASTLE, Ayr	The Baron de Fresnes	*Written appointment only*
DUNTRUNE CASTLE, Lochgilphead	Robin Malcolm of Poltalloch	*Written appointment only*
KELBURN CASTLE, Fairlie	Rear Admiral the Earl of Glasgow	*Written appointment only*
KILKERRAN, Maybole, KA19 7SJ	Sir Charles Fergusson, Bt.	*Written appointment only*
NEW LANARK, Caithness Row	New Lanark Association, The Counting House, New Lanark, ML11 9DG	0555 61345
PLACE OF PAISLEY (THE), Paisley	Paisley Abbey, Kirk Session *Written appt. only, apply to Minister*	
SADDELL CASTLE, nr. Campbeltown	The Landmark Trust, Shottesbrooke, nr. Maidenhead, Berks.	*Written appointment only*
TANGY MILL, nr. Campbeltown	The Landmark Trust, Shottesbrooke, nr. Maidenhead, Berks.	*Written appointment only*
TANNAHILL'S COTTAGE, Queen Street, Paisley	Secretary, Paisley Burns Club	041–887 7500
TAYSIDE REGION		
ARDBLAIR CASTLE, Blairgowrie	Laurence P. K. Blair Oliphant	*Blairgowrie* 3155
CRAIG HOUSE, Montrose		
KINROSS HOUSE, Kinross (*Garden only*)	Sir David Montgomery Bt.	*Written appointment only*
MICHAEL BRUCE'S COTTAGE, Kinnesswood	*Apply to* the Caretaker	
TULLIEBOLE CASTLE, Crook of Devon	The Lord Moncreiff	*Fossoway* 236

INDEX TO HOUSES, CASTLES AND GARDENS

PROPERTIES NEW TO THE 1984 EDITION

Printed in England by Index Printers and published by **ABC HISTORIC PUBLICATIONS**, World Timetable Centre, Church Street, Dunstable, Bedfordshire LU5 4HB.